James L. Hall

SEMIMICRO QUALITATIVE ANALYSIS

HARPER'S CHEMISTRY SERIES

Under the Editorship of William Marshall MacNevin

SEMIMICRO QUALITATIVE ANALYSIS

REVISED EDITION

Hervey Hubbard Barber

Professor Emeritus of Chemistry, University of Minnesota

Professor of Chemistry, Lincoln Memorial University

and

T. Ivan Taylor

Professor of Chemistry, Columbia University

HARPER & BROTHERS NEW YORK

SEMIMICRO QUALITATIVE ANALYSIS, REVISED EDITION

Printed in the United States of America

C-E

Library of Congress Catalog Card Number: 53-9410

CONTENTS

Part 2. Qualitative Analysis for the Anions

Appendixes

PREFACE

Some of the general aims of a first course in qualitative chemical analysis are: (1) to aid in classifying and systematizing information about the properties and chemical reactions of the more common inorganic substances; (2) to study the principles of chemical equilibrium and to apply them to solutions of electrolytes; (3) to learn the general methods of systematically separating and identifying inorganic substances; (4) to acquire skill and practice in using certain laboratory techniques. The relative emphasis placed upon the various aspects of qualitative chemical analysis may vary considerably, depending upon the aims of the instructor, the time available for the course, and the interests and previous training of the students in the class. This book, which is based in part on a previous edition, will be found suitable for many of the courses now given in qualitative chemical analysis.

Instead of the theoretical material being presented in a separate section of the book, it is integrated with the laboratory work. Specific applications of ionic equilibria to the analysis of each group of cations is covered rather completely in the discussions of the analytical procedures. Since students with a normal training in general chemistry have been introduced to the ideas of solutions of acids, bases and salts, equilibria, ionization of weak electrolytes, solubility products, complex ions, oxidation-reduction, etc., they should be able to follow these discussions without difficulty. The rather extensive series of questions and problems should aid the students in their work and provide the instructor with material for problem assignments.

The reference tables on the reactions of the ions will be found informative. Time may not be available for discussion of all these reactions or even for thorough study by the student. However, the tables are valuable as a review and for reference during the laboratory work. Similarly the students will find that the equations for the reactions in each procedure will be a valuable aid in their study of the analysis of each group.

The subject matter has been arranged to make the selection of material for different types of courses relatively easy. For example, a course devoting a full semester or more to qualitative analysis will probably use material from Part 1 (cations) and Part 2 (anions). Schools on the quarter system will use material primarily from Part 1 on the analysis for the cations, with some work on alloys and simple tests for anions. In schools that give qualitative analysis as a laboratory course during the second semester of inorganic or general chemistry, material from Part 1 can be selected and the theoretical aspects can be discussed in class work or laboratory conferences.

The organization of the material relative to the analysis of each group of cations also makes the book adaptable to the time available. Thus for each group of cations, the arrangement is as follows: preliminary experiments, summary of reactions, outline and discussion of the procedure, theory of ionic equilibria applicable to the analysis, analysis of knowns and unknowns, chemical reactions in the analysis, questions and problems. An instructor with a minimum of time for the course could select only a few of the preliminary experiments and the analysis of knowns and unknowns, omitting as much of the other material as necessary.

The procedures for the analyses are essentially those that have been more or less standard since they were introduced by A. A. Noyes many years ago. Some innovations, however, have been introduced without changing the general scheme of analysis. The most important of these are sulfide precipitations with thioacetamide, CH_3CSNH_2 (*Anal. Chem.* **21,** 192, 1949), and the pressure bulb method of filtration (*Ind. Eng. Chem. Anal. Ed.* **12,** 58, 1940).

Thioacetamide hydrolyzes at elevated temperatures in acid solution to form hydrogen sulfide, acetic acid, and ammonium ion. In alkaline solution the hydrolysis is more rapid than in acid solutions. Hydrolysis in alkaline solution results in the formation of sulfide ion, acetate ion, and ammonia. In neutral solution at room temperature there is negligible hydrolysis so no difficulty is involved in keeping solutions of thioacetamide. There is no essential difference in the chemistry of sulfide precipitation when thioacetamide is used instead of hydrogen sulfide because thioacetamide is essentially a source of hydrogen sulfide. It is only necessary to keep the solution hot by setting it in a boiling water bath during the precipitation. An important advantage in using thioacetamide instead of hydrogen sulfide gas is that it eliminates the need of tanks or generators of hydrogen sulfide with the consequent danger and the disagreeable odor. Other advantages and the techniques of using thioacetamide are discussed in Chapter 4.

The usefulness of the pressure bulb method for filtration in semimicro qualitative analysis has been established by continued use in many laboratories since it was described by the authors in their earlier book. Besides its simplicity, rapidity, and versatility, the pressure bulb method of filtration is low in cost and provides each student with his own filtration assembly. Other advantages and the techniques of using the pressure bulb method are given in Chapter 4.

Although the authors prefer the use of thioacetamide for sulfide precipitations and the pressure bulb method for filtrations, there is no reason why the book cannot be used by those who prefer to use hydrogen sulfide gas and the centrifuge. Directions are given for both these techniques and no fundamental changes in the procedures will be needed. Some instructors may prefer to use the centrifuge for some filtrations and the pressure bulb method for others. The filter tube, described in Chapter 4, can also be used with the centrifuge. Usually, however, after one starts using the pressure bulb, he seldom turns on the centrifuge except when he actually wants to recover and save a precipitate for one reason or another. In most cases a precipitate obtained in one procedure is dissolved and further tests are made on it in another procedure. Consequently it is not necessary to remove a precipitate from the filter medium in the pressure bulb method. The precipitate is simply dissolved by the appropriate reagents and further tests are then made as needed.

Acknowledgments are made with gratitude to the many good textbooks on qualitative analysis and to such standard reference books as those by A. A. Noyes, Stieglitz, Prescott and Johnson, Treadwell and Hall, Lundell and Hoffman, Latimer and Hildebrand, Sneed and Maynard, etc. The authors are grateful to Edward Grzeskowiok for his help with some of the experimental work on the analytical procedures. The valuable suggestions of those who used the previous edition are gratefully acknowledged.

H. H. Barber
T. I. Taylor

Minneapolis, Minnesota
New York, N. Y.
August 1, 1953

PART 1

SEMIMICRO QUALITATIVE ANALYSIS FOR THE CATIONS

Using Thioacetamide for Precipitation of Sulfides

CHAPTER 1

INTRODUCTION—TERMS OF QUALITATIVE ANALYSIS

SCOPE OF QUALITATIVE ANALYSIS

Whenever an object or sample of material is under consideration for one purpose or another, some of the first questions asked about it are: "What is it?" and "What is its composition?" Before these questions are answered, it is usually found necessary to ask: "How much of this or that substance is in it?" **Analytical chemistry** is concerned with the answers to these questions.

Qualitative analysis is the branch of analytical chemistry that is concerned primarily with the identification of the elements, ions, or compounds contained in a sample of material. Such an analysis should also give some idea of the approximate relative proportions of the substances in the sample. In **quantitative analysis** a precise determination is made of the percentage of one or more of the substances in the sample. The procedure selected for the quantitative determination depends, in many cases, upon the presence or absence of interfering substances. Consequently a qualitative analysis usually precedes a quantitative analysis.

In order to perform a qualitative analysis intelligently, not only is it necessary to acquire skill in the application of certain experimental techniques, but it is also necessary to learn the properties and behavior of the substances for which tests are made. Therefore, the study of qualitative analysis includes (1) the laboratory procedures employed for the separation and identification of substances, (2) the properties and chemical reactions of the elements and their compounds, and (3) the laws and theories which describe and explain the behavior of substances. It appears, in fact, that the usefulness of the knowledge derived from a study of the reactions and of the principles involved in the procedures for separating and identifying ions will probably outweigh the practical training in analytical techniques.

Inorganic qualitative analysis is usually carried out in aqueous solutions; consequently it is concerned primarily with the identification of ions that exist in such solutions. From the results of an analysis for the ions it is possible to list the elements that were present in the original sample, but it is not always possible to infer which specific compounds were in the mixture. For example, an analysis of a mixture of zinc chloride, calcium chlorate, and aluminum nitrate dissolved in water would show the presence of the following ions: Zn^{++}, Ca^{++}, Al^{3+}, Cl^-, ClO_3^-, and NO_3^-. There is no way to infer from this analysis whether the original compound of zinc was $ZnCl_2$, $Zn(ClO_3)_2$, or $Zn(NO_3)_2$. Some information, however, is obtained about the state of combination of the element chlorine in the original mixture. It is known, for example, that a chloride and a chlorate were present, but it is not possible to conclude which of the three metallic elements these two ions were originally combined with. Physical examination of the original dry salts by optical methods or by x-ray diffraction would be required to identify definitely the actual compounds.

Elementary courses in qualitative analysis are limited in scope to the separation and identification of a number of the more common cations and anions. The identification is carried out in a systematic manner by precipitating successive groups of ions from solution with *group reagents* (see p. 106). The ions in each of these smaller groups are then separated from one another and are finally identified positively by specific confirmatory tests. The reason for limiting the number of elements studied is primarily a matter of the time available. Many of the analytically important separations and techniques are included; and once these are mastered, it is easy to extend them to other problems in analytical chemistry.

In order to understand the methods employed to precipitate the ions into their respective groups, to know why certain reagents are selected to dissolve the precipitates, and to apply specific tests for the individual ions, it is necessary to have a thorough knowledge of the properties of the ions and of the principles of ionic equilibria in solutions of electrolytes. Therefore, a large part of the theory of elementary qualitative analysis is concerned with the chemistry of the ions and their behavior in solution.

METHODS OF QUALITATIVE ANALYSIS

The principles involved in a qualitative analysis of aqueous solutions of electrolytes are essentially the same whether relatively large or small quantities are used. If the analysis is made on comparatively large volumes of solutions (10 to 100 ml.) and with ordinary test tubes, beakers, and funnels, the procedure is called **macroanalysis** (Fig. 1.1). The analysis of very small samples of substances, using diminutive apparatus and special instruments such as the microscope, is called **microanalysis.** In **semimicroanalysis,** volumes of solutions from 1 drop to about 5 ml. are employed. Small test tubes, centrifuge tubes, pressure filter tubes, semimicro suction funnels, spot plates, glass slides, drop-reaction papers, etc., are used to carry out the identification tests. Usually the analysis can be made more rapidly by semimicro methods. The chemical reactions

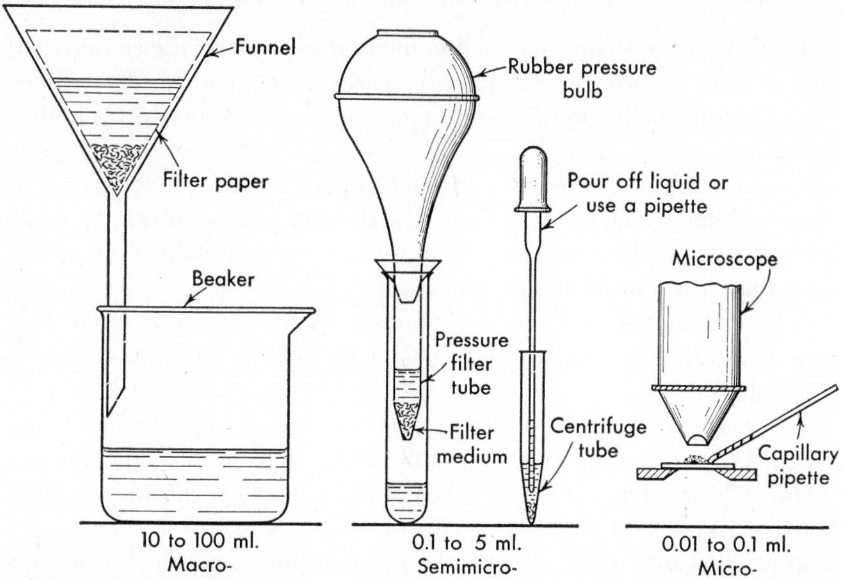

FIG. 1.1. Filtration Techniques in Macro, Semimicro, and Micro Methods of Qualitative Analysis.

and the procedures used for both macro and semimicro qualitative analysis are, however, practically the same. Likewise, with some practice and with the use of solutions of known concentration for comparative tests, the approximate number of milligrams of an ion in the original sample can be estimated. Similarly, experience with the sensitivity of the confirmatory tests enables one to conclude that certain ions are not present in more than a certain concentration.*

Other Methods of Analysis

Although the procedures commonly employed in qualitative analysis are devised for solutions of electrolytes, other important methods are

* See the discussion on sensitivity of tests, p. 8, and problems, p. 9.

often used. Among them are spectroscopic analysis and flame colorations, blowpipe analysis and bead tests, microscopic examination, x-ray analysis, polarographic analysis, fluorescence, etc. Indeed, in practice it may be more expedient to use one or more of these other methods to determine the presence or absence of certain elements. The principles and applications of these methods are studied in more advanced courses in analytical chemistry.

SUMMARY OF TERMS USED IN QUALITATIVE ANALYSIS

Terms that are frequently used in qualitative analysis are summarized here so that the student will have a clearer understanding of the directions given in the laboratory work and of the explanations in theoretical discussions.

1. A **solution** is a homogeneous mixture of a **solute** in a **solvent** (generally a liquid). The solute is dispersed throughout the solvent as molecules or ions (cations and anions) or, at the most, as aggregates of not more than a few molecules or ions.

2. A **test solution** is one that contains a specific cation or anion. It is used to study characteristic reactions of the ion, or to make comparative tests.

3. A **reagent** is a solution of an acid, base, salt, or other chemical that is added to another solution to produce a reaction. For example, hydrochloric acid is a reagent which, when added to a silver nitrate test solution, precipitates the silver ion as silver chloride. Reagents may be classed as **group reagents** when used for the precipitation of a group of ions, or as **specific reagents** when employed to test for individual ions or to bring about specific reactions.

4. A **reaction** is the chemical change that takes place when a reagent is added to a solution of another material. The substances produced by the **reactants** are called the **products.** A reagent which is added for the specific purpose of forming a slightly soluble substance (a precipitate) is called a **precipitant.** A **chemical equation** is used to give a qualitative and quantitative expression of the chemical reaction by means of formulas and symbols.

5. A **precipitate** is a slightly soluble solid that is formed when a reagent is added to a solution. The process is called **precipitation.** Precipitates are usually described by their color and their physical appearance. If the precipitate resembles curdled milk, it is called a **curdled** precipitate. Other precipitates may be described as **flocculent** (of flaky appearance);

granular (grainy in appearance); **crystalline** (like transparent or shiny crystals); **heavy** (a precipitate that settles rapidly); **colloidal** (a very finely dispersed or cloudy precipitate that does not settle or cannot be filtered out). A solution that contains a colloidal precipitate is called a **sol.** In order to make **translucent** precipitates more visible, a dye that is adsorbed by the precipitate is added to the solution. After the dye has been adsorbed, the precipitate is called a **lake.**

6. A precipitate is separated from the solution in which it is formed by **filtration** or **centrifugation.** Filtration is the process of removing a precipitate or solid from a liquid by pouring the mixture on a **filter medium** which allows the liquid to flow through but retains the solid. The filter medium may be filter paper, cotton, glass fiber, asbestos, porous glass, or porous porcelain. In centrifugation, the mixture is rotated at high speed in a centrifuge. This causes the precipitate to settle in a compact mass at the bottom of the centrifuge tube. The **supernatant** liquid above the precipitate may then be decanted (poured off), leaving the precipitate in the tube. Frequently precipitation and filtration or centrifugation will be more complete and rapid if the solution is **digested** (heated) in a **hot water bath.** The technique of filtration and centrifugation will be considered in detail in the discussion of laboratory techniques (Chapter 4).

7. A **residue** is the solid remaining on a filter medium or in a centrifuge tube after one or more components have been extracted from the precipitate or solid. The term **residue** is also applied to the solid obtained when a solution is evaporated almost to dryness (**incipient dryness**) or to dryness. Often the residue is **ignited** (*heated strongly*) when it is desired to volatilize or decompose one or more of its components.

8. Precipitates and residues are usually **washed** with small quantities of distilled water or other specified solutions to remove the supernatant liquid that remains on the solid or in the filter medium.

9. The **filtrate** is the solution that passes through the filter medium; more generally, it is the solution that has been separated from a precipitate or solid.

10. A **test** is a procedure designed to determine whether a given substance or group of substances is present. In general, a test is made by adding a reagent and noting whether a specific reaction takes place. If the expected reaction occurs, the test is **positive;** if it does not occur, the test is **negative.** Most tests depend upon the formation or disappearance of a color or a precipitate when certain reagents are added to the solution. Other tests, however, depend upon the colors, odors, and reactions of evolved gases; the adsorption of dyes; the colors imparted to

flames; the formation of colored borax or microcosmic salt beads; and the colors imparted to drop-reaction papers, etc.

11. **Identification** is a process which involves precipitation of an ion or group of ions and the confirmation of the presence of the ion, or group, in the precipitate by further tests. Characteristic properties exhibited by the precipitate with respect to color, form, or solubility may **indicate** the presence of a certain ion.

12. In order to **confirm** the presence of the ion, the members of the group are further segregated and a special **confirmatory test** is applied. This test is a specific test for an individual ion. The confirmatory test is applied after all the ions which may interfere with the test have been removed from the solution.

13. A **comparative** or **control test** is made on solutions known to contain the ion for which a test is being made.

14. A **blank test** is made by testing for the presence of a given ion in all the reagents that have been used for the separation and identification of the ion. If the ion for which a test is being made is shown to be present as an impurity in the reagents, the ion is reported as present in the original solution *only* when the confirmatory test is more pronounced than the blank test.

15. **Spot tests** are drop reactions carried out on spot plates, glass slides, watch glasses, filter papers, or other filter mediums. A white **spot plate** (porcelain plate with indentations) is used to increase the visibility of dark-colored precipitates; a black one is used to increase the visibility of light-colored precipitates.

16. The **sensitivity** of a test is the concentration below which the solution is so dilute with respect to a given ion that the ion fails to respond to the test under the conditions specified. These concentrations are usually expressed in grams per milliliter (g./ml.) of solution, or sometimes in micrograms per milliliter.

$$1 \text{ microgram } (1\ \mu\text{g.}) = \begin{cases} 1 \text{ gamma } (1\ \gamma) \\ 0.001 \text{ milligram (mg.)} \\ 0.000001 \text{ gram (g.)} \\ \dfrac{1}{1{,}000{,}000} \text{ g.} \\ 1 \times 10^{-6} \text{ g.} \end{cases}$$

That is, 1 microgram, or 1 gamma, is one millionth of a gram. The sensitivity of various tests varies from 1 mg. to 0.01 μg. per ml. Sensitivities depend upon a number of factors, such as the solubility, color, and form of a precipitate; the intensity of the color developed by organic reagents; the type of illumination used; and the effect of other substances that are present when the test is made. Conditions may often be varied to increase the sensitivity of a given test.

The sensitivity of a test is determined by diluting a solution containing a known quantity of the ion until a specified quantity of the diluted solution (usually 1 ml. or 1 drop, 0.05 ml.) fails to respond to the specified test. The number of grams of the ion present in 1 ml. of the most dilute solution that responded to the test is then calculated. For example, 1.58 g. of silver nitrate contains 1 g. of silver ions. When this weight (1.58 g.) of silver nitrate is dissolved in water and diluted to 400 liters (400,000 ml.), a faint precipitate of silver chloride can be seen when hydrochloric acid is added to 1 ml. of this solution. However, at greater dilutions the visibility of the precipitate is so low that it cannot be seen easily. The **limit of dilution** is, then, 1 part of silver to 400,000 parts of water and is expressed by the ratio, 1:400,000. The sensitivity of the test is $1 \div 400{,}000 = 0.0000025$ g./ml. $= 2.5 \times 10^{-6}$ g./ml., or 2.5 μg./ml. Smaller concentrations of Ag^+ than this cannot be detected easily by precipitation as AgCl.

REVIEW QUESTIONS

1. Distinguish between qualitative and quantitative analysis.
2. Why is a qualitative analysis frequently necessary before a quantitative analysis is made?
3. State the aims of a course in qualitative analysis.
4. What information does a qualitative analysis give about an aqueous solution of inorganic salts? Why is it not possible to determine which salts were originally dissolved to make the solution? By what methods could the original salts be identified in the original dry salt mixture?
5. Describe the general scheme of a systematic analysis. Why is it not possible in most cases to make individual specific tests for an ion without separation into groups?
6. Distinguish between macro, micro, and semimicro analysis.
7. List a number of methods, other than chemical reactions in solutions, that are used to determine the composition of a sample of material.
8. Define each of the boldface terms on pages 6–8.
9. Upon what factors does the sensitivity of a test depend? How is it determined? In what units may the sensitivity of a test be expressed?

PROBLEMS

1. If the sensitivity of a test for Sn^{++} is 2 μg./ml., what weight of Sn^{++} will be contained in 1 liter of a solution of this concentration?

2. To what volume can 1 drop of 0.1-M $AgNO_3$ be diluted and still respond to the AgCl test with HCl?
3. The limit of dilution for the detection of Ni^{++} with the organic reagent dimethylglyoxime is 1 part of Ni^{++} in 6×10^6 parts of water. What weight (in μg.) of Ni^{++} will there be in 1 drop (0.05 ml.) of a solution of this concentration? How many nickel ions will be contained in 1 drop? (58.69 g. of Ni^{++} contains 6.023×10^{23} atoms.)
4. One liter of a silver nitrate solution contains 1 g. of Ag^+. How many silver ions are there in 1 drop of this solution?
5. The solubility of AgI is 2.2×10^{-9} g./ml. at 25° C. Would a precipitate of AgI be obtained if 1 drop of a solution containing one billion Ag^+ were added to 1 drop of a solution containing one billion I^-?
6. The solubility of AgCl is 1.9×10^{-6} g./ml. What volume of water in liters will be required to dissolve 1 mg. of AgCl?

CHAPTER 2

CONCENTRATION OF SOLUTIONS—CALCULATIONS

In order to prepare solutions for the laboratory work in qualitative analysis, it is necessary that the student review some of the terms and calculations involved. Also, it is necessary that he review some of the calculations involved in chemical reactions if he is to proceed intelligently. It is frequently necessary, for example, to calculate the volume of a reagent required to precipitate a known amount of certain ions in a solution, to calculate the volume of acid required to neutralize the base in another solution, etc. For this reason a summary is given here of the methods of expressing concentrations and the calculations involved in chemical reactions.

CONCENTRATION OF SOLUTIONS

1. **Dilute solutions** (usually below 6-M) contain relatively small proportions of solute, whereas solutions which contain relatively large proportions of solute are said to be **concentrated.** Hence these terms are only relative, not exact. However, when the term concentrated (concd.) is applied to solutions of certain acids and bases, it usually refers to the solutions commonly supplied by the manufacturers for laboratory use. The composition of these acids and bases is given in Appendix B.

2. The **density** of a material is its mass per unit volume; in the metric system this is the mass, in grams, of 1 cc. of the material. The density of a solid is usually expressed in grams per cc., but the density of a liquid is frequently expressed in grams per ml. Since 1 ml. = 1.000028 cc., densities expressed in either of these volume units are, for most practical purposes, the same. The temperature should be specified since a change in temperature affects the density of a solid or liquid.

Frequently **specific gravity** is used in place of density. It is defined as the ratio of the weight of a substance to the weight of an equal volume of water at 4° C. or some other specified temperature. Since the weight of 1 ml. of water at 4° C. is 1 g., the specific gravity of a substance at 25° C., for example, compared with water at 4° C. (sp. gr. 25°/4°) is the same as the density of the substance at 25° C.

If, instead of 4° C., the comparison is made with water at some other temperature—for example, sp. gr. 25°/20° = 1.125—the density of the substance at 25° C. is

$$\text{density at } 25° = (\text{sp. gr. } 25°/20°)(\text{density of water at } 20°)$$
$$= (1.125)(0.998) = 1.123 \text{ g./ml.}$$

3. **Percentage concentration** by weight is equal to the grams of solute present in 100 g. of solution. Thus a 38 percent (38%) solution of hydrochloric acid is one that contains 38 g. of HCl in 100 g. of solution, that is, 38 g. of HCl and 62 g. of water. The density of this solution is 1.19 (Appendix B). Hence, 1 ml. of a 38% solution of hydrochloric acid contains (1)(1.19)(0.38) = 0.45 g. of HCl. Thus,

$$\text{grams of solute} = (\text{volume of solution})(\text{density})\left(\frac{\text{percent of solute}}{100}\right)$$
$$\text{g.} = (V)(D)\left(\frac{\%}{100}\right)$$

If the density or the percentage concentration is not known, it is necessary to weigh a quantity of the solution in order to obtain a definite weight of solute. Consequently, this system of expressing concentrations is not as useful as many of the others.

The term "percent by weight" solution should be reserved for the solutions defined here and should not be used for solutions such as the following: grams of solute per 100 g. of solvent, or grams of solute per 100 ml. of solvent. It is, however, acceptable to state a "percent by volume" as the milliliters of solute per 100 ml. of solution.

4. **Weight per unit volume.** For many purposes concentrations are conveniently expressed in terms of a weight per unit volume of solution because a measured volume of the solution will give a definite weight of the solute. Concentrations may be expressed, for example, as grams of solute per liter of solution, or as grams of solute per ml. of solution. For work in qualitative analysis, concentrations of test solutions or of known solutions are frequently prepared to contain a certain number of milligrams per ml. of solution—for example, 10 mg./ml. of Pb^{++}. Very dilute solutions used in determining the sensitivity of certain tests are often expressed in terms of micrograms per ml. (μg./ml.). The weight of $Pb(NO_3)_2$ required to prepare 250 ml. of a solution containing 10 mg./ml. of Pb^{++} is obtained as follows:

$$\text{g. of Pb}^{++} = \frac{(10)(250)}{(1000)} = 2.50 \text{ g.}$$

$$\text{g. of Pb(NO}_3)_2 = \frac{2.50}{\text{Pb}} \times \text{Pb(NO}_3)_2$$

$$= \left(\frac{2.50}{207.2}\right)(331.2) = 4.00 \text{ g.}$$

That is, the number of gram-atomic weights of Pb needed is 2.50/207.2; and since 1 mole of $Pb(NO_3)_2$ is required for each gram atom of Pb, the weight of $Pb(NO_3)_2$ needed is obtained by multiplying the gram atoms of Pb by the weight of 1 mole of $Pb(NO_3)_2$.

5. The **molar concentration** of a solution is equal to the number of gram-molecular weights (moles) of solute dissolved in 1 liter of solution. This concentration is called the **molarity** of the solution and is designated by the letter M. A two-molar (2-M) solution, for example, contains 2 moles of solute in 1 liter of solution. To illustrate, the molarity of commercial concentrated hydrochloric acid (Appendix B) is calculated as follows:

$$\text{weight of HCl in 1 liter} = (1000)(1.19)(0.38) = 452.2 \text{ g.}$$

$$\text{molarity} = \frac{\text{grams of solute in 1 liter}}{\text{molecular weight of solute}} = \frac{452.2}{36.47} = 12.4\text{-}M$$

The molecular weight (or formula weight) is equal to the sum of the atomic weights of all the atoms in the compound. The formula weight of a salt is often referred to as its molecular weight. On this basis the molecular weight of $CuSO_4$ is 63.57 + 32.06 + 64 = 159.63 g.; that of $CuSO_4 \cdot 5H_2O$ is 159.63 + 5(18.016) = 249.71 g. This means that only 159.63 g. of $CuSO_4$ are required to prepare 1 liter of a 1-M solution of copper (II) sulfate, whereas 249.71 g. of $CuSO_4 \cdot 5H_2O$ are required to prepare a 1-M solution using the hydrate.

6. The **normality** of a solution is equal to the number of gram-equivalent weights (equivalents) of solute dissolved in 1 liter of solution. This concentration is called the normality of the solution, and is designated by the letter N. Thus a 5-N solution of sulfuric acid contains 5 equivalent weights of H_2SO_4 in 1 liter of solution.

The equivalent weight of a molecule, ion, or radical is the weight that contains, reacts with, or displaces 1.008 g. of hydrogen, 8 g. of oxygen, or an equivalent quantity of another element. From this relationship it can be shown that the equivalent weight of an acid, base, or salt is equal to the gram-molecular weight divided by the total valence of the reacting radical, except in oxidation-reduction reactions. Here the formula weight is divided by the change in oxidation state and this is numerically equal to the electrons gained by an oxidizing agent or to the electrons lost by a reducing agent. Table 2.1 shows the method of determining the equivalent weight of a substance. The normality of a solution may be calculated as follows:

TABLE 2.1. Equivalent Weight of Acids, Bases, and Salts

Substance	Equivalent Weight	Examples
Acids	$\frac{\text{Formula weight}}{\text{Number of ionizable protons}}$	$\frac{H_2SO_4}{2}$, $\frac{CH_3COOH}{1}$
Hydroxides	$\frac{\text{Formula weight}}{\text{Number of hydroxide groups}}$	$\frac{Ca(OH)_2}{2}$, $\frac{Fe(OH)_3}{3}$
Bases	$\frac{\text{Formula weight}}{\text{Number of protons accepted}}$	$\frac{NH_3}{1}$, $\frac{OH^-}{1}$, $\frac{CO_3^=}{2}$
Normal salts	$\frac{\text{Formula weight}}{\text{Total valence of + or − radical}}$	$\frac{Al_2(SO_4)_3}{6}$, $\frac{KMnO_4}{1}$
Mixed, hydrogen, hydroxy-, oxy-, complex, or double salts	$\frac{\text{Formula weight}}{\text{Total valence of reacting radical}}$	$\frac{Na_2HPO_4}{2}$ for Na^+ $\frac{Na_2HPO_4}{1}$ for H^+ $\frac{Na_2HPO_4}{3}$ for PO_4^{3-}
Oxidizing agents	$\frac{\text{Formula weight}}{\text{Electrons gained}}$	$\frac{KMnO_4}{5}$ for $MnO_4^- \rightarrow Mn^{++}$
Reducing agents	$\frac{\text{Formula weight}}{\text{Electrons lost}}$	$\frac{SnCl_2}{2}$ for $Sn^{++} \rightarrow Sn^{4+}$

$$\text{normality} = \text{gram equivalents per liter of solution}$$

$$N = \frac{\text{grams of solute in 1 liter of solution}}{\text{equivalent weight}}$$

$$= \frac{(\text{grams of solute})(1000)}{(\text{ml. of solution})(\text{equivalent weight})}$$

Since, in certain cases, the normality of a solution is ambiguous unless the reaction for which the solution was made is fully specified, it is preferable to label all bottles with the molar concentration. The normality for specific reactions can also be stated if desired. It is hoped by many that normality will ultimately be dropped as a method of expressing concentrations.

7. The **gram-ion concentration** of a solution is equal to the number of gram-ion weights (moles of an ion) present in 1 liter of solution. A gram-ion weight is equal to the sum of the atomic weights of the atoms in the ion: $Na^+ = 22.997$ g.; $SO_4^{--} = 96.06$ g.; $NH_4^+ = 18.04$ g. It follows that a 1-*M* solution of Na_2SO_4 contains 2 gram ions of Na^+ and 1 gram ion of SO_4^{--}. Or, since 1 gram-ion weight of an ion contains 6.02×10^{23} (Avogadro's number) individual ions, a 1-*M* solution of Na_2SO_4 contains $2(6.02 \times 10^{23}) = 12.04 \times 10^{23}$ sodium ions, whereas it contains only 6.02×10^{23} sulfate ions. This means that a 0.5-*M* solution of Na_2SO_4 contains 6.02×10^{23} sodium ions or 1 gram ion of Na^+. If the test solutions used in the laboratory contain 0.1 gram cation per liter of solution, equal volumes of these solutions will contain equal numbers of the ions for which tests are made.

The relation between molar, normal, and gram-ion concentrations is shown by the following tabulation for lead nitrate and sodium alum:

Molarity	Normality	Gram Ion
1-*M* $Pb(NO_3)_2$	2-*N* for Pb^{++}	1 gram ion for Pb^{++}
	2-*N* for NO_3^-	2 gram ion for NO_3^-
1-*M* $Na_2SO_4 \cdot Al_2(SO_4)_3 \cdot 24H_2O$	2-*N* for Na^+	2 gram ion for Na^+
	6-*N* for Al^{3+}	2 gram ion for Al^{3+}
	8-*N* for SO_4^{--}	4 gram ion for SO_4^{--}

This illustrates again that, in the case of complex or double salts, normality has meaning only when the nature of the reaction for which the solution is to be used is specified. A 0.1 gram-ion solution of Pb^{++} will contain 20.72 g. of Pb^{++} per liter, or 20.72 mg./ml. In order to prepare this solution it would be necessary to prepare a 0.1-*M* solution of $Pb(NO_3)_2$ by dissolving one-tenth of a gram-formula weight of $Pb(NO_3)_2$, or 33.12 g., in 1 liter of solution. The general procedure for preparing a solution of definitely known concentration is illustrated in Fig. 2.1.

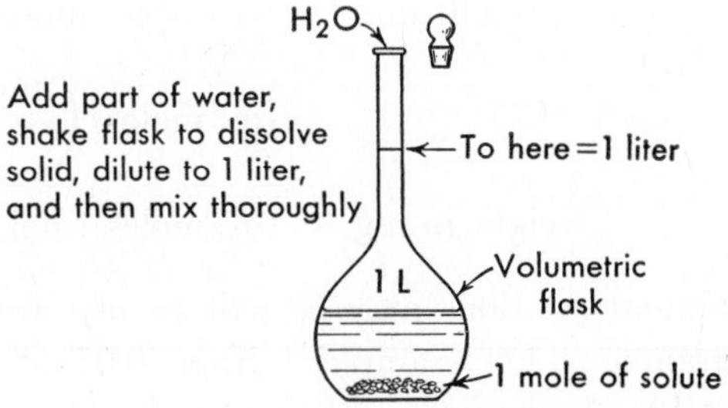

FIG. 2.1. Preparation of a 1-*M* Solution.

8. **Millimoles and milliequivalents.** A millimole (m. mole) is one thousandth of a mole (gram-molecular weight) and a milliequivalent (m.

equiv.) is one thousandth of a gram-equivalent weight of a substance. It can be seen that 1 m. mole of a substance dissolved in 1 ml. of solution has the same concentration as 1 mole dissolved in 1 liter of solution. That is, the number of millimoles per ml. of solution is equal to the molarity:

$$M = \frac{\text{m. moles}}{\text{ml.}} = \frac{\text{moles}}{\text{liter}}$$

Similarly,

$$N = \frac{\text{m. equiv.}}{\text{ml.}} = \frac{\text{equivalents}}{\text{liter}}$$

These units are particularly useful in laboratory work where volumes are usually measured in milliliters rather than in liters. For example, if 30 ml. of a 0.1-M solution of $Pb(NO_3)_2$ is used for a particular experiment, the number of millimoles used is (30)(0.1), or 3.0. This value times the weight of 1 m. mole $\left(\frac{\text{molecular weight}}{1000}\right)$ gives the number of grams of the substance present.

The following is a summary of these relations:

$$\text{no. of millimoles} = \frac{\text{grams}}{\text{molecular weight}/1000}$$

$$= \frac{\text{milligrams}}{\text{molecular weight}}$$

Also,

$$\text{no. of millimoles} = (\text{ml.})(M)$$

If the number of millimoles is known, the weight of the substance is given by:

$$\text{weight in g.} = (\text{no. of m. moles})(\text{weight of 1 m. mole})$$

$$= (\text{m. moles})\left(\frac{\text{mol. wt.}}{1000}\right)$$

$$\text{weight in mg.} = (\text{m. moles})(\text{mol. wt.})$$

Similar relations may be written in terms of milliequivalents and milligram ions. For example, 2 drops (0.05 ml. each) of a 0.1 gram-ion solution of Pb^{++} contains

$$\text{mg. of } Pb^{++} = (\text{ml.})(\text{gram-ion conc.})(\text{gram-ion wt. of } Pb^{++})$$

$$= (0.05 \times 2)(0.1)(207.2) = 2.07 \text{ mg.}$$

Other Methods of Expressing Concentration

9. **Molality (m).** The molality of a solution is equal to the number of moles of solute dissolved in 1000 g. of solvent. Thus, a 0.2-*m* solution of acetic acid contains (0.2)(60.05) = 12.01 g. of CH_3COOH in 1000 g. of water. Molality is used when the degree of ionization is calculated from the freezing-point depression or from the boiling-point elevation. The difference between molality and molarity should be carefully noted.

10. **Mole fraction.** This is the fraction of solute molecules present in a given solution. It is obtained by dividing the number of moles of the solute present in the solution by the total number of moles of solute and solvent present. That is,

$$N_2 = \frac{n_2}{n_1 + n_2}$$

where N_2 is the mole fraction of the solute molecules and n_1 and n_2 are the number of moles of solvent and solute molecules respectively. Concentrations are not often expressed in terms of mole fractions in qualitative analysis, but this unit is useful in advanced courses in chemistry.

Expressing the Solubility of Substances

The **solubility** of a substance at a given temperature is defined as the concentration of solute in its saturated solution. A saturated solution is one that is in equilibrium with excess undissolved solute. Any of the methods described previously can be used to express the concentration of a saturated solution. The methods most useful for qualitative analysis are: grams of solute per ml. of solution, milligrams or micrograms of solute per ml., or moles per liter.

SOLUBILITY IN GRAMS, MILLIGRAMS, OR MICROGRAMS PER MILLILITER. Many solubility tables list the solubility of substances in grams per 100 ml. of solution (g./100 ml.). The solubility in grams per ml. is then 1/100 of this value. Thus, if the solubility of silver chloride is 0.00019 g./100 ml. at 25° C., its solubility in grams per ml. is

$$\begin{aligned} 0.00019 \div 100 = 0.0000019 &= 1.9 \times 10^{-6} \text{ g./ml.} \\ &= 1.9 \times 10^{-3} \text{ mg./ml.} \\ &= 1.9\ \mu\text{g./ml.} \end{aligned}$$

For substances that are rather insoluble, expressing the concentration in terms of micrograms per ml. (1 μg. = 10^{-6} g.) is convenient.

MOLAR SOLUBILITY. Rather extensive use is made of solubilities of salts expressed in moles per liter of solution when the solubility product principle is discussed. The **molar solubility** can readily be calculated from the solubility in grams per ml. as follows: The solubility in grams per ml. multiplied by 1000 gives the solubility in grams per liter of solution. This divided by the molecular weight of the solute is equal to the moles of solute dissolved in 1 liter of solution, i.e., the molar solubility. Thus the molar solubility of silver chloride is

$$\frac{(0.0000019)(1000)}{143.34} = \frac{(1.9 \times 10^{-6})(1 \times 10^{3})}{(1.43 \times 10^{2})} = 1.3 \times 10^{-5} \text{ moles/liter}$$

Sometimes the molar solubility is known and it is desired to determine the grams of a particular ion in 1 ml. of the saturated solution. The molar solubility of $PbSO_4$, for example, is 1.3×10^{-4} moles per liter. How many grams of Pb^{++} are present in 1 ml. of this solution?

Since $1PbSO_4$ yields $1Pb^{++}$, the number of gram atoms of Pb in 1 liter of solution is 1.3×10^{-4}. Therefore, the number of grams of Pb in 1 liter of solution is $(1.3 \times 10^{-4})(207.2)$, and in 1 ml.,

$$\frac{(1.3 \times 10^{-4})(207.2)}{1000} = \frac{(1.3 \times 10^{-4})(2.07 \times 10^{2})}{1 \times 10^{3}} = 2.7 \times 10^{-5} \text{ g./ml.}$$

In micrograms per ml. this becomes

$$(2.7 \times 10^{-5})(1 \times 10^{6}) = 2.7 \times 10^{1} = 27\ \mu\text{g./ml.}$$

CALCULATIONS

Concentrations

1. *Molarity and Normality of Solutions.* The molarity of a solution containing a given weight of solute is determined by calculating the number of moles of solute in 1 liter of solution. Consider the following example.

What is the molarity of a solution that contains 15 g. of $Pb(NO_3)_2$ in 50 ml. of solution?

$$\text{weight in 1 ml.} = \frac{15 \text{ g.}}{50 \text{ ml.}}$$

$$\text{weight in 1000 ml.} = \frac{(15)(1000)}{(50)}$$

$$\text{molecular weight of } Pb(NO_3)_2 = 331.2$$

$$\text{molarity} = \frac{(15)(1000)}{(50)(331.2)} = 0.91\text{-}M$$

This may be expressed by the equation

$$M = \frac{(\text{g.})(1000)}{(\text{ml.})(\text{mol. wt.})}$$

or, in terms of the normality of the solution,

$$N = \frac{(\text{g.})(1000)}{(\text{ml.})(\text{equiv. wt.})}$$

The following example illustrates the method of converting percentage concentrations to concentrations in terms of molarities and normalities.

Calculate the molarity and normality of concentrated sulfuric acid which has a specific gravity (25°/4°) of 1.84 and contains 95% by weight of H_2SO_4.

$$\text{weight of } H_2SO_4 \text{ in 1 liter} = (1000)(1.84)(0.95) = 1748 \text{ g.}$$

$$\text{molarity} = \frac{1748}{98.08} = 17.8\text{-}M$$

$$\text{normality} = \frac{1748}{49.04} = 35.6\text{-}N$$

2. *Weight of Solute to Prepare, or Contained in, a Given Volume of Known Concentration.* The weight of solute in 1000 ml. of solution is equal to the molarity of the solution times the molecular weight of the solute, and the weight of solute in 1 ml. is one thousandth of the weight of the solute in 1000 ml. The weight of solute in any volume is then obtained by multiplication. The following example illustrates these steps.

How many grams of HCl are there in 5 ml. of 4-*M* HCl?

$$\text{weight of HCl in 1 liter} = (4)(36.47)$$

$$\text{weight of HCl in 1 ml.} = \frac{(4)(36.47)}{1000}$$

$$\text{weight of HCl in 5 ml.} = \frac{(4)(36.47)(5)}{1000} = 0.729 \text{ g.}$$

These relations are expressed by the general equations:

$$\text{grams of solute (g.)} = (\text{liters})(M)(\text{mol. wt.})$$

$$= \left(\frac{\text{ml.}}{1000}\right)(M)(\text{mol. wt.})$$

These equations are derived from the fact that the volume in liters multiplied by the molarity of the solution is equal to the number of moles of solute present. Thus 3 liters of 2-*M* HCl contains (3)(2) = 6 moles of HCl. The number of grams of solute is then equal to the number of moles of solute times the number of grams in 1 mole.

The equation can be expressed in a more useful form in terms of millimoles or milliequivalents:

$$g. = (\text{no. of millimoles})(\text{weight of 1 m. mole})$$

$$g. = (\text{ml.})(M)\left(\frac{\text{mol. wt. of solute}}{1000}\right)$$

The following example illustrates the use of this equation.

What weight of HCl is required to prepare 250 ml. of 0.25-*M* HCl? Substituting in the above equation, we have

$$g. = (\text{millimoles})(\text{weight of 1 m. mole})$$

$$g. = (250)(0.25)\left(\frac{36.47}{1000}\right) = 2.28 \text{ g. of HCl}$$

If we want to prepare this solution from concentrated hydrochloric acid, the volume required to give 2.28 g. of HCl is

$$\text{ml.} = \frac{(2.28)}{(1.19)(0.38)} = 5.04 \text{ ml.}$$

Equations similar to the one above can be used in calculations involving normalities and gram-ion concentrations. Thus:

$$g. = (\text{ml.})(N)\left(\frac{\text{equiv. wt.}}{1000}\right)$$

$$g. = (\text{ml.})(\text{gram-ion conc.})\left(\frac{\text{gram-ion wt.}}{1000}\right)$$

If three of these terms are given, or if they can be obtained from other data, the remaining term can be calculated.

3. *Dilution Problems.* The amount of solute dissolved in a given volume is equal to the amount of solute per unit volume multiplied by the given volume. That is,

$$(\text{volume})(\text{concentration}) = \text{amount of solute}$$

When the volume is expressed in liters or milliliters (ml.), and the concentration is expressed in grams, milligrams, moles, equivalents, gram ions, milliequivalents, or millimoles per unit volume, the amount of the solute in the given volume is as follows:

$$\begin{aligned}
(\text{liters})(M) &= \text{moles of solute}\\
(\text{ml.})(M) &= \text{millimoles of solute}\\
(\text{liters})(N) &= \text{equivalents of solute}\\
(\text{ml.})(N) &= \text{milliequivalents of solute}\\
(\text{liters})(\text{gram-ion conc.}) &= \text{gram ions of the ion}\\
(\text{ml.})(\text{gram-ion conc.}) &= \text{milligram ions of the ion}\\
(\text{ml.})(\text{grams/ml.}) &= \text{weight of solute in grams}\\
(\text{ml.})(\text{milligrams/ml.}) &= \text{weight of solute in milligrams}
\end{aligned}$$

Since the amount of solute is not changed by diluting the solution, it follows that

$$(\text{vol.})(\text{conc.}) = (\text{vol.})'(\text{conc.})'$$

Or, for example,

$$(\text{ml.})(M) \text{ before dilution} = (\text{ml.})'(M)' \text{ after dilution}$$
$$(\text{ml.})(\text{g./ml.}) \text{ before dilution} = (\text{ml.})'(\text{g./ml.})' \text{ after dilution}$$

If three of these terms are known, the fourth can be calculated.

Actually it is not necessary to set dilution problems up in this way. We can simply say, for example, that the number of millimoles of solute measured out before dilution is (ml.)(M). The concentration after dilution is the millimoles of solute per ml. of the diluted solution, or

$$M' = \frac{(\text{ml.})(M)}{\text{ml.}'}$$

Also, since (ml.)′(M)′ is equal to the number of millimoles,

$$\text{ml.}' = \frac{\text{millimoles}}{M'} = \frac{(\text{ml.})(M)}{M'}$$

This expression can be used to calculate the volume to which a solution must be diluted to obtain another solution of specified molarity.

Example 1. To what volume must 1 ml. of 4-M HCl be diluted to obtain a 0.3-M solution?

$$(\text{ml.})(M) = (\text{ml.})'(M)'$$
$$(1)(4) = (\text{ml.})'(0.3)$$
$$(\text{ml.})' = \frac{(1)(4)}{(0.3)} = 13.3 \text{ ml.}$$

Following the reasoning of the second method above, we see that the number of millimoles of HCl is (1)(4) = 4. The 0.3-M solution is obtained when this number of millimoles is dissolved in the following volume:

$$\text{ml.}' = \frac{(\text{ml.})(M)}{M'} = \frac{(1)(4)}{(0.3)} = 13.3 \text{ ml.}$$

Example 2. A 0.1 gram-ion solution of Ag^+ contains 0.01079 g./ml. of Ag^+. To what extent must 1 ml. of this solution be diluted to obtain a solution with a concentration of 2 mg./ml.?

Convert g./ml. to mg./ml.:

$$0.01079 \text{ g./ml.} = 10.79 \text{ mg./ml.}$$

Then, since 1 ml. of the solution is diluted,

$$(1)(10.79) = (\text{ml.})'(2)$$
$$(\text{ml.})' = \frac{(1)(10.79)}{(2)} = 5.4 \text{ ml.}$$

Example 3. What is the concentration in g./ml. of a solution made by adding 1 drop of silver nitrate test solution (0.1 gram-ion of Ag^+) to 1 ml. of water?

Calculate the concentration in g./ml. from the gram-ion concentration:

$$0.1 \text{ gram ion of } Ag^+ \text{ per liter} = 0.01079 \text{ g./ml.}$$

Then since the volume of 1 drop is 0.05 ml. (20 drops per ml.),

$$(0.05)(0.01079) = (1.05)(\text{g./ml.})'$$

$$(\text{g./ml.})' = \frac{(0.05)(0.01079)}{(1.05)} = 0.00051, \text{ or } 0.51 \text{ mg./ml.}$$

Reactions

In chemical reactions involving a combination or interchange of ions in solution, the use of equivalents and normalities simplifies the calculations. It follows, from the definition of the equivalent weight of a substance, that for reactions which are substantially complete, the number of equivalents of one reactant is equal to the number of equivalents of the other reactant. Also for such reactions equal volumes of solutions with the same normality are equivalent and therefore react to completion. The application of these concepts is illustrated in the examples that follow. It should be pointed out that, although this system is useful, confusion may arise because the equivalent weight of a substance for one type of reaction may not be the same as it is for another reaction. Thus the equivalent weight of $KMnO_4$ for nonoxidizing reactions would be $KMnO_4 \div 1$, whereas for an oxidation reaction in acid solution it would be $KMnO_4 \div 5$, and $KMnO_4 \div 3$ for such a reaction in basic solution. Because of this confusion the tendency now is to use moles and molarities in connection with the appropriate equivalency factor obtained from the equation for the actual chemical reaction.

1. *Neutralization.* This type of reaction takes place when, for example, a solution of an acid is added to a solution of a base. At the **equivalence point** the number of equivalents of acid added is equal to the number of equivalents of the base. Thus

$$\text{equivalents of the acid} = \text{equivalents of the base}$$

From the discussion in the preceding section it follows that

$$(\text{liters})(N) \text{ of the acid} = (\text{liters})'(N)' \text{ of the base}$$

In terms of milliequivalents,

$$\text{milliequivalents of the acid} = \text{milliequivalents of the base}$$

or

$$(\text{ml.})(N) \text{ of the acid} = (\text{ml.})'(N)' \text{ of the base}$$

If three of these terms are known, the fourth can be calculated.

Example 1. What is the normality of a solution of sodium hydroxide if 15.5 ml. of 4-N HCl is required to neutralize 10 ml. of the NaOH solution?

$$(\text{ml.})(N) = (\text{ml.})'(N)'$$
$$(15.5)(4) = (10)(N)'$$
$$(N)' = \frac{(15.5)(4)}{(10)} = 6.2\text{-}N$$

Example 2. How many drops of 4-N HCl are required to neutralize a solution to which have been added 3 drops of concentrated ammonia with a normality of 14.8?

The volume of 1 drop is 0.05 ml. Therefore,

$$(\text{no. of drops} \times 0.05)(4) = (3 \times 0.05)(14.8)$$

Since 0.05 appears on both sides of the equation, it can be canceled. Hence

$$(\text{drops})(N) = (\text{drops})'(N)'$$

or

$$(\text{drops})(4) = (3)(14.8)$$
$$(\text{drops}) = \frac{(3)(14.8)}{(4)} = 11 \text{ drops}$$

Such problems can be solved as readily by using molarities as by using normalities, as is shown in the following example.

Example 3. How many grams of NaOH are there in a solution which requires 30 ml. of 0.1-M H_2SO_4 to reach the equivalence point?

The millimoles of H_2SO_4 used are:

$$\text{millimoles of } H_2SO_4 = (30 \text{ ml.})(0.1\text{-}M) = 3 \text{ m. moles}$$

Each millimole of H_2SO_4 reacts with 2 m. moles of NaOH:

$$(2H_3O^+ + SO_4^{--}) + 2(Na^+ + OH^-) \rightleftarrows 2Na^+ + SO_4^{--} + 4H_2O$$

Therefore, the number of millimoles of NaOH is twice the number of millimoles of H_2SO_4, or

$$\text{millimoles of NaOH} = (3.0)(2) = 6 \text{ m. moles}$$

and the grams of NaOH are:

$$\text{grams of NaOH} = (\text{millimoles})(\text{weight of 1 m. mole})$$
$$= (6.0)\left(\frac{40.01}{1000}\right) = 0.24 \text{ g.}$$

Actually in working the problem it is not necessary to write down each stage as is done above. The answer can be written simply as

$$\text{grams of NaOH} = (30 \times 0.1)(2)\left(\frac{40.01}{1000}\right) = 0.24 \text{ g.}$$

If normalities are used, this problem is solved as follows: The normality of 0.1-M H_2SO_4 is 0.2-N. Hence,

$$\begin{aligned} \text{milliequivalents of NaOH} &= \text{milliequivalents of } H_2SO_4 \\ &= (30)(0.2) = 6 \\ \text{grams of NaOH} &= (\text{milliequivalents})(\text{wt. of 1 m. equiv.}) \\ &= (6.0)\left(\frac{40.01}{1000}\right) = 0.24 \text{ g.} \end{aligned}$$

2. *Solutions of Other Reactants.* The procedure used for precipitation reactions is the same as that outlined for neutralization. Since 1 m. equiv. of one reactant interacts with 1 m. equiv. of another reactant, it follows that

$$(\text{ml.})(N) = (\text{ml.})'(N)'$$

Example 1. How many milliliters of 4-N HCl are required to precipitate Ag^+ as AgCl from 5 ml. of 0.2-N solution of $AgNO_3$?

$$\begin{aligned} (\text{ml.})(4) &= (5)(0.2) \\ \text{ml.} &= \frac{(5)(0.2)}{4} = 0.25 \text{ ml., or 5 drops} \end{aligned}$$

Example 2. How many milliliters of 0.1-M $Ca(CH_3COO)_2$ are required to precipitate PO_4^{3-} as $Ca_3(PO_4)_2$ from 3 ml. of 0.2-M Na_2HPO_4? This problem is done without using normalities as follows:

The equation for the reaction is

$$3Ca^{++} + 2PO_4^{3-} \rightleftharpoons \underline{Ca_3(PO_4)_2} \downarrow$$

Here 3 m. moles of Ca^{++} are required for 2 m. moles of PO_4^{3-}, or for every millimole of PO_4^{3-} there are required 1.5 m. moles of Ca^{++}:

$$\underbrace{1PO_4^{3-} \equiv 1.5Ca^{++}}_{\text{“reacts with” or “is equivalent to”}}$$

The number of millimoles of Ca^{++} needed is then 1.5 times the millimoles of PO_4^{3-}, or

$$\begin{aligned} \text{millimoles of } Ca^{++} &= (\text{millimoles of } PO_4^{3-})(1.5) \\ &= (3)(0.2)(1.5) \end{aligned}$$

and

$$\begin{aligned} \text{milliliters of 0.1-}M\ Ca(CH_3COO)_2 &= \frac{\text{millimoles of } Ca^{++}}{M} \\ &= \frac{(3)(0.2)(1.5)}{(0.1)} = 9 \text{ ml.} \end{aligned}$$

Thus we see that such problems are as easily solved by using millimoles and molarities as by using normalities and milliequivalents. Further examples will be given later in connection with oxidation-reduction reactions.

3. *A Solid and a Solution.* As was explained in the preceding section, the number of equivalents of one reactant is equal to the number of equivalents of the other reactant. Thus,

$$(\text{equivalents})_{\text{solid}} = (\text{equivalents})_{\text{solute in solution}}$$

or

$$(\text{equivalents})_{\text{solid}} = (\text{liters})(N)_{\text{solution}}$$

Since volumes are usually measured in milliliters, this equation may be expressed as

$$(\text{milliequivalents})_{\text{solid}} = (\text{ml.})(N)_{\text{solution}}$$

Example 1. How many milliliters of 4-N HCl are required to dissolve 0.5 g. of FeS? The number of milliequivalents of FeS is equal to the number of milligrams of solid (0.5 × 1000 = 500 mg.) divided by the equivalent weight of FeS (87.90 ÷ 2 = 43.95 g.). Therefore,

$$\frac{(0.5)(1000)}{43.95} = (\text{ml.})(4)$$

$$(\text{ml.}) = \frac{(0.5)(1000)}{(43.95)(4)} = 2.84 \text{ ml.}$$

Example 2. How many drops of 4-N HCl are required to precipitate 50 mg. of AgCl from a solution that contains Ag^+?

$$\frac{50}{\text{AgCl}} = (\text{ml.})(4)$$

$$(\text{ml.}) = \frac{50}{(143.34)(4)} = 0.087 \text{ ml.}$$

and

$$(0.087)(20) = 1.74, \text{ or 2 drops}$$

Example 3. How many drops of 4-N HCl solution are required to precipitate the ions of Group I if 20 mg. of Ag^+, 50 mg. of $Hg_2{}^{++}$, and 40 mg. of Pb^{++} are present? The number of milliequivalents of HCl required is equal to the sum of the milliequivalents of Ag^+, $Hg_2{}^{++}$, and Pb^{++}. Thus,

$$\frac{20}{Ag^+} + \frac{50}{Hg_2{}^{++} \div 2} + \frac{40}{Pb^{++} \div 2} = (\text{ml.})(4)$$

or

$$\frac{20}{107.9} + \frac{50}{200.6} + \frac{40}{103.6} = (\text{ml.})(4)$$

$$0.185 + 0.249 + 0.386 = (\text{ml.})(4)$$

$$(\text{ml.}) = \frac{0.821}{4} = 0.205 \text{ ml.}$$

The number of drops required is therefore

$$(0.205 \text{ ml.})(20) = 4.10, \text{ or 4 drops}$$

Example 4. How many milliliters of 4-*M* HCl are required to dissolve 500 mg. of $BaCO_3$? The equation for the reaction is

$$2H_3O^+ + \underline{BaCO_3} \rightleftharpoons Ba^{++} + 3H_2O + CO_2\uparrow$$

One millimole of $BaCO_3$ requires 2 m. moles of H_3O^+. Hence for every millimole of $BaCO_3$, 2 m. moles of HCl are required, i.e.,

$$1BaCO_3 \equiv 2HCl$$

Therefore, the number of millimoles of $BaCO_3$ multiplied by 2 equals the number of millimoles of HCl needed:

$$\text{millimoles of } BaCO_3 = \frac{500}{197.4}$$

$$\text{millimoles of HCl} = \left(\frac{500}{197.4}\right)(2)$$

$$\text{milliliters of 4-}M\text{ HCl} = \frac{\text{millimoles of HCl}}{M}$$

$$= \frac{(500)(2)}{(197.4)(4)} = 1.27 \text{ ml.}$$

This example again illustrates the method of calculating such problems without the use of normalities and equivalents. The student should practice solving the problems at the end of this chapter with both methods. He will save much time in doing the problems if he uses logarithms or a slide rule.

4. *Oxidation-Reduction.* The methods outlined above are also applicable to oxidation-reduction reactions, as the following examples make clear.

Example 1. How many milliliters of 0.02-*M* $KMnO_4$ solution will be required to react with 6 ml. of 0.2-*M* NaCl in acid solution?

The reaction is as follows (see the next chapter for balancing oxidation-reduction equations):

$$2MnO_4^- + 10Cl^- + 16H_3O^+ \rightleftharpoons 2Mn^{++} + 5Cl_2 + 24H_2O$$

From this equation we see that 2 moles of MnO_4^- react with 10 moles of Cl^-, or 1 mole of Cl^- requires ⅕ mole of MnO_4^-. That is,

$$1Cl^- \equiv \tfrac{1}{5}MnO_4^-$$

In terms of millimoles, every millimole of Cl^- requires ⅕ of a millimole of MnO_4^-. Hence, all we need to do to obtain the number of millimoles of MnO_4^- is to multiply the number of millimoles of Cl^- by ⅕:

$$\text{millimoles of } MnO_4^- = (\text{millimoles of } Cl^-)(\tfrac{1}{5})$$

$$= (6)(0.2) \times \tfrac{1}{5} = 0.24 \text{ m. mole}$$

Then, since

$$(\text{ml.})(M) = \text{millimoles}$$

or

$$\text{ml.} = \text{millimoles}/M$$

the number of milliliters of the 0.02-M $KMnO_4$ solution needed is

$$\text{milliliters of 0.02-}M\ KMnO_4 = \frac{\text{millimoles of } KMnO_4}{M}$$

$$= \frac{0.24}{0.02} = 12 \text{ ml.}$$

This calculation has been done in detail to show the steps in the reasoning process. Actually in doing the problem we would write down the steps one after the other:

$$\text{milliliters of } MnO_4^- = \frac{\text{millimoles}}{M} = \frac{(6)(0.2)(\frac{1}{5})}{0.02} = 12 \text{ ml.}$$

In some respects calculations with normalities are simpler because the number of equivalents of one reactant is just equal to the number of equivalents of the other reactant, i.e.,

$$(\text{ml.})(N) = (\text{ml.})'(N)'$$

$$(\text{ml.}) = \frac{(\text{ml.})'(N)'}{N}$$

The normalities of the solutions in the above problem are 0.1-N $KMnO_4$ and 0.2-N NaCl. Hence, the number of milliliters of the $KMnO_4$ solution required for 6 ml. of 0.2-N NaCl is

$$\text{ml.} = \frac{(\text{ml.})'(N)'}{N} = \frac{(6)(0.2)}{(0.1)} = 12 \text{ ml.}$$

One important precaution is necessary when expressing solutions in terms of normalities. The normalities apply to particular reactions carried out under definite acidity conditions, etc. Thus, in basic solutions where the product from MnO_4^- is usually MnO_2, the normality of a 0.02-M solution of $KMnO_4$ is 0.06-N instead of 0.1-N.

Example 2. How many drops of 4-M HNO_3 are required to dissolve 200 mg. of PbS?

The equation for the dissolution of PbS in HNO_3 is:

$$2NO_3^- + \underline{3PbS} + 8H_3O^+ \rightarrow 2NO\uparrow + 3Pb^{++} + \underline{3S}\downarrow + 12H_2O$$

From this equation

$$3PbS \equiv 2NO_3^-$$

or

$$1PbS \equiv \tfrac{2}{3}NO_3^-$$

That is, for every millimole of PbS, ⅔ of a millimole of NO_3^- is needed. The millimoles of NO_3^- required is ⅔ times the millimoles of PbS, or

$$\text{millimoles of } NO_3^- = \left(\frac{200}{239.3}\right)\left(\frac{2}{3}\right)$$

The number of milliliters of 4-M HNO_3 is

$$\text{milliliters} = \frac{\text{millimoles}}{M} = \frac{(200)(2)}{(239.3)(3)(4)} = 0.14 \text{ ml.}$$

Since there are 20 drops in 1 ml., the number of drops of HNO_3 required is

$$\text{no. of drops} = (0.14)(20) = 2.8 \text{ drops}$$

This is calculated on the assumption that the solution contains sufficient acid from other sources for the reaction. If the HNO_3 added is to furnish the H_3O^+ required for the reaction, more HNO_3 will be required than was calculated above, since $1PbS \equiv \frac{8}{3}H_3O^+$. Then

$$\text{millimoles of } H_3O^+ = \left(\frac{200}{239.3}\right)\left(\frac{8}{3}\right)$$

or the number of milliliters of 4-M HNO_3 required is

$$\text{milliliters} = \frac{\text{millimoles}}{M} = \frac{(200)(8)}{(239.3)(3)(4)} = 0.56 \text{ ml.}$$

The number of drops needed is $(0.56)(20) = 11.2$.

REVIEW QUESTIONS

1. List the different ways of expressing the concentration of solutions.
2. What are the approximate molarity and normality of the following concentrated acids and bases as ordinarily supplied by the manufacturer: HCl, HNO_3, H_2SO_4, CH_3COOH, NH_3? (See Appendix B.)
3. Define the following terms: (a) specific gravity; (b) percentage concentration; (c) molarity; (d) a 1-M solution; (e) normality; (f) gram-ion weight; (g) gram-ion concentration.
4. Describe the procedure for preparing a 0.1-M solution of $AgNO_3$.
5. Give examples to illustrate the calculation of the equivalent weight of acids, bases, and salts, and of oxidizing and reducing agents.
6. State and illustrate the relation between molar, normal, and gram-ion concentrations. List the normalities and the gram-ion concentrations with respect to each ion in 0.3-M $Na_2SO_4 \cdot Al_2(SO_4)_3 \cdot 24H_2O$.
7. Define milliequivalents, millimoles, and milligram ions. State how each is determined for a given volume of solution.
8. What is the difference between molarity and molality?
9. What is the mole fraction of solute in a 1-m solution of HCl?
10. Define solubility. How may it be expressed? Illustrate.
11. Write the equations in general terms for (a) molarity and normality of a solution; (b) grams of solute in a volume of solution of known concentration; (c) concentration of a solution after dilution to a new volume; (d) volume of a given solution to produce a specified volume of specified concentration; (e) neutralization reactions; (f) precipitation reactions; (g) dissolution of a precipitate; (h) oxidation-reduction reactions.

PROBLEMS

(Note: Review the use of exponents, logarithms, and the slide rule before doing these problems.)

Density and Specific Gravity

1. If 2.4 cc. of a solid substance at 25° weighs 12.4 g., what is the density of the substance?
2. The density of iron is 7.6 g./cc. What is the weight of 4 cc. of iron?
3. The density of gold is 19.32 g./cc. What volume of gold weighs 1 kg.?
4. If 12 ml. of 70% HNO_3 weighs 17 g. at 25°, what is the density of the acid in g./ml.?
5. If 25 ml. of 95% ethyl alcohol weighs 19.2 g. at 25°, what is the density of the alcohol solution in g./ml.?
6. The specific gravity (25°/4°) of a 15% by weight ethyl alcohol solution is 0.978. What volume will 10 g. of this alcohol solution occupy?
7. A concentrated solution of HCl has a specific gravity (25°/4°) of 1.19 and contains 37% HCl. What is the weight of HCl in 100 ml. of this solution? In 1 liter of the solution?
8. The density of concd. NH_3 solution is 0.90 g./ml. If 100 ml. of water and 10 ml. of concd. NH_3 are mixed, what is the approximate density of the diluted NH_3 solution? (Assume additivity of the volumes.)
9. What volume of concd. H_2SO_4 (specific gravity 25°/4° = 1.84) must be added to 100 ml. of water to obtain a solution with a specific gravity (25°/4°) of 1.25? (Assume additivity of the volumes.)

Molecular, Equivalent, and Gram-Ion Weights

10. For the compounds listed in the following table, determine:
    a. The molecular weights.
    b. The equivalent weight of the compounds for each of the ions or radicals in parentheses.
    c. The weight of the compound required for 1 gram-ion weight of each cation.

Compound	Molecular Weight	Equivalent Weight	Weight for 1 Gram Cation
(H)Cl			
$(H_2)SO_4$			
$H(NO_3)$			
$(H_3)PO_4$			
(Na)Cl			
$(Na_2)(H)(PO_4)$			
Na(OH)			
$(Ca)CO_3$			
$CH_3COO(H)$			
$(Cu)SO_4 \cdot 5H_2O$			

Compound	Molecular Weight	Equivalent Weight	Weight for 1 Gram Cation
$Ca(H)PO_4$			
$(Ca)(HCO_3)_2$			
$H(ClO_4)$			
$(Al_2)(SO_4)_3$			
$(Zn)NH_4(PO_4)\cdot 2H_2O$			
$Pb(H)AsO_4$			
$(K)MnO_4$			
$K_2(Cr_2O_7)$			
$(Na_2)CO_3$			
$(Cu_2)Cl_2$			
$Hg_2(Cl_2)$			
$(NH_4)Cl$			
$K_4(Fe)(CN)_6$			

Dilution

11. To what volume must 1 drop of 6-*M* HCl be diluted to obtain a 0.15-*M* solution?
12. If 50 ml. of a sulfuric acid solution with a normality of 0.25 is desired, what volume of a 0.4-*N* solution of sulfuric acid must be used to obtain the desired quantity of the diluted acid?
13. To what volume must 10 ml. of a 0.2-*M* solution of nitric acid be diluted for the concentration of HNO_3 to be 0.01 g./ml.?
14. To what volume must 1 ml. of a 0.1 gram-ion solution of $Pb(NO_3)_2$ be diluted for the concentration of the Pb^{++} to be 1×10^{-7} g./ml.?
15. In what ratio must acids 0.562-*N* and 0.232-*N* be mixed to obtain one that is 0.372-*N*?

Reactions Between Solutions of Acids and Bases

16. If 50 ml. of a 0.4-*N* acid requires 35 ml. of a base to neutralize it, what is the normality of the base?
17. How many milliliters of a 0.25-*N* base are required to neutralize 100 ml. of a 0.30-*N* acid?
18. If 80 ml. of a solution of sulfuric acid is required to neutralize 300 ml. of a 0.14-*M* solution of sodium hydroxide, what is the molarity of the acid? What is its normality?
19. If 50 ml. of a 0.335-*N* NaOH is required to neutralize the acetic acid in 25 ml. of solution, what is the normality of the acid?
20. If 35 ml. of a 0.145-*N* acid is added to 35 ml. of a 0.250-*N* base, what is the concentration of the base in the resultant solution?
21. When 80 ml. of a 0.145-*N* acid is added to 90 ml. of a 0.140-*N* base, is the resultant solution acidic or basic, and what is its normality?
22. After 50 ml. of a 0.460-*N* acid is added to 75 ml. of a base, the resultant acid solution has a normality of 0.02 to H_3O^+. What was the normality of the base?

23. If 350 ml. of a 0.256-N sulfuric acid is equivalent to 250 ml. of a hydrochloric acid solution, what is the normality of the hydrochloric acid solution?
24. One drop of a 0.10-N acid solution is required to neutralize the base in 500 ml. of solution. What was the normality of the base solution?
25. Two drops of a 0.02-N solution of NaOH are required to neutralize the acid in 2 liters of alcohol. What was the normality of the alcoholic acid solution?

Normal Solutions, Molar Solutions, and Percentage Concentrations

26. What weight of HCl is required to prepare 100 ml. of a solution of this acid with a molarity of 0.25?
27. If 250 ml. of sulfuric acid solution contains 4.29 g. of H_2SO_4, calculate the normality of the sulfuric acid.
28. If 2.5 liters of a sulfuric acid solution contains 2 g. of H_2SO_4, what is the molarity of this solution? What is its normality?
29. How many milliliters of a nitric acid solution with a molarity of 0.175 will be required to obtain 5 g. of HNO_3?
30. What weight of HNO_3 is there in 10 ml. of concd. HNO_3 which has a density of 1.42 g./ml. and contains 70% HNO_3?
31. What volume (ml.) of concd. H_2SO_4 which has a density of 1.84 and contains 98% of H_2SO_4 will be required to make 500 ml. of a sulfuric acid solution with a molarity of 0.426?
32. What weight of NaOH will be required to make 300 ml. of a 0.037-M solution of sodium hydroxide?
33. What weight of acetic acid is contained in 1 ml. of solution if the acetic acid concentration is 4% and the specific gravity of the solution is 1.0?
34. What is the normality of the acetic acid solution in Problem 33?
35. What weight of sodium carbonate (Na_2CO_3) will be required to make 700 ml. of a 0.253-M solution of this salt?
36. If 1 g. of commercial sodium hydroxide (92% NaOH) is required to neutralize 50 ml. of an acid, what is the normality of the acid?
37. A precipitate of 0.256 g. of $BaSO_4$ was obtained when an excess of $BaCl_2$ was added to 40 ml. of a sodium sulfate (Na_2SO_4) solution. What were the molarity and normality of the sodium sulfate solution?
38. If 0.1762 g. of AgCl is obtained when an excess of $AgNO_3$ is added to 50 ml. of a solution of calcium chloride ($CaCl_2$), what was the molarity of the $CaCl_2$ solution?
39. An experiment yielded the following result: 0.1230 g. of CO_2 was liberated from 250 ml. of a solution by the addition of 8.66 ml. of 0.321-N sulfuric acid. What is the normality of the solution relative to Ca^{++} if the salt in the water was $Ca(HCO_3)_2$?
40. What weight of NaCl could be obtained from 50 ml. of a 0.234-M solution of hydrochloric acid if an excess of NaOH were added to the acid?
41. At 25°, 1.9×10^{-6} g. of AgCl dissolves in 1 ml. of water. What is the molarity of this solution?
42. At 25°, 6.7×10^{-4} g. of $CaSO_4$ dissolves in 1 ml. of water. What are the normality and molarity of a saturated solution of $CaSO_4$?

43. What weight of $CaCO_3$ is equivalent to the H_2SO_4 contained in 75 ml. of a solution of sulfuric acid with a molarity of 0.175?
44. What is the molarity of a solution that contains 1 drop of concd. H_2SO_4 (density 1.84 g./ml., 98% H_2SO_4) in 12 ml. of solution?
45. What weight of hydrochloric acid is equivalent to the weight of sulfuric acid contained in 50 ml. of sulfuric acid solution with a molarity of 0.526?
46. If 1.10 g. of MgO is required to neutralize 35 ml. of an acid, what was the normality of the acid?
47. If 10 ml. of hydrochloric acid with a normality of 0.35 is added to 30 ml. of sodium hydroxide with a normality of 0.20, what is the normality of the resulting solution to OH^-?
48. Excess barium chloride solution is added to 10 ml. of H_2SO_4 with a molarity of 0.272. What weight of $BaSO_4$ will be precipitated?
49. What volume of a 0.072-*M* HCl solution is required to dissolve 0.5 g. of Fe_2O_3?
50. What volume of a 0.121-*M* H_2SO_4 solution is required to dissolve 0.2 g. of Zn, 0.1 g. of Mg, and 0.3 g. of Al?
51. What volume of a 0.142-*M* HNO_3 is required to change 0.25 g. of Cu to $Cu(NO_3)_2$?
52. An acid with a normality of 0.455 is desired from one with a normality of 0.572. In what ratio must the 0.572-*N* acid be mixed with a 0.350-*N* base to obtain an acid with the desired normality (0.455-*N*)?
53. If 1.2 g. of zinc metal is dissolved in 100 ml. of a 0.645-*M* HCl solution, (a) what is the molarity of the resultant acid? (b) What weight of $ZnCl_2$ is formed?
54. One hundred ml. of a 0.35-*N* acid solution were required to dissolve 0.5 g. of a mixture of iron and magnesium metals. The iron was oxidized to the iron (III) state. What weight of iron and of magnesium was contained in the mixture?
55. A mixture of pure Na_2CO_3 and $BaCO_3$ weighed 0.2 g. Thirty ml. of 0.1-*N* acid was required to react with the 0.2 g. of carbonate. What percentage of each component was there in the mixture?
56. A mixture of NaCl and KCl weighed 1 g. This mixture of chlorides was converted into Na_2SO_4 and K_2SO_4. The sulfates weighed 1.19 g. Find the percentage of NaCl and KCl in the mixture.
57. A mixture of $CaCO_3$ and $BaCO_3$ weighed 10 g. When decomposed by an acid, 1.47 liters of CO_2 was obtained at S.T.P. What weights of $CaCO_3$ and $BaCO_3$ were there in the mixture?
58. A student has two acids, (a) and (b). Acid (a) has a normality of 1.42 and acid (b) has a normality of 2.10. Only 50 ml. of acid (b) is available. What volumes of the two acids must he use to obtain 250 ml. of an acid with a normality of 1.54?

Factors, Percentage Composition, and Calculations from Chemical Equations

a. $$\text{Factor of O to KClO}_3 = \frac{(3)(0)}{\text{KClO}_3} = \frac{48}{122.56} = 0.3914$$

b. Factor of $CuSO_4 \cdot 5H_2O$ to Cu $= \dfrac{CuSO_4 \cdot 5H_2O}{Cu} = \dfrac{249.71}{63.57} = 3.928$

c. Factor of $CuSO_4$ to $CuSO_4 \cdot 5H_2O = \dfrac{CuSO_4}{CuSO_4 \cdot 5H_2O} = \dfrac{159.63}{249.71} = 0.6393$

d. Percent of oxygen in $KClO_3 = \left(\dfrac{3(0)}{KClO_3}\right)(100) = \left(\dfrac{48}{122.56}\right)(100)$

$$= 39.14\%$$

e. Weight of CuS produced by the reaction of 5 mg. of Cu^{++} with excess H_2S:

$$\left(\frac{CuS}{Cu^{++}}\right)(5) = \left(\frac{95.63}{63.57}\right)(5) = 7.52 \text{ mg.}$$

f. Weight of HNO_3 required to react with 10 g. of CuS:

$$\underset{3 \times 95.63}{\overset{10}{3CuS}} + \underset{8 \times 63.02}{\overset{x}{8HNO_3}} \rightleftharpoons 3Cu^{++} + 6NO_3^{-} + \underline{3S}\downarrow + 2NO\uparrow$$

$$\frac{x}{504.16} = \frac{10}{286.89}; \quad x = \left(\frac{10}{286.89}\right)(504.16) = 17.58 \text{ g.}$$

59. Calculate the factor and the percentage of lead in the following compounds: (a) $Pb(NO_3)_2$; (b) $PbSO_4$; (c) PbO; (d) PbO_2; (e) PbS; (f) Pb_3O_4.

60. Calculate the number of grams of the following compounds which can be made from 10 g. of Ag: (a) $AgNO_3$; (b) Ag_2SO_4; (c) Ag_3PO_4; (d) AgCl; (e) CH_3COOAg.

61. Calculate the number of milligrams of Ag^+ contained in 1 ml. and in 1 liter of the following saturated solutions:

Salt	Solubility	mg. Ag^+/ml.	mg. Ag^+/liter
Ag_2SO_4	7.1×10^{-3} g./ml.		
Ag_2CrO_4	2.2×10^{-5} g./ml.		
AgCl	1.9×10^{-6} g./ml.		
AgBr	1.1×10^{-7} g./ml.		
AgI	2.2×10^{-9} g./ml.		

62. Calculate the molar solubility of each of the salts listed in Problem 61.

63. What weight of chlorine can be obtained by the reaction of 50 g. of MnO_2 with excess HCl? What volume of Cl_2 would be obtained at 0° and 760 mm. pressure? What volume would be obtained at 25° C. and 720 mm. pressure?

64. If excess HCl is added to a solution which contains 8 mg. of $Hg_2(NO_3)_2$, how many milligrams of Hg_2Cl_2 will be formed?

65. How many milliliters of 3-*N* CH_3COOH are required to dissolve 10 g. of $CaCO_3$? To dissolve a mixture of 5 g. of $CaCO_3$ and 15 g. of $BaCO_3$?

66. How many drops of 1-*N* HCl are required to precipitate 3 mg. of Ag^+, 50 mg. of Hg_2^{++}, and 100 mg. of Pb^{++} as chlorides?

CHAPTER 3

CHEMICAL REACTIONS AND EQUATIONS

WRITING EQUATIONS

Chemical Equations

In procedures for identifying substances, many chemical reactions are used. The correct representation of these reactions by means of chemical equations not only aids the student in understanding the method of analysis, but also affords him a very effective means of learning many of the chemical properties of substances. For this reason a review of writing equations for several types of chemical reactions is given here.

A chemical equation not only is a shorthand method of stating what happens in a chemical reaction, but for reactions that go essentially to completion it states the quantitative relationships between reactants and products. Thus, when properly written and balanced, an equation shows: (1) the formulas of the reactants and the products; (2) the weight relationships between the reactants and the products; (3) whether the reaction is reversible and, if it is, the relative extent of the two reverse reactions; (4) the formation of a precipitate or the evolution of a gas; (5) the form in which the largest proportion of the reactants or products are present—that is, whether they are present largely as weak electrolytes (slightly ionized substances), complex ions, or simple ions—and (6) the changes in oxidation state of any ions or atoms in the case of oxidation-reduction reactions.

To write a chemical equation, it is necessary to know the formulas of the reactants as well as of the products. The skeleton or incomplete equation is obtained by writing the formulas of the reactants on the left-hand side of the arrows and the products on the right-hand side. The next step is to balance the equation by selecting coefficients for the reactants and the products such that the same number and kind of atoms appear on each side of the equation.

Furthermore, if charged ions are involved in the reaction, the net charge must be the same on both sides of the arrows when the equation is properly balanced. These general rules are illustrated for different types of reactions in the later sections of this chapter.

Formulas and Conventions for Oxidation States

If the formulas of the reactants or products of a reaction are not known, they must be looked up in a textbook or deduced from a knowledge of the *oxidation state* or *valence number* of the elements in the compound or ion. In the case of a simple ion or of a complex ion considered as a unit, the oxidation state is taken as equal to the charge on the ion. The assignment of the oxidation state to the elements in certain ionic compounds such as NaCl and $CaCl_2$ is relatively unambiguous. However, in covalent compounds and complex ions the assignment is based on certain conventions which in effect assign the electrons of a bond to only one of the atoms even though there has not been a complete transfer. The more electronegative element partially takes electrons from the other element forming the bond. The total number of electrons thus partially taken is the negative oxidation state or valence number of the atom in the compound. Similarly, the number of electrons which are partially lost on the above basis is the positive oxidation state or valence number of the elements in the compound. This is equivalent to saying that the oxidation state is the charge assumed to be on an atom such that it would account for the number of electrons involved in changing the atom to the free state. The conventions usually adopted for assigning oxidation states and writing the formulas of compounds are summarized as follows:

1. The oxidation state of free or uncombined elements, as well as of elements combined with themselves, is taken as zero: Cu, Ag, H_2, N_2, O_2, Cl_2, Zn, etc.

2. Simple ions or complex ions taken as a unit are assigned an oxidation state equal to the charge on the ion, and are positive or negative according to the sign of the charge. Thus the oxidation state of Hg^{++} is $+2$, and that of PO_4^{3-} is -3.

3. Oxygen is assigned an oxidation state of -2 in most of its compounds such as CaO, MnO_2, etc. This has some justification, because oxygen is one of the most electronegative elements (except fluorine) and therefore at least partially takes electrons from the other elements with which it forms bonds. (In peroxides the oxidation state of oxygen is taken as -1.)

The oxidation state of the central atom of an oxy-ion such as MnO_4^- is deduced on the basis of an oxidation state of -2 for each oxygen atom (see rule 6), even though there may not be a complete transfer of electrons to the oxygen atoms.

4. The oxidation state of hydrogen in most compounds is +1. In metallic hydrides and in compounds with elements that are below it in electronegativity it is negative. Thus the oxidation state of hydrogen is +1 in the following compounds: HCl, H_2O, HI, H_2SO_4, etc.; it is −1 in LiH, CaH_2, etc.

5. The algebraic sum of the positive and negative oxidation states in a compound is equal to zero. That is, the sum of the positive oxidation states is equal to the sum of the negative oxidation states. Thus, in the compound $AlCl_3$, aluminum has an oxidation state of +3, and the total oxidation states of the three chloride ions is −3, making an algebraic sum of zero. In the compound $Ca_3(PO_4)_2$, the total of the positive oxidation states for calcium is $(+2)(3) = +6$. It follows that the negative oxidation state for the phosphate radical must be −3 so that the total negative oxidation states will be $(-3)(2) = -6$. Hence, if the oxidation state of one ion or radical of a compound is known, the other can readily be deduced.

6. The algebraic sum of the positive and negative oxidation states of the atoms in a complex ion or a radical is equal to the oxidation state of the ion or radical. For example, the oxidation state of the sulfate ion (SO_4^{--}) is −2 because this is the algebraic sum of the oxidation states of the oxygen atoms $(-2)(4) = -8$ and the oxidation state of sulfur (+6). Thus,

$$\begin{aligned} \text{Total oxidation states of } 4O^{--} &= (-2)(4) = -8 \\ \text{Oxidation state of S in sulfates} &= \underline{+6} \\ \text{Charge or oxidation state of sulfate ion} &= -2 \end{aligned}$$

Similarly, the permanganate ion (MnO_4^-) has an oxidation state of −1 because the total of the oxidation states of the oxygen atoms is $(-2)(4) = -8$, and the oxidation state of Mn in MnO_4^- is +7. The sum of −8 and +7 is −1, which is the oxidation state of the permanganate ion.

By reversing the procedure, the oxidation state of the central atom of an ion or radical can be deduced. The oxidation state of Cr in $K_2Cr_2O_7$ is determined as follows: Because 2 potassium atoms $(+1 \times 2 = +2)$ are combined with the dichromate radical, the oxidation state of the latter is −2. The total of the oxidation states of the oxygen atoms is $(-2)(7) = -14$ (see rule 3). In order for the oxidation state of $Cr_2O_7^{--}$ to be −2, the total oxidation states of the two Cr atoms must be +12, so that −14 + 12 = −2. Therefore each chromium atom has an oxidation state of +12 ÷ 2 = +6.

A list of the principal oxidation states of most of the elements encountered in elementary courses in qualitative analysis is given in Table 3.1. The most common state is given first.

TABLE 3.1. Principal Oxidation States of the Elements Encountered in Qualitative Analysis

	Oxidation States and Examples
Aluminum	$+3(AlCl_3)$
Antimony	$+3(SbCl_3)$; $+5(Sb_2O_5)$; $-3(SbH_3)$; $+4(Sb_2O_4)$
Arsenic	$+3(AsCl_3)$; $+5(H_3AsO_4)$; $-3(AsH_3)$
Barium	$+2(BaCl_2)$
Bismuth	$+3(BiCl_3)$; $+5(NaBiO_3)$; $-3(BiH_3$ or $Na_3Bi)$
Boron	$+3(H_3BO_3)$
Bromine	$-1(HBr)$; $+1(HBrO)$; $+5(HBrO_3)$
Cadmium	$+2(CdCl_2)$
Calcium	$+2(CaCl_2)$
Carbon	$+4(Na_2CO_3)$; $-4(CH_4)$; $+2(CO)$
Chlorine	$-1(HCl)$; $+1(HClO)$; $+3(HClO_2)$; $+4(ClO_2)$; $+5(KClO_3)$; $+7(KClO_4)$
Chromium	$+3(CrCl_3)$; $+6(K_2CrO_4)$; $+2(CrCl_2)$
Cobalt	$+2(CoCl_2)$; $+3(Co(OH)_3$ or $Na_3Co(NO_2)_6)$
Copper	$+2(CuCl_2)$; $+1(Cu_2O)$
Fluorine	$-1(HF)$
Hydrogen	$+1(HCl)$; $-1(NaH)$
Iodine	$-1(HI)$; $+1(HIO)$; $+5(KIO_3)$; $+7(KIO_4)$
Iron	$+3(FeCl_3)$; $+2(FeCl_2)$
Lead	$+2(PbSO_4)$; $+4(PbO_2)$
Magnesium	$+2(MgCl_2)$
Manganese	$+2(MnCl_2)$; $+3(Mn(OH)_3$; $+4(MnO_2)$; $+6(Na_2MnO_4)$; $+7(KMnO_4)$
Mercury	$+2(HgCl_2)$; $+1(Hg_2Cl_2)$
Nickel	$+2(NiCl_2)$; $+3(Ni_2O_3)$
Nitrogen	$-3(NH_4Cl)$; $+5(HNO_3)$; $+4(NO_2)$; $+3(HNO_2)$; $+2(NO)$; $+1(N_2O)$; $-1(NH_2OH)$; $-2(N_2H_4)$
Oxygen	$-2(H_2O)$; $-1(H_2O_2)$
Phosphorus	$+5(H_3PO_4)$; $-3(PH_3)$; $+1(H_3PO_2)$; $+3(H_3PO_3$ or $PCl_3)$; $+4(H_4P_2O_6)$
Potassium	$+1(KCl)$
Silicon	$+4(Na_2SiO_3$ or $SiF_4)$
Silver	$+1(AgCl)$
Sodium	$+1(NaCl)$
Strontium	$+2(SrCl_2)$
Sulfur	$+6(Na_2SO_4)$; $-2(H_2S)$; $+4(Na_2SO_3)$
Tin	$+2(SnCl_2)$; $+4(SnCl_4)$
Zinc	$+2(ZnCl_2)$

IONIC REACTIONS

Most of the reactions studied in qualitative analysis involve ions. Hence *ionic equations* are used to represent these reactions. Reactions involving ions are usually divided into two main classes: (1) those in which no change occurs in oxidation state of an element, and (2) oxidation-reduction reactions (sometimes abbreviated O-R reactions). For purposes of discussion the first group of reactions may be subdivided into (a) ionic combinations and (b) protolytic (proton-transfer) reactions.

Conventions for Writing Equations

By means of a number of conventions, ionic equations can be used to indicate several important facts relative to the reactants and products of a reaction. Writing an equation correctly in accordance with these conventions requires a certain amount of knowledge concerning the properties of the substances involved and also some understanding of the conditions under which substances interact. The following conventions are useful in this connection.

1. Since strong electrolytes are completely ionized, only the ions that actually take part in a reaction should appear in the equation.

2. If the ions of soluble strong electrolytes are products of a reaction in dilute aqueous solution, they are written as separate ions, not as molecules.

3. Weak electrolytes (slightly ionized acids, bases, and salts) are represented by their *molecular formulas*, even though a small concentration of one of their ions is responsible for the particular reaction.

4. If an ion is present *mainly* as a slightly ionized *complex ion*, the formula of this complex ion is used, even though a small concentration of one of its ionization products is responsible for the reaction. In other words, an ionic equation does not necessarily indicate the mechanism of the reaction. As will be shown later, this may require two or more ionic equations.

5. Slightly soluble or solid substances taking part or formed in a reaction are represented by their molecular or empirical formulas and are underlined: $\underline{AgCl}$.

6. The formation of a slightly soluble precipitate is indicated by an arrow pointing downward: $\underset{\text{white}}{\underline{AgCl\downarrow}}$, and the color of the precipitate is often put below the formula. The formation of a slightly soluble gas that

escapes from the solution is indicated by an arrow pointing upward: $CO_2\uparrow$.

7. If a substance is added in excess, its formula is often doubly underscored: $\underline{\underline{NH_4^+}}$.

8. A single arrow $\rightarrow$ is used to represent an equation that proceeds practically completely in the direction indicated.

9. A double arrow $\rightleftharpoons$ indicates a reversible reaction in which an equilibrium exists between the products and the reactants.

10. A double arrow in which one is longer than the other $\rightleftharpoons$ indicates the direction in which a reversible reaction is more complete. The presence of a catalyst, the temperature, or the application of heat is sometimes indicated below or above the arrow:

$$\underline{PbCl_2} + H_2O \underset{\text{heat}}{\rightleftharpoons} Pb^{++} + 2Cl^- + H_2O$$

11. Ionic equations must be balanced, not only with respect to number and kinds of atoms, but also with respect to electrical charges. The net charge must be the same on both sides of the equation.

The method of writing and balancing ionic equations may be illustrated by the reaction of hydrogen sulfide (H_2S) with a solution of bismuth nitrate ($Bi^{3+} + 3NO_3^-$). The incomplete equation, showing reactants and products, is written first:

$$Bi^{3+} + H_2S + H_2O \rightleftharpoons \underset{\text{brown}}{\underline{Bi_2S_3}}\downarrow + H_3O^+ \text{ (incomplete)}$$

By inspection it can be seen that the coefficient of Bi^{3+} must be 2 and that the coefficient of H_2S must be 3. Hence

$$2Bi^{3+} + 3H_2S + H_2O \rightleftharpoons \underset{\text{brown}}{\underline{Bi_2S_3}}\downarrow + H_3O^+ \text{ (incomplete)}$$

It is now evident that the six H^+ from the three H_2S molecules will require six H_2O molecules for the formation of six H_3O^+. Hence the completed equation is

$$2Bi^{3+} + 3H_2S + 6H_2O \rightleftharpoons \underset{\text{brown}}{\underline{Bi_2S_3}}\downarrow + 6H_3O^+$$

The equation is balanced because the same number and kind of atoms appear on both sides of the arrow, and because the net charge is the same on both sides (+6). It will be noted that only the ions and molecules that actually take part in the reaction are included in the equation. If all the ions were included, the reaction would be written as follows:

$$2(Bi^{3+} + 3NO_3^-) + 3H_2S + 6H_2O \rightleftharpoons \underset{\text{brown}}{\underline{Bi_2S_3}} \downarrow + 6(H_3O^+ + NO_3^-)$$

It is obvious that the six nitrate ions from the bismuth nitrate do not enter into the reaction and hence they need not be included in the equation. Occasionally it is desirable to write these complete equations, but there is rarely any advantage in writing a molecular equation like the following unless the molecules are actually involved:

$$2Bi(NO_3)_3 + 3H_2S \rightleftharpoons Bi_2S_3 \downarrow + 6HNO_3$$

While this equation does represent the reaction, it does not give as much information as the ionic equations.

Calculations involving quantities of a salt or electrolyte can be made as readily from ionic as from molecular equations. For instance, suppose we want to determine the quantity of bismuth nitrate pentahydrate that would be required to produce 10 g. of bismuth sulfide.

$$2Bi^{3+} + 3H_2S + 6H_2O \rightleftharpoons \underset{\text{brown}}{\underline{Bi_2S_3}} \downarrow + 6H_3O^+$$

Inspection of this equation shows that 2 gram ions (moles) of Bi^{3+}, and hence 2 moles of $Bi(NO_3)_3 \cdot 5H_2O$, are required to produce 1 mole of Bi_2S_3. Since the number of moles of Bi_2S_3 is $\frac{10}{Bi_2S_3}$, or $\frac{10}{514.2}$, the number of moles of $Bi(NO_3)_3 \cdot 5H_2O$ is $\frac{10}{Bi_2S_3} \times 2$ and the weight in grams is

$$\frac{10}{Bi_2S_3} \times 2 \times Bi(NO_3)_3 \cdot 5H_2O = \frac{(10)(2)(485.1)}{514.2} = 18.8 \text{ g.}$$

In order to illustrate further the application of the above conventions in writing ionic equations, we shall consider examples of several types of reactions. This discussion will also aid the student in determining the conditions under which ionic reactions take place.

Reactions Involving No Change in Oxidation State

REACTIONS INVOLVING IONIC COMBINATIONS. Ionic combinations take place between ions or between ions and molecules when there is a possibility of the formation of (1) a slightly soluble solid, (2) a slightly soluble or volatile gas, (3) a slightly ionized product, (4) a complex ion.

1. *Formation of Slightly Soluble Solids.* When a solution of hydrochloric acid is added to a solution of silver nitrate, a white precipitate of silver chloride is formed.

$$(H_3O^+ + Cl^-) + (Ag^+ + NO_3^-) \rightleftharpoons \underset{\text{white}}{\underline{AgCl}}\downarrow + H_3O^+ + NO_3^-$$

According to the equation, only silver ions and chloride ions react; H_3O^+ and NO_3^- remain in solution in ionic form. Since these ions are on both sides of the equation, they are omitted. Thus, according to the conventions adopted, the ionic equation for this reaction is

$$Ag^+ + Cl^- \rightleftharpoons \underset{\text{white}}{\underline{AgCl}}\downarrow$$

Because silver chloride is only slightly soluble (1.9×10^{-6} g./ml.), a precipitate is formed, even with low concentrations of Ag^+ and Cl^-.

The following examples of ionic reactions which result in the formation of a precipitate are selected to illustrate some of the conventions adopted regarding these equations. The second equation in each case is the preferred one because it is the simplified ionic equation.

Mercury (I) nitrate + hydrochloric acid

$$(Hg_2^{++} + 2NO_3^-) + 2(H_3O^+ + Cl^-) \rightleftharpoons \underset{\text{white}}{\underline{Hg_2Cl_2}}\downarrow + 2H_3O^+ + 2NO_3^-$$

$$Hg_2^{++} + 2Cl^- \rightleftharpoons \underset{\text{white}}{\underline{Hg_2Cl_2}}\downarrow \text{ (ionic)}$$

Diammine silver chloride + nitric acid

$$(Ag(NH_3)_2^+ + Cl^-) + 2(H_3O^+ + NO_3^-) \rightleftharpoons$$
$$\underset{\text{white}}{\underline{AgCl}}\downarrow + 2NH_4^+ + 2NO_3^- + 2H_2O$$

$$Ag(NH_3)_2^+ + Cl^- + 2H_3O^+ \rightleftharpoons \underset{\text{white}}{\underline{AgCl}}\downarrow + 2NH_4^+ + 2H_2O \text{ (ionic)}$$

Diammine silver chloride + potassium bromide

$$(Ag(NH_3)_2^+ + Cl^-) + (K^+ + Br^-) \rightleftharpoons \underset{\text{cream}}{\underline{AgBr}}\downarrow + 2NH_3 + K^+ + Cl^-$$

$$Ag(NH_3)_2^+ + Br^- \rightleftharpoons \underset{\text{cream}}{\underline{AgBr}}\downarrow + 2NH_3 \text{ (ionic)}$$

Copper (II) sulfate + hydrogen sulfide

$$(Cu^{++} + SO_4^{--}) + H_2S + 2H_2O \rightleftharpoons \underset{\text{black}}{\underline{CuS}}\downarrow + 2H_3O^+ + SO_4^{--}$$

$$Cu^{++} + H_2S + 2H_2O \rightleftharpoons \underset{\text{black}}{\underline{CuS}}\downarrow + 2H_3O^+ \text{ (ionic)}$$

Cadmium chloride + hydrogen sulfide

$$CdCl_2 + H_2S + 2H_2O \rightleftharpoons \underset{\text{yellow}}{\underline{CdS}}\downarrow + 2H_3O^+ + 2Cl^-$$

(The above is the same as the ionic equation.)

Strontium sulfate + sodium carbonate

$$\underline{SrSO_4} + (2Na^+ + CO_3^{--}) \rightleftharpoons \underset{\text{white}}{\underline{SrCO_3}}\downarrow + 2Na^+ + SO_4^{--}$$

$$\underline{SrSO_4} + CO_3^{--} \rightleftharpoons \underset{\text{white}}{\underline{SrCO_3}}\downarrow + SO_4^{--} \text{ (ionic)}$$

Bismuth nitrate + ammonium hydroxide

$$(Bi^{3+} + 3NO_3^-) + 3NH_3 + 3H_2O \rightleftharpoons \underset{\text{white}}{\underline{Bi(OH)_3}}\downarrow + 3NH_4^+ + 3NO_3^-$$

$$Bi^{3+} + 3NH_3 + 3H_2O \rightleftharpoons \underset{\text{white}}{\underline{Bi(OH)_3}}\downarrow + 3NH_4^+ \text{ (ionic)}$$

These equations are written according to the conventions given previously. Knowledge of the properties of the electrolytes involved in the reactions, especially knowledge as to which of them are strong, weak, complex, or slightly soluble, is essential.

Ionic equations do not necessarily give the *mechanism of the reaction*. The mechanism of the last reaction above may be represented as follows:

$$\begin{array}{l} 3NH_3 + 3H_2O \rightleftharpoons 3NH_4^+ + \boxed{3OH^-} \\ (Bi^{3+} + 3NO_3^-) \rightleftharpoons 3NO_3^- + \boxed{Bi^{3+}} \\ \qquad\qquad\qquad\qquad\qquad\qquad \uparrow\downarrow \\ \qquad\qquad\qquad\qquad\qquad\qquad \underline{Bi(OH)_3}\downarrow \end{array}$$

The bismuth ion in the bismuth nitrate solution reacts with the small amount of the hydroxide ion present to form a slightly soluble precipitate of $Bi(OH)_3$. The reduction in concentration of the hydroxide ion causes more ammonia to ionize, thereby producing more hydroxide ions to interact with more bismuth ions. Consequently, the equilibria are all shifted in the forward direction and the bismuth ion is precipitated almost completely as $Bi(OH)_3$.

2. *Formation of Slightly Soluble or Volatile Gases.* When hydrochloric acid ($H_3O^+ + Cl^-$) is added to a solution of sodium carbonate ($2Na^+ + CO_3^{--}$), the hydronium ion and the carbonate ion unite to form the slightly ionized bicarbonate ion, HCO_3^-. This ion then unites with another hydronium ion to form the slightly ionized and unstable acid, H_2CO_3. Carbonic acid decomposes into water and the slightly soluble gas, CO_2. After the solution becomes saturated with CO_2, the latter escapes. The reaction is formulated as follows:

$$\begin{array}{l} H_3O^+ + CO_3^{--} \rightleftharpoons HCO_3^- + H_2O \\ \qquad\qquad\qquad\quad \llcorner + H_3O^+ \rightleftharpoons H_2CO_3 + H_2O \\ \qquad\qquad\qquad\qquad\qquad\qquad\quad \llcorner \rightleftharpoons H_2O + CO_2\uparrow \end{array}$$

As long as carbon dioxide escapes from solution, the equilibria are all shifted in the forward direction so the reaction proceeds nearly to completion.

Other reactions in which a slightly soluble gas is formed are:

Nitric acid + sodium hydrogen carbonate

$$H_3O^+ + HCO_3^- \rightleftharpoons H_2CO_3 + H_2O$$
$$\quad \llcorner\rightleftharpoons H_2O + CO_2\uparrow$$

Acetic acid + sodium hydrogen carbonate

$$CH_3COOH + HCO_3^- \rightleftharpoons H_2CO_3 + CH_3COO^-$$
$$\quad \llcorner\rightleftharpoons H_2O + CO_2\uparrow$$

Hydrochloric acid + iron (II) sulfide

$$2H_3O^+ + \underline{FeS} \rightleftharpoons Fe^{++} + 2H_2O + H_2S\uparrow$$

Ammonium chloride + sodium hydroxide + heat

$$NH_4^+ + OH^- \underset{\text{heat}}{\rightleftharpoons} H_2O + NH_3\uparrow$$

3. *Formation of Slightly Ionized Acids, Bases, and Salts.* If the ions of a slightly ionized acid, base, or salt are present when two solutions are mixed, the ions unite to form the weak electrolyte. Thus, when hydrochloric acid is added to a solution of sodium acetate, the hydronium ions and the acetate ions combine to form the weak acid, CH_3COOH:

$$H_3O^+ + CH_3COO^- \rightleftharpoons CH_3COOH + H_2O$$

The weaker (less ionized) the acid, the greater the extent to which the ions unite.

Examples of other reactions involving the formation of weak electrolytes are:

Slightly ionized acids

Dilute sulfuric acid + sodium cyanide

$$H_3O^+ + CN^- \rightleftharpoons H_2O + HCN$$

Zinc sulfide + hydrochloric acid

$$\underline{ZnS} + H_3O^+ \rightleftharpoons Zn^{++} + HS^- + H_2O$$
$$\quad \llcorner + H_3O^+ \rightleftharpoons H_2S\uparrow + H_2O$$

Strontium chromate + hydrochloric acid

$$\underline{2SrCrO_4} + 2H_3O^+ \rightleftharpoons 2Sr^{++} + 2HCrO_4^- + 2H_2O$$
$$\quad \llcorner\rightleftharpoons Cr_2O_7^{--} + H_2O$$

Slightly ionized bases

Ammonium chloride + sodium hydroxide

$$NH_4^+ + OH^- \rightleftharpoons H_2O + NH_3$$

Magnesium hydroxide + ammonium chloride

$$\underline{Mg(OH)_2} + 2NH_4^+ \rightleftharpoons Mg^{++} + 2NH_3 + 2H_2O$$

Formation of water

Hydrochloric acid + sodium hydroxide

$$H_3O^+ + OH^- \rightleftharpoons H_2O + H_2O$$

Hydrochloric acid + ammonium hydroxide

$$H_3O^+ + NH_3 \rightleftharpoons NH_4^+ + H_2O$$

Aluminum hydroxide + hydrochloric acid

$$\underline{Al(OH)_3} + 3H_3O^+ \rightleftharpoons Al^{3+} + 6H_2O$$

Slightly ionized salts

Lead chloride + ammonium acetate

$$\underline{PbCl_2} + 2CH_3COO^- \rightleftharpoons 2Cl^- + Pb(CH_3COO)_2$$

4. *Formation of Complex Ions.* When ammonium hydroxide is added to a precipitate of silver chloride, the solid dissolves. The mechanism of this reaction may be formulated as follows:

$$\begin{array}{ccc} \underline{AgCl} \rightleftharpoons & Ag^+ & + \; Cl^- \\ & + & \\ & 2NH_3 & \\ & \updownarrow & \\ & Ag(NH_3)_2^+ & \end{array}$$

The ammonia molecules react with the small amount of silver ions present in the saturated solution of AgCl. This reaction reduces the concentration of the silver ion and shifts the equilibrium in the forward direction until the precipitate dissolves. The ionic equation for this reaction is:

$$\underline{AgCl} + 2NH_3 \rightleftharpoons Ag(NH_3)_2^+ + Cl^-$$

The color of a copper (II) sulfate solution becomes deep blue when ammonium hydroxide is added to it because of the formation of the complex tetrammino copper (II) ion, $Cu(NH_3)_4^{++}$.

$$Cu^{++} + 4NH_3 \rightleftharpoons Cu(NH_3)_4^{++}$$

Examples of other reactions which occur because of the formation of complex ions are:

Mercury (II) chloride + potassium iodide

$$HgCl_2 + 4I^- \rightleftharpoons HgI_4^{--} + 2Cl^-$$

Arsenic (III) sulfide + ammonium sulfide

$$\underline{As_2S_3} + 3S^{--} \rightleftharpoons 2AsS_3^{3-}$$

Aluminum hydroxide + sodium hydroxide

$$\underline{Al(OH)_3} + OH^- \rightleftharpoons Al(OH)_4^- \xrightleftharpoons{\text{heat}} AlO_2^- + 2H_2O$$

Cadmium chloride + potassium cyanide

$$CdCl_2 + 4CN^- \rightleftharpoons Cd(CN)_4^{--} + 2Cl^-$$

PROTOLYTIC (PROTON-TRANSFER) REACTIONS. Protolytic reactions are those in which a proton is transferred from one substance to another, that is, from an acid to a base. The fundamental reaction is

$$\text{Acid}_1 + \text{Base}_2 \rightleftharpoons \text{Acid}_2 + \text{Base}_1$$

These reactions may be classed as (1) ionization of acids and bases, (2) hydrolysis of ions, and (3) neutralization. The nature of these reactions is considered in more detail in connection with the theories of acids and bases; hence, only one or two illustrations of each are given here.

1. *Ionization of Acids and Bases.* When hydrogen chloride is added to water, the proton is transferred from the HCl molecule to the H_2O molecule.

$$\begin{matrix} HCl + H_2O & \rightarrow & H_3O^+ + Cl^- \\ \text{acid}_1 + \text{base}_2 & & \text{acid}_2 + \text{base}_1 \end{matrix}$$

Other reactions of this type are:

$$CH_3COOH + H_2O \rightleftharpoons H_3O^+ + CH_3COO^-$$

$$H_2O + NH_3 \rightleftharpoons NH_4^+ + OH^-$$

2. *Hydrolysis of the Ions of a Salt.* Hydrolysis as applied to solutions of electrolytes is the protolytic reaction between the ions of a *salt* and water. The effect of these reactions on the acidity and the basicity of the solutions of salts will be considered later (p. 208). When sodium acetate is added to water, the acetate ion interacts with water because of its tendency to take protons from water and form a weak acid, CH_3COOH.

$$H_2O + CH_3COO^- \rightleftharpoons CH_3COOH + OH^-$$

The addition of sodium sulfide to water results in a strongly basic solution, owing to hydrolysis of the sulfide ion.

$$H_2O + S^{--} \rightleftharpoons HS^- + OH^-$$

Other hydrolysis reactions are:

Ammonium chloride + water

$$NH_4^+ + H_2O \rightleftharpoons H_3O^+ + NH_3$$

Sodium carbonate + water

$$H_2O + CO_3^{--} \rightleftharpoons HCO_3^- + OH^-$$

3. *Neutralization.* Neutralization is a protolytic reaction that occurs when acids and bases other than water are mixed (p. 22). For example, in the reaction of hydrochloric acid ($H_3O^+ + Cl^-$) with sodium hydroxide ($Na^+ + OH^-$), a proton is transferred from the hydronium ion to the hydroxide ion.

$$H_3O^+ + OH^- \rightleftharpoons H_2O + H_2O$$

Other neutralization reactions are:

Hydrochloric acid + sodium acetate

$$H_3O^+ + CH_3COO^- \rightleftharpoons CH_3COOH + H_2O$$

Sodium hydroxide + ammonium chloride

$$NH_4^+ + OH^- \rightleftharpoons H_2O + NH_3$$

Hydrochloric acid + ammonium hydroxide

$$H_3O^+ + NH_3 \rightleftharpoons NH_4^+ + H_2O$$

It should be noted that neutralization reactions are essentially the reverse of ionization and hydrolysis reactions. Also some of these reactions could be grouped with the ionic combinations discussed in the preceding section. These classifications are not rigid but are made arbitrarily as a convenience in discussing the large number of reactions encountered in qualitative analysis.

Oxidation-Reduction Reactions

Originally oxidation referred to reactions involving the addition of oxygen, and reduction to those involving the removal of oxygen. Although the two terms are still used to designate these reactions, oxidation-reduction is now used in a more general sense to include any reactions in which there is a change in oxidation state (a valence number). On the basis of electronic concepts, this means a loss or gain of electrons. Thus, an **oxidation-reduction reaction** is a chemical change in which there is a transfer of electrons from one element, ion, or radical to another. The part of the reaction in which there is a loss of electrons is called **oxidation,** and the part in which there is a gain of electrons is called **reduction.** For example, in the reaction of mercury with sulfur to form mercury (II) sulfide,

$$Hg + S \rightarrow HgS$$

$$Hg \rightarrow Hg^{++} + 2e \text{ (oxidation)}$$

$$S + 2e \rightarrow S^{--} \text{ (reduction)}$$

Two electrons are said to be transferred from the mercury to the sulfur. The mercury is said to be oxidized because it loses electrons, and the sulfur is reduced because it gains electrons.

It can be seen that oxidation resulting from a loss of electrons increases the positive oxidation state or decreases the negative oxidation state of an element. This is frequently referred to as an algebraic increase in the oxidation state. Similarly, reduction may be referred to as an algebraic decrease in the oxidation state. In the above reaction the oxidation state of mercury changes from zero to plus two ($0 \rightarrow +2$), and that of sulfur is reduced from zero to minus two ($0 \rightarrow -2$). Sulfur is said to be an oxidizing agent because it takes electrons from mercury and thereby causes the mercury to be oxidized. Mercury may be called a reducing agent in this reaction because its tendency to lose electrons to sulfur causes a reduction in the oxidation state of the sulfur atoms. It is obvious that oxidation and reduction must occur together because the electrons gained by one substance must be lost by another.

The tendency of one substance to take electrons from another can be expressed quantitatively in terms of oxidation-reduction potentials (Appendix N). Qualitatively, however, it may be said that strong oxidizing agents are substances which have a marked tendency to take electrons from other substances. Strong reducing agents, on the other hand, lose electrons easily and are therefore easily oxidized. Examples of strong oxidizing agents are: (1) certain radicals and molecules which contain an element in one of its higher positive oxidation states, such as MnO_4^-, $HClO$, ClO_3^-, $Cr_2O_7^{--}$, BrO_3^-, IO_3^-, NO_3^-, H_2O_2, etc.; (2) certain elements such as Cl_2, Br_2, O_2, I_2, and S; (3) certain ions of the less active metals, especially in their higher oxidation states, as for example Hg^{++},

Fe^{3+}, and Sn^{4+}. Examples of good reducing substances—that is, substances which readily lose electrons to strong oxidizing agents—are: (1) certain active metals such as Na, Ca, Mg, Al, and Zn; (2) certain ions of an element in one of its lower states of valence, such as I^-, Br^-, Sn^{++}, Fe^{++}, Hg_2^{++}, S^{--}; (3) certain radicals and molecules such as $S_2O_3^{--}$, SO_3^{--}, $Fe(CN)_6^{4-}$, NO_2^-, H_2S, etc.

WRITING OXIDATION-REDUCTION EQUATIONS. Examples of oxidation-reduction are found in most varieties of chemical changes. Many of these are simple and can be balanced easily by inspection from a knowledge of the oxidation states of the elements in some of their most common compounds (Table 3.1). This will be evident from an examination of the examples that follow. In each case the student should determine the loss and gain of electrons from the change in oxidation state and thereby identify the oxidizing agent and the reducing agent. The equation is balanced if (1) the same number and kind of atoms are present on both sides of the equation; (2) the net charge on both sides of the equation is the same; and (3) the gain of electrons by the oxidizing agent is equal to the loss of electrons by the reducing agent.

Combination Reactions. Many combination reactions involve a change in oxidation state, as is illustrated by the following:

$$2Mg + O_2 \rightarrow 2MgO$$
$$2Ag + S \rightarrow Ag_2S$$
$$2H_2 + O_2 \rightarrow 2H_2O$$
$$Zn + Cl_2 \rightarrow ZnCl_2$$
$$2Sb + 3Br_2 \rightarrow 2SbBr_3$$

Ionic combinations discussed in earlier sections and such reactions as $CaO + H_2O \rightarrow Ca(OH)_2$ and $H_2O + P_2O_5 \rightarrow 2HPO_3$ are not oxidation-reduction reactions because no change in oxidation state occurs.

Decomposition Reactions. These reactions are the converse of combination reactions and often involve oxidation and reduction. However, unless there is a change in oxidation state of some of the atoms, the decomposition is not considered to be an oxidation-reduction reaction. For example, none of the elements change their oxidation state in the decomposition of calcium carbonate ($CaCO_3 \rightarrow CaO + CO_2$); therefore the reaction is not an oxidation-reduction reaction. The following are examples of decomposition reactions which do involve a change in oxidation state:

$$2HgO \rightarrow 2Hg + O_2$$
$$2HI \rightarrow H_2 + I_2$$
$$2H_2O_2 \rightarrow 2H_2O + O_2$$
$$2KClO_3 \rightarrow 2KCl + 3O_2$$

In the decomposition of $KClO_3$, the oxidation state of chlorine changes from +5 to −1. This corresponds to a gain of 6 electrons for each chlorine atom, or a total of 12 for the two molecules of $KClO_3$. The oxidation state of oxygen changes from −2 to 0. This corresponds to a loss of 2 electrons for each oxygen atom, or a total loss of 12. Thus it is seen that the gain and loss of electrons are equal.

Displacement Reactions. Displacement reactions are usually accompanied by changes in oxidation state corresponding to the transfer of electrons from one substance to another, as the following examples show:

$$Cu^{++} + \underline{Zn} \rightleftharpoons Zn^{++} + \underline{Cu}$$
$$2Sb^{3+} + \underline{3Zn} \rightleftharpoons 3Zn^{++} + \underline{2Sb}$$
$$Cl_2 + 2I^- \rightleftharpoons I_2 + 2Cl^-$$
$$6H_3O^+ + \underline{2Al} \rightleftharpoons 2Al^{3+} + 3H_2\uparrow + 6H_2O$$

In all these reactions it is clear that the total number of electrons taken by the oxidizing agent (the first substance in each case) is just equal to the number of electrons lost by the reducing agent.

Relatively simple oxidation-reduction reactions also take place between certain ions or between certain ions and elements, as is shown by the following:

$$2Fe^{3+} + Sn^{++} \leftrightarrows 2Fe^{++} + Sn^{4+}$$
$$2Hg^{++} + Sn^{++} \leftrightarrows Hg_2{}^{++} + Sn^{4+}$$
$$Cl_2 + 2Fe^{++} \leftrightarrows 2Fe^{3+} + 2Cl^-$$

In the first of these reactions, for example, two Fe^{3+} ions are required to take the two electrons from one Sn^{++} and change it to Sn^{4+}. Hence, the coefficient of Fe^{3+} is 2 and that of Sn^{++} is 1.

BALANCING OXIDATION-REDUCTION EQUATIONS INVOLVING COMPLEX IONS. All oxidation-reduction reactions can be balanced by inspection, provided, of course, that all the reactants and the products are known. However, when complex ions are involved, a systematic procedure is usually advisable. Two different methods are in general use: (1) the oxidation-state method (sometimes called the valence-number method), and (2) the ion-electron partial equation method (abbreviated ion-electron method). The first method is particularly applicable in writing equations involving nonionic reactions but may also be used for ionic reactions as well. The second method is preferred by many for writing equations that involve ions.

Oxidation-State Method. In the oxidation-state method the reactants and products are written down as is done with other reactions. The number of electrons taken by the oxidizing agent is deduced from the change in oxidation state of the elements comprising the oxidizing agent. The number of electrons lost by the reducing agent is determined in a similar manner. Coefficients are then supplied so that the number of electrons taken by the oxidizing agent is equal to the number of electrons lost by the reducing agent. In the case of oxycompounds in aqueous solution, H_3O^+, OH^-, and H_2O are added as needed to balance the equation. The following simple rules will be helpful in using the oxidation-state method for writing equations for oxidation-reduction reactions.

1. Uncombined (free) elements have an oxidation state of zero: Ag°, $O_2{}^\circ$, Mg°, $Cl_2{}^\circ$.

2. Whenever an atom or ion loses electrons, it is oxidized: $Mg^\circ - 2e \rightleftharpoons Mg^{++}$.

3. Whenever an atom or ion gains electrons, it is reduced: $Cl_2{}^\circ + 2e \rightleftharpoons 2Cl^-$.

4. The same number and kind of atoms must be present on both sides of the equation.

5. In any reaction, the number of electrons lost must equal the number of electrons gained.

6. In acid solution, H_3O^+ and H_2O are used in the equation, if needed; and in basic solution, OH^- and H_2O are used.

7. The number and sign of the charges on one side of the equation must be equal to the number and sign of the charges on the other side of the equation.

The following procedure for the reaction of potassium permanganate with hydrochloric acid summarizes the application of the general rules.

1. Write the incomplete equation: oxidant + reductant → products.

$$MnO_4{}^- + Cl^- \rightleftharpoons Mn^{++} + Cl_2 \text{ (incomplete)}$$

2. Note the change in oxidation state of the oxidizing agent and the reducing agent.

$$Mn^{7+} \rightarrow Mn^{++} \quad \text{or} \quad 7 - (2) = +5e \text{ (gained)}$$
$$Cl^- \rightarrow Cl^\circ \quad \text{or} \quad -1 - (0) = -1e \text{ (lost)}$$

The least common multiple (L.C.M.) of 5 and 1 is 5. Divide this L.C.M. by each change in oxidation state to find the coefficients needed to make the electrons gained equal to the electrons lost. Supply these coefficients and balance the incomplete equation with respect to the products of the oxidizing agent and reducing agent:

$$MnO_4{}^- + 5Cl^- \rightleftharpoons Mn^{++} + 2.5Cl_2 \text{ (incomplete)}$$

(NOTE: The above procedure is equivalent to using the change in oxidation state of the oxidizing agent (5) as the *coefficient of the reducing agent* and the change in oxidation state of the reducing agent (1) as the *coefficient of the oxidizing agent.*)

3. When necessary, complete the equation by using H_3O^+ and H_2O in acid solution, or OH^- and H_2O in basic solution. The coefficient of the H_3O^+ or the OH^- required is the one needed to make the net charge the same on both sides of the arrow.

Inspection of the above equation shows that 8 plus charges are needed on the left side of the arrow to make the net charge +2 on both sides. The use of $8H_3O^+$ on the left side gives $(24 \div 2) = 12H_2O$ on the right side. Hence,

$$\begin{array}{l} MnO_4^- + 5Cl^- + 8H_3O^+ \rightleftharpoons Mn^{++} + 2.5Cl_2 + 12H_2O \\ (-1) + (-5) + (+8) = +2 \\ \qquad\qquad +2 = +2 \end{array}$$

(NOTE: It can also be seen that the number of H_3O^+ is equal to twice the number of O atoms lost by the MnO_4^-.)

4. Multiply all the coefficients by 2 if necessary to make them all whole numbers, or divide all of them by 2 when possible.

According to this rule, the above equation must be multiplied by 2 to give the final balanced equation.

$$2MnO_4^- + 10Cl^- + 16H_3O^+ \rightleftharpoons 2Mn^{++} + 5Cl_2 + 24H_2O$$

The equation is balanced because (a) the same number and kind of atoms appear on both sides: (b) the net charge on both sides of the equation is the same (4); and (c) the electrons taken by the oxidizing agent MnO_4^- ($2 \times 5e = 10e$) are equal to the electrons lost by the reducing agent Cl^- ($10 \times 1e = 10e$).

In an alkaline solution, OH^- ions are used when needed to balance the equation electrically. This is illustrated in the following equation for the reaction of potassium permanganate with sodium sulfite in an alkaline solution.

1. Incomplete equation

$$\begin{array}{l} \text{oxidant} + \text{reductant} \rightarrow \text{products} \\ MnO_4^- + SO_3^{--} \rightleftharpoons \underline{MnO_2}\downarrow + SO_4^{--} \text{ (incomplete)} \end{array}$$

2. Changes in oxidation state

$$\begin{array}{lcl} Mn^{7+} \rightarrow Mn^{4+} & \text{or} & 7 - (4) = +3 \\ S^{4+} \rightarrow S^{6+} & \text{or} & 4 - (6) = -2 \end{array}$$

The L.C.M. is 6. Hence, use 3 as the coefficient of SO_3^{--} and 2 as the coefficient of MnO_4^-.

$$2MnO_4^- + 3SO_3^{--} \rightleftharpoons \underline{2MnO_2}\downarrow + 3SO_4^{--} \text{ (incomplete)}$$

3. Completing the equation

There is a total of $(-2) + (-6)$ or 8 negative charges on the left side of the arrow, and only 6 negative charges on the right side. Therefore, two OH^- ions are needed on the right side to balance the equation electrically, and one

H_2O on the left side to balance it with respect to atoms. Hence, the balanced equation is:

$$\begin{array}{c} 2MnO_4^- + 3SO_3^{--} + H_2O \rightleftharpoons \underline{2MnO_2}\downarrow + 3SO_4^{--} + 2OH^- \\ (-2) \ + \ (-6) \qquad = \qquad (-6) \ + \ (-2) \\ -8 = -8 \end{array}$$

In the reaction of HNO_3 with As_2S_3, the nitric acid oxidizes both the arsenic and the sulfur to higher oxidation states. The above steps applied to this reaction are as follows:

1. Incomplete equation

$$\text{oxidant} + \text{reductant} \rightarrow \text{products}$$

$$NO_3^- + \underline{As_2S_3} \rightleftharpoons NO_2\uparrow + H_2AsO_4^- + \underline{S}\downarrow$$

2. Changes in oxidation state

$$\begin{array}{lcr} N^{5+} \rightarrow N^{4+} & \text{or} & [5 - (4)] \times 1 = +1 \\ 2As^{3+} \rightarrow 2As^{5+} & \text{or} & [3 - (5)] \times 2 = -4 \\ 3S^{--} \rightarrow 3S^0 & \text{or} & [-2 - (0)] \times 3 = \underline{-6} \\ & & -10 \end{array}$$

The L.C.M. is 10. Hence, use 10 as the coefficient of NO_3^- and 1 as the coefficient of As_2S_3.

$$10NO_3^- + \underline{As_2S_3} \rightleftharpoons 10NO_2\uparrow + 2H_2AsO_4^- + \underline{3S}\downarrow$$

3. Completing the equation

Examination of the above equations shows 10 negative charges on the left side and only 2 on the right. Therefore, $8H_3O^+$ are required on the left side to balance the equation electrically. Hence,

$$\begin{array}{c} 10NO_3^- + \underline{As_2S_3} + 8H_3O^+ \rightleftharpoons 10NO_2\uparrow + 2H_2AsO_4^- + \underline{3S}\downarrow + 10H_2O \\ (-10) \qquad + \ (+8) \quad = \qquad (-2) \end{array}$$

Other Oxidation-Reduction Reactions

Potassium dichromate + hydrogen sulfide in acid solution

1. Incomplete equation

$$Cr_2O_7^{--} + H_2S \rightleftharpoons 2Cr^{3+} + \underline{S}\downarrow$$

2. Changes in oxidation state

$$\begin{array}{lcr} 2Cr^{6+} \rightarrow 2Cr^{3+} & \text{or} & [6 - (3)] \times 2 = +6 \\ S^{--} \rightarrow S^0 & \text{or} & [-2 - (0)] \times 1 = -2 \end{array}$$

The L.C.M. is 6. Therefore,

$$Cr_2O_7^{--} + 3H_2S \rightleftharpoons 2Cr^{3+} + \underline{3S}\downarrow \ \text{(incomplete)}$$

3. Completing the equation

Balance charges with H_3O^+. Add $8H_3O^+$ on the left.

$$\underset{(-2)}{Cr_2O_7^{--}} + 3H_2S + \underset{+\ (+8)}{8H_3O^+} \rightleftharpoons \underset{=\ (+6)}{2Cr^{3+}} + \underline{3S}\downarrow + 15H_2O$$

Potassium chlorate + iodine in acid solution

1. Incomplete equation

$$ClO_3^- + I_2 \rightleftharpoons Cl^- + IO_3^-$$

2. Changes in oxidation state

$$Cl^{5+} \rightarrow Cl^- \quad \text{or} \quad [5 - (-1)] \times 1 = +6$$
$$I_2^0 \rightarrow 2I^{5+} \quad \text{or} \quad [0 - (5)] \times 2 = -10$$

The L.C.M. is 30. Therefore,

$$5ClO_3^- + 3I_2 \rightleftharpoons 5Cl^- + 6IO_3^- \text{ (incomplete)}$$

3. Completing the equation

Balance charges with H_3O^+. Add $6H_3O^+$ on the right.

$$\underset{(-5)}{5ClO_3^-} + 3I_2 + 9H_2O \rightleftharpoons \underset{=\ (-5)}{5Cl^-} + \underset{+\ (-6)}{6IO_3^-} + \underset{+\ (+6)}{6H_3O^+}$$

Potassium permanganate + sodium sulfite in alkaline solution

1. Incomplete equation

$$MnO_4^- + SO_3^{--} \rightleftharpoons \underline{MnO_2}\downarrow + SO_4^{--}$$

2. Changes in oxidation state

$$Mn^{7+} \rightarrow Mn^{4+} \quad \text{or} \quad 7 - (4) = +3$$
$$S^{4+} \rightarrow S^{6+} \quad \text{or} \quad 4 - (6) = -2$$

The L.C.M. is 6. Therefore,

$$2MnO_4^- + 3SO_3^{--} \rightleftharpoons \underline{2MnO_2}\downarrow + 3SO_4^{--} \text{ (incomplete)}$$

3. Completing the equation

Balance charges using OH^-. Add $2OH^-$ on the right.

$$\underset{(-2)}{2MnO_4^-} + \underset{+\ (-6)}{3SO_3^{--}} + H_2O \underset{=}{\rightleftharpoons} \underline{2MnO_2}\downarrow + \underset{(-6)}{3SO_4^{--}} + \underset{+\ (-2)}{2OH^-}$$

Sodium hypochlorite + iodine in alkaline solution

1. Incomplete equation

$$ClO^- + I_2 \rightleftharpoons IO_3^- + Cl^-$$

2. Changes in oxidation state

$$Cl^{+} \rightarrow Cl^{-} \quad \text{or} \quad [1 - (-1)] \times 1 = +2$$
$$I_2{}^0 \rightarrow 2I^{5+} \quad \text{or} \quad [0 - (+5)] \times 2 = -10$$

The L.C.M. is 10. Therefore,

$$5ClO^{-} + I_2 \rightleftharpoons 2IO_3{}^{-} + 5Cl^{-} \text{ (incomplete)}$$

3. Completing the equation

Balance charges using OH^-. Add $2OH^-$ on the left.

$$5ClO^{-} + I_2 + 2OH^{-} \rightleftharpoons 2IO_3{}^{-} + 5Cl^{-} + H_2O$$
$$(-5) \quad + \quad (-2) \; = \; (-2) + (-5)$$

Bismuth hydroxide + sodium stannite in alkaline solution

1. Incomplete equation

$$\underline{Bi(OH)_3} + Sn(OH)_4{}^{--} \rightleftharpoons \underline{Bi}\downarrow + Sn(OH)_6{}^{--}$$

2. Changes in oxidation state

$$Bi^{3+} \rightarrow Bi^{0} \quad \text{or} \quad 3 - (0) = +3$$
$$Sn^{++} \rightarrow Sn^{4+} \quad \text{or} \quad 2 - (4) = -2$$

The L.C.M. is 6. Therefore,

$$\underline{2Bi(OH)_3} + 3Sn(OH)_4{}^{--} \rightleftharpoons \underline{2Bi}\downarrow + 3Sn(OH)_6{}^{--}$$
$$-6 \quad = \quad -6$$

3. Completing the equation

The equation is already balanced with respect to charges.

Mercury (I) chloride + ammonia

$$\underline{Hg_2Cl_2} + 2NH_3 \rightleftharpoons \underline{Hg}\downarrow + \underline{Hg(NH_2)Cl}\downarrow + NH_4{}^{+} + Cl^{-}$$

In this equation part of the mercury is oxidized and part of it is reduced. That is, $Hg_2{}^{++} \rightarrow Hg^0 + Hg^{++}$. Instead of forming $HgCl_2$, $Hg(NH_2)Cl_2$ is formed in ammoniacal solution.

The above examples should suffice to illustrate the procedure for balancing oxidation equations by the oxidation-state method. However, in oxidation-reduction reactions, as in any others, it is necessary that the products of the oxidizing agent and of the reducing agent be known or be deduced from the general behavior of similar substances. Once they are known, balancing the equation becomes routine.

As an aid in writing oxidation-reduction equations, the products obtained when certain oxidizing agents react with a number of different reducing agents are listed in Table 3.2. This is not intended to be a com-

TABLE 3.2. Products in Typical Oxidation-Reduction Reactions

Oxidizing Agent	Nature of Solution	Usual Product of Oxidizing Agent	Reducing Agent	Usual Product of Reducing Agent
BiO_3^-	Acid	Bi^{3+}	Cl^-, Cr^{3+}, Mn^{++} (also many other oxidizable substances)	Cl_2, $Cr_2O_7^=$, MnO_4^-
H_2O_2	Acid	H_2O	H_2S, $S_2O_3^=$, H_2SO_3, PbS, Fe^{++}, $Fe(CN)_6^{4-}$, I^-	$SO_4^=$, $SO_4^=$, $SO_4^=$, $PbSO_4$, Fe^{3+}, $Fe(CN)_6^{3-}$, I_2
MnO_4^-	Acid	Mn^{++} (Some give MnO_2 in very dil. acid)	$C_2O_4^=$, CNS^-, Ti^{3+}, Sn^{++}, H_2S, $S_2O_3^=$, H_2SO_3, $Fe(CN)_6^{4-}$, I^-, H_3AsO_3, H_3SbO_3, Fe^{++}, H_2O_2, HNO_2, Hg_2^{++}, Br^-, Cl^-	CO_2, ($HCN + SO_4^=$), Ti^{4+}, Sn^{4+}, (SO_4+some$^=$ $S_2O_3^=$ in very dil. acid), $SO_4^=$, $SO_4^=$, $Fe(CN)_6^{3-}$, I_2, H_3AsO_4, $HSb(OH)_6$, Fe^{3+}, O_2, NO_3^-, Hg^{++}, Br_2, Cl_2
HClO	Acid	Cl^-	$C_2O_4^=$, CNS^-, H_2PO_3, Sn^{++}, H_2S, $S_2O_3^=$, H_2SO_3, (HgS + HCl), $Fe(CN)_6^{4-}$, I^-, H_3AsO_3, Fe^{++}, H_2O_2, HNO_2, Hg_2^{++}, Hg, Br^- (Mn^{++} + concd. HCl)	CO_2, ($HCN + SO_4^=$), H_3PO_4, Sn^{4+}, $SO_4^=$, $SO_4^=$, $SO_4^=$, ($HgCl_4^= + S$), $Fe(CN)_6^{3-}$, (I_2 dil., IO_3^- concd. acid), H_3AsO_4, Fe^{3+}, O_2, NO_3^-, Hg^{++}, Hg^{++}, Br_2, MnO_2
ClO_3^-	Acid	Cl^-	Zn, Sn^{++}, H_2SO_3, I^-, Fe^{++}, HNO_2, Mn^{++}, etc.	Zn^{++}, Sn^{4+}, $SO_4^=$, I_2, Fe^{3+}, NO_3^-, Mn^{3+}
PbO_2	Acid	Pb^{++}	H_2SO_3, CNS^-, Br^-, $Fe(CN)_6^{4-}$, (Mn^{++} + HNO_3)	$PbSO_4$, ($PbSO_4$ + HCN), Br_2, (Fe^{3+} + HCN), MnO_4^-
$Cr_2O_7^=$	Acid	Cr^{3+}	$C_2O_4^=$, Sn^{++}, H_2S, $S_2O_3^=$, H_2SO_3, $Fe(CN)_6^{4-}$, I^-, Fe^{++}, H_2O_2, HNO_2, (Br^-, highly acid), (Cl^-, highly acid), (Mn^{++} + concd. HCl)	CO_2, Sn^{4+}, (S in dil., $SO_4^=$ in concd. acid), $SO_4^=$, $SO_4^=$, $Fe(CN)_6^{3-}$, I_2, Fe^{3+}, O_2, NO_3^-, Br_2, Cl_2, MnO_2

TABLE 3.2. Products in Typical Oxidation-Reduction Reactions (*Continued*)

Oxidizing Agent	Nature of Solution	Usual Product of Oxidizing Agent	Reducing Agent	Usual Product of Reducing Agent
Cl_2	Acid	Cl^-	Zn, Sn^{++}, H_2SO_3, $Fe(CN)_6^{4-}$, I^-, Fe^{++}, H_2O_2, Hg, NH_4^+, Br^-	Zn^{++}, Sn^{4+}, $SO_4^=$, $Fe(CN)_6^{3-}$, (I_2 and IO_3^-), Fe^{3+}, O_2, Hg^{++}, N_2, Br_2
MnO_2	Acid	Mn^{++}	Sn^{++}, H_2SO_3, I^-, Fe^{++}, H_2O_2, HNO_2, Br^-	Sn^{4+}, $SO_4^=$, I_2, Fe^{3+}, O_2, NO_3^-, Br_2
O_2	Acid	H_2O	H_2S, H_2SO_3, Sn^{++}, I^-, Fe^{++}	S, $SO_4^=$, Sn^{4+}, I_2, Fe^{3+}
IO_3^-	Acid	I_2	Zn, H_2SO_3, I^-, H_3AsO_3, P, Hg_2^{++}, Br^-, (Cl^- highly acid)	Zn^{++}, $SO_4^=$, I_2, H_3AsO_4, H_3PO_4, Hg^{++}, Br_2, Cl_2
IO_3^-	Acid	I^-	Sn^{++}, H_2S, H_3PO_3	Sn^{4+}, S, H_3PO_4
Br_2	Acid	Br^-	H_2S, H_2SO_3, CNS^-, I^-, Fe^{++}, Mn^{++}	$SO_4^=$, $SO_4^=$, (HCN + $SO_4^=$), I_2, Fe^{3+}, Mn^{3+}
HNO_3	Dil. acid	NO, etc.*	H_2S, H_2SO_3, $S_2O_3^=$, $Fe(CN)_6^{4-}$, I^-, Fe^{++}	S, $SO_4^=$, $SO_4^=$, $Fe(CN)_6^{3-}$, I_2, Fe^{3+}
HNO_3	Concd.	NO_2, etc.*	Cu, Ag, H_2S, $S_2O_3^=$, H_2SO_3, CuS, I^-, Fe^{++}, (Mn^{++} + HCl)	Cu^{++}, Ag^+, S, $SO_4^=$, $SO_4^=$, (Cu^{++} + S), I_2, Fe^{3+}, MnO_2
$SO_4^=$	Concd. H_2SO_4	SO_2	Cu, Bi, Br^-	Cu^{++}, Bi^{3+}, Br_2
$SO_4^=$	Concd. H_2SO_4	S	H_2S	S
$SO_4^=$	Concd. H_2SO_4	H_2S	Zn, I^-	Zn^{++}, I_2
Hg^{++}	Dil. HCl	Hg_2Cl_2	Sn^{++}	Sn^{4+}
Fe^{3+}	Acid	Fe^{++}	Zn, Sn^{++}, Ti^{3+}, H_2S, H_2SO_3, $S_2O_3^=$, (NO_3^- + concd. H_2SO_4)	Zn^{++}, Sn^{4+}, Ti^{4+}, S, $SO_4^=$, $SO_4^=$, $Fe(NO)^{++}$

* Besides the main products listed for the reduction of nitric acid, varying amounts of NO_2, HNO_2, NO, N_2O, N_2, NH_3, NH_2OH, N_2H_2, etc., are also obtained.

TABLE 3.2. Products in Typical Oxidation-Reduction Reactions (*Continued*)

Oxidizing Agent	Nature of Solution	Usual Product of Oxidizing Agent	Reducing Agent	Usual Product of Reducing Agent
I_2	Acid	I^-	Sn^{++}, H_2S, ZnS, H_2SO_3, $S_2O_3^{=}$, H_3AsO_3, H_3SbO_3, HCHO	Sn^{4+}, S, (Zn^{++} + S), $SO_4^{=}$, $S_4O_6^{=}$, H_3AsO_4, $HSb(OH)_6$, $HCOO^-$
$Fe(CN)_6^{3-}$	Dil. acid	$Fe(CN)_6^{4-}$	H_2S, H_2SO_3, $S_2O_3^{=}$, I^-, HNO_2 (dil. acid), (Mn^{++} + concd. HCl)	S, $SO_4^{=}$, $SO_4^{=}$, I_2, NO_3^-, MnO_2
ClO^-	Alkaline	Cl^-	$S^{=}$, $SO_3^{=}$, $S_2O_3^{=}$, CN^-, CNS^-, I^- (dil. acid), $Fe(CN)_6^{4-}$, NO_2^-, $Fe(OH)_2$, $Mn(OH)_2$, $Co(OH)_2$, $Pb(OH)_2$, $Cr(OH)_3$, I_2 (hot)	(S and $SO_4^{=}$), $SO_4^{=}$, $SO_4^{=}$, CNO^-, (CNO^- + $SO_4^{=}$), I_2, $Fe(CN)_6^{3-}$, NO_3^-, $Fe(OH)_3$, $MnO(OH)_2$, $Co(OH)_3$, PbO_2, $CrO_4^{=}$, IO_3^-
HO_2^-	Alkaline	OH^-	$S^{=}$, AsS_4^{3-}, CN^-, $Cr(OH)_3$, $Co(OH)_2$, $Mn(OH)_2$	$SO_4^{=}$, (AsO_4^{3-} + $SO_4^{=}$), CNO^-, $CrO_4^{=}$, $Co(OH)_3$, $MnO(OH)_2$
MnO_4^-	Neutral or alkaline	MnO_2	$S^{=}$, $SO_3^{=}$, I^-, NO_2, CN^-, CNS^-, $HCOO^-$	$SO_4^{=}$, $SO_4^{=}$, IO_3^-, NO_3^-, CNO^-, (CNO + $SO_4^{=}$), $CO_3^{=}$
$Fe(CN)_6^{3-}$	Alkaline	$Fe(CN)_6^{4-}$	$S^{=}$, $SO_3^{=}$	S, $SO_4^{=}$

plete list of reactions, but it does present many that are encountered in analytical chemistry. The student should practice balancing oxidation-reduction equations by writing the equations for typical reactions indicated in this table. It should be emphasized that the oxidizing power of many of the oxidizing agents is markedly affected by the acid concentration. Consequently, the nature of the products obtained may vary as the acidity of the solution is changed; in some cases, a mixture of products will be obtained. This is particularly true of reactions involving nitric acid, compounds of sulfur, etc. Except for the concentrated acids, the substances are listed in the table in the approximate order of their oxidizing power in 1-*M* acid solution. Also the substances oxidized most easily under these conditions are listed first in the column headed reducing agent.

Ion-Electron Partial Equation Method. In this method of balancing oxidation-reduction reactions, *ion-electron partial equations* are written for the oxidizing agent and for the reducing agent. These partial equations are essentially the electrode reactions that occur in a suitable electrochemical cell in which the oxidant system is one electrode and the reductant system is the other. (Such cells are described more completely in the discussion of the theoretical aspects of oxidation-reduction reactions.) The two ion-electron partial equations are multiplied by factors which make the number of electrons taken by the oxidizing agent equal to the number lost by the reducing agent. Adding the two partial equations gives the final balanced equation for the reaction. For example, the reaction of potassium permanganate with a solution of hydrochloric acid is written as follows:

$$[MnO_4^- + 8H_3O^+ + 5e \rightleftharpoons Mn^{++} + 12H_2O] \times 2$$
$$[2Cl^- \rightleftharpoons Cl_2 + 2e] \times 5$$
$$\overline{2MnO_4^- + 10Cl^- + 16H_3O^+ \rightleftharpoons 2Mn^{++} + 5Cl_2 + 24H_2O}$$

It should be noted that when the partial equation for MnO_4^- is multiplied by 2 and the one for Cl^- by 5, the total number of electrons taken by the MnO_4^- is equal to the total number lost by the Cl^-.

The following example, using MnO_4^- in acid solution, illustrates the steps involved in writing ion-electron partial equations:

1. Write the incomplete equation: oxidized form → reduced form.

$$MnO_4^- \rightleftharpoons Mn^{++} \text{ (incomplete)}$$

2. Balance the equation with respect to atoms; if necessary, use H_3O^+ and H_2O in acid solutions, or OH^- and H_2O in alkaline solutions.

$$MnO_4^- + 8H_3O^+ \rightleftharpoons Mn^{++} + 12H_2O \text{ (incomplete)}$$

3. Balance the equation electrically, using as many electrons as necessary to make the net charge the same on both sides of the arrow. The net charge on the left side is +7, and that on the right is +2. Hence, 5e must be added to the left side of the arrow to make the net charge +2 and thus balance the equation electrically.

$$MnO_4^- + 8H_3O^+ + 5e \rightleftharpoons Mn^{++} + 12H_2O$$

The following general statements with respect to the use of H_3O^+, H_2O, or OH^- apply to writing ion-electron partial equations.

In acid solution

1. When the oxidizing agent loses oxygen atoms, H_3O^+ is used as one of the reactants and H_2O is one of the products.

$$NO_3^- + 2H_3O^+ + 1e \rightleftharpoons NO_2\uparrow + 3H_2O$$

2. When the reducing agent gains oxygen atoms, H_2O is a reactant and H_3O^+ is a product.

$$HNO_2 + 4H_2O \rightleftharpoons NO_3^- + 3H_3O + 2e$$

In basic solution

3. When the oxidizing agent loses oxygen atoms, H_2O is used as a reactant and OH^- is one of the products.

$$MnO_4^- + 2H_2O + 3e \rightleftharpoons \underline{MnO_2}\downarrow + 4OH^-$$

4. When the reducing agent gains oxygen atoms, OH^- is one of the reactants and H_2O is a product.

$$Cr^{3+} + 8OH^- \rightleftharpoons CrO_4^{--} + 4H_2O + 3e$$

To aid the student in writing equations for the many oxidation-reduction reactions encountered in qualitative analysis, a list of ion-electron partial equations for some common oxidizing and reducing agents is given in Table 3.3. The conditions under which the partial reactions take place are also indicated. The partial equations listed under "oxidizing agents" may be read from right to left to obtain the ion-electron partial for the oxidation of the reduced form of the substance concerned. Similarly, the ion-electron partials listed under "reducing agents" may be read from right to left to obtain the ion-electron partial for the reduction of the oxidized form. The oxidizing agents are listed in the approximate order of their oxidizing power. The best reducing agents are likewise listed first under the reducing agents. A more complete table in Appendix N lists these and other substances in the order of their standard oxidation potentials.

The use of Table 3.3 may be illustrated by writing the equation for the reaction of dilute nitric acid with lead sulfide. All that is necessary is to combine the partial equation for dilute nitric acid listed under oxidizing agents with the one for PbS, as follows:

$$[NO_3^- + 4H_3O^+ + 3e \rightleftharpoons NO\uparrow + 6H_2O] \times 2$$

$$[\underline{PbS} \rightleftharpoons Pb^{++} + \underline{S}\downarrow + 2e] \times 3$$

$$2NO_3^- + 3\underline{PbS} + 8H_3O^+ \rightleftharpoons 2NO\uparrow + 3Pb^{++} + 3\underline{S}\downarrow + 12H_2O$$

Similarly, the oxidation of $Cr(OH)_3$ to CrO_4^{--} in basic solution by hydro-

TABLE 3.3. Ion-Electron Partial Equations

Equations	Conditions
For substances reacting as oxidizing agents	
$BiO_3^- + 6H_3O^+ + 2e \rightleftharpoons Bi^{3+} + 9H_2O$	Acid solution
$H_2O_2 + 2H_3O^+ + 2e \rightleftharpoons 4H_2O$	Acid solution
$MnO_4^- + 8H_3O^+ + 5e \rightleftharpoons Mn^{++} + 12H_2O$	Acid solution
$HClO + H_3O^+ + 2e \rightleftharpoons Cl^- + 2H_2O$	Acid solution
$PbO_2 + 4H_3O^+ + 2e \rightleftharpoons Pb^{++} + 6H_2O$	Acid solution
$ClO_3^- + 6H_3O^+ + 6e \rightleftharpoons Cl^- + 9H_2O$	Acid solution
$BrO_3^- + 6H_3O^+ + 6e \rightleftharpoons Br^- + 9H_2O$	Acid solution
$Cr_2O_7^= + 14H_3O^+ + 6e \rightleftharpoons 2Cr^{3+} + 21H_2O$	Acid solution
$HBrO + H_3O^+ + 2e \rightleftharpoons Br^- + 2H_2O$	Acid solution
$Cl_2 + 2e \rightleftharpoons 2Cl^-$	Acid solution
$MnO_2 + 4H_3O^+ + 2e \rightleftharpoons Mn^{++} + 6H_2O$	Acid solution
$O_2 + 4H_3O^+ + 4e \rightleftharpoons 6H_2O$	Acid solution
$2IO_3^- + 12H_3O^+ + 10e \rightleftharpoons I_2 + 18H_2O$	Acid solution
$IO_3^- + 6H_3O^+ + 6e \rightleftharpoons I^- + 9H_2O$	Acid solution
$Br_2 + 2e \rightleftharpoons 2Br^-$	Acid solution
$HNO_2 + H_3O^+ + e \rightleftharpoons NO + 2H_2O$	Acid solution
$NO_3^- + 4H_3O^+ + 3e \rightleftharpoons NO + 6H_2O$	Dilute HNO_3. Other products: HNO_2, N_2O, NH_2OH, N_2, N_2H_4
$NO_3^- + 10H_3O^+ + 8e \rightleftharpoons NH_4^+ + 13H_2O$	Very dilute HNO_3 with active metals
$NO_3^- + 2H_3O^+ + e \rightleftharpoons NO_2 + 3H_2O$	Concd. HNO_3
$SO_4^= + 4H_3O^+ + 2e \rightleftharpoons SO_2 + 6H_2O$	Concd. H_2SO_4 with less active metals, C, S, HBr, etc.
$SO_4^= + 8H_3O^+ + 6e \rightleftharpoons S + 12H_2O$	Concd. H_2SO_4 with H_2S
$SO_4^= + 10H_3O^+ + 8e \rightleftharpoons H_2S + 14H_2O$	Concd. H_2SO_4 with active metals, HI, etc.
$2Hg^{++} + 2e \rightleftharpoons Hg_2^{++}$	Acid solution
$Hg_2^{++} + 2e \rightleftharpoons 2Hg$	Acid solution
$Fe^{3+} + e \rightleftharpoons Fe^{++}$	Acid solution
$H_3SbO_4 + 2H_3O^+ + 2e \rightleftharpoons H_3SbO_3 + 3H_2O$	Acid solution
$H_3AsO_4 + 2H_3O^+ + 2e \rightleftharpoons H_3AsO_3 + 3H_2O$	Acid solution
$I_2 + 2e \rightleftharpoons 2I^-$	Acid solution
$Fe(CN)_6^{3-} + e \rightleftharpoons Fe(CN)_6^{4-}$	Acid solution
$Cu^{++} + 2e \rightleftharpoons Cu$	Acid solution
$Sn^{4+} + 2e \rightleftharpoons Sn^{++}$	Acid solution
$ClO^- + H_2O + 2e \rightleftharpoons Cl^- + 2OH^-$	Alkaline solution
$HO_2^- + H_2O + 2e \rightleftharpoons 3OH^-$	Alkaline solution
$BrO^- + H_2O + 2e \rightleftharpoons Br^- + 2OH^-$	Alkaline solution

TABLE 3.3. Ion-Electron Partial Equations (*Continued*)

Equations	Conditions
$ClO_3^- + 3H_2O + 6e \rightleftharpoons Cl^- + 6OH^-$	Alkaline solution
$MnO_4^= + 2H_2O + 3e \rightleftharpoons MnO_2 + 4OH^-$	Alkaline solution
$Fe(CN)_6^{3-} + e \rightleftharpoons Fe(CN)_6^{4-}$	Alkaline solution
$O_2 + 2H_2O + 4e \rightleftharpoons 4OH^-$	Alkaline solution
$IO_3^- + 3H_2O + 6e \rightleftharpoons I^- + 6OH^-$	Alkaline solution
$NO_3^- + H_2O + 2e \rightleftharpoons NO_2^- + 2OH^-$	Alkaline solution
$CrO_4^{--} + 4H_2O + 3e \rightleftharpoons Cr(OH)_3 + 5OH^-$	Alkaline solution
For substances reacting as reducing agents	
$Al \rightleftharpoons Al^{3+} + 3e$	Acid solution
$Zn \rightleftharpoons Zn^{++} + 2e$	Acid solution
$C_2O_4^= \rightleftharpoons 2CO_2 + 2e$	Acid solution
$H_3PO_3 + 3H_2O \rightleftharpoons H_3PO_4 + 2H_3O^+ + 2e$	Acid solution
$H_2S + 2H_2O \rightleftharpoons S + 2H_3O^+ + 2e$	Acid solution
$PbS \rightleftharpoons Pb^{++} + S + 2e$	Acid solution
$Sn^{++} + 6Cl^- \rightleftharpoons SnCl_6^= + 2e$	Acid solution
$2S_2O_3^= \rightleftharpoons S_4O_6^= + 2e$	Acid solution
$H_2SO_3 + 5H_2O \rightleftharpoons SO_4^= + 4H_3O^+ + 2e$	Acid solution
$Fe(CN)_6^{4-} \rightleftharpoons Fe(CN)_6^{3-} + e$	Acid solution
$2I^- \rightleftharpoons I_2 + 2e$	Acid solution
$H_3AsO_3 + 3H_2O \rightleftharpoons H_3AsO_4 + 2H_3O^+ + 2e$	Acid solution
$H_3SbO_3 + 3H_2O \rightleftharpoons H_3SbO_4 + 2H_3O^+ + 2e$	Acid solution
$H_2O_2 + 2H_2O \rightleftharpoons O_2 + 2H_3O^+ + 2e$	Acid solution
$Fe^{++} \rightleftharpoons Fe^{3+} + e$	Acid solution
$HNO_2 + 4H_2O \rightleftharpoons NO_3^- + 3H_3O^+ + 2e$	Acid solution
$Hg_2^{++} \rightleftharpoons 2Hg^{++} + 2e$	Acid solution
$2Br^- \rightleftharpoons Br_2 + 2e$	Acid solution
$I^- + 9H_2O \rightleftharpoons IO_3^- + 6H_3O^+ + 6e$	Acid solution
$2Cl^- \rightleftharpoons Cl_2 + 2e$	Acid solution
$Al + 4OH^- \rightleftharpoons Al(OH)_4^- + 3e$	Alkaline solution
$Zn + 4OH^- \rightleftharpoons Zn(OH)_4^= + 2e$	Alkaline solution
$CN^- + 2OH^- \rightleftharpoons CNO^- + H_2O + 2e$	Alkaline solution
$Sn(OH)_4^= + 2OH^- \rightleftharpoons Sn(OH)_6^= + 2e$	Alkaline solution
$SO_3^= + 2OH^- \rightleftharpoons SO_4^= + H_2O + 2e$	Alkaline solution
$AsO_3^{3-} + 2OH^- \rightleftharpoons AsO_4^{3-} + H_2O + 2e$	Alkaline solution
$Fe(OH)_2 + OH^- \rightleftharpoons Fe(OH)_3 + e$	Alkaline solution
$S^= \rightleftharpoons S + 2e$	Alkaline solution
$Mn(OH)_2 + OH^- \rightleftharpoons Mn(OH)_3 + e$	Alkaline solution
$Mn(OH)_2 + 2OH^- \rightleftharpoons MnO_2 + 2H_2O + 2e$	Alkaline solution
$Cr(OH)_3 + 5OH^- \rightleftharpoons CrO_4^= + 4H_2O + 3e$	Alkaline solution
$HO_2^- + OH^- \rightleftharpoons O_2 + H_2O + 2e$	Alkaline solution
$NO_2^- + 2OH^- \rightleftharpoons NO_3^- + H_2O + 2e$	Alkaline solution
$Co(OH)_2 + OH^- \rightleftharpoons Co(OH)_3 + e$	Alkaline solution
$I^- + 6OH^- \rightleftharpoons IO_3^- + 3H_2O + 6e$	Alkaline solution

gen peroxide is written by combining the ion-electron partial equations as follows:

$$[HO_2^- + H_2O + 2e \rightleftharpoons 3OH^-] \times 3$$
$$[Cr(OH)_3 + 5OH^- \rightleftharpoons CrO_4^{--} + 4H_2O + 3e] \times 2$$
$$\overline{3HO_2^- + 2Cr(OH)_3 + OH^- \rightleftharpoons 2CrO_4^{--} + 5H_2O}$$

Thus, it is relatively simple to write equations for oxidation-reduction reactions by this method.

REVIEW QUESTIONS

1. What facts are shown by a chemical equation?
2. What conventions regarding oxidation states have been adopted in writing equations? Illustrate.
3. Using Table 3.1, list all the elements with an oxidation state of +1. Repeat for each of the other oxidation states.
4. What conventions have been adopted for writing ionic equations? Illustrate.
5. Under what conditions do reactions classed as ionic combinations take place? Give two or three examples of each. Be able to write the equations for all the reactions in the section on ionic reactions.
6. Describe a possible mechanism for the precipitation of $Bi(OH)_3$ with ammonium hydroxide, and one for the dissolution of AgCl in ammonium hydroxide.
7. Define a protolytic reaction and state the general formula which illustrates the fundamental reaction. Give examples of three different classes of protolytic reactions.
8. Define (a) oxidation; (b) reduction; (c) oxidizing agent; (d) reducing agent. Give a few examples of oxidizing and reducing agents.
9. Write several equations illustrating oxidation-reduction in combination and in decomposition reactions. Name two or three combination and decomposition reactions which are not oxidation-reduction reactions. Write some equations illustrating oxidation-reduction in displacement reactions.
10. Summarize the steps in balancing oxidation-reduction equations by the oxidation-state method. Illustrate by means of the reaction of $KMnO_4$ with HCl.
11. Be able to write the equations for all the examples given on pages 47–54.
12. Practice writing oxidation-reduction equations by balancing the equations for the reactions of each oxidizing agent listed in the first column of Table 3.2 with the reducing agents in the fourth column.
13. What is meant by "ion-electron partial equation"? Illustrate.
14. List and illustrate the steps in writing ion-electron partial equations. State the rules relative to the use of H_3O^+, H_2O, and OH^-. Illustrate each.
15. Balance all the oxidation-reduction equations on pages 47–54, using the ion-electron method. Practice using this method by balancing the equations for the reactions of the oxidizing and reducing agents listed in Table 3.2.

16. Why is the oxidation state of free elements taken as zero?
17. The oxidation state of the oxygen in H_2O_2 and other peroxides is taken as -1. Explain.
18. What is the oxidation state of the hydrogen in CaH_2?
19. In balancing oxidation-reduction equations, why is it logical to include only the ions that take part in the reactions?
20. What reasons are advanced for saying that H^+ does not exist in a water solution but that the ion is H_3O^+?
21. When H_3O^+ is added to a solution containing NH_3, why is the ion NH_4^+ obtained?
22. What types of valences are shown by the compound, NH_4Cl? Explain.
23. Why is hydrochloric acid in water solution written $(H_3O^+ + Cl^-)$ instead of HCl?
24. Why is mercury (I) chloride written Hg_2Cl_2 instead of HgCl? Would it be correct to write Hg_2^+ instead of Hg_2^{++}? Why or why not?
25. Why is acetic acid in solution written CH_3COOH instead of $(CH_3COO^- + H_3O^+)$?
26. Why is lead acetate written $Pb(CH_3COO)_2$ instead of $(Pb^{++} + 2CH_3COO^-)$?
27. The solubility of AgCl is 1.9×10^{-6} g./ml. Why is AgCl in solution written $(Ag^+ + Cl^-)$ instead of AgCl?
28. When NaOH is added to a solution containing NH_4^+, NH_3 is liberated. Why?
29. AgCl is only slightly soluble in water but may be dissolved in a solution of ammonia by the formation of a very soluble compound. How can we account for this reaction?
30. Distinguish between (a) ionization reaction, (b) hydrolysis reaction, (c) neutralization reaction. In what respect are they all similar?
31. Is there a clear distinction between a strong acid and a weak acid?
32. Is there a clear distinction between an oxidizing agent and a reducing agent?
33. Show by equations where hydrogen peroxide may act (a) as an oxidizing agent, (b) as a reducing agent.
34. What types of salts are (a) acid in reaction, (b) basic in reaction, (c) neutral in reaction?
35. When Hg_2Cl_2 is acted on by an ammonia solution, some Hg° is formed. What reaction will Hg° have on Ag^+?

CHAPTER 4

LABORATORY METHODS IN SEMIMICRO QUALITATIVE ANALYSIS

The laboratory work in qualitative analysis is designed with the following aims in mind: (1) It affords the student an opportunity to acquire a certain amount of skill and proficiency in laboratory techniques. (2) It gives him practice in making systematic separations and identifications of many common ions. (3) It makes learning the properties and reactions of the ions easier both because of the systematic approach and because of direct observation of the reactions. Finally (4) study of procedures and of the reasons for the various operations provides dramatic illustrations of many of the theories of chemistry, particularly those relating to solutions of electrolytes.

In this chapter some details of the laboratory methods and techniques used in qualitative analysis are described and discussed. The other aspects and aims of the laboratory work are developed in the chapters that follow.

EQUIPMENT

The equipment needed for the laboratory work is shown in Fig. 4.1, and a complete list of the items needed appears in Appendix A. Detailed directions for the operations in which this equipment is used are given in the following sections.

FILTRATION OF PRECIPITATES

One of the most frequently used operations in qualitative analysis is the separating of a precipitate from the solution in which it is formed. Several methods are available; of them, decantation, centrifugation, and filtration are the most important. The choice of method depends upon the nature of the precipitate, the completeness of the separation desired, the equipment available, and the time available for the separation.

Nature of Precipitates

If all precipitates were in the form of large dense crystals, any of the three methods of separation would be applicable. However, many precipitates form in a fine, a flocculent, a gelatinous, or a colloidal condition. Slow precipita-

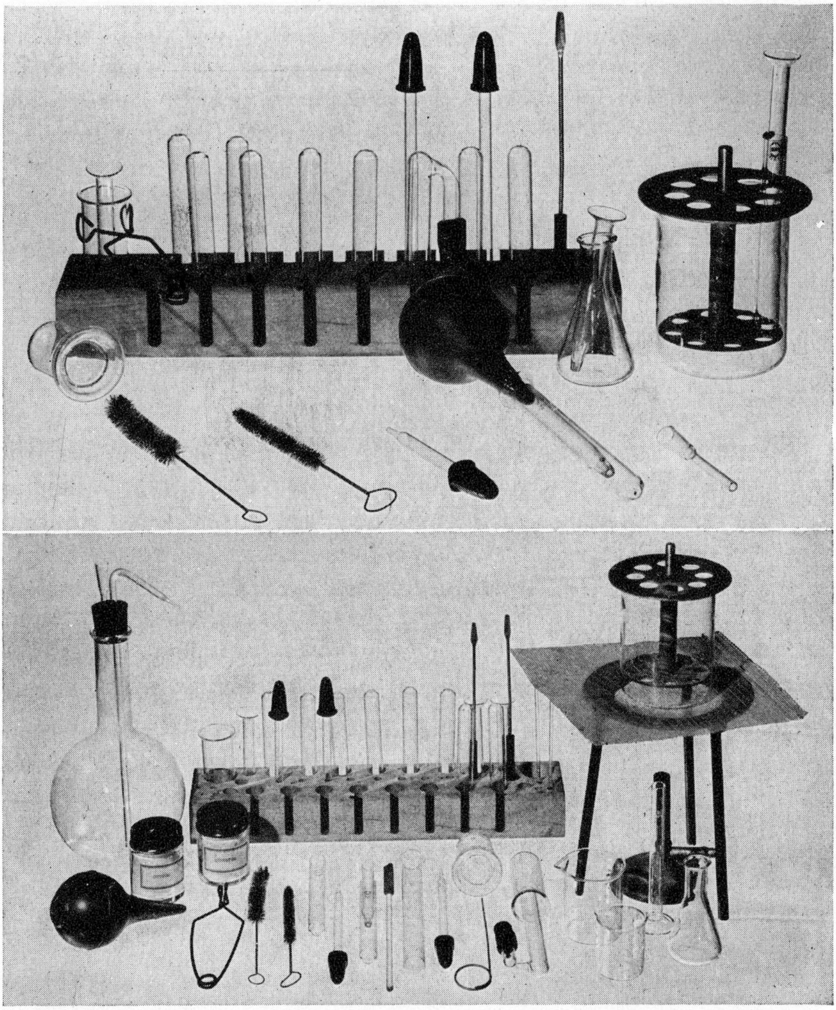

FIG. 4.1. Apparatus for Semimicro Qualitative Analysis by the Pressure Bulb Method.

tion usually favors the formation of larger particles. Furthermore, fine crystalline precipitates tend to increase in size when allowed to stand in the liquid from which they are precipitated. The reason is that finely divided particles of a solid are more soluble than larger particles. Consequently the smaller particles dissolve and reprecipitate on the larger crystals. This process is more rapid when the solution is shaken or stirred, and especially when it is maintained at elevated temperatures. Hence the test tubes in which precipitates are formed are usually set in a hot water bath and shaken occasionally. Higher temperatures and shaking also favor the coagulation of colloidal and gelatinous precipitates. Often the addition of certain electrolytes causes the coagulation of precipitates in a form more easily separated from the supernatant liquid.

Careful control of the conditions under which precipitation is carried out prevents the formation of colloidal precipitates and produces precipitates in a form that is easily separated from the liquid. The temperature, the concentration of the precipitant, and the presence of other ions in the solution are controllable factors which affect the nature of the precipitate. Control of conditions is especially important in the precipitation of the sulfides. Here the regulation of the hydronium ion concentration (the pH of the solution) is an important factor. Indicators are frequently used to aid in controlling the acidity or alkalinity of solutions before precipitation is carried out.

Decantation and the Settling of Precipitates

Decantation (Fig. 4.2) is the least satisfactory of the three methods mentioned above for separating a precipitate from its supernatant liquid. It is applicable only in case the precipitate consists of large crystalline particles that settle rapidly. Decantation as a means of separating the liquid from the solid not only requires rapid settling; it also requires that the precipitate pack into a reasonably compact mass at the bottom of the test tube so that it will not be drawn off or poured off with the liquid. Decantation is often used during filtrations to allow a large part of the liquid to run through the filter before solids which tend to plug the pores of the filter medium are transferred to the filter.

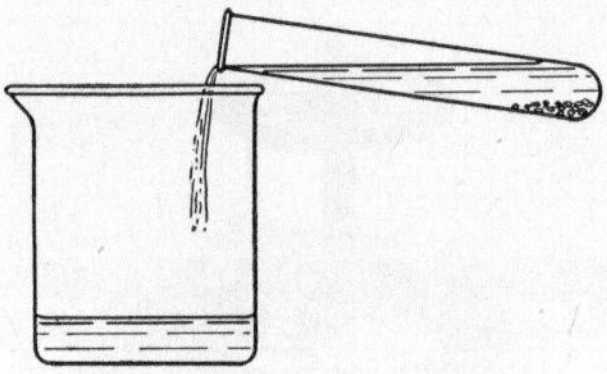

FIG. 4.2. Decantation.

The rate of settling of spherical particles is given by Stokes' equation:

$$R_s = \frac{2r^2g}{9\eta}(d - d')$$

where R_s is the rate of settling in centimeters per sec.; r is the radius of the particle in centimeters; g is the acceleration of gravity (981 cm./sec.^{2}); η is the viscosity of the liquid in c.g.s. units (poises); d is the density of the solid; and d' is the density of the liquid.

It is seen from this equation that the rate of settling is increased by (1) an increase in size of the particles (r); (2) an increase in the acceleration of gravity (g); (3) a decrease in the viscosity of the liquid (η); and (4) an increase in the difference between the density of the solid (d) and the density of the liquid (d'). For a given crystalline precipitate the factors which cannot be changed easily are g and d. However, the radius of the particles can be increased by the methods described in the preceding section. Furthermore, an increase in temperature not only reduces the viscosity but also decreases the density of the liquid more than it does the density of the solid, so that the term $(d - d')$ becomes larger, thereby increasing the rate of settling. Moreover, heating often changes the nature and composition of the precipitate by coagulating smaller particles into larger ones, or by dehydrating certain types of gelatinous precipitates. Many gelatinous or flocculent precipitates never settle sufficiently to allow decantation. Indeed, if the density of the solid is equal to or less than that of the liquid, the precipitate floats rather than settles. At times air bubbles trapped in a precipitate cause it to rise rather than settle.

Centrifugation

With the use of a centrifuge (Fig. 4.3) it is possible to increase greatly the rate at which a precipitate settles. This is true because the high speed of rotation increases the force that causes the particle to settle.

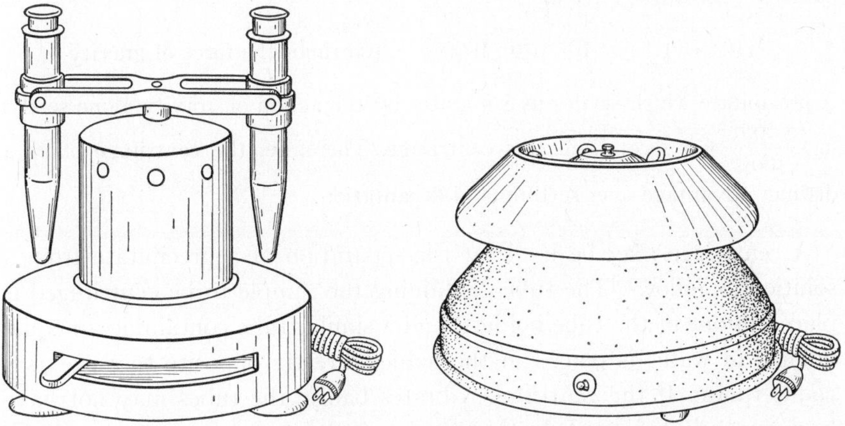

FIG. 4.3. Centrifuges.

The relative rate of settling of a precipitate in a centrifuge and in a stationary tube may be derived as follows (Fig. 4.4). The force of centrifugal motion of a particle of effective mass m is given by

$$f = (m)(a) = (m)\left(\frac{v^2}{R}\right) = (m)\left[\frac{(2\pi Rn)^2}{R}\right] = (m)(4\pi^2 Rn^2)$$

where f is the centrifugal force; m is the effective mass of the particle in grams; a is the acceleration in cm. per sec.^{2}; v is the velocity in cm. per sec.; $\pi = 3.1416$;

R is the distance from the center of the centrifuge to the precipitate in centimeters; and n is the number of revolutions per second.

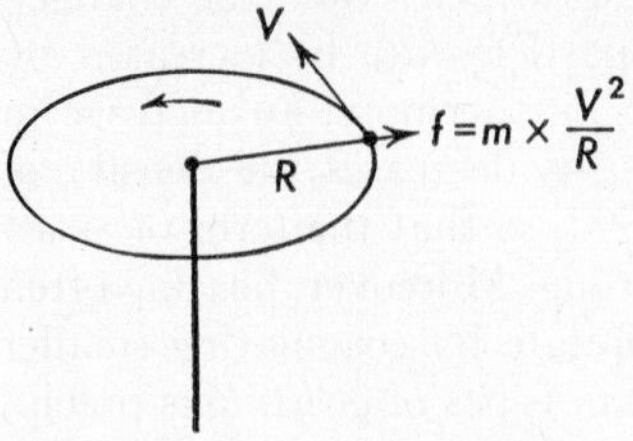

FIG. 4.4. Principle of Centrifugation.

Comparing the centrifugal force (f) with the force of gravity (F) on the same particle gives

$$f = (m)(4\pi^2 Rn^2) \quad \text{and} \quad F = (m)(g)$$

Dividing the first equation by the second, we have

$$\frac{f}{F} = \frac{(m)(4\pi^2 Rn^2)}{(m)(g)} = \frac{4\pi^2 Rn^2}{g}$$

The m's cancel because they are the effective mass of the same particle. If the speed of rotation of the centrifuge is expressed in revolutions per minute (r.p.m.), the comparative centrifugal force (c.c.f.) is

$$\text{c.c.f.} = \frac{f}{F} = \frac{4\pi^2 R(\text{r.p.m.})^2}{(981)(60^2)} = (1.12 \times 10^{-5})(R)(\text{r.p.m.})^2$$

Thus a centrifuge with a radius of 9 cm. and a speed of 1000 r.p.m. has a comparative centrifugal force of

$$\text{c.c.f.} = (1.12 \times 10^{-5})(9)(1000)^2 = 100 \text{ times the force of gravity}$$

A precipitate which settles in 5 minutes by the action of gravity alone settles in $\frac{(5)(60)}{100} = 3$ seconds in this centrifuge. Therefore, the centrifuge offers a distinct advantage over settling and decantation.

A centrifuge may be used for the separation of a precipitate from a solution as follows. The tube containing the sample to be centrifuged is placed in one of the tube holders, and a similar tube containing an equal volume of water is placed in the holder directly opposite to serve as a counterpoise. If the centrifuge vibrates badly, the tubes may not have been properly balanced. In this case the centrifuge should be stopped immediately because the bearings may be ruined or a serious accident may result.

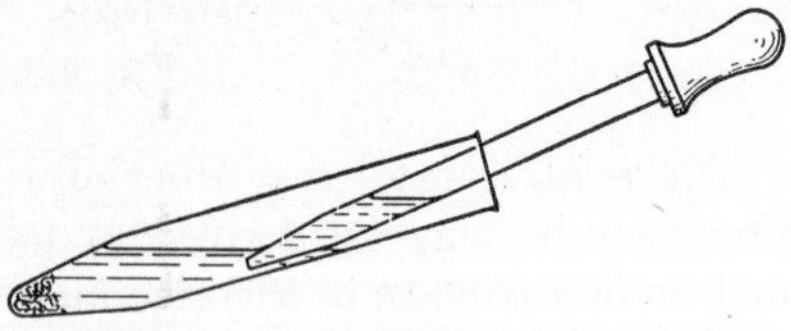

FIG. 4.5. Removal of Supernatant Liquid.

After 30 seconds to 1 minute, the centrifuge is stopped and the supernatant liquid is drawn off, as illustrated in Fig. 4.5. The bulb of the dropper is depressed and the capillary tip is kept just below the surface of the liquid as the bulb is released. As the level of the liquid approaches the precipitate, care must be used to prevent dispersing the precipitate. Sometimes a small piece of cotton placed in the end of the dropper will aid in removing the supernatant liquid from precipitates that disperse easily. The supernatant liquid (filtrate) may be transferred to another test tube or centrifuge tube for further treatment. To wash the precipitate, several drops of the wash liquid are added to the tube, the precipitate is stirred up, the tube is centrifuged, and the supernatant liquid is removed as before. This process is repeated three or four times.

If the precipitate forms a compact mass at the bottom of the tube, the supernatant liquid may be poured off carefully rather than pipetted off as described above.

Difficulty may be encountered with gelatinous or colloidal precipitates. Sometimes heating the mixture or adding the appropriate electrolyte causes coagulation so that the precipitate can be separated by centrifugation. The test tube plus filter tube assembly (see Fig. 4.8) may be used with the centrifuge in many cases where there is difficulty. To do this, the assembly is balanced with a second one by adding sufficient water. The two assemblies are then placed in opposite tube holders of the centrifuge. The rotation of the centrifuge causes the liquid to pass through the filter medium and the precipitate to remain on it.

Although the centrifuge is widely used for semimicro qualitative analysis, the method this book prefers is a special filtration technique discussed in the next section. If the instructor wishes, centrifugation may be designated as the method of separating precipitates from solutions, either in centrifuge tubes or in the test tube plus filter tube assembly. The procedures need no significant modifications.

Filtration

Filtration is the most commonly used method of removing solids from liquids. In this method the mixture is poured on a filter medium which retains the precipitate and allows the liquid to pass through. A number of methods have been devised for filtrations, some of which are illustrated in Fig. 4.6. Since the standard macro filtration techniques have already been learned in earlier courses in chemistry, no discussion of the macro method need be given here. Many texts specify that a small suction flask and funnel with filter paper be used for filtrations in semimicro qualitative analysis. If suction is to be used, the system illustrated in Fig. 4.6*C* is convenient because the filter medium above the constricted part of the stem is not susceptible to breaking as are filter papers.

From the authors' point of view, the system shown in Fig. 4.6*D* is the most rapid and convenient system of filtration. This will be described in detail, because the description of the procedures calls for the use of this

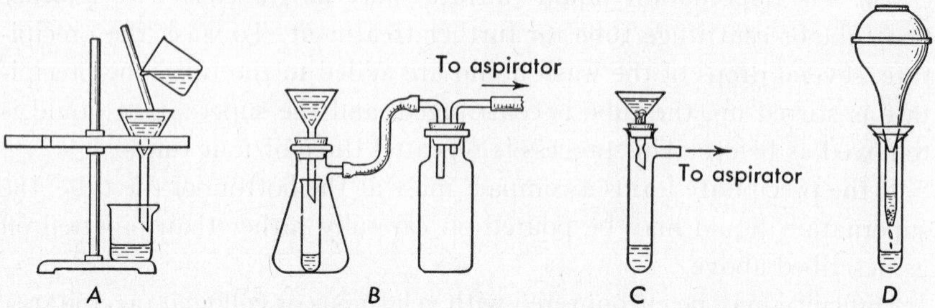

FIG. 4.6. Methods of Filtration. *A*, Macro method; *B*, semimicro method with filter paper; *C*, semimicro method with filter medium and suction; *D*, semimicro method with pressure bulb and filter tube assembly.

filtration assembly; however, any of the other methods illustrated may be used.

THE PRESSURE FILTER TUBE. The dimensions of the pressure filter tube (Fig. 4.7*A*) were chosen so that it could be used with a No. 2370

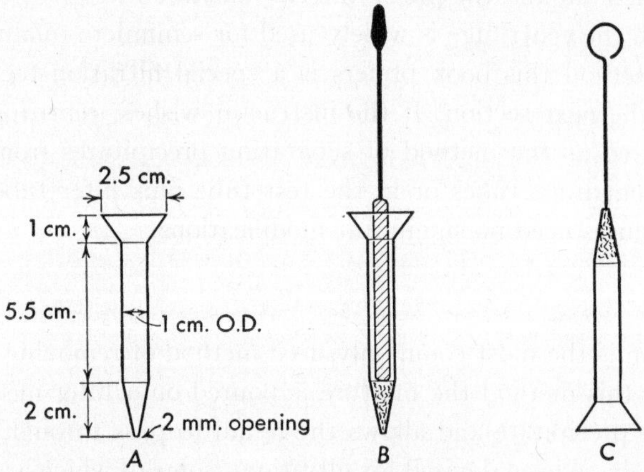

FIG. 4.7. The Pressure Filter Tube. *A*, Dimensions of the tube; *B*, packing the tube; *C*, removing the filter medium.

(13 x 100 mm.) Pyrex test tube. The outside diameter of the filter tube is 10 mm., slightly less than the inside diameter (11 mm.) of the test tube. The volume of liquid held by the filter tube is slightly less than the volume of the test tube below the constricted end of the filter tube. An over-all length of 8½ cm. with a taper 2 cm. long satisfies this condition. The

top of the pressure filter tube is flared so that it will rest on the top of the test tube when inserted into the latter. A 2-mm. opening in the constricted end of the tube allows the filter medium to be packed in the filter tube with the 4-mm. handle of a semimicro spatula or a 4-mm. glass rod, and prevents the medium from being forced through the opening.

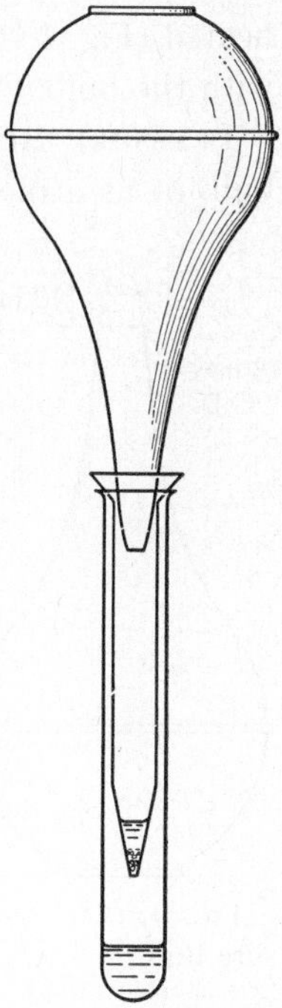

FIG. 4.8. The Filtration Assembly.

To use the pressure filter tube the constricted end is packed with (1) ordinary surgical cotton, (2) glass fiber (Corning Brand No. 790), or (3) asbestos fiber. A Monel metal micro spatula with a handle about 4 mm. in diameter or a 4-mm. glass rod is used to press the filter media into the constricted end of the tube (Fig. 4.7*B*). The depth and extent of the packing of the filter media determine the retentiveness of the filter and the rate of filtration. Cotton is the least expensive filter medium and is satisfactory for most filtrations. The cotton should be removed from the pressure filter tube after each filtration with a short piece (4 in.) of No. 18 Chromel or Nichrome wire (Fig. 4.7*C*). When glass or asbestos fiber is used as a filter medium it is not necessary to change these media for each filtration because they are not acted on by chemicals that do not react with glass. The medium must, however, be kept thoroughly clean at all times so as not to carry contamination from one filtration to the next. To clean the glass fiber or the asbestos, add to the filter tube 2 drops of 5% NaClO and 2 drops of 6-*N* HCl and force the solution through the medium. Rinse the medium thoroughly by forcing distilled water through it a number of times.

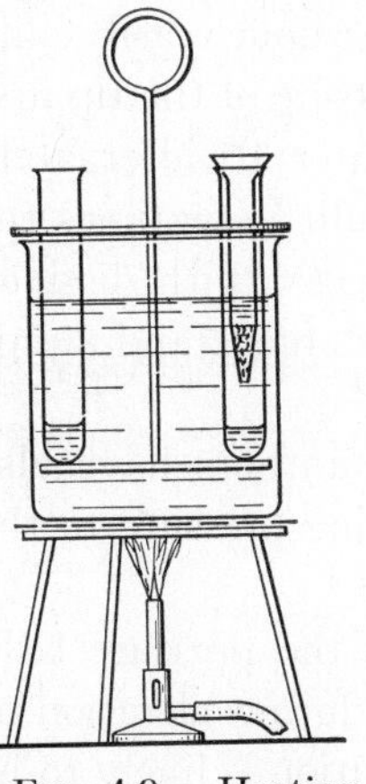

FIG. 4.9. Heating Solutions for Filtration While They Are Hot or for Dissolving Precipitates at Elevated Temperatures.

After the pressure filter tube is packed with the appropriate filter medium, it is inserted into a No. 2370 Pyrex test tube. The solution to be filtered is poured into the filter tube and pressure is applied to the solution by means of the pressure bulb (Fig. 4.8). The applied pressure is easily regulated by the pressure the hand exerts on the bulb.

If the solution is to be filtered while it is hot, the assembly is placed in a hot water bath (Fig. 4.9), or the filter tube is placed in an evaporation test tube or flask in which a small amount of the filtrate or water may be heated (Fig. 4.16). After the solution has been heated, pressure is applied with the bulb.

PRESSURE BULB. A common ear syringe can be used as a pressure bulb or as a means of obtaining a partial vacuum. Suitable dimensions for the bulb are given in Fig. 4.10. A 2-oz. No. 527 Duvol or No. A 591 Meinecke ear and ulcer syringe, when new, produces sufficient vacuum to raise a column of mercury 10 to 15 cm. high, and a pressure of 1 atmosphere (760 mm. of mercury) may be produced by depressing the bulb with the hand. The taper on these bulbs and the "give" of the rubber render them particularly desirable for semimicro work. The flat end of the bulb is placed on the desk to prevent the tip of it from becoming contaminated.

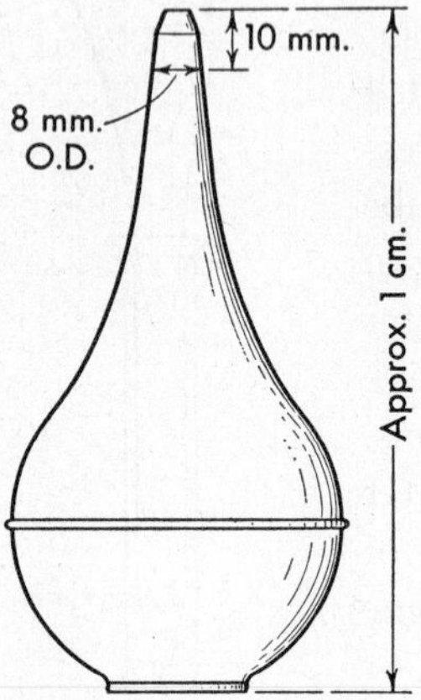

FIG. 4.10. The Pressure Bulb.

The bulb must be cleaned frequently to prevent contamination. This is done easily and rapidly by washing off the outside of the tip first and then drawing in a little water. By alternately squeezing and releasing the bulb a few times the water is expelled and the bulb is dried. This is repeated with distilled water. Occasionally it may be necessary to use a detergent and a pipe cleaner if solids have entered the tip.

Besides using the pressure bulb for pressure, the authors have also equipped low-pressure lines with adapters for supplying pressure to the filter tubes.

(NOTE: Care should be used when filtering with the pressure bulb method. If too great pressure is exerted on the bulb during filtration or after the filtrate has passed through the filter, the solution is likely to be blown on to the hands or into the eyes of the operator.)

FILTER MEDIA. Cotton, glass fiber (Corning Brand No. 790), and asbestos fiber are the three most suitable filter media. Other media, including fritted glass or porous porcelain in specially designed filter tubes and funnels, have been used for special purposes and for semimicro quantitative analysis.

Cotton may be used for most filtrations in semimicro qualitative analysis because the solutions used are usually not concentrated or destructive to cotton. It is inexpensive and, by the extent of packing in the pressure filter tube, it may be adjusted to retain both fine and coarse precipitates. The finer grained the precipitate, the more tightly must the filter medium be packed. However, the more tightly the cotton is packed, the more slowly the solution filters. Hence the student should learn to judge the extent of packing required for each type of precipitate. Sometimes a second more loosely packed plug aids in filtering gelatinous precipitates. If the filtrate is not clear it should be repassed through the filter medium, or the medium may be retamped.

Glass fiber or asbestos is employed whenever there is a possibility that the substances in solution, or the reagents required to dissolve the precipitate, will react with cotton. Glass fiber is suitable for all filtrations normally encountered in qualitative analysis when cotton cannot be used. Asbestos is a more retentive medium than glass fiber, but filtration proceeds more slowly.

With all types of filter media it is essential that the *amount of precipitate be small;* otherwise the filter may become plugged and filtration will be slow.

Factors Affecting the Rate of Filtration

A filter medium may be represented as a system of parallel capillaries through which the liquid flows (Fig. 4.11). The flow of liquid through such capillaries is given by Poiseuille's equation:

$$R_s = \frac{P\pi r^4}{8l\eta}$$

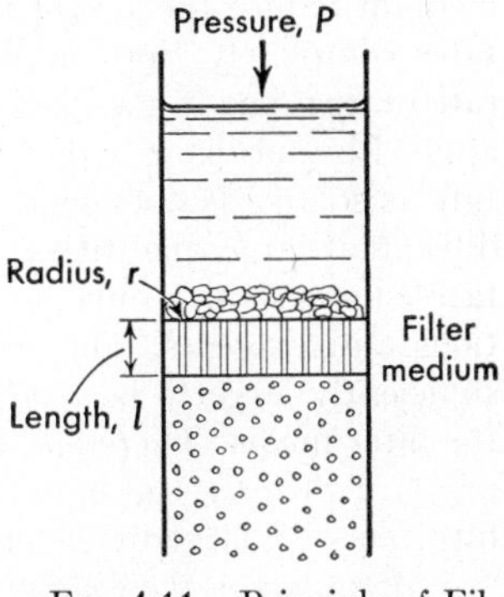

FIG. 4.11. Principle of Filtration.

where R_s is the rate of flow in cm.^{3}/sec.; π is 3.1416; P is the pressure in dynes/cm.^{2}; r is the radius of the pores in cm.; l is the length of the pores in cm.; and η is the viscosity in poises or dyne-seconds/cm.^{2}. Inspection of this equation and consideration of the nature of the filtration process show that the rate of filtration through a single pore depends on the following factors: (1) the size of the pores, r, and the thickness, l, of the medium; (2) the nature of the precipitate; (3) the viscosity, η, of the liquid; and (4) the pressure or force, P, that causes the liquid to pass through the filter medium. The total rate will be given by the number of pores per unit area times the total area.

1. *Size of Pores.* To retain a precipitate, the diameter of the pores of the filter medium must be smaller than the diameter of the precipitated particles.

However, to obtain rapid filtration, the size of the pores should be as large as possible because the filtration rate depends upon the fourth power of the radius of the pores; i.e., a filter medium with pores twice as large as a given medium will allow the liquid to pass through 16 times faster. Therefore a filter medium is chosen which has large pores but still retains the precipitate. Often the first filtrate that passes through the filter medium contains some of the smaller particles of the precipitate. Repeated filtration through the same medium usually removes the precipitate because the coarser particles tend to close the larger pores in the filter medium. The small particles cannot pass through the remaining pores the next time the solution is passed through the filter.

Many different types of filter media are available. Filter papers with very small pores (fine filter paper) and with large pores (coarse filter paper) are made for filtering different types of precipitates in macro qualitative analysis. Porous or fritted glass filters and porous porcelain filters are also available with different pore sizes. Gooch filters, prepared by placing a mat of asbestos over a perforated plate in a funnel or a crucible with a perforated bottom, can be adjusted for filtering different types of precipitates. As was said above, the filter media preferred for the pressure bulb method of filtration are cotton, glass fiber, or asbestos, packed in the pressure filter tube or the semimicro suction filter funnel. The size of the pores may be varied widely by the extent of packing, as was brought out in earlier sections.

2. *Nature of the Precipitate.* Coarse crystalline precipitates are more easily filtered than gelatinous or flocculent precipitates. The conditions that favor the formation of easily filtered precipitates have already been discussed (p. 65).

Gelatinous precipitates and precipitates that pack solidly over the filter medium reduce the size of the pores in the medium. Sometimes these precipitates completely stop the flow of liquid. Application of suction increases the rate of flow but it also packs the precipitate more solidly. The use of pressure applied by means of a pressure bulb or air pressure does not pack the precipitate as solidly as does suction; but, even with pressure, filtration is sometimes difficult if large quantities of the precipitate are present. In semimicro qualitative analysis this difficulty is obviated by the use of small quantities of solutions and reagents. The amounts of precipitates formed (1 to 0.1 mg.) are sufficiently large to be seen easily but not so large as to form thick layers on the filter media. Therefore, by using small quantities of reagents and by using pressure to force the liquid through the filter medium, the time required for filtrations is markedly reduced.

3. *Viscosity of the Liquid.* Poiseuille's equation shows that the less the viscosity, η, of the liquid, the more rapidly the liquid flows through the filter medium. The viscosity of water at 20° C. is 10×10^{-3} poises (dyne-seconds per cm.^{2}) and at 100° C. it is only 2.8×10^{-3} poises. Therefore, water passes through a given filter medium almost four times faster at 100° C. than at 20° C. As will be shown later, the pressure filter tube is easily adapted to filtrations at elevated temperatures.

4. *Force on the Liquid.* The greater the force (P) which causes the liquid to flow through the filter medium, the greater is the rate of filtration. The

rate of filtration may be increased over that obtained by the force of gravity alone by the use of centrifugation, suction, or pressure.

As previously shown, a centrifuge with a 9-cm. radius and a speed of 1000 revolutions per minute produces a force 100 times greater than gravity. The rate of filtration is therefore increased by placing the filter in a centrifuge in such a way that the liquid is thrown outward through the filter medium.

Suction may be applied in several ways to speed up filtration. When ordinary funnels are used for filtrations, it is customary to tear off one edge of the folded filter paper and fit the latter snugly to the walls of the funnel in such a way that the stem of the funnel remains filled with a liquid. If the length of the stem is 15 cm., the force causing the liquid to flow through the filter is $(15)(981) = 14{,}700$ dynes per cm.^{2}, or about 15 times greater than gravity alone on a 1-cm. column of water. Thus the rate of filtration is increased 10 to 15 times by keeping the stem filled with the filtrate. Application of suction by means of a suction pump or a pressure bulb greatly increases the rate of filtration unless complications occur as a result of the packing of the precipitate.

Pressures equal to 1 atmosphere (76 cm. of mercury) or greater may be applied to the liquid by means of the pressure bulb. This pressure is equivalent to the pressure of a column of water $(76)(13.6) = 1034$ cm. high. Thus, a force about 1000 times that of gravity alone on a 1-cm. column of water is obtained. It is clear that filtrations can be carried out much more rapidly by means of the pressure bulb and consequently the filtration process is greatly accelerated.

WASHING PRECIPITATES

Regardless of the procedure employed to remove a solid from the solution in which it forms, the precipitate must be washed to remove the small amount of solution which adheres to it or is absorbed in the filter medium. This solution contains ions for which tests are to be made later on in the analysis. Furthermore, these ions may interfere with tests for ions in the precipitate. Therefore, the precipitate is usually washed with a liquid that has very little solvent action on the precipitate. Either the liquid should be a solvent for the substances to be removed, or it should not cause them to precipitate. The wash liquid is usually water, or water to which has been added a small amount of the reagent used to produce the precipitate. Sometimes water mixed with an organic solvent is used.

The procedure for washing a precipitate after it has been separated from the solution by centrifugation has already been described (p. 69).

To wash a precipitate after filtration in a filter tube, a small amount of distilled water is put in the tube and slowly forced through the filter medium with the pressure bulb. Often it is necessary to wash the precipitate with distilled water to which have been added one or two drops of certain electrolytes. In this case the distilled water is first transferred to the filter tube from a wash bottle and then the electrolyte is added to the water. The solution is mixed with the micro stirring rod and finally forced through the medium with the pressure bulb.

Wash Bottles

A number of types of wash bottles are available commercially or they may be constructed by the students. Two are illustrated in Fig. 4.12. If the pressure bulb and filter tubes are being used for the filtrations, the pressure bulb wash bottle is preferred. This is prepared by fitting a 500-ml.

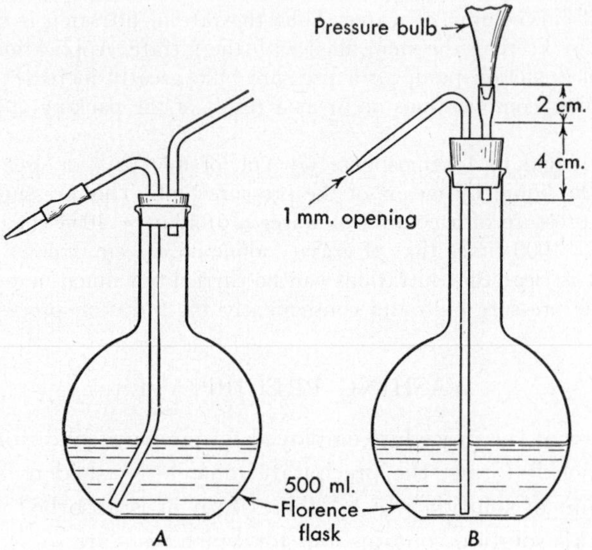

FIG. 4.12. Wash Bottles. *A*, Ordinary type; *B*, pressure bulb type.

Florence flask with a delivery tube and a short tapered tube by means of a two-hole rubber stopper. The exit end of the delivery tube should have an opening with a diameter no larger than that of an ordinary pin. Water is forced from the flask by inserting the end of the rubber bulb into the tapered tube and applying pressure. This wash bottle is an improvement over the older type (Fig. 4.12*A*) for semimicro work because the operator does not have to lift the flask from the desk and force the water out with his mouth. A second wash bottle made from a 250-ml. flask is useful for supplying hot water or special solutions. Polyethylene wash bottles are also very useful. They can be purchased from laboratory supply houses or they can be made by placing a one-hole rubber stopper in a polyethylene bottle and fitting it with an exit tube that extends to the bottom of the bottle. Water is forced out through the exit tube by squeezing the polyethylene bottle.

Efficiency of Washing Precipitates

The removal of undesired substances from a precipitate is more complete if the precipitate is washed several times, using small volumes of wash liquid each time, than if it is washed with an equal volume of wash liquid in larger portions. The removal is also more complete if the volume of the liquid remaining on the precipitate each time is small.

The determination of the completeness of removal of the ions originally present in the solution adhering to the precipitate is essentially a problem in dilution. Thus, the addition of a given volume of wash liquid to the filter does not change the quantity of the ions present, but merely dilutes the solution. Removal of this wash liquid leaves a small volume of liquid adhering to the precipitate, but the concentration of the ions is less than the concentration of the ions in the original solution. Repetition of this process reduces the concentration of the ions to a very low value. These statements may be expressed quantitatively as follows.

Let

v_r = the residual volume. (This is the volume of solution which adheres to the precipitate and which is absorbed in the filter medium, about 0.05 ml., in the pressure filter tube technique.)

c = the concentration in g./ml. of the undesired material in the residual volume.

c_1 = the concentration in g./ml. of the undesired material when diluted with the wash liquid.

V = the volume of the wash liquid added each time.

The weight of the undesired ions remaining on the precipitate and in the filter medium is equal to the residual volume times the concentration ($v_r c$). After the addition of the wash solution, the total volume of liquid is $(V + v_r)$ and the weight of the undesired ions is then expressed by $(V + v_r)c_1$. Therefore, since the amount of material does not change by diluting the solution,

$$\left.\begin{matrix}\text{amount of material before}\\ \text{the addition of the wash liquid}\end{matrix}\right\} = \left\{\begin{matrix}\text{amount of material after the}\\ \text{addition of the wash liquid}\end{matrix}\right.$$

That is,

$$v_r c = (V + v_r)c_1$$

or

$$c_1 = \frac{v_r c}{(V + v_r)}$$

After the wash solution passes through the filter medium, the same residual volume of liquid remains on the precipitate and in the filter medium, but the concentration of the undesired ions is now equal to c_1, and the amount of undesired ions remaining in the filter is $v_r c_1$.

Addition of a second portion of the wash liquid of volume (V) dilutes the residual volume to ($V + v_r$) and the concentration becomes c_2. Hence,

$$v_r c_1 = (V + v_r)c_2$$

or

$$c_2 = \frac{v_r c_1}{(V + v_r)}$$

Substituting the value of c_1 from the equation above, we have

$$c_2 = \frac{v_r \left[\frac{v_r c}{V + v_r}\right]}{(V + v_r)} = \frac{v_r^2 c}{(V + v_r)^2} = \left[\frac{v_r}{(V + v_r)}\right]^2 c$$

Thus the concentration of the undesired ions is reduced to the value of c_2 after the second washing, and the amount of undesired ions remaining on the filter is equal to $v_r c_2$.

After n such washings, the original concentration, c, is reduced to c_n, as given by the following equation:

$$c_n = \left[\frac{v_r}{(V + v_r)}\right]^n c$$

The amount of undesired ions remaining on the precipitate and in the filter medium after n washings is equal to $v_r c_n$. The following problem illustrates the use of this equation.

The precipitated chlorides of Group I were washed with cold water to remove the ions of the other groups. Calculate the amount of Cu^{++} which will be left on the filter after washing the precipitate (1) once with 2 ml. of water and (2) four times with 0.5 ml. of water each time. Assume that the volume, v_r, of solution remaining on the precipitate and in the filter medium is 1 drop (0.05 ml.) and that the concentration of Cu^{++} is 0.002 g./ml.

Case 1:

$$v_r = 0.05 \text{ ml.}; \quad c = 0.002 \text{ g./ml.}; \quad n = 1; \quad V = 2 \text{ ml.}$$

$$c_1 = \left[\frac{0.05}{(2 + 0.05)}\right](0.002) = \left(\frac{0.05}{2.05}\right)(0.002)$$

$$= 0.000049 = 4.9 \times 10^{-5} \text{ g./ml.}$$

The weight of Cu^{++} remaining in the filter is then

$$v_r c_1 = 0.05 \times 4.9 \times 10^{-5} = \underline{2.45 \times 10^{-6} \text{ g. of } Cu^{++}}$$

Case 2:

$$v_r = 0.05 \text{ ml.}; \quad c = 0.002 \text{ g./ml.}; \quad n = 4; \quad V = 0.5 \text{ ml.}$$

$$c_4 = \left[\frac{0.05}{(0.5 + 0.05)}\right]^4 (0.002) = \left(\frac{0.05}{0.55}\right)^4 (0.002)$$

$$= 1.37 \times 10^{-7} \text{ g./ml. of } Cu^{++}$$

The weight of Cu^{++} remaining after four washings of 0.5 ml. each is

$$v_r c_4 = 0.05 \times 1.37 \times 10^{-7} = \underline{6.8 \times 10^{-9} \text{ g. of } Cu^{++}}$$

The relative effectiveness of these two cases is

$$\frac{2.45 \times 10^{-6}}{6.8 \times 10^{-9}} = \frac{0.00000245}{0.0000000068} = \frac{24{,}500}{68} = 360$$

Therefore, the four washings of 0.5 ml. each are theoretically 360 times more effective than one washing of 2 ml.

Washing of precipitates is more effective in a pressure filter tube than in an ordinary funnel. If 2 ml. of wash liquid is added to the filter tube, the liquid fills the tube about two-thirds full. Only the liquid in contact with the filter medium (about 0.2 ml.) is effective in diluting the residual volume. As the remaining liquid is slowly forced through the filter medium, it may be assumed that successive 0.2-ml. portions of the wash liquid become separate, effective portions of wash liquid. When the 2 ml. of wash liquid passes through the filter medium, 10 washings of 0.2 ml. each are made. The amount of Cu^{++} remaining in the filter medium in this case is approximately

$$c_{10} = \left[\frac{0.05}{(0.2 + 0.05)}\right]^{10} (0.002) = 2.0 \times 10^{-10} \text{ g./ml.}$$

and

$$v_r c_{10} = 0.05 \times 2.0 \times 10^{-10} = \underline{1.0 \times 10^{-11} \text{ g. of } Cu^{++}}$$

Thus, this washing is theoretically more effective in removing Cu^{++} than either of the preceding cases discussed. If the filter medium is not evenly packed or if too much is used, channeling may occur and the washing will not be as effective as calculated in the example. Packing of gelatinous precipitates may also cause channeling and decrease the efficiency of washing. Hence precipitates of this type are stirred before each washing.

The above calculations are made on the assumption that the Cu^{++} remaining in the filter is uniformly distributed throughout each portion of the wash liquid before the latter is allowed to pass through the filter. If the undesired ions are strongly adsorbed on the precipitate or the filter medium, *co-precipitated*, or *occluded*, the removal of the ions is incomplete. Some ions form a precipitate when allowed to stand in contact with certain finely divided solids. This phenomenon is known as *post-precipitation*. Washing does not completely remove undesired ions which have been post-precipitated. Therefore, unless otherwise directed, precipitates are filtered and washed as soon as they have been allowed to stand in contact with the supernatant liquid a sufficient length of time to form large particles, or to cause the conversion of gelatinous precipitates into a more readily filtered form.

HEATING SOLUTIONS

The use of the pressure bulb filtration technique makes it convenient to carry out precipitations, filtrations, and dissolution of precipitates at elevated temperatures. The advantages of elevated temperatures are (1) more rapid precipitation, especially in the case of the sulfides; (2) coagulation of precipitates; (3) formation of larger crystals; (4) decrease in the extent of adsorption of impurities; (5) more rapid filtration; (6) more rapid dissolution of precipitates. Consequently, whenever higher temperatures do not interfere, the reaction mixture or the filtration assembly is set in a hot water bath rack.

The Hot Water Bath Rack (Fig. 4.13)

This piece of apparatus is convenient for heating reaction mixtures and the filtration assembly. It is essentially a holder for eight 13 x 100 mm. No. 2370 Pyrex test tubes. The two Monel metal plates (0.7 mm. thick)

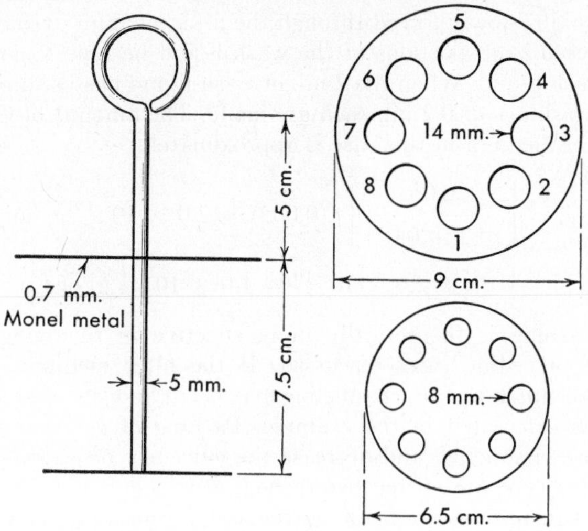

FIG. 4.13. Hot Water Bath Rack.

are spaced 7.5 cm. apart by means of a 5-mm. Monel metal rod. The rod is cut off flush with the bottom of the lower plate, but extends 5 cm. above the top of the upper plate with a ring at the top to facilitate handling the rack while it is hot. The top plate (9 cm. in diameter) is bored with eight 14-mm. (9/16-in.) holes evenly spaced on a circle with a diameter of 5 cm. (2 in.). The holes should be numbered to facilitate identification of the test tubes placed in the rack. The bottom plate (6.5 cm. in diameter) is bored with eight 8-mm. (5/16-in.) holes spaced evenly on a circle with a diameter of 5 cm. (2 in.). Satisfactory racks may also be made from ½-in. aluminum rod and 1/16-in. aluminum plate.

The rack is placed in a 250-ml. Pyrex beaker. The beaker is filled with water and placed on a wire gauze which is supported by a 5-in. tripod

(Fig. 4.9). The water in the beaker is maintained near the boiling point by the flame of a micro burner. A small electric hot plate is also convenient for heating the water.

An ordinary tripod and burner may be used if the semimicro equipment is not available. Improvised hot water bath racks or even a small Erlenmeyer flask containing water may also be employed for heating the solutions.

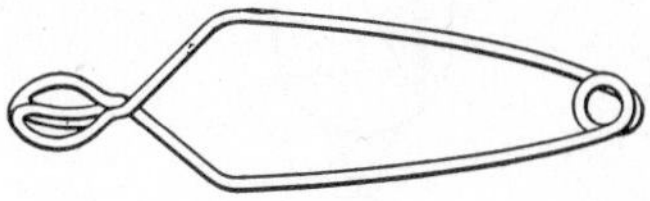

FIG. 4.14. Semimicro Test Tube Holder.

When solutions are heated directly in the flame, hold the test tube with a semimicro test tube holder (Fig. 4.14). Turn down the flame until it is no more than 2 cm. high and heat the solution a short distance below the surface of the liquid. Shaking the tube has a tendency to prevent the solution from spurting out.

DISSOLVING PRECIPITATES

When a mixture is filtered, the filter medium selected is one that is not attacked by the substances being filtered or by the reagents required to dissolve or extract part or all of the precipitate. Hence, the appropriate reagents are added directly to the pressure filter tube or the semimicro funnel. If the precipitate reacts rapidly with the reagents added, the pressure bulb is used to force the reagent through the filter medium. If the precipitates dissolve slowly, the filtration assembly may be placed in the hot water bath rack (Fig. 4.13). The reagent is allowed to flow through the filter medium under the force of gravity until the precipitate dissolves. The rate of dissolution is increased by stirring the precipitate on the filter medium with a micro stirring rod (Fig. 4.15). After the precipitate dissolves, the solution should be forced through the medium.

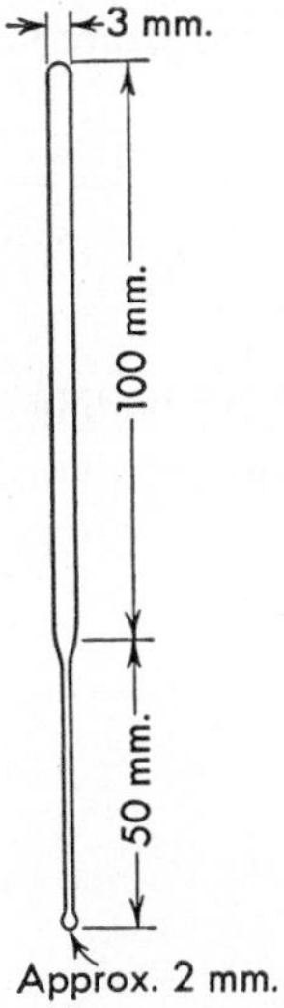

FIG. 4.15. Micro Stirring Rod.

The pressure filter tube may be placed in an evaporation test tube (Fig. 4.16) or a 25-ml. Erlenmeyer flask to which about 2 ml. of water has been added. The assembly is then heated in the flame. The vapors heat the solution in the pressure filter tube and cause the dissolution of part or all of the precipitates as the solution flows slowly through the filter medium. As soon as the precipitate has dissolved, the remaining solution may be forced through the medium. The filtrate is

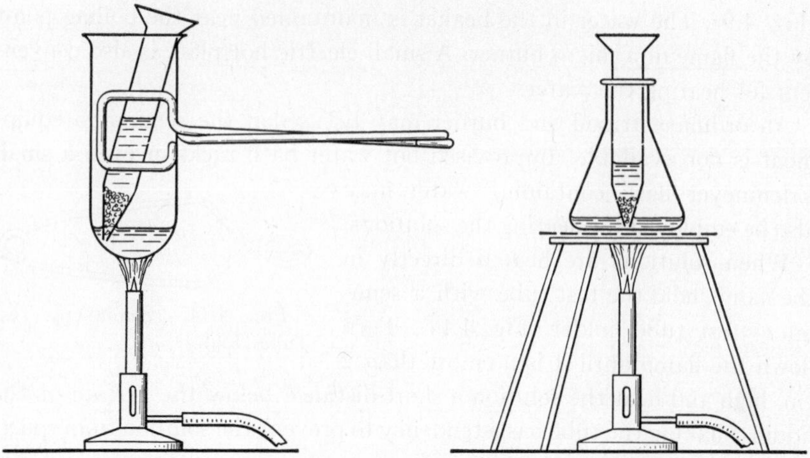

FIG. 4.16. Dissolving Precipitates at Elevated Temperatures.

then placed in the evaporation test tube and may be evaporated to a smaller volume or to dryness.

Micro Stirring Rods

Five or more 15-cm. micro stirring rods should be prepared from 3- to 5-mm. glass rod, as shown in Fig. 4.15.

EVAPORATION

Evaporation Test Tube

When it is desired to decrease the volume of a solution by boiling off the liquid, or to evaporate a solution to dryness, it is transferred to an

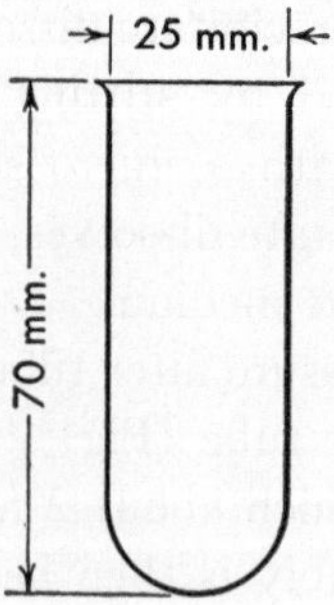

FIG. 4.17. Evaporation Test Tube.

evaporation test tube (Fig. 4.17). The evaporation test tube is held with the semimicro test tube holder and heated with continual shaking in the flame of a micro burner.

A 20-ml. beaker or a 25-ml. Erlenmeyer flask may also be used for this purpose. It is not feasible to evaporate solutions to a small volume in the small (13 x 100 mm.) test tubes.

Rubber Policeman to Loosen and Transfer a Residue

A rubber policeman is a small piece of gum rubber tubing sealed and flattened at one end. It is placed on the end of a glass rod (Fig. 4.18) or

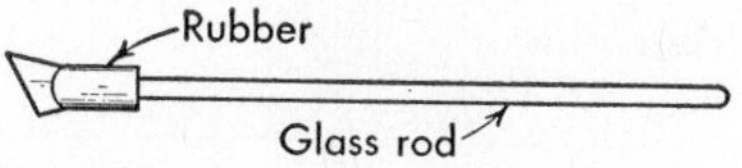

FIG. 4.18. Rubber Policeman.

on the end of the handle of the micro spatula. When solutions are evaporated to dryness, a precipitate is often formed that must be transferred to a filter tube. This is done by adding a few drops of water and then rubbing the walls and bottom of the evaporation test tube or other vessel with the rubber policeman. The suspension is then transferred to the filter tube. Two or three such operations are sometimes necessary to remove all the residue from the evaporation test tube.

CLEANING APPARATUS

Cleanliness is essential for successful analyses by the semimicro technique. Many of the tests are very sensitive and slight contamination from dirty apparatus may produce the wrong result.

All apparatus must be thoroughly cleaned with cleaning solution or with a brush and a detergent. The apparatus should then be rinsed several times with tap water and several times with distilled water. Special filter tube brushes (Fig. 4.19*A*) and test tube brushes (Fig. 4.19*B*) are available. Medicine droppers, precipitation tubes, and stirring rods should be carefully cleaned and rinsed, and kept in distilled water. The outside of the pressure filter tubes should also be cleaned when they are removed from the test tubes. The tip and inside of the rubber bulb should be washed frequently to remove possible contamination.

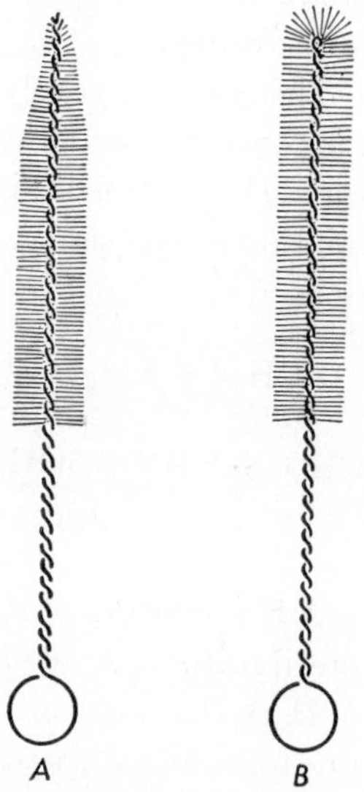

FIG. 4.19. *A*, A brush for cleaning a pressure filter tube; *B*, a test tube brush.

APPARATUS AND METHODS FOR PRECIPITATING THE SULFIDES

Precipitation of sulfides at different acid concentrations is an important and frequently used method for separating a number of the cations into analytical groups. After the acid concentration has been adjusted, the sulfides may be precipitated by adding a solution of thioacetamide ($CH_3CS \cdot NH_2$) which hydrolyzes to give hydrogen sulfide, or by passing H_2S gas into the solution.

With Thioacetamide

Thioacetamide (m.p. 108°) is a white crystalline solid with a faint spicy odor. It may be purchased from the Eastman Kodak Co. (Item 1719) or prepared in the laboratory.* It is very soluble in water and in alcohol. A water solution is relatively stable and hydrolyzes very slowly. After several months of standing in a closed flask, a 5% solution of thioacetamide produces no appreciable pressure of H_2S and only a slight deposit of sulfur is formed.

The rate of hydrolysis of thioacetamide is increased by an increase in the concentration of either H_3O^+ or OH^- and by an increase in temperature. The hydrolysis is more rapid in an alkaline solution than in an acid solution of the same strength. Equations for the overall hydrolysis reactions are:

$$CH_3CS \cdot NH_2 + 2H_2O \xrightleftharpoons{H_3O^+} CH_3COO^- + NH_4^+ + H_2S \text{ (acid)}$$

$$CH_3CS \cdot NH_2 + 3OH^- \xrightleftharpoons{OH^-} CH_3COO^- + NH_3 + H_2O + S^{--} \text{ (alkaline)}$$

A 5% solution of thioacetamide is used in the following way for sulfide precipitations in semimicro qualitative analysis. After the concentration of H_3O^+ has been adjusted to the proper value (about 0.2-*M* HCl) for the precipitation of the cations of Group II (p. 157), thioacetamide is added directly to the solution. The test tube containing the mixture is sealed with a rubber-tipped filter tube into which a plug of cotton has been placed, as shown in Fig. 4.20. To this filter tube is added about 2 ml. of water. The assembly is placed in the hot (*boiling*) water bath for *five min-*

* *Annalen der Chemie* **250**, 264 (1889). Five moles (295.4 g.) of acetamide, CH_3CONH_2, and 1 mole (222.3 g.) of finely powdered phosphorus pentasulfide, P_2S_5, are boiled for 20 minutes under a reflux condenser with a large excess (about 50 parts) of benzene. The solution is then filtered and concentrated until the thioacetamide crystallizes out.

utes or longer. When the precipitation of the sulfides is complete, bubbles of H_2S will form at the surface in the test tube and some of it will be dissolved by the water in the filter tube.

After the sulfides have been precipitated, the water in the filter tube is forced into the test tube. This reduces the H_3O^+ concentration somewhat and insures complete precipitation of the more soluble sulfides of Group II (PbS, CdS, and the tin sulfides). This method of precipitating the sulfides produces a well-coagulated precipitate which can be filtered easily.

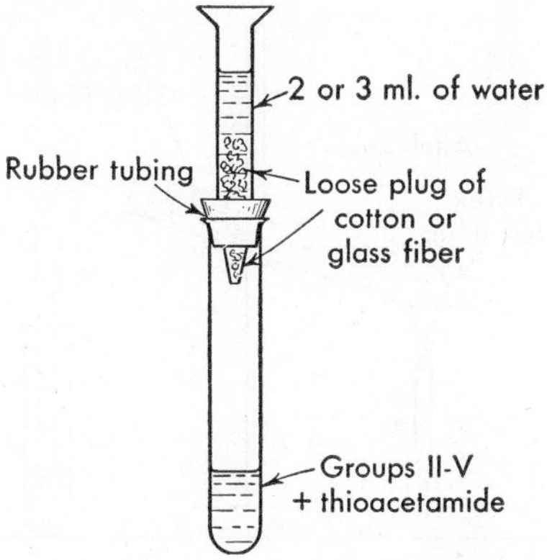

FIG. 4.20. Assembly for Precipitation of Sulfides with Thioacetamide.

The filtrate from the above precipitation contains the ions of Groups III, IV, and V, along with unhydrolyzed thioacetamide. To this mixture NH_4OH is added until the solution is alkaline. The sulfides and hydroxides of Group III form readily and can be filtered easily from the mixture. The filtrate from this group, which may still contain some thioacetamide, may be treated with $(NH_4)_2CO_3$ to precipitate the carbonates of Group IV without interference. Finally, the filtrate from Group IV is acidified with HNO_3 and the solution is evaporated to dryness and heated to drive off the ammonium salts. During this process any remaining thioacetamide or sulfide is oxidized to sulfur which is expelled by the heating. Thus it is seen that the thioacetamide causes no difficulties throughout the analysis.

With Hydrogen Sulfide Gas

Some instructors may want their students to use hydrogen sulfide gas for certain precipitations. If a supply of H_2S is not available in hoods or special rooms, a convenient source is an intimate mixture of sulfur, paraffin, and asbestos sold under the trade name Aitch-tu-ess. A vial of the material is placed in a Pyrex test tube that has been equipped with a delivery tube, as shown in Fig. 4.21. When hydrogen sulfide is needed, the Aitch-tu-ess is heated gently and the gas is passed through a precipitation tube into the solution. It is important to remember that the tube must be removed from the solution as soon as the heating is stopped. In large, well-ventilated rooms with small classes, the amount of H_2S which escapes into the room is not sufficient to be dangerous, as only small quantities of solutions are saturated. If very small bubbles are formed, most of the gas is absorbed in the solution and relatively small amounts escape. It must be remembered, however, that small concentrations of H_2S often produce nausea and unconsciousness, and high concentrations

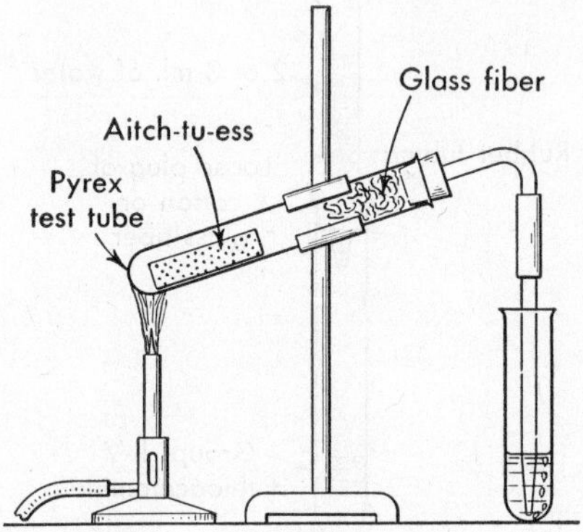

FIG. 4.21. H_2S Generator.

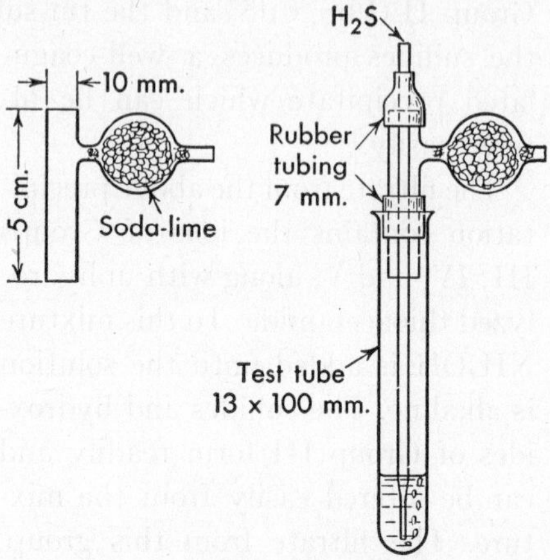

FIG. 4.22. Precipitation Tube Designed to Prevent the Escape of Hydrogen Sulfide into the Laboratory.

are fatal. The special precipitating tube illustrated in Fig. 4.22 eliminates the escape of H_2S into the laboratory when individual hydrogen sulfide generators are employed.

Besides H_2S generators of the above type, a number of suitable semimicro Kipp-type H_2S generators have been described in which FeS and a solution of HCl are used. These can be obtained from a number of laboratory supply companies.

Notes on the Use of Thioacetamide Instead of H_2S Gas

The use of thioacetamide eliminates the escape of noticeable quantities of H_2S into the laboratory. Not only is the odor of H_2S practically eliminated, but possible ill effects of small concentrations of the gas such as nausea and fatigue are reduced to a minimum. The possibility of fatal accidents from high concentrations of H_2S due to failure of hydrogen sulfide supplies, tanks, or distribution lines need not be considered when thioacetamide is used.

The convenience of adding a water solution of the precipitant is obvious. Because the sulfide-ion concentration is low during the precipitations, the sulfides are precipitated in a coagulated and easily filtered form. Hydrolysis of the thioacetamide produces H_2S in acid solution for precipitation of Group

II, and S^{--} in alkaline solution for precipitation of Group III cations. Unhydrolyzed thioacetamide introduces no difficulties because it is oxidized by HNO_3 without liberation of H_2S during the evaporation to dryness prior to analyzing for Group V cations. Excess H_2S from the precipitation of Group II is absorbed in the water used as a seal in the filter tube. To obtain a higher pressure of H_2S for the precipitation of such sulfides as MoS_3, a tube smaller in diameter and longer may be used for the water seal.

The use of thioacetamide introduces no fundamental changes in the usual theoretical treatment of the precipitation of the sulfides because the thioacetamide is essentially a source of H_2S.

APPARATUS BLOCK

A useful holder for the test tubes, medicine droppers, evaporation test tubes, filter tubes, stirring rods, spatula, and wires for removing filter media is shown in Fig. 4.23. It consists of a block of rock maple wood

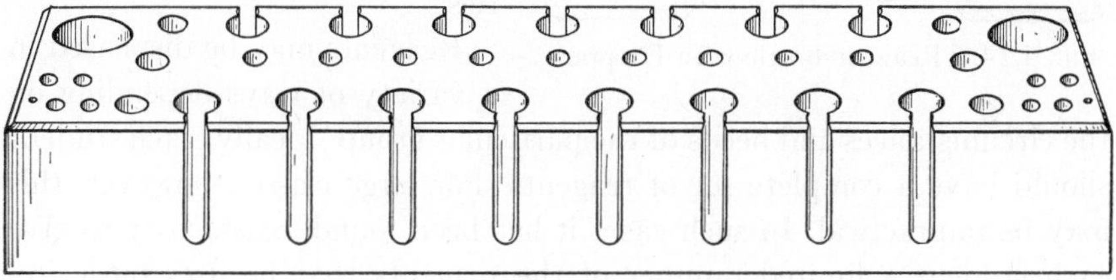

FIG. 4.23. Apparatus Block.

29 x 6 cm. with 42 holes drilled as follows. Fifteen 14-mm. holes suitable for the test tubes are spaced along the two outer sides of the block, with a 5-mm. slot to the surface for drainage. Between these holes and along the middle of the block there are nine 6-mm. holes for medicine droppers. At each end of the block there are 9 holes; one of them has a diameter of 26 mm. and is used for the evaporation test tube. Three of the holes are 11 mm. in diameter and are used for the filter tubes. Four of the holes have a diameter of 5 mm. and are used for stirring rods and the semimicro spatula. The other hole has a diameter of 2 mm. and is used for holding the Nichrome or Chromel wire used to push the filter medium from the filter tubes. The block is sprayed with lacquer or dipped in melted paraffin after the holes have been drilled.

REAGENTS

Reagent Bottles and Racks

Several types of bottles fitted with droppers can be purchased. One of the most useful is a square 30-ml. (1-oz.) bottle with a small neck, like that shown in Fig. 4.24. Each bottle should be clearly labeled and numbered to prevent the interchange of droppers. It is also advisable to number the rubber bulb with India ink. Droppers with rubber or Neoprene bulbs are available from supply companies.

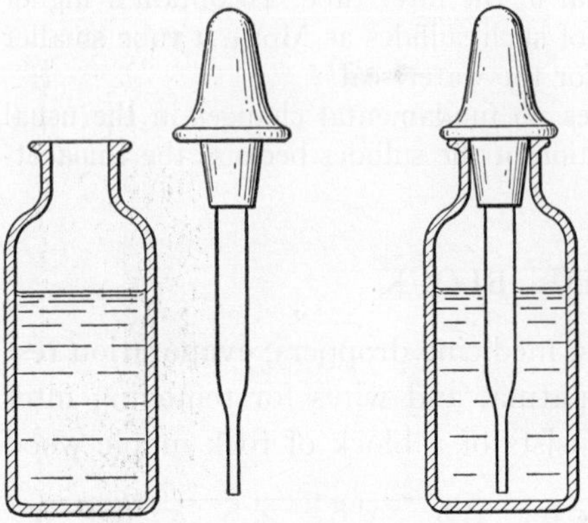

FIG. 4.24. Reagent Bottle with Dropper.

The reagent racks may be built in accordance with the specifications in the following sections, or they may be obtained from laboratory supply companies. The racks are designed to hold the bottles firmly in place so that the droppers can be removed without holding on to the bottles.

Reagents may be dispensed in a variety of ways depending on the circumstances and needs of the particular group. Ideally, each student should have a complete set of reagents. For large classes, however, this may be impractical. In such cases it has been found satisfactory to give each student a limited number of the reagents that he uses most frequently. The remainder of the reagents and the test solutions are used in common by a number of students.

Individual Reagent Set

The reagents in the individual set are the ones that are used frequently. Each student is given a reagent rack (Fig. 4.25) with a set of ten 30-ml. reagent bottles containing the following solutions:

1. Ammonium Hydroxide, concentrated	15-*N*
2. Ammonium Hydroxide, diluted	4-*N*
3. Ammonium Hydroxide	1-*N*
4. Sodium Hydroxide	4-*N*
5. Acetic Acid, diluted	4-*N*
6. Hydrochloric Acid, diluted	6-*N*
7. Hydrochloric Acid, diluted	1-*N*
8. Nitric Acid, diluted	4-*N*
9. Sulfuric Acid, diluted	4-*N*
10. Thioacetamide	5%

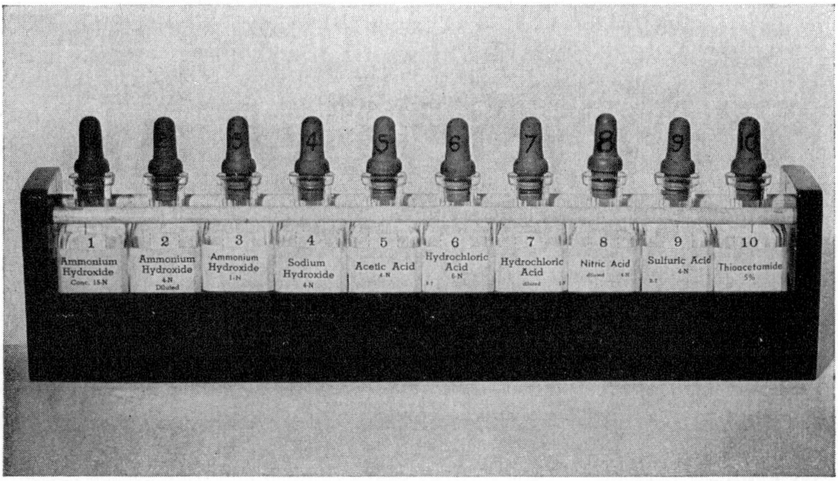

FIG. 4.25. Individual Reagent Set and Rack.

General Reagent Set

The reagents in this set are used less frequently in the Preliminary Experiments and Procedures than the reagents in the individual sets. Consequently, in large classes one such set (Fig. 4.26) is provided for a

FIG. 4.26. Reagent Rack Set.

group of 10 to 20 students. The reagents in this set and the procedure for preparing them are given in Appendix D.

The reagents are arranged in the rack so that the *inorganic reagents* are together in one group and the *organic reagents* and *indicators* are in another group. The suggested order for each group is the order in which they are listed in Appendix D.

In addition to the established inorganic reagents for confirmatory tests, organic reagents have been given as an alternative test in a number of cases. Some of these are well known and widely used, such as dimethylglyoxime for nickel, aluminon for aluminum, and 2-nitroso-1-naphthol for cobalt. Of the many such organic reagents known,* only a few have been selected. Although our primary emphasis is on the use of inorganic reagents, it is well for the student to become familiar with a few of the organic reagents because they are now used widely in both qualitative and quantitative analysis.

The indicators selected are those that have color changes at the appropriate pH range and whose colors interfere least with the analysis.

Test Solution Set

The solutions in this set contain the ions for which tests are made in the Procedures. They are also used in the Preliminary Experiments to study some of the characteristic reactions of the ions. During the analysis they are used to make comparative tests in estimating the approximate quantity of the ion in the unknown. The composition of suitable test solutions is given in Appendix C. Although the procedures are based on the use of 0.1 gram-ion test solutions, some instructors may prefer to use test solutions containing 10 mg. of the ion per ml. No essential change in procedure is required in this case.

Several suitable methods can be devised for dispensing the test solutions. Three of them are as follows.

Method 1. Ideally each student should have a set of test solutions. For large classes one for every 10 or 15 students is satisfactory. The rack may be like that illustrated in Fig. 4.27, capable of holding twenty-four 30-ml. reagent bottles. The bottles should be labeled with the name and concentration of the solute, and arranged preferably in the order of the analytical groups (p. 106).

If laboratory arrangements permit, a double set of the test solutions may be put in a suitable rack. This rack can be placed on the reagent shelves over the center of the laboratory table so that students from both sides may use the solutions.

Method 2. If a sufficient number of racks and dropping bottles is not available, the student may obtain the test solutions in 5-ml. vials, one analytical group at a time, or he may obtain all of them at the same time in 24 suitably

* Feigl, *Qualitative Analysis by Spot Tests*, Elsevier Publishing Co., Inc., New York, 1946; Hopkins and Williams, Ltd., *Organic Reagents for the Metals;* and The British Drug Houses, Ltd., *B.D.H. Reagents for Delicate Analysis and Spot Tests.*

labeled vials. The vials can be filled either in the storeroom or from large dispensing bottles in the laboratory.

Method 3. The student obtains from the storeroom 5-ml. vials which contain the ion solutions used in the Preliminary Experiments. These vials are *not* labeled with the name of the solute. They are dispensed in analytical groups, and the student is required to identify the ion in the different vials by means of the known reactions and the tests for individual ions given in the

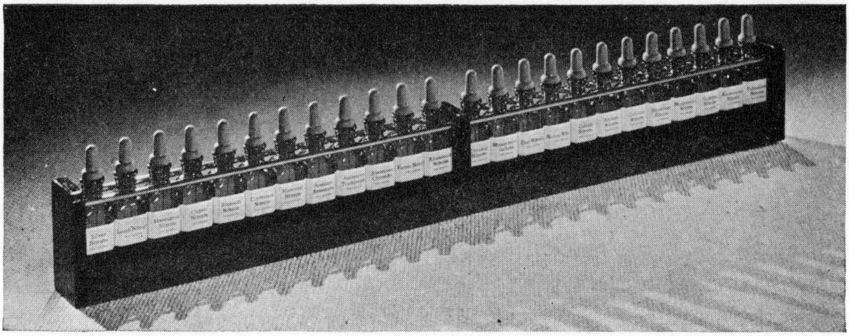

FIG. 4.27. Test Solutions and Rack.

Preliminary Experiments and the Procedures. After the ion is identified, the vial is labeled, and the solution is kept for further use. This method requires a technique and perspicuity on the part of the student that are not demanded by either of the other methods; because identifying an ion, even within the limitations of one group, requires considerable thought and stimulates greater interest. (This method is suitable where sufficient dispensing service and laboratory instruction are provided.)

Concentration of Test Solutions

Because concentrations can be readily converted one into the other (p. 15), any one of several methods may be used in preparing the test solutions. If in addition to the qualitative identification of the ions an estimate of the approximate quantity of the ion is desired, test solutions containing 10 mg. of the ion per ml. are convenient. Thus 1 drop of such a solution contains about $10 \div 20 = 0.5$ mg., and this diluted to 5 ml. with water gives a solution that contains 0.1 mg./ml. The approximate number of milligrams of the ion in the unknown can be estimated by comparing the amount of precipitate or the depth of color with that in known solutions. For example, the samples may be reported as containing approximately 5 mg./ml., 1 mg./ml., or 0.1 mg./ml.

Test solutions which are 0.1 gram ion with respect to the ion under consideration are convenient in other respects. Equal volumes of such solutions contain equal numbers of ions, whereas this is not true in the case of normal, molar, or weight concentrations. For instance, 1 ml. of a 0.1 gram-ion solution of Ag^+ contains the same number of ions as 1 ml. of a 0.1 gram-ion solution of Al^{3+}. This would not be true if the solutions were either 0.1-N or 0.1-M with respect to their sulfates, Ag_2SO_4 and $Al_2(SO_4)_3$. It should be remembered in using gram-ion concentrations that 1 drop of a 0.1 gram-ion solution of Al^{3+}, for instance, requires 3 drops of a 0.1-*N* solution of a given reagent to be equivalent in reactive value. Actually, the reagents are usually of a relatively high molar or normal concentration, so that one or two drops are more than sufficient to complete the reaction with one or two drops of the test solution.

Conversion from gram-ion concentration to the concentration of the ion in milligrams per milliliter is very simple. For example, a 0.1 gram-ion solution of Ag^+ contains 10.79 g. of Ag per liter, or 10.79 mg. per ml. Similarly, a 0.1 gram-ion solution of Al^{3+} contains 2.7 g. of Al^{3+} per liter, or 2.7 mg. per ml. The milligrams of ion per milliliter of solution in 0.1 gram-ion solutions of the cations range from 1.8 mg./ml. for NH_4^+ to 40.12 mg./ml. for Hg_2^{++}.

Use of Reagents

Before using a reagent, read carefully the label on the bottle and make certain that it is the reagent called for in the directions. It may take only a few seconds to add a wrong reagent, but it may take an hour to correct a mistake if you make one. Usually a student does not detect his mistake in using a wrong reagent, and misses the ion for which the test is being made.

The specified amount of a reagent is sufficient. The addition of an excess often gives concentrations which prevent or hinder the desired reaction.

Be certain to return the droppers to the bottle from which they were removed. If the reagents are accidentally mixed because the dropper is placed in the wrong bottle, the bottle must be emptied, washed, and refilled at the storeroom.

Avoid dropping or spilling the reagents on the racks.

Neatness and cleanliness are essential for a correct analysis.

REVIEW QUESTIONS

1. List some of the aims of the laboratory work in a course on qualitative analysis. Illustrate.
2. State three methods of separating precipitates from the solution in which they are formed and discuss the important points of technique in using each of them.
3. What types of precipitates might be difficult to separate from the solution in which they are formed?
4. What conditions of precipitation favor the formation of more easily filtered precipitates?
5. For what kind of precipitates is decantation suitable as a means of separating a precipitate from a solution? When is it used during filtration and centrifugation?

6. On the basis of Stokes' equation, what factors contribute toward the more rapid settling of a precipitate?
7. Upon what factors does the rate of separation of a precipitate by means of a centrifuge depend?
8. Make schematic drawings of apparatus suitable for three methods of filtration.
9. Discuss the choice of filter media for the filter tube.
10. How may filtrations be carried out at elevated temperatures in the filter tube?
11. What difficulties may be encountered if the quantity of precipitate to be removed from a liquid is large?
12. On the basis of Poiseuille's equation, what factors influence the rate of filtration through a filter medium? Discuss each of these factors.
13. What factors contribute to the most effective washing of precipitates?
14. What conditions contribute to the incomplete removal of undesired ions from precipitates by washing?
15. Discuss some of the techniques of washing precipitates. What are the most common difficulties encountered in washing precipitates effectively?
16. Show that washing precipitates with a given volume of water is more effective if several small portions are used rather than one large one.
17. Discuss the important points of techniques for heating solutions, dissolving precipitates, and evaporating solutions.
18. Write equations for the formation of H_2S in acid solution and S^{--} in alkaline solution from thioacetamide. What conditions favor precipitation of sulfides by thioacetamide?
19. What precautions must be used when sulfide precipitations are made with H_2S gas? Sketch an apparatus for generating H_2S and write the equations for the reactions involved.
20. State the ways in which the concentration of test solutions may be expressed. Show how the concentration of an ion in mg. per ml. of solution can be obtained from a concentration expressed in terms of normality, molarity, or gram-ion.

PROBLEMS

1. Calculate from the following data the rate at which a spherical particle will settle at 25° C. and 100° C.: r = 0.001 cm.; g = 981 cm./sec.^{2}, η at 25° C. = 0.894 centipoises = 0.00894 poises (dyne-sec./cm.^{2}); η at 100° C. = 0.284 centipoises = 0.00284 poises; density of solid at 25° C. = 2.93 g./ml.; density of solid at 100° C. = 2.92 g./ml.; density of water at 25° C. = 0.997 g./ml.; density of water at 100° C. = 0.958 g./ml. (*Ans.*: 25° C., R_s = 0.0471 cm./sec.; 100° C., R_s = 0.151 cm./sec.) How many minutes will it take the particle to fall 2 cm. at each temperature? (*Ans.*: 25° C., 3.53 min.; 100° C., 1.13 min.)
2. Repeat the calculations in Problem 1 for a particle with a radius of 0.0001 cm.
3. How many times the force of gravity will be achieved in a centrifuge with a radius of 9 cm. that runs at a speed of 1500 r.p.m.?

4. How many times the force of gravity will be achieved in a centrifuge 24 cm. in diameter that runs at 1500 r.p.m.?
5. From Poiseuille's equation, show the effect of the following on the time required for a given volume of liquid to flow through small capillaries:
   a. The pressure is doubled.
   b. The radius of the pores is doubled.
   c. The thickness of the filter medium is doubled.
   d. The viscosity is doubled.
6. How many times faster will a given volume of liquid be forced through the filter medium by a pressure equivalent to 700 mm. of mercury than by a pressure equivalent to a column of water 15 cm. high?
7. In washing the chlorides of Group I with water to remove the ions of the other groups, calculate the amount of Cu^{++} which will be left absorbed in a filter paper and on the precipitate after washing the precipitate (a) once with 2 ml. of water and (b) four times with 0.5 ml. of water. Assume that the filter paper and precipitate absorb 0.4 ml. of solution and that the concentration of Cu^{++} is 0.002 g./ml. How many times more effective is washing when the residual volume is 0.05 ml. than when it is 0.4 ml.? (See the example on p. 78.)
8. Calculate the concentration of the *cation* in mg./ml. in each of the following solutions: (a) 0.1-*M* $MgNO_3$; (b) 0.1-*N* $AlCl_3$; (c) 0.1 gram ion Fe^{3+}; (d) 0.1-*M* $Cr_2(SO_4)_3$; (e) 0.1-*N* $Pb(NO_3)_2$; (f) 0.1-*M* $Al_2(SO_4)_3$.

CHAPTER 5

DIRECTIONS FOR LABORATORY WORK *

GENERAL INSTRUCTIONS

1. After a laboratory desk has been assigned, check the apparatus in the desk set according to the directions given by the laboratory instructor.

2. Obtain from the storeroom the special semimicro apparatus that is required but is not in the desk set.

3. Prepare the following special apparatus if it is not supplied by the storeroom: 6 micro stirring rods (Fig. 4.15), a wash bottle (Fig. 4.12), and a rubber policeman (Fig. 4.18).

4. Fill the reagent bottles in the reagent sets if they are supplied without the solutions.

5. Wash all the apparatus to be used in the course and keep it clean at all times. The filter tubes are washed with water and a tapered brush (Fig. 4.19*A*) and the test tubes are washed with water and a small test tube brush (Fig. 4.19*B*). A detergent such as Tide or some other similar product is useful in cleaning glassware. The apparatus should not be allowed to dry before being washed and rinsed with distilled water. Medicine droppers must be cleaned thoroughly and always kept clean to prevent contamination of solutions being analyzed. To clean them, remove the rubber bulb and wash the glass tube with a detergent and pipe cleaner if necessary. The rubber bulb should be washed with a detergent solution, rinsed with tap water, and rinsed again with distilled water.

6. Observe all the standard laboratory rules with respect to conduct, storeroom service, disposal of liquids and solids, use of reagents (p. 92), etc. Use an empty beaker or other receptacle to dispose of used filter media, matches, etc., and empty it into the waste jars at the close of the laboratory period.

7. Perform the Preliminary Experiments for Group I, using the test solutions for this group. The test solutions will be dispensed by one of the three procedures described on page 91.

* Because of special laboratory situations and aims, some instructors may prefer to omit this chapter and substitute their own directions for the laboratory work.

Record the observations, write and *learn* the equations for the reactions, and answer all the questions at the time the experiment is performed. (See the suggestions for recording notes in a later section.)

8. After the Preliminary Experiments have been checked, and after any other special requirements are completed, obtain a "known solution" from the storeroom. Analyze it and take notes on your analysis in the manner suggested below unless you are given other directions by the laboratory instructor.

9. After the known solution has been analyzed and the results checked for correctness by the instructor, study the procedures and prepare for a short examination on such topics as the following: the reactions involved in the analysis, the reason for the different operations, and the colors of the ions and precipitates. The instructor will then sign a blank with which you may obtain an unknown solution from the storeroom.

Analyze the unknown solution and record your observations and conclusions. If the test for any ion is not definite, make a comparative test by using the test solutions. If less than 0.01 mg./ml. of an ion is found (use a comparative test to determine this), report the ion present as a "trace." If there is an abnormally large amount of any ion, indicate the fact by doubly underscoring the ion on the report blank. Some instructors may ask their students to indicate the approximate quantity of each ion in milligrams per milliliter, as determined by comparative tests with solutions of known concentration. Concentrations of the unknown solutions may range from 0.1 mg./ml. to 5 mg./ml. Fill out the Unknown Report Blank and hand it in for correction.

10. Follow the above directions in analyzing each known and unknown solution assigned by the laboratory instructor.

GENERAL ASPECTS OF LABORATORY TECHNIQUE

1. The actual operations of qualitative analysis are relatively simple, so the work should proceed without delay.

2. Working efficiently should be the rule from the beginning. This requires some planning and forethought so that the work may be approached methodically. Two or more operations which do not interfere can be carried on simultaneously. There is no reason to "wait" for something. Efficiency does not mean working so fast that mistakes are made. Such work may be very inefficient because it is usually followed by another hurried experiment with contradictory results.

3. Each observation should be recorded concisely, as suggested in the next section on notebook records.

4. Judgment and good chemical sense should be used in drawing conclusions from the data carefully recorded during the analysis.

5. Although the loss of a small amount of the solutions or precipitates in various steps of the analysis will not affect the results within the precision required for qualitative analysis, great care is necessary to prevent contamination during the analysis.

6. Test tubes, filter tubes, stirring rods, droppers, pressure bulbs, etc., must be scrupulously cleaned before use. Stirring rods, droppers, or stoppers that have touched the top of the desk should be thoroughly cleaned before they are used. Particular care should be taken to clean the pressure bulb after each use.

7. Whenever possible, containers should be kept covered to prevent dust from getting into the solutions.

8. Reagents should never be returned to the bottle from which they have been poured. Stoppers should be put back on reagent bottles immediately to prevent contamination and reduce the possibility of interchanging the stoppers.

9. The purity of reagents is questionable because they may have been made from impure chemicals or they may have been contaminated through carelessness. Consequently, when contamination is indicated, a "blank test" should be made by adding all the reagents used in the test to distilled water and then testing for the ion in question. A negative test shows that the contamination is not sufficient to influence the analytical test.

10. The quantitative aspects of qualitative tests must not be ignored. A negative test means little unless the sensitivity of the test is known. When an ion is said to be absent, what is meant is that so far as the tests used are concerned, the particular ion was not detected. A more sensitive reagent would probably show that the ion is present. A reagent or test that is so sensitive as to show the presence of an ion in almost everything is likewise not too useful. Consequently it is important to make some kind of estimate as to the quantity of the ion present. As previously explained, this can be done by comparative tests with known amounts of the ion. A trace is reported if the amount is below 0.01 mg./ml. It is also possible to estimate whether an ion is present to the extent of 0.1 mg./ml., 1 mg./ml., or 5 mg./ml. simply by comparing the amount of precipitate or depth of color obtained with these amounts of the ion.

If the sensitivity of a test is known and if no indication of the ion is obtained, it is easy to calculate the maximum quantity that could be present in the solution analyzed. Suppose, for example, that the sensitivity of a test for an ion is 2.5 μg./ml. If 5 drops of an unknown solution is diluted to 1 ml. for analysis, a negative test will mean that there was not as much as 2.5 μg. of the ion in the 5 drops of the unknown solution. Since 5 drops is about 0.25 ml. (0.05 ml./drop), the total quantity of the ion per ml. of the unknown solution will be $2.5 \div 0.25 = 10$ μg. If the unknown solution had been prepared by dissolving about 100 mg. of a solid in 10 ml. of solution so that the concentration of solid would be about 10 mg./ml., the maximum percentage of the ion that could be present in the solid sample would be $\frac{10 \times 10^{-6}}{10 \times 10^{-3}} \times 100 = 0.1\%$, or one part per thousand.

NOTEBOOK RECORDS

Keeping a good notebook record is essential for an intelligent report on the results of an analysis. It is important that the results be recorded *immediately* after performing an experiment or making a test. The notes should not be too detailed, but they should be complete enough to give all the essential facts about the experiment.

Equations should be written in the ionic form (p. 38), and all the conventions with regard to designating the formation of precipitates, gases, and slightly ionized compounds should be used. The color and physical appearance (powdery, granular, flocculent, gelatinous, or curdy) should be stated for each precipitate. Likewise the color formed when a reagent is added to a solution should be described with respect to hue and intensity.

Suggested Form of Notebook Record for the Preliminary Experiments

The form shown in Table 5.1 is suggested as suitable for recording notes. Some instructors prefer special methods of recording the results. It is suggested that the experiment be recorded in a form on the right-hand page of the notebook and that any questions not answered in the form be answered on the left-hand page. Special notes, instructions, and scratch work can also be put on that page.

One of the primary purposes of the Preliminary Experiments is to acquaint the student with a number of the important reactions of the ions. These experiments also afford him an opportunity to observe the

TABLE 5.1. Suggested Form for Notes on Preliminary Experiments

SILVER ION Ag^+

Exp. No.	Procedure	Results	Equations, Answers, and Conclusions
1	$AgNO_3 + HCl$	White curdy ppt.	$Ag^+ + Cl^- \rightleftharpoons \underset{\text{white}}{AgCl} \downarrow$
	Suspension of AgCl heated.	Ppt. does not dissolve but coagulates.	Solubility of AgCl is not greatly different in hot and in cold water.
2	AgCl ppt. from Exp. 1 + hot water.	Does not dissolve.	Apparently not soluble.
etc.			

appearance of many precipitates that are formed during the analysis. Consequently, careful observation while the Preliminary Experiments are being performed will make the analyses easier and more certain.

Each operation has a purpose and the student should try to understand the reason for each step in the experiment. He should try to understand each reaction in terms of the theories learned in the classroom.

The following indicates the type of questions the student should ask himself and the type of information he may get from even the simplest Preliminary Experiments. Consider, for example, the silver ion experiment, Ag-1 (p. 111).

> To 1 ml. of distilled water add 1 drop of the silver test solution. To this solution add 1 drop of 6-*N* HCl. Write the equation for the reaction. Warm the solution and filter off the precipitate. To the clear filtrate add 1 drop of 1-*N* HCl and note whether a precipitate is formed. If a precipitate is not formed, what does this indicate? Solubility of AgCl = 1.9×10^{-6} g./ml. of water.

1. "To 1 ml. of distilled water add 1 drop of the silver test solution." A measured volume of water, 1 ml., should be placed in a clean test tube (13 x 100 mm.). (1 ml. is about 20 drops, depending somewhat on the tip of the dropper. Check yours.) The height to which this volume comes in the test tube should be noted. Distilled water is used because tap water contains a number of dissolved substances, one of which is the chloride ion. The drop of silver nitrate test solution contains $0.01079 \div 20 = 0.00054$ g. (0.54 mg.) of Ag^+ so that the concentration of Ag^+ is about 0.54 mg./ml. and its molar concentration is $(0.05)(0.1) \div 1.05 = 0.0048$-*M*.

2. "To this solution add 1 drop of 6-*N* HCl." This makes the solution about 0.27-*N* with respect to H_3O^+ and Cl^- ($0.05 \times 6 \div 1.1 = 0.27$-*N*). Accord-

ing to the solubility product principle, a precipitate of AgCl will form if the product of the molar concentrations of Ag^+ and Cl^- exceeds the solubility product constant. That is, a precipitate will form if

$$[Ag^+][Cl^-] \underbrace{>}_{\text{is greater than}} 1.7 \times 10^{-10}$$

Consequently, since $(0.0048)(0.27) = 1.3 \times 10^{-3}$, the ion concentration product is much greater than the solubility product constant (1.7×10^{-10}) and a precipitate of AgCl will form.

3. "Write the equation for the reaction." The equation is as follows:

$$(Ag^+ + NO_3^-) + (H_3O^+ + Cl^-) \rightleftharpoons \underset{\text{white}}{AgCl\downarrow} + (H_3O^+ + NO_3^-)$$

or, preferably,

$$Ag^+ + Cl^- \rightleftharpoons \underset{\text{white}}{AgCl\downarrow}$$

Note that ionic equations are used.

4. "Warm the solution." The solution is warmed in order to observe whether the AgCl precipitate has a marked difference in solubility in hot and cold water. In this case the difference in solubility is slight, and therefore no difference in the quantity of the precipitate is observed. In most cases, warming also helps to coagulate the precipitate and make filtration easier.

5. "Filter off the precipitate." To separate the precipitate from the filtrate, a small plug of cotton or glass fiber is placed in the tapered end of the pressure filter tube (Fig. 4.7) by using the handle of the micro spatula or a glass rod. The pressure filter tube is inserted in a test tube (13 x 100 mm.). The solution to be filtered is added to the pressure filter tube and with the pressure bulb (Fig. 4.8) the filtrate is forced through the filter medium into the test tube. The precipitate remains on the filter. The filtrate should be clear. If it is not, it is passed through the filter medium until a clear solution is obtained. Sometimes it is necessary to repack the filter medium more tightly in the pressure filter tube. The longer the precipitate is allowed to remain in the solution, the larger the particles become. Shaking and heating also tend to coagulate precipitates and thereby facilitate filtration. Other methods of filtration or centrifugation can be used to separate the precipitate from the solution.

The following questions should arise in the student's mind. Has enough HCl been added to interact with all the silver ions? The answer is Yes, because the number of milliequivalents of Cl^- added is greater than the number of milliequivalents of Ag^+ in the solution. Thus, if 1 drop is 0.05 ml. (20 drops per ml.),

$$(\text{ml.} \times N)_{Cl^-} > (\text{ml.} \times N)_{Ag^+}$$
$$(0.05)(6.0) > (0.05)(0.1)$$

or 0.30 milliequivalent of Cl^- was added to a solution which contained only 0.005 milliequivalent of Ag^+. Hence an excess of Cl^- was added.

Does this excess cause all the Ag^+ to precipitate as AgCl? The answer is No, because AgCl is soluble to a slight extent in water. The excess Cl^- reduces the solubility of AgCl but does not completely remove the Ag^+. The amount of Ag^+ left in solution can be calculated from the common ion effect on solubilities. In general, an excess of a precipitant is added to a solution in order to reduce the quantity of the cation in the solution.

If an excess of HCl decreases the solubility of AgCl, should a large excess be added? The answer is best obtained by adding 1 drop of $AgNO_3$ test solution to a clean test tube and then adding several drops of concentrated HCl. No precipitate is formed because the large excess of Cl^- forms the complex ion $AgCl_2^-$.

$$\underline{AgCl} + (H_3O^+ + Cl^-) \rightleftharpoons H_3O^+ + AgCl_2^-$$

or

$$\underline{AgCl} + Cl^- \rightleftharpoons AgCl_2^-$$

Many slightly soluble compounds dissolve when a large excess of a reagent is added. Hence a *large* excess of any reagent should be avoided.

6. "To the clear filtrate add 1 drop of 1-*N* HCl and note whether a precipitate is formed." This extra drop of HCl is added to see whether sufficient HCl was supplied previously to precipitate the silver ion "completely." If a visible precipitate formed on the addition of the extra drop of HCl, this would be evidence of incomplete precipitation. If no visible precipitate is formed when additional precipitant is added to the filtrate, precipitation for the particular ion or ions is considered *analytically complete.* It is usual to test for *complete precipitation* in this manner.

7. "Solubility of AgCl = 1.9×10^{-6} g./ml. of water." This is 0.0000019 g./ml. = 0.0019 mg./ml. = 1.9 μg./ml. If the temperature is not stated, room temperature is assumed (21° to 25° C.). A volume of about 526 liters of water (139 U.S. gallons, or about 3 fifty-gallon barrels) would be required to dissolve 1 g. of silver chloride. Thus, the quantity of Ag^+ in 1 ml. of solution is reduced to a very small value (less than 1.9×10^{-6} g.) by the addition of HCl. Although a precipitate of AgCl will form when a substance yielding chloride ion is added to a solution containing 1.9 μg./ml. of Ag^+, the precipitate is not easily seen by the eye unless about 2.5 μg./ml. of Ag^+ is present. In other words, the sensitivity of the test for Ag^+ by precipitation with chloride ion is about 2.5 μg./ml.

Suggested Form for Notes for the Analysis of a Known Solution

The analysis of a "known solution" which contains all the ions of a group gives the student an opportunity to observe the tests for each ion in that group. The procedures should be studied as the analysis proceeds and the reason for each step should be recorded in the notes. The ionic equations for all the reactions involved in the analysis should also be written. A form similar to the one in Table 5.2 is suitable for recording the results of an analysis.

TABLE 5.2. Suggested Form of Notes for the Analysis of Known Solutions

Analysis of Known Solution for Group . . . .

Date . . . . Name . . . .

Procedure No.	Procedure	Results	Purpose, Conclusions, and Equations
1	Known solution + HCl	White curdy ppt.	Precipitates the ions of Group I: $Ag^+ + Cl^- \rightleftharpoons \underset{\text{white}}{\underline{AgCl}} \downarrow$ $Hg_2^{++} + 2Cl^- \rightleftharpoons \underset{\text{white}}{\underline{Hg_2Cl_2}} \downarrow$ ($Pb^{++} + 2Cl^- \rightleftharpoons \underset{\text{white}}{\underline{PbCl_2}} \downarrow$ if present in large amounts)
	Ppt. + hot water	——	Dissolves $PbCl_2$ if it is present.
2	Ppt. + NaClO + HCl	Part of ppt. dissolves.	Dissolves Hg_2Cl_2: $Hg_2Cl_2 + HClO + 5Cl^- + H_3O^+ \rightleftharpoons 2HgCl_4^= + 2H_2O$
3	Filtrate (2) + NH_4OH + NH_4I + NaOH	Brown ppt.	Shows the presence of Hg^{++}: $2HgCl_4^= + NH_3 + I^- + 3OH^- \rightleftharpoons \underset{\text{brown}}{\underline{HOHgNHHgI}} \downarrow + 2H_2O + 8Cl^-$
4	Ppt. (2) + NH_3	Ppt. dissolves.	Dissolves AgCl: $AgCl + 2NH_3 \rightleftharpoons Ag(NH_3)_2^+ + Cl^-$
4a	Solution (4) + H_3O^+	White ppt.	Confirms the presence of Ag^+: $Ag(NH_3)_2^+ + 2H_3O^+ + Cl^- \rightleftharpoons \underset{\text{white}}{\underline{AgCl}} \downarrow + 2NH_4^+ + 2H_2O$
	etc.		

Suggested Form for Notes on the Analysis of Unknown Solutions

The form used for notes here should be similar to that for known solutions, but with the modifications shown in Table 5.3. The color of the unknown solutions should be noted because this *indicates* the presence or absence of certain ions. For example, if a general unknown solution is colorless, the absence of appreciable quantities of Cu^{++}, Fe^{3+}, Cr^{3+}, Mn^{++}, Co^{++}, and Ni^{++} is *indicated* but not *proved*. Small quantities of colored ions may be present or certain ions may be present in such proportions as to make the solution nearly colorless. Similarly, the presence of two colored ions gives a hue intermediate between the colors of the two ions. Hence, the absence of color or the presence of a certain color only *indicates* or suggests the presence of certain ions. The presence and behavior of a precipitate in the original unknown also indicate the presence of certain ions. Hence, all observations which may lead to establishing the presence or absence of the ions should be recorded, and the final conclusion should follow as a result of these evidences and the confirmatory test. Furthermore, if the final result is correct, all the observations should be explainable.

A form similar to the one shown in Table 5.3 is suitable for recording the results of analyzing an unknown solution.

TABLE 5.3. Suggested Form for Notes for the Analysis of Unknown Solutions

Unknown 2, Group II

Date . . . . Name . . . .

Procedure No.	Reagent or Procedure	Result	Conclusions
—	Visual examination	Light blue. White ppt. present.	Indicates the presence of Cu^{++}. The white ppt. indicates one or more of the following: Bi^{3+}, Sb^{3+}, Sn^{4+}.
7	Adjust acidity + CH_3CSNH_2. Heat in boiling water bath.	Black ppt. forms. White ppt. originally present disappears.	The black ppt. indicates the presence of one or more of the following: PbS, HgS, CuS. Lighter-colored sulfides may also be present.
8	Ppt. + NaOH + CH_3CSNH_2	Black residue remains.	Indicates one or more of the following: PbS, CuS, Bi_2S_3. CdS (yellow) may also be present.
9	Residue + HNO_3 + H_2SO_4. Evaporate to SO_3.	White ppt. remains.	Indicates $PbSO_4$.
10	White ppt. + CH_3COONH_4 + K_2CrO_4	Yellow ppt. $PbCrO_4$.	Confirms Pb^{++}.
	etc.		

CHAPTER 6

GENERAL SCHEME OF QUALITATIVE ANALYSIS FOR THE CATIONS

Before the analysis is started, it is necessary to make certain that the sample of material is representative. If the material is not already in solution it must be dissolved by the appropriate procedure (p. 360). In general, it is not possible to make direct, specific tests for each ion in the solution. This is particularly true if the number of elements that may be present is large. Instead, it is necessary to separate the ions into smaller groups so that interferences will not occur. Only when the possible number of elements in the solution is limited to a few can specific or confirmatory tests be devised for most of the elements.

The number of separations into groups and the number of possible interferences increase if we attempt to devise a scheme that will include all the elements. Consequently, for an elementary course, a scheme of qualitative analysis must be limited in scope to a reasonable number of the more common elements. Hence a more complete treatise on qualitative analysis * must be consulted for the general analysis of a sample containing some of the rarer elements.

One of the primary tasks of a method of analysis such as is given in this book is to teach the technique and principles of a number of the more important analytical methods of separation and identification. Although the scheme of analysis applies to a limited number of the more common ions, its extension to a greater number would involve primarily a greater number of similar types of separation and identification techniques. The study of the methods in the subsequent chapters affords one of the best opportunities to learn and systematize many of the reactions of the ions.

Provision is made for the systematic separation and identification of twenty-four of the more common cations. These cations are removed

* A. A. Noyes and W. C. Bray, *A System of Qualitative Analysis for the Rare Elements*, Macmillan, New York, 1927; R. K. McAlpine and B. A. Soule, *Prescott and Johnson's Qualitative Chemical Analysis*, Van Nostrand, New York, 1933; E. H. Swift, *A System of Chemical Analysis*, Prentice-Hall, New York, 1939.

successively by groups from solution by the so-called group reagents. The ions in each group are then separated from one another where necessary, and finally identified by specific tests.

SEPARATION OF THE CATIONS INTO GROUPS

Group Reagents

The twenty-four cations that are usually considered in elementary courses in qualitative analysis are separated into five groups on the basis of group reagents:

1. Hydrochloric acid.
2. H_2S or thioacetamide (CH_3CSNH_2) in acid solution.
3. H_2S or thioacetamide in ammoniacal solution.
4. Ammonium carbonate.
5. No group reagent.

Groups of Ions

The formulas and colors of the precipitates that are formed by the cations of each group with the group reagent are summarized in Table 6.1.

Schematic Outline for the Separation of Cations into Groups

Usually the first samples analyzed by the students are already dissolved and are in a dilute nitric acid solution. If the samples are solids they must be dissolved by one of the general methods described in a later section of the book. The general scheme for separating the ions into groups and subgroups is shown in Table 6.2.

Tests for the Ions

After a group of ions has been precipitated and separated from the solution, it is necessary to separate each ion from the group in order to apply tests that will positively identify the ion. This separation is accomplished by differential dissolution and precipitation, or by the formation of weak salts or complex ions. In some cases where the group is sufficiently small, the addition of special inorganic or organic reagents may be sufficient to confirm the presence of the ion. Many of these confirmatory tests are included in the Preliminary Experiments so that the student may recognize them easily when the samples are analyzed. Schematic outlines for the separation and identification of the ions in each group will be presented when each group of ions is considered.

TABLE 6.1. Cation Groups and Group Reagents

Group	Ions	Group Reagent	Precipitates Formed by Group Reagents
I	Ag^+ (colorless) Hg_2^{++} (colorless) Pb^{++} (colorless)	HCl	AgCl (white) Hg_2Cl_2 (white) $PbCl_2$ (white)
II Division A	Pb^{++} (colorless) Bi^{3+} (colorless) Cu^{++} (greenish blue) Cd^{++} (colorless)	H_2S or CH_3CSNH_2 in 0.2-*N* HCl	PbS (black) Bi_2S_3 (brown) CuS (black) CdS (yellow)
Division B	Hg^{++} (colorless) As^{3+}, As^{5+} (colorless) Sb^{3+}, Sb^{5+} (colorless) Sn^{++}, Sn^{4+} (colorless)		HgS (black) As_2S_3 (yellow) Sb_2S_3 (orange) SnS_2 (yellow)
III Division A	Fe^{3+} (reddish brown) Ni^{++} (light green) Co^{++} (faint red) Mn^{++} (faint pink)	H_2S or CH_3CSNH_2 in NH_4OH	FeS (black) NiS (black) CoS (black) MnS (flesh)
Division B	Al^{3+} (colorless) Cr^{3+} (dark green to blue) Zn^{++} (colorless)		$Al(OH)_3$ (white) $Cr(OH)_3$ (faint greenish blue) ZnS (white)
IV	Ba^{++} (colorless) Sr^{++} (colorless) Ca^{++} (colorless)	$(NH_4)_2CO_3$	$BaCO_3$ (white) $SrCO_3$ (white) $CaCO_3$ (white)
V	Mg^{++} (colorless) K^+ (colorless) Na^+ (colorless) NH_4^+ (colorless)	No group reagent (special tests)	—— —— —— ——

Other Ions Precipitated by the Group Reagents *

It may be of interest to list other ions that are precipitated by the group reagents. Although this information is not necessary for the analyses in this book, it will give interested students a feeling of the scope of the general scheme for separating all the ions into groups.

* For further details, see Lundell and Hoffman, *Outlines of Methods of Chemical Analysis*, Wiley, New York, 1938.

TABLE 6.2. Schematic Outline for Separation of Cations into Groups

<table>
<tr><td colspan="7">Solution: All Groups, I–V.
Add HCl.</td></tr>
<tr><td rowspan="4">Precipitate:
AgCl
Hg_2Cl_2
$PbCl_2$(?)</td><td colspan="6">Filtrate: Groups II–V.
Adjust H_3O^+ to 0.2- to 0.3-M. Add CH_3CSNH_2. Heat 5 minutes.</td></tr>
<tr><td colspan="2" rowspan="2">Precipitate:
PbS As_2S_3
Bi_2S_3 Sb_2S_3
CuS SnS
CdS SnS_2
HgS

Add NaOH +
CH_3CSNH_2</td><td colspan="4">Filtrate: Groups III–V.
Add NH_4OH (CH_3CSNH_2 already present). Heat 2 minutes.</td></tr>
<tr><td colspan="2">Precipitate:
$Al(OH)_3$ MnS
$Cr(OH)_3$ CoS
ZnS NiS
FeS

Dissolve in HNO_3. Add NaOH + H_2O_2.</td><td colspan="2">Filtrate: Groups IV–V.
Add $(NH_4)_2CO_3$.</td></tr>
<tr><td>Residue:
PbS
Bi_2S_3
CuS
CdS</td><td>Solution:
$HgS_2^{=}$
AsS_3^{3-}
SbS_3^{3-}
$SnOS^{=}$
SnS_4^{4-}</td><td>Filtrate:
$Al(OH)_4^-$
$CrO_4^{=}$
$Zn(OH)_4^{=}$</td><td>Precipitate:
$Fe(OH)_3$
MnO_2
$Ni(OH)_2$
$Co(OH)_3$</td><td>Precipitate:
$BaCO_3$
$SrCO_3$
$CaCO_3$</td><td>Filtrate: Group V.
No group reagent.
Special tests.</td></tr>
<tr><td>Group I</td><td>Group IIA</td><td>Group IIB</td><td>Group IIIB</td><td>Group IIIA</td><td>Group IV</td><td>Group V</td></tr>
</table>

1. Addition of HCl to a dilute nitric acid *solution* of the elements will cause the precipitation of only Ag^+ and Hg_2^{++}. Pb^{++} will also precipitate if its concentration is above 4 to 5 mg./ml. Sometimes BiOCl or SbOCl will form if too little HCl is added or if the solution becomes diluted. A moderate excess of HCl or of HNO_3 will dissolve these salts, but not the AgCl or the Hg_2Cl_2. $Sn(OH)_4$ may also precipitate if the acid concentration is too low.

A number of other substances are precipitated when a solution of the elements is evaporated with hydrochloric or other acids. This evaporation frequently follows the direct treatment of the sample with HCl or the addition of HCl to the sample after it has been fused in a suitable flux. During evaporation with HCl, a number of elements form relatively insoluble acids, oxides, or hydrous oxides rather than salts. Of these the most important is silicic acid, H_4SiO_4. Niobium (Nb), tantalum (Ta), and tungsten (W) are also rather completely precipitated by this treatment. Some Ti and Zr, if present, will also be found in the precipitate. P, S, Cl, Br, or I may be found in the precipitate because anions containing them may form insoluble compounds with certain cations. S as SO_4^{--} may form insoluble $PbSO_4$ and $BaSO_4$, for example. P as PO_4^{3-} may form insoluble phosphates with Zr, Hf, Ti, and Th. Phosphates of other cations may dissolve in the acid but they may reprecipitate later if the solution is diluted or if it is made less acidic (see the discussion of Group III, p. 207). The halogens will, of course, form insoluble precipitates with Ag^+, Hg_2^{++}, Pb^{++}, and Tl^+ if present in high concentrations. Some elements such as As and Ge are lost during evaporation with HCl.

2. In addition to Group II cations (Pb^{++}, Bi^{3+}, Cu^{++}, Cd^{++}, Hg^{++}, As^{3+}, As^{5+}, Sb^{3+}, Sb^{5+}, Sn^{++}, Sn^{4+}), a number of other ions form insoluble sulfides in 0.2- to 0.5-*M* acid solution. Among those that are rather completely precipitated are the following: Ag^+, Au^{3+}, Ge^{4+}, Mo^{4+}, Pd^{4+}, Se^{4+}, and Te^{4+}; among those partially precipitated are Ir^{4+}, Os^{4+}, Pt^{4+}, Re^{7+}, Rh^{3+}, and Ru^{4+}. Most of the sulfides except those of Cd^{++}, Pb^{++}, In^{3+}, and Mo^{4+} can be precipitated from a 1-*M* HCl solution about as well as from 0.2-*M* HCl. Such ions as As^{5+}, Ge^{4+}, and Re^{7+} require a high acid concentration for complete precipitation as sulfides in a reasonable time. Se^{4+}, Te^{4+}, and As^{5+} will precipitate in 12-*M* HCl solutions. As can be seen, special conditions are frequently needed for complete precipitation of all the acid hydrogen sulfide group.

Most of the sulfides of this group are either black or brownish black, except those of Ge^{4+} (white); As^{3+}, As^{5+}, Cd^{++}, Sn^{4+} (yellow); Sb^{3+}, Sb^{5+}, Se^{6+} (orange-yellow to orange-red). Actually the color of some of the sulfides varies with the condition of precipitation.

Besides the elements that will precipitate in 0.2-*M* HCl when in solution alone, small amounts of a number of other sulfides may be carried down with the sulfides of this group by adsorption and co-precipitation. The principal ones are the sulfides Zn^{++}, Fe^{++}, Co^{++}, Ni^{++}, V^{4+}, W^{6+}, Tl^{3+}, and In^{3+}. A second precipitation (or the use of a higher acid concentration when permissible) will make negligible the contamination by the first four elements.

3. When ammonium hydroxide and thioacetamide (or H_2S) is added to a solution from which Groups I and II have been removed, the following precipitates are obtained: (a) hydroxides of Al, Cr, Be, Sc, Y, La, rare earths, Ti, Zr, Hf, Th, Nb, Ta, Ga; and (b) sulfides of Zn, Fe, Mn, Co, Ni, In, Tl, U. The precipitate may be contaminated with V, W, Ru, Pt, B, Si, P, F, as well as with some of the alkaline earth elements.

If ammonium hydroxide alone were added to a solution of the elements after removal of Groups I and II, the following would be rather completely precipitated: Al, Cr, Fe, Be, Sc, Y, La, rare earths, Ti, Zr, Hf, Th, Nb, Ta, Pa, U, Ga, In. Though not precipitated when alone in solution, Si, P, V, W, and lesser amounts of Zn and Co would be more or less completely carried down with the precipitate. It can be seen from the above that the hydroxides of Fe, U, and In would be converted to sulfides if the ammonium hydroxide precipitate were treated with H_2S.

Removal of the ammonium hydroxide precipitate and addition of H_2S or

TABLE 6.3. Elements Precipitated from Solutions from Which No Groups Have Been Removed

Reagent and Solution or Operation	Elements More or Less Completely Precipitated	Partially Precipitated	May Precipitate, React Under Special Circumstances, or Co-precipitate
1. HCl + evaporation	Ag, (Hg_2^{++}), Si, Nb, Ta, W	Pb, Tl	B, F, P, S, Cl, Br, I, Ba, Ra, Ti, Zr, Hf, Th
2. H_2SO_4 + evaporation	Pb, Ba, Ra, Si, Nb, Ta, W, Ag-halide	Sr, Ca	Al, Cr, Fe, Ni, Sn, Sb, Ge, P, S, Cl, Br, I, B, Ti, Zr, Hf, Th
3. H_2S or CH_3CSNH_2 in dil. acid solution	Pb, Bi, Cu, Cd, Hg, As, Sb, Sn, Ag, Au, Ge, Mo, Pd, Se, Te	Ir, Os, Pt, Re, Rh, Ru, Pa	Zn, Fe, Co, Ni, In, Tl, V, W
4. NH_4OH	Al, Cr, Fe, Be, Sc, Y, La, rare earths, Ti, Zr, Hf, Th, Nb, Ta, Ga, In, Sn, Tl	Au, Hg, Sb, Pb, Bi	Mg, Ca, Sr, Ba, Ra, V, Mo, W, Mn, Co, Ni, Cu, Zn, Ru, Rh, Pd, Ag, Cd, Re, Os, In, Pt, B, Si, P, S, Ge, Te
5. NH_4OH + H_2S or CH_3CSNH_2	Hydroxides: Al, Cr, Be, Sc, Y, La, rare earths, Ti, Zn, Hf, Th, Nb, Ta Sulfides: Zn, Fe, Mn, Co, Ni, Cu, Cd, Hg, Pb, Bi, Ag, Rh, Pd, In, Tl, Os, Ga, U	Re, Ru, Pt, V, W	B, Si, P, F, Mg, Ca, Sr, Ba, Ra
$(NH_4)_2C_2O_4$ in faintly acid solutions (pH, 3–4)	Ca, Sr, Sc, Y, La, rare earths, Th, Au	Ba, Mn, Ta, Co, Ni, Cu, Zn, Ag, Cd, Sn, Pb, Bi	
$(NH_4)_2HPO_4$ + NH_3	Mg, Mn, Ca, Be, Sc, Y, La, rare earths, Zr, Hf, Th, Pb, Bi	Sr, Ba, Ra, Al, In, Tl, Ti, Nb, Ta, Pa, U, Cr, Fe, Rh, Pt, Au, Hg, Sb	
H_3PO_4 + acid	Ti, Zr, Hf, Pa	Cb, Ta	
NaOH (5%)	Fe, Mn, Cr, Co, Ni, Cu, Ag, Cd, Mg, Sc, Y, La, rare earths, Ti, Zr, Hf, Th, Pa, U, In, Tl	Si, Bi, Hg, Nb, Ta, Ru, Rh, Os	Ca, Sr, Ba, Ra, P, F, Pd, Ir, Pt
NaOH (5%) + Na_2CO_3	Same as above, plus Ca, Sr, Ba, and Ra. U remains in solution.		

thioacetamide to the ammoniacal solution would result in the formation of sulfides of the following: Zn, Mn, Co, Ni, and Tl, with some contamination by V, W, and Si.

4. After the preceding groups are removed, ammonium carbonate in the presence of NH_4^+ allows the precipitation of Group IV (Ca, Sr, Ba) and Ra as carbonates. In the absence of NH_4^+, Mg and some Li are precipitated with this group.

5. The only elements not separated from the solution by the group reagents are the alkali elements (Li, Na, K, Rb, Cs) and, of course, the nonmetals including such ions as NH_4^+.

Reagents Plus Solutions Containing All the Elements

The elements that are precipitated when a number of common group reagents are added to solutions of all the ions are summarized in Table 6.3. For each reagent there is listed in Column 2 the elements that are more or less completely precipitated when they are either alone or mixed with ions of the other elements. In the third column are listed elements whose ions are only partially precipitated by the reagent. Elements that may be found in the precipitate because of special circumstances even though they are not precipitated when alone in solution are listed in the last column. In some cases the elements are carried down by co-precipitation and adsorption. In other cases they may be present because the element was in solution as an anion that forms an insoluble compound.

Examination of this table shows that quite a number of elements are removed from solution by each reagent. Except for cases in which certain ions are known to be absent, the addition of these reagents to solutions of all the elements is not very useful in qualitative analysis. In order to reduce the numbers of ions precipitated by each reagent, it is necessary to remove one group after another systematically from the solution, as was said above. Each small group of ions may then be treated individually, as will be described in the following chapters.

REVIEW QUESTIONS

1. Why is it not possible to make direct tests for all the cations before separating them into groups?
2. List the reagents used to separate the cations into groups.
3. For each analytical group of cations, give the formula and color of the precipitates formed with the group reagent.
4. Make a schematic outline for separating the cations into groups.
5. After the ions have been separated into groups, what is the general procedure for identifying them?
6. Summarize the general scheme of qualitative analysis for the cations.
7. What ions other than those listed in Table 6.1 might be precipitated with each group reagent?

CHAPTER 7

PRELIMINARY EXPERIMENTS AND REACTIONS FOR GROUP I CATIONS *

IONS OF GROUP I

Test Solution †	Ion	Concentration (mg./ml.)
0.1-*M* Silver nitrate	Ag^+	10.8
0.1-*M* Mercury (I) nitrate	Hg_2^{++}	40.1
0.1-*M* Lead nitrate	Pb^{++}	20.7

† If desired, test solutions may be prepared to contain 10 mg. of cation per ml. (Appendix C).

The Silver Ion, Ag^+

Ag-1. Precipitation of AgCl. To 1 ml. of distilled water add 1 drop of the silver nitrate test solution. To this solution add 1 drop of 6-*N* HCl. Write the equation for the reaction. Place the tube in the hot water bath and note the behavior of the precipitate. Filter off the precipitate and wash it with a little water (about 10 drops). To the clear filtrate add 1 drop of 1-*N* HCl. If a precipitate is not formed, what does this indicate?

Solubility: AgCl $= 1.9 \times 10^{-6}$ g./ml. (1.4 μg. Ag^+/ml.).

(NOTE: Solubilities of salts are given in grams per milliliter of water at room temperature unless otherwise stated.)

Ag-2. Test for Solubility of AgCl in Hot Water. Pass 2 ml. of boiling water through the AgCl precipitate from Ag-1. Cool the filtrate and add 1 drop of 1-*N* HCl. Does a precipitate form? What does this experiment show as to the solubility of AgCl in hot water?

Ag-3. Dissolution of AgCl by NH_4OH, and Confirmatory Test. Add 5 drops of 4-*N* NH_4OH to the AgCl precipitate that remains on the filter medium from Ag-2. Force the solution through the filter and wash the medium with about 1 ml. of water. Did the precipitate dissolve? Write

* Study the discussion of the Procedures for Group I (pp. 119 ff.) and the chemical reactions in the analysis of Group I (pp. 130 ff.) before doing these Preliminary Experiments.

the equation for the reaction. To the filtrate add 1 drop of phenolphthalein indicator and then add HCl until the red color of the indicator disappears. What is the white precipitate that forms? Write the equation for the reaction. Why was the indicator added?

(NOTE: The formula NH_4OH is used to designate the ammonium hydroxide reagent which is essentially a solution of NH_3 (gas) in water. The fact that it contains a small percentage of the NH_4^+ and the OH^- is sufficient justification for the use of the formula NH_4OH. This formula is not used to suggest the presence of NH_4OH molecules, for their existence at room temperature is doubtful.)

Ag-4. Test for Dissolution of AgCl by HClO. To 1 ml. of water add 1 drop of the silver nitrate test solution. To this solution add 2 drops of 1-*N* HCl and 2 drops of a 5% solution of NaClO. Place the tube in the hot water bath. What does this experiment show as to the solubility of AgCl in a hot acid solution that contains NaClO? (Compare this result with that in Hg-2.)

Ag-5. Confirmatory Test. Reduction of Ag^+ by HCHO. To 1 ml. of water add 1 drop of the silver nitrate test solution. To this solution add 1 drop of formalin (HCHO) and 1 drop of 4-*N* NaOH. Note the color of the precipitate and write the equation for the reaction.

The Mercury (I) Ion, Hg_2^{++}

Hg-1. Precipitation of Hg_2Cl_2 and Solubility in Hot Water. To 1 ml. of water add 1 drop of the mercury (I) nitrate test solution. To this solution add 2 drops of 1-*N* HCl. Note the color of the precipitate and write the equation for the reaction. Place the tube in the hot water bath and note whether the precipitate dissolves to any great extent. Filter off the precipitate and wash it with water.

Solubility: $Hg_2Cl_2 = 3.1 \times 10^{-7}$ g./ml. (0.25 μg. Hg_2^{++}/ml.).

Hg-2. Dissolution of Hg_2Cl_2 by HClO. To the precipitate on the filter medium add about 10 drops of water, 2 drops of 1-*N* HCl, and 1 or 2 drops of a 5% solution of NaClO. Stir the precipitate with a micro stirring rod. Did the precipitate dissolve? (See Ag-4.) Write the equation for the reaction. Force the solution through the filter medium and wash it with a little water (about 10 drops).

Hg-3. Confirmatory Test. Nessler's Test. To the test tube containing the mercury solution add 1 drop of 4-*N* NH_4OH. Note the color of the precipitate and write the equation for the reaction. To this solution add 1-*N* NH_4I, drop by drop, until the precipitate dissolves. Write the equation for the reaction. To this solution, which may be colorless or have a brown color (I_2), add 2 or 3 drops of 4-*N* NaOH. Note the color of the precipitate and write the equation for the reaction.

Hg-4. Confirmatory Tests. Reaction of Hg_2^{++} *and* Hg_2Cl_2 *with* NH_4OH. To 1 ml. of water add 1 drop of the mercury (I) nitrate test solution. To this solution add 1 drop of 4-*N* NH_4OH. Note the color of the precipitate and write the equation for the reaction. Repeat this experiment, using a precipitate of Hg_2Cl_2 on a filter medium. Describe the results and write the equation for the reaction.

(Note the difference in behavior of the mercury (II) ion, Hg-3, and the mercury (I) ion, Hg-4, with NH_4OH.)

Hg-5. Confirmatory Test. Oxidation of Hg_2Cl_2 *with HClO and Then Reduction with* $(H_2NOH)_2H_2SO_4$. To 1 ml. of water add 1 drop of the mercury (I) nitrate test solution. To this solution add 1 drop of 1-*N* HCl. Note the color of the precipitate and write the equation for the reaction. Place the tube in the hot water bath and add 1 or 2 drops of a 5% solution of NaClO. Did the precipitate dissolve? Write the equation for the reaction. To the solution add 2 or 3 drops of 4-*N* NaOH and 2 or 3 drops of hydroxylamine sulfate. Note the color of the precipitate and write the equation for the reaction.

The Lead Ion, Pb^{++}

Pb-1. Precipitation of $PbCl_2$ *and Solubility in Hot Water.* To 1 ml. of water add 1 drop of the lead nitrate test solution. To this solution add 2 or 3 drops of 1-*N* HCl. If a precipitate is not obtained, add the lead nitrate test solution, drop by drop, shaking the tube after the addition of each drop, until a precipitate has formed. Write the equation for the reaction. Place the tube in the hot water bath and allow the solution to become hot. Did the precipitate dissolve?

Solubilities: $PbCl_2 = 4.5 \times 10^{-3}$ g./ml. at 20°; 13.6×10^{-3} g./ml. at 100°. The solubility decreases in the presence of excess Cl^-. $PbCl_2$, however, is soluble in concd. HCl by reason of the formation of the complex, $PbCl_4^{--}$.

Pb-2. Precipitation and Dissolution of $PbSO_4$. *Formation of* $PbCrO_4$. To 10 ml. of water add 1 drop of lead nitrate test solution. Calculate the mg./ml. of Pb^{++} in this diluted solution. (Usually 20 drops = 1 ml. Droppers should be checked for approximate size of drops delivered.) Add

(Text continues on page 118.)

SUMMARY OF REACTIONS OF GROUP I CATIONS

Reagents	Silver—$AgNO_3$	Lead—$Pb(NO_3)_2$	Mercury (I)—$Hg_2(NO_3)_2$
Acids	Metal $3Ag + NO_3^- + 4H_3O^+ \rightleftharpoons 3Ag^+ + NO\uparrow + 6H_2O$ $2Ag + \underset{\text{(hot concd.)}}{H_2SO_4} + 2H_3O^+ \rightleftharpoons 2Ag^+ + SO_2\uparrow + 4H_2O$ Silver is not soluble in nonoxidizing acids.	Metal $3Pb + 2NO_3^- + 8H_3O^+ \rightleftharpoons 3Pb^{++} + 2NO\uparrow + 12H_2O$ $Pb + \underset{\text{(hot concd.)}}{2H_3O^+ + 2Cl^-} \rightleftharpoons PbCl_2\downarrow + H_2\uparrow + 2H_2O$ $PbCl_2$ $+ 2Cl^- \rightarrow PbCl_4^=$ $Pb + \underset{\text{(hot concd.)}}{H_2SO_4} + 2H_3O^+ \rightleftharpoons Pb^{++} + 4H_2O + SO_2\uparrow$ Dilute H_2SO_4 and HCl do not dissolve Pb because of a protective layer of insoluble salt.	Metal $\underset{\text{(excess)}}{6Hg} + 2NO_3^- + 8H_3O^+ \rightleftharpoons 3Hg_2^{++} + 2NO\uparrow + 12H_2O$ $\underset{\text{(excess)}}{2Hg} + \underset{\text{(hot concd.)}}{H_2SO_4} + 2H_3O^+ \rightleftharpoons Hg_2^{++} + SO_2\uparrow + 4H_2O$ Hg_2^{++} is formed when an excess of Hg is present (cf. mercuric salts).
Precipitants	Insoluble salts (order of increasing solubility): Ag_2S, AgI, $Ag_4Fe(CN)_6$, AgBr, AgCN, AgSCN, $Ag_3Fe(CN)_6$, AgCl, Ag_3PO_4, Ag_2O, Ag_2CrO_4, Ag_2CO_3, $Ag_2C_2O_4$, $AgIO_3$, AgCNO, Ag_2SO_3, $AgBrO_3$, Ag_2SO_4, $AgNO_2$, $Ag(CH_3COO)$, $AgBO_2$.	Insoluble salts: PbS, $Pb_3(PO_4)_2$, $PbCrO_4$, $PbCO_3$, PbC_2O_4, $Pb(IO_3)_2$, $Pb(OH)_2$, $PbSO_4$, $PbSO_3$, PbF_2, PbS_2O_3, PbI_2, $PbBr_2$, $PbCl_2$.	Insoluble salts: Hg_2S, Hg_2I_2, Hg_2Br_2, Hg_2Cl_2, Hg_2O, Hg_2CO_3, $Hg_2C_2O_4$, $Hg_2(SCN)_2$, Hg_2CrO_4, $Hg_2(OH)NO_3$, Hg_3PO_4, $Hg_2(NO_2)_2$, $Hg_2(IO_3)_2$.
Excess reagent	Complex ions (order of decreasing stability): $Ag(CN)_2^-$, $[Ag_2(S_2O_3)_3]^{4-}$, $Ag(SO_3)_2^{3-}$, $Ag(NH_3)_2^+$, $AgCl_2^-$.	Complex ions: $Pb(CH_3COO)_4^=$, $Pb(OH)_4^=$, $PbI_4^=$, $PbBr_4^=$, $PbCl_4^=$.	Complex ions: (cf. mercury (II) salts).

HCl	$Ag^+ + Cl^- \rightleftharpoons \underset{\text{white}}{\underline{AgCl}}\downarrow$ AgCl dissolves in solutions of concd. HCl, NH_4OH, KCN, $Na_2S_2O_3$, $Hg(NO_3)_2$, and Zn + HCl, with the formation of the following products respectively: $AgCl_2^-$, $Ag(NH_3)_2^+$, $Ag(CN)_2^-$, $[Ag_2(S_2O_3)_3]^{4-}$, $Ag^+ + HgCl_4^=$, and $Ag + Zn^{++}$. AgCl is transposed by ions which form less soluble silver salts, but it does not dissolve in a solution of CH_3COONH_4 or of HNO_3.	$Pb^{++} + 2Cl^- \rightleftharpoons \underset{\text{white}}{\underline{PbCl_2}}\downarrow$ $PbCl_2$ is soluble in hot water and in solutions of concd. HCl, NaOH, Zn + HCl, $Hg(NO_3)_2$, and CH_3COONH_4, with the formation of $PbCl_4^=$, $Pb(OH)_4^=$, $Pb + Zn^{++}$, $Pb^{++} + HgCl_4^=$, and $Pb(CH_3COO)_2$ respectively. With NH_4OH, $PbCl_2$ forms Pb(OH)Cl, which is not soluble in excess NH_4OH. $PbCl_2$ is transposed by ions which form less soluble lead salts.	$Hg_2^{++} + 2Cl^- \rightleftharpoons \underset{\text{white}}{\underline{Hg_2Cl_2}}\downarrow$ Hg_2Cl_2 reacts with NH_3 to form Hg and $Hg(NH_2)Cl$, both of which are soluble in aqua regia or HClO. The products formed are $HgCl_4^=$ and $HgCl_4^= + N_2$ respectively. Hg_2Cl_2 dissolves in concd. HNO_3, Zn + HCl, and $Hg(NO_3)_2$, with the formation of Hg^{++}, $Hg + Zn^{++}$, and $Hg_2^{++} + HgCl_4^=$ respectively. Hg_2Cl_2 is not soluble in a solution of CH_3COONH_4, but it is transposed by ions which form less soluble mercurous salts.
KBr	$Ag^+ + Br^- \rightleftharpoons \underset{\text{cream}}{\underline{AgBr}}\downarrow$ AgBr dissolves in solutions of concd. NH_4OH, KCN, $Na_2S_2O_3$, and Zn + HCl, with the formation of the products similar to those listed in the preceding section.	$Pb^{++} + 2Br^- \rightleftharpoons \underset{\text{white}}{\underline{PbBr_2}}\downarrow$ $PbBr_2$ dissolves in solutions of concd. KBr, NaOH, CH_3COONH_4, and Zn + HCl, with the formation of products similar to those listed in the preceding section.	$Hg_2^{++} + 2Br^- \rightleftharpoons \underset{\text{whitish-yellow}}{\underline{Hg_2Br_2}}\downarrow$ The precipitate is soluble in concd. HNO_3 and in Zn + HCl, with the formation of $Hg^{++} + Br_2$ and $Hg + Zn^{++}$ respectively.
KI	$Ag^+ + I^- \rightleftharpoons \underset{\text{yellow}}{\underline{AgI}}\downarrow$ AgI dissolves in solutions of KCN, $Na_2S_2O_3$, and Zn + HCl, but not in concd. NH_4OH.	$Pb^{++} + 2I^- \rightleftharpoons \underset{\text{yellow}}{\underline{PbI_2}}\downarrow$ PbI_2 dissolves in solutions of concd. KI, NaOH, and Zn + HCl, with the formation of $PbI_4^=$, $Pb(OH)_4^=$, and $Pb + Zn^{++}$. PbI_2 reprecipitates when a solution of $PbI_4^=$ is diluted.	$Hg_2^{++} + 2I^- \rightleftharpoons \underset{\text{greenish-yellow}}{\underline{Hg_2I_2}}\downarrow$ With excess KI, $\underline{Hg_2I_2} + 2I^- \rightleftharpoons \underset{\text{black}}{\underline{Hg}}\downarrow + \underset{\text{scarlet}}{\underline{HgI_2}}\downarrow +$ $2I^- \rightleftharpoons \underset{\text{black}}{\underline{Hg}}\downarrow + HgI_4^=$

SUMMARY OF REACTIONS OF GROUP I CATIONS (*Continued*)

Reagents	Silver—$AgNO_3$	Lead—$Pb(NO_3)_2$	Mercury (I)—$Hg_2(NO_3)_2$
NH_4OH	$Ag^+ + NH_3 + H_2O \rightleftharpoons \underline{AgOH}\downarrow + NH_4^+$ $\underline{2AgOH} \rightleftharpoons \underset{\text{brown}}{\underline{Ag_2O}}\downarrow + H_2O$ Ag_2O is soluble in excess NH_4OH, HNO_3, and in solutions of the substances that dissolve AgCl.	$Pb^{++} + 2NH_3 + 2H_2O \rightleftharpoons \underset{\text{white}}{\underline{Pb(OH)_2}}\downarrow + 2NH_4^+$ $Pb(OH)_2$ does not dissolve in excess NH_4OH, but it is soluble in solutions of acids, alkali hydroxides, and soluble acetates.	$Hg_2^{++} + NO_3^- + NH_3 + H_2O \rightleftharpoons \underset{\text{black}}{\underline{Hg}}\downarrow + \underset{\text{white}}{\underline{Hg(NH_2)NO_3}}\downarrow + H_3O^+$ The precipitate is soluble in aqua regia and in $HClO + HCl$.
NaOH	$2Ag^+ + 2OH^- \rightleftharpoons \underset{\text{white}}{\underline{2AgOH}}\downarrow$ $\rightleftharpoons \underline{Ag_2O}\downarrow + H_2O$ Ag_2O does not dissolve in excess NaOH.	$Pb^{++} + 2OH^- \rightleftharpoons \underset{\text{white}}{\underline{Pb(OH)_2}}\downarrow$ The precipitate dissolves in excess NaOH. $\underline{Pb(OH)_2} + 2OH^- \rightleftharpoons Pb(OH)_4^=$ or $PbO_2^= + 2H_2O$	$Hg_2^{++} + 2OH^- \rightleftharpoons \underset{\text{black}}{\underline{Hg_2O}}\downarrow + H_2O$ Hg_2O is insoluble in excess NaOH.
$(NH_4)_2CO_3$ $+NH_4OH$	$2Ag^+ + CO_3^= \rightleftharpoons \underset{\text{white}}{\underline{Ag_2CO_3}}\downarrow$ Ag_2CO_3 dissolves in excess of the reagent with the formation of $Ag(NH_3)_2^+$. The precipitate is soluble in all acids stronger than carbonic acid.	$Pb^{++} + CO_3^= \rightleftharpoons \underset{\text{white}}{\underline{PbCO_3}}\downarrow$ $PbCO_3$ is not soluble in excess reagent but is soluble in solutions of acids, alkali hydroxides, and soluble acetates.	$Hg_2^{++} + CO_3^= \rightleftharpoons \underset{\text{yellowish-brown}}{\underline{Hg_2CO_3}}\downarrow$ The precipitate rapidly decomposes: $\underline{Hg_2CO_3} \rightleftharpoons \underline{Hg}\downarrow + \underset{\text{gray}}{\underline{HgO}}\downarrow + CO_2\uparrow$
H_2S	$2Ag^+ + S^= \rightleftharpoons \underset{\text{black}}{\underline{Ag_2S}}\downarrow$ Ag_2S dissolves in hot HNO_3 and in acid solutions of thiourea, but not in KCN, $Na_2S_2O_3$, or NH_4OH.	$Pb^{++} + S^= \rightleftharpoons \underset{\text{black}}{\underline{PbS}}\downarrow$ PbS is soluble in concd. HCl and in hot 4-*N* HNO_3, but it is insoluble in solutions of alkali hydroxides and soluble acetates. PbS does not form complex sulfide ions.	$Hg_2^{++} + S^= \rightleftharpoons \underset{\text{black}}{\underline{Hg_2S}}\downarrow$ The precipitate immediately decomposes. $\underline{Hg_2S} \rightleftharpoons \underline{Hg}\downarrow + \underset{\text{black}}{\underline{HgS}}\downarrow$

			Both products are soluble in aqua regia or HClO, and HgS is soluble in Na_2S with the formation of $HgS_2^{=}$.
K_2CrO_4	$2Ag^+ + CrO_4^{=} \rightleftharpoons \underset{\text{dull red}}{\underline{Ag_2CrO_4}} \downarrow$ Ag_2CrO_4 is soluble in solutions of HNO_3, NH_4OH, and in the reagents that dissolve AgCl.	$Pb^{++} + CrO_4^{=} \rightleftharpoons \underset{\text{yellow}}{\underline{PbCrO_4}} \downarrow$ $PbCrO_4$ is soluble in excess alkali hydroxide and in HNO_3 but not in acetic acid.	$Hg_2^{++} + CrO_4^{=} \rightleftharpoons \underset{\text{brick red}}{\underline{Hg_2CrO_4}} \downarrow$ The precipitate is soluble in HNO_3 with difficulty.
Na_3PO_4	$3Ag^+ + PO_4^{3-} \rightleftharpoons \underset{\text{yellow}}{\underline{Ag_3PO_4}} \downarrow$ Ag_3PO_4 is soluble in CH_3COOH, NH_4OH, and in the reagents that dissolve AgCl.	$3Pb^{++} + 2PO_4^{3-} \rightleftharpoons \underset{\text{white}}{\underline{Pb_3(PO_4)_2}} \downarrow$ $Pb_3(PO_4)_2$ is soluble in strong acids and alkali hydroxides, but not in solutions of acetates or acetic acid.	$3Hg_2^{++} + 2PO_4^{3-} \rightleftharpoons \underset{\text{white}}{\underline{2Hg_3PO_4}} \downarrow$ The precipitate is soluble in dilute HNO_3.
$SnCl_2$	$Ag^+ + Cl^- \rightleftharpoons \underset{\text{white}}{\underline{AgCl}} \downarrow$	$Pb^{++} + 2Cl^- \rightleftharpoons \underset{\text{white}}{\underline{PbCl_2}} \downarrow$	$Hg_2^{++} + 2Cl^- \rightleftharpoons \underset{\text{white}}{\underline{Hg_2Cl_2}} \downarrow$ $\underline{Hg_2Cl_2} + Sn^{++} + 4Cl^- \rightleftharpoons$ $\underset{\text{black}}{\underline{2Hg}} \downarrow + SnCl_6^{=}$
H_2O	—	—	$\underline{Hg_2(NO_3)_2} \rightleftharpoons Hg_2^{++} + 2NO_3^-$ $Hg_2^{++} + 2NO_3^- + 2H_2O \rightleftharpoons$ $\underset{\text{white}}{\underline{Hg_2(OH)NO_3}} \downarrow + H_3O^+ + NO_3^-$ Dilute nitric acid dissolves the precipitate.

1 drop of 4-*N* H_2SO_4 to 1 ml. of this dilute Pb^{++} solution. Note the color of the precipitate. Write the equation for the reaction. Filter off the precipitate and wash the filter medium with water. To the filter tube add 4 drops of 1-*N* CH_3COONH_4 and 1 ml. of water. Force the solution through the filter medium into a test tube. The $PbSO_4$ precipitate dissolves in CH_3COONH_4. Write the equation for the reaction. To the test tube add 1 drop of 0.5-*M* K_2CrO_4. Note the color of the precipitate. Write the equation for the reaction.

Solubilities: $PbSO_4 = 4.0 \times 10^{-5}$ g./ml. (27 μg. Pb^{++}/ml.).
$PbCrO_4 = 4.3 \times 10^{-8}$ g./ml. (0.028 μg. Pb^{++}/ml.).

CHAPTER 8

ANALYSIS OF GROUP I CATIONS

SCHEMATIC OUTLINE OF THE PROCEDURE

<table>
<tr><td colspan="4">1. Ag^+, Hg_2^{++}, (Pb^{++}) + Groups II–V for general unknowns
Add HCl.</td></tr>
<tr><td colspan="2">2. Precipitate: AgCl, Hg_2Cl_2, ($PbCl_2$)
Add NaClO + HCl.</td><td colspan="2" rowspan="1">5. Filtrate: Analyze for Groups II–VI. For Group I ions only, two parts.</td></tr>
<tr><td>3. Filtrate: Hg^{++}
a. Add NH_4OH + NH_4I + NaOH.
Brown ppt.:
HOHgNHHgI
b. Add NaOH + $(H_2NOH)_2H_2SO_4$.
White, gray, or black ppt.:
Hg_2Cl_2 or Hg</td><td>4. Residue: AgCl
Add NH_4OH.

Filtrate: $Ag(NH_3)_2^+$
a. Add HCl.
White ppt.:
AgCl
b. Add NH_4I.
Yellowish-white ppt.:
AgI
c. Add HCHO + NaOH.
Gray to black ppt.:
Ag</td><td>6. First part:
Test for Hg^{++} by 3a or 3b.</td><td>Second part:
Add CH_3COONH_4+ K_2CrO_4.
Yellow ppt.:
$PbCrO_4$</td></tr>
<tr><td>Mercury (I)</td><td>Silver</td><td>Mercury (II)</td><td>Lead</td></tr>
</table>

DISCUSSION OF THE PROCEDURE

The ions of Group I (Ag^+, Hg_2^{++}, and Pb^{++}) are separated from the aqueous solution to be analyzed by precipitating their chlorides with HCl. The oxychlorides of antimony (SbOCl) and bismuth (BiOCl) may also precipitate, but they are readily dissolved by adding sufficient acid to make the final concentration of H_3O^+ from 0.5- to 2-M. Silicic acid (H_2SiO_3) may form if SiO_3^{--} is present, and free sulfur could form if polysulfides (S_2^{--}), $S_2O_3^{--}$, or complex thiosulfates such as AsS_4^{--} are in the solution. Sometimes certain oxides or hydroxides such as $Sn(OH)_4$ may be formed if a strong acid solution of the ion is diluted too much. The procedure to be used in this case is discussed later.

The accompanying tabulation lists the solubilities of the chlorides of this group. These values show that the solubility of $PbCl_2$ in g./ml. is

Precipitate	$K_{s.p.}$	Solubility Moles/Liter	Solubility g./ml.	Quantity of Cation/ml.
Hg_2Cl_2	1.1×10^{-18}	6.5×10^{-7}	3.1×10^{-7}	0.25 μg./ml.
AgCl	1.7×10^{-10}	1.3×10^{-5}	1.9×10^{-6}	1.4 μg./ml.
$PbCl_2$	1.7×10^{-5}	1.6×10^{-2}	4.5×10^{-3}	3.4×10^3 μg./ml.

about 2400 times greater than the solubility of AgCl and about 14,500 times greater than the solubility of Hg_2Cl_2. Thus, it can be seen that Ag^+ and Hg_2^{++} are more completely removed from solution than is Pb^{++} when HCl is added to a solution containing these three ions in about equal amounts. A saturated solution of $PbCl_2$ at 20° C. contains 4.5 mg. of $PbCl_2$ or 3.4 mg. of Pb^{++} per ml., whereas only 1.4 μg. of Ag^+ and 0.25 μg. of Hg_2^{++} are contained in 1 ml. of a saturated solution of their chlorides. If the known or unknown solutions contain, or are adjusted to contain, about 5 mg. of each cation per ml., and if only 2 or 3 drops of such a solution is added to 1 ml. of water for analysis, less than 1 mg./ml. of Pb^{++} will be present. Consequently, Pb^{++} will normally not be precipitated with Ag^+ and Hg_2^{++} unless it is present in reasonably large concentrations (3.4 mg./ml. when an equivalent amount of Cl^- is added). Actually, however, an excess of Cl^- is added so that the final concentration is about 0.3-M. On the basis of the common-ion effect on the solubility of $PbCl_2$, this concentration of Cl^- should reduce the quantity of Pb^{++} remaining in solution to about 0.04 mg./ml. The presence of HNO_3 or a large excess of HCl tends to increase the solubility of $PbCl_2$ so that the amount of Pb^{++} remaining is not as low as might be predicted from the above calculations. Washing the precipitate with water removes the excess chloride ions and increases the solubility of $PbCl_2$ to its normal value.

If Pb^{++} is found in Group I, it will always be found in Group II; but the fact that it is not found in Group I does not indicate its absence. It must always be tested for in Group II. When the unknown is for Group I only, a test for Pb^{++} is made with the filtrate that normally contains Groups II–V (see Procedures 5 and 6).

If mercury is present only in the oxidation state of +1 [mercury (I) ion, Hg_2^{++}] it is almost entirely precipitated in Group I. However, since Hg_2^{++} is easily oxidized to Hg^{++}, mercury may be found in both Groups I and II even though originally all of it was present as Hg_2^{++}. Mercury (I) chloride (Hg_2Cl_2) is slightly soluble in water, whereas mercury (II) chloride ($HgCl_2$) is a soluble, slightly ionized molecule. From this it can be seen that silver will be found only in Group I, but lead may be found in both Groups I and II because of its incomplete precipitation as $PbCl_2$. Tests for mercury must be made in both groups because it forms two different ions (Hg_2^{++} and Hg^{++}) that have marked differences in the solubility of their chlorides.

After the ions of this group have been precipitated, the ions are separated from one another by utilizing the following properties and reactions of the ions and their compounds.

1. Pb^{++} probably does not precipitate, so it is in the filtrate from the Group I precipitate. However, to make certain that no $PbCl_2$ remains with the AgCl and Hg_2Cl_2, the precipitate is washed with *hot* water. This is done because $PbCl_2$ is about three times more soluble in hot than in cold water.

2. Hg_2Cl_2 is separated from AgCl by treatment with HClO and HCl. This reagent oxidizes Hg_2^{++} to Hg^{++} and the excess Cl^- forms $HgCl_4^{--}$. It does not affect the AgCl. If the concentration of Cl^- were high, as is required in using aqua regia, some AgCl would dissolve because of the formation of the complex ion $AgCl_2^-$.

Alternatively, the AgCl could have been dissolved by NH_4OH with the formation of the stable complex ion $Ag(NH_3)_2^+$, the mercury being left in the residue as finely divided black Hg and a white precipitate of $Hg(NH_2)Cl$. This procedure has some difficulties such as reduction of AgCl by the Hg, and solution of some of the $Hg(NH_2)Cl$ because of the tendency of Hg^{++} to form $Hg(NH_3)_2^{++}$ and $Hg(NH_3)_4^{++}$. Small amounts of Ag^+ in the presence of large amounts of Hg_2^{++} usually escape detection if this procedure is followed. The method of analysis used in the Procedures obviates this difficulty.

Once the ions of a group have been separated one from the other, it is easy to apply any one of a number of confirmatory tests in order finally to establish the presence or absence of a given ion in amounts corresponding to the sensitivity limits of the procedure.

CONDITIONS FOR THE PRECIPITATION AND DISSOLUTION OF PRECIPITATES IN GROUP I

Solubility Product Principle

The principles relating to the precipitation and dissolution of the slightly soluble salts of this group may be summarized in the following statements of the solubility product principle.

1. In a *saturated solution* of a slightly soluble salt, the product of the molar concentrations of the ions (raised to the appropriate power) is equal to the solubility product constant. For a saturated solution of AgCl,

$$[Ag^+][Cl^-] = K_{s.p.} = 1.7 \times 10^{-10}$$

whereas for Hg_2Cl_2,

$$[Hg_2{}^{++}][Cl^-]^2 = K_{s.p.} = 1.1 \times 10^{-18}$$

The square brackets indicate concentrations in moles per liter of solution.

2. Precipitation occurs when the value of the ion concentration product exceeds the value of the solubility product constant. That is, silver chloride will precipitate when

$$[Ag^+][Cl^-] \underbrace{>}_{\text{is greater than}} K_{s.p.}$$

3. A slightly soluble salt will *dissolve* or be *prevented from forming* if the ion concentration product is maintained at a value below that of the solubility product constant. Thus, silver chloride dissolves or is prevented from forming if

$$[Ag^+][Cl^-] \underbrace{<}_{\text{is less than}} K_{s.p.}$$

Common Ion Effect on Solubility

According to statements 1 and 2, the addition of Cl^- to a solution of Ag^+ will cause precipitation to occur as soon as $[Ag^+][Cl^-]$ exceeds 1.7×10^{-10}. When an equivalent amount of Cl^- has been added, $[Ag^+]$ and $[Cl^-]$ will be the same, and equal to 1.3×10^{-5} moles/liter. Any further addition of Cl^- will make the ion concentration product $[Ag^+][Cl^-]$ momentarily larger than $K_{s.p.}$. This requires that precipitation of some AgCl take place until the ion concentration product is again equal to $K_{s.p.}$. In this precipitation the concentration of Ag^+ must decrease. The new value for the concentration of Ag^+ can be calculated if the concentration of Cl^- is known.

The same qualitative conclusion will be reached from the application of Le Chatelier's principle to the equilibrium:

$$\underline{AgCl} \rightleftharpoons Ag^+ + Cl^-$$

Addition of Cl^- shifts the equilibrium toward the formation of more AgCl, thereby reducing the concentration of Ag^+. This effect is called the **common-**

ion effect on the solubility of a slightly soluble salt. Because of this effect, an excess of the precipitant is usually added to obtain more complete removal of the ion from solution. For example, the common-ion effect will reduce the concentration of Ag^+ from 1.3×10^{-5} moles/liter (1.4 μg. of Ag^+/ml.) in a saturated solution of AgCl to 5.7×10^{-10} moles/liter (6.1×10^{-5} μg. of Ag^+/ml.) in a solution 0.3-*M* to Cl^-.

Effect of Excess Reagent

In many cases too great an excess of the reagent must be avoided because of the tendency of certain ions to form relatively stable complex ions. Thus, high concentrations of Cl^- increase the solubility of AgCl, rather than decrease it. This is so because $AgCl_2^-$ forms and thereby reduces the concentration of Ag^+, with the result that the ion concentration product momentarily is less than $K_{s.p.}$. More AgCl will dissolve until the ion concentration product is again equal to $K_{s.p.}$. The equations for this reaction are:

$$\begin{array}{lcl} \underline{AgCl} \rightleftharpoons & Ag^+ & + Cl^- \\ & + & \\ & 2Cl^- & \rightleftharpoons AgCl_2^- \end{array}$$

Here the formation of $AgCl_2^-$ reduces the concentration of Ag^+, thereby shifting the equilibrium in a direction that increases the solubility of AgCl. From the above discussion it can be seen why an excess of a precipitant is added and why a large excess is avoided.

Dissolution of Hg_2Cl_2

In order to dissolve Hg_2Cl_2 from the Group I precipitate it is necessary to reduce the concentration of one or both of the ions in its saturated solution so that the ion concentration product will become less than $K_{s.p.}$. That is, $[Hg_2][Cl^-]^2$ must be made less than $K_{Hg_2Cl_2}$. This is done by oxidizing the Hg_2^{++} ion with HClO:

$$\begin{array}{lcl} \underline{Hg_2Cl_2} \rightleftharpoons & Hg_2^{++} & + 2Cl^- \\ & + & \\ HClO + 7Cl^- + & H_3O^+ & \rightleftharpoons 2HgCl_4^{--} + 2H_2O \end{array}$$

The reduction of the concentration of Hg_2^{++} in the saturated solution shifts the equilibrium in a direction that increases the solubility of Hg_2Cl_2. The Hg_2^{++} ion is oxidized so completely that all the precipitate dissolves.

Complex Ions in the Dissolution of Precipitates of Group I

In dissolving AgCl, the tendency of Ag^+ to form a relatively stable complex ion with NH_3 is utilized. Thus

$$\begin{array}{lcl} \underline{AgCl} \rightleftharpoons & Ag^+ & + Cl^- \\ & 2NH_3 & \rightleftharpoons Ag(NH_3)_2^+ \end{array}$$

The reduction in the concentration of Ag^+ in the saturated solution, because of the formation of $Ag(NH_3)_2^+$, decreases the ion concentration product, so that

$$[Ag^+][Cl^-] < K_{s.p.}$$

and some of the precipitate must dissolve. The complex ion $Ag(NH_3)_2^+$ is sufficiently stable so that a moderate excess of NH_3 will completely dissolve the amount of precipitate usually formed.

The concentration of Ag^+ in a solution containing NH_3 can be calculated from the **instability constant** for the complex ion:

$$Ag(NH_3)_2^+ \rightleftharpoons Ag^+ + 2NH_3$$

Hence

$$\frac{[Ag^+][NH_3]^2}{[Ag(NH_3)_2^+]} = K_{Ag(NH_3)_2^+} = 6.0 \times 10^{-8}$$

If the concentration of NH_3 is 1-*M*, 0.053 m. mole (7.6 mg.) of AgCl will dissolve in 1 ml. of solution and the concentration of Ag^+ will be 3.2×10^{-9}. Addition of HNO_3 or HCl will reduce the concentration of NH_3, thereby increasing the concentration of Ag^+, so that

$$[Ag^+][Cl^-] > K_{s.p.}$$

and a precipitate of AgCl will form. This reaction is used to confirm the presence of Ag^+ (Procedure 4a). Alternatively, a solution of an iodide may be added to the ammoniacal solution to confirm the presence of silver. If the concentration of Ag^+ is 3.2×10^{-9} moles/liter in the 1-*M* NH_3 solution, addition of sufficient NH_4I to give a solution 0.1-*M* to I^- will cause the precipitation of AgI because

$$[Ag^+][I^-] = [3.2 \times 10^{-9}][0.1] \gg K_{AgI}(8.5 \times 10^{-17})$$

Precipitation will continue until the ion concentration product is equal to $K_{s.p.}$ for AgI.

Even though AgI is very insoluble, it can be readily dissolved by adding a soluble cyanide such as NaCN. In a saturated solution of AgI

$$[Ag^+][I^-] = 8.5 \times 10^{-17}, \quad \text{and} \quad [Ag^+] = 9.2 \times 10^{-9}$$

If the concentration of Ag^+ can be reduced appreciably below this value, the ion concentration product will be less than K_{AgI} and the precipitate will dissolve. Assuming that 1 mg. of silver is present for each milliliter of solution, its concentration when dissolved is about 0.01-*M*. Addition of 2 drops of 1-*N* NaCN to 1 ml. of this solution will dissolve the AgI and give a solution that is approximately 0.01-*M* with respect to $Ag(CN)_2^-$ and about 0.1-*M* with respect to CN^-. The concentration of $[Ag^+]$ in such a solution can be calculated from the instability constant of the complex ion $Ag(CN)_2^-$:

$$\frac{[Ag^+][CN^-]^2}{[Ag(CN)_2^-]} = K_{Ag(CN)_2^-} = 3.8 \times 10^{-19}$$

or

$$\frac{[Ag^+](0.1)^2}{(0.01)} = 3.8 \times 10^{-19}, \qquad \text{and} \qquad [Ag^+] = 3.8 \times 10^{-19}$$

This very low value for $[Ag^+]$ shows that the ion concentration product $[Ag^+][I^-]$ will be much lower than K_{AgI} and the AgI will dissolve in the NaCN solution.

Although the concentration of Ag^+ is very low in a solution of $Ag(CN)_2^-$, silver sulfide with a $K_{s.p.}$ of 1×10^{-51} is so insoluble that it can be precipitated from the cyanide solution. Thus if the pH of the solution is kept at 7 and if H_2S is passed in until it is saturated (about 0.1-*M* to H_2S), the concentration of HS^- is about 0.12-*M* and the concentration of S^{--} will be about 1.2×10^{-9} moles/liter because

$$\frac{[H_3O^+][HS^-]}{[H_2S]} = \frac{(1 \times 10^{-7})(HS)}{(0.1)} = 1.2 \times 10^{-7}, \text{ and } [HS^-] = 0.12$$

and

$$\frac{[H_3O^+][S^{--}]}{[HS^-]} = \frac{(1 \times 10^{-7})[S^{--}]}{(0.12)} = 1 \times 10^{-15}, \qquad \text{and} \qquad [S^{--}] = 1.2 \times 10^{-9}$$

Then, since the ion concentration product $[Ag^+]^2[S^{--}]$ is

$$(3.8 \times 10^{-19})^2(1.2 \times 10^{-9}) = 1.7 \times 10^{-46}$$

Ag_2S will precipitate from the cyanide solution because this value is larger than 1×10^{-51}. In the presence of a large excess of CN^-, however, the precipitation is rather incomplete. An acid solution of thiourea will dissolve the very insoluble Ag_2S by formation of an exceptionally stable complex ion with Ag^+.

The formation of the relatively stable complex ion HgI_4^{--} is involved in the Nessler test for Hg^{++} or for NH_4^+. In Group I, mercury is precipitated as Hg_2Cl_2 and then dissolved by HCl and HClO to give a solution of Hg^{++} or $HgCl_4^{--}$. Addition of NH_4OH produces a white precipitate of $Hg(NH_2)Cl$ (p. 130). Excess NH_4I dissolves this precipitate because of the formation of HgI_4^{--}, which is very stable, as shown by its instability constant:

$$\frac{[Hg^{++}][I^-]^4}{[HgI_4^{--}]} = K_{HgI_4^{--}} = 5.3 \times 10^{-31}$$

However, addition of NaOH produces a very insoluble yellowish-brown compound of HOHgNHHgI. This reaction can also be used as a test for the NH_4^+ ion (p. 130).

LABORATORY WORK—ANALYSIS OF KNOWN AND UNKNOWN SOLUTIONS

1. Obtain from the storeroom a solution that contains the ions of Group I and analyze it by using Procedures 1 through 6 for Group I, given below. Use 2 drops of the solution in 1 ml. of water for the analysis. (NOTE: If the known solution contains approximately 5 mg. of each cation per ml. of solution, 2 drops will give about 0.5 mg. of each cation. If too large an amount is taken for analysis, difficulty may arise in the filtrations.)

2. (Optional). Request a student to prepare an unknown solution from the test solutions. Analyze it in accordance with the Procedures for Group I. (Preparation of the unknown: To 1 ml. of water add 1 drop of the test solutions for each ion. One, two, or three of the ions of Group I may be included in this solution.)

3. Obtain from the storeroom Unknown No. 1 and analyze it by means of the Procedures for Group I. For the analysis, use 2 drops of the unknown in 1 ml. of water. Report the results of the analysis on an Unknown Report Blank, indicating, if requested by the instructor, the approximate concentration of each ion in the unknown solution (0.1, 1, or 5 mg./ml.). To make this estimate, use comparative tests (p. 8) by making up solutions of these concentrations from the test solutions. Use 2 drops and compare the size of precipitates or intensity of color with that obtained with the unknown solution.

Preliminary Examination and Preparation of the Sample for Analysis

Before the analysis of a general unknown sample by the Procedures is begun, its physical appearance should be recorded; attempts must also be made to dissolve completely any precipitate that is present or forms when the sample is added to water. The first unknown samples are usually made up from solutions of the cations—usually their nitrates, acetates, or chlorides, with sufficient acid to prevent the precipitation of the oxysalts of bismuth and antimony, $BiOCl$ or $BiONO_3$ and $SbOCl$ or $SbONO_3$. With insufficient acid these substances may precipitate. Moreover, solutions of Sn^{++}, on standing in contact with air, will become turbid because of the formation of a precipitate of the hydrous oxide of tin (IV), $SnO_2 \cdot xH_2O$, sometimes referred to as stannic hydroxide, $Sn(OH)_4$, or as metastannic acid, H_2SnO_3. Since these precipitates might be filtered off with Group I and hence missed in later groups, they must be dissolved, if present, before HCl is added for the precipitation of Group I. Furthermore, if a precipitate forms when HCl is added, the analyst must make certain, as outlined below, that the precipitate is the chlorides of Group I and not BiOCl and/or SbOCl. (The methods of dissolving metal samples and other solids are described in later chapters; see pages 269 and 359.)

COLOR AND OTHER PHYSICAL CHARACTERISTICS. A general discussion of the physical examination of solid samples is presented in a later chapter on pages 359 ff. In the case of solutions, the color, the existence of a precipitate, and the pH of the solution, if possible, should be recorded. The color imparted to solutions by the cations is discussed on pages 106 and 361. Conclusions based on color alone, however, may be quite erroneous because mixtures of certain colored ions may produce misleading colors. In dilute solutions, the appearance of the faintly colored ions is often completely masked by other colored ions. The concentration and kind of anion present may also affect the color. Occasionally the color may be due to organic substances.

Usually the first unknown samples for cation analyses are solutions or soluble solid salts (largely the nitrates, acetates, or chlorides of the cations). If the unknowns are prepared by mixing *solutions* of cations, the treatment of the sample prior to analysis will depend upon whether a precipitate is present. Such a precipitate may result from hydrolysis or interaction of certain cations with the anions present. Similarly, soluble solid salts may dissolve completely or a solid precipitate may form and remain undissolved.

1. TREATMENT IF NO PRECIPITATE IS PRESENT. As stated at the beginning of the Procedures for analysis, add the required number of drops of the solution to 1 ml. of water. If no precipitate is formed, proceed with the analysis as outlined in the Procedures. However, if a white precipitate is obtained, the presence of either bismuth or antimony, or both, is indicated because they tend to form the slightly soluble oxysalts, BiOCl, $BiONO_3$, SbOCl, $SbONO_3$. In this case, place the test tube in a hot water bath and allow the solution to heat to the temperature of boiling water. If the precipitate has not dissolved, add 4-*N* HNO_3 drop by drop, until the precipitate goes into solution:

$$BiONO_3 + 2H_3O^+ \leftrightharpoons Bi^{3+} + 3H_2O + NO_3^-$$
$$BiOCl + 2H_3O^+ \leftrightharpoons Bi^{3+} + 3H_2O + Cl^-$$

Similar reactions take place for the oxysalts of antimony. Continue with the analysis by adding HCl as directed for the precipitation of Group I. Any precipitate that forms when the HCl is added to the above solution is probably due to the ions of Group I.

2. Treatment If a Precipitate Is Present. a. If the unknown samples were prepared by mixing solutions of the cations, a precipitate that remains in a solution which is somewhat acidic may be AgCl, Hg_2Cl_2, $PbCl_2$, BiOCl, $BiONO_3$, SbOCl, $SbONO_3$, or $Sn(OH)_4$. In this case shake up the solution and the precipitate so as to get a representative sample. With a medicine dropper, transfer the specified quantity of the sample to an evaporation test tube and add 1 ml. of water. To this add 5 drops of 4-*N* HNO_3 and heat the mixture to boiling over a small flame. If the precipitate is due only to the oxysalts of bismuth and/or antimony, it will dissolve and a clear solution will result. In this case continue with the analysis, in accordance with the Procedures, by adding HCl for the precipitation of Group I.

b. If a precipitate or turbid solution remains after the above treatment, the presence of $Sn(OH)_4$ and/or Group I chlorides is indicated. In this case add 10 drops of 6-*N* HCl to the evaporation test tube and evaporate the solution carefully, almost *but not quite* to dryness. Add 10 drops more of 6-*N* HCl and repeat the evaporation. This treatment usually converts $Sn(OH)_4$ to stannic chloride. To the residue add 1 drop of 6-*N* HCl and 1 ml. of water. If a clear solution results, the presence of tin is indicated and Ag^+ and Hg_2^{++} are absent. In this case, the analysis for Group I is omitted and the solution is analyzed according to the Procedures for Group II. Some of the Hg_2^{++} may be oxidized to Hg^{++} by the above treatment, so mercury may be found in both groups even though it was added originally as Hg_2^{++}.

c. If a precipitate remains after evaporation with HCl and the addition of HCl and water as described above, the presence of Group I ions is indicated. In this case, filter the mixture and test the precipitate for Group I cations, starting with Procedure 2. Analyze the filtrate according to the Procedures for Group II.

3. Unknown Containing Only Group I Cations. If the solution is clear, proceed with the analysis according to Procedures 1 through 6. If a precipitate is present, it can be assumed to be due to one of the Group I cations. In this case, shake the solution to obtain a suspension and transfer the required amount to a test tube. Continue with the analysis outlined in Procedures 1 through 6.

PROCEDURES FOR THE ANALYSIS OF GROUP I

Analysis of Group I, Known or Unknown. Follow Procedures 1 through 6. Use 2 drops of the solution. This usually gives from 0.1 to 1 mg. of each cation.

Analysis of a General Known or Unknown for Groups I Through V. See Preliminary Examination and Preparation of Samples for Analysis, p. 126. Use 5 drops of the solution and follow Procedures 1 through 35. Reserve part of the original solution to test for NH_4^+ by Procedure 35.

---

1. To a test tube add the specified amount of the known or unknown solution. To this solution add 1 ml. of water and 1 drop of 6-*N* HCl. Place the tube in the hot water bath and allow it to remain for 1 or 2 minutes. Shake the tube occasionally. (Usually the precipitate coagulates and settles to the bottom of the tube.) Filter the hot solution through a cotton filter medium (Fig. 4.8), and add 1 ml. of water to the precipitate. Heat the mixture by placing the assembly in the hot water bath (Fig. 4.9) and then force the water that remains in the filter medium into the test tube. Reserve the filtrate for the analysis of Groups II through V if the known or unknown contains all the groups. If the known or unknown contains Group I only, test the filtrate for Pb^{++} and Hg^{++}. See Procedure 5.

---

2. **Precipitate:** AgCl, Hg_2Cl_2, ($PbCl_2$). To the precipitate on the filter medium add 10 drops of water, 2 drops of a 5% solution of NaClO, and 2 drops of 1-*N* HCl. Stir the precipitate with a micro stirring rod. Place the filter tube in a test tube, set the assembly in the hot water bath, and allow the solution to pass slowly through the filter medium. (Refilter the solution if the filtrate in the test tube is not clear.) Wash the filter medium with about 1 ml. of water.

---

3. **Filtrate:** Hg^{++}. Confirm the presence of Hg^{++} by one of the following tests:

a. Add 1 drop of 15-*N* NH_4OH, 1 drop of NH_4I, and 3 to 5 drops of 4-*N* NaOH. If mercury is present, a brown precipitate (HOHgNHHgI) will form. The precipitation of low concentrations of Hg^{++} is facilitated by warming the tube in the hot water bath.

b. Add 2 drops of 4-*N* NaOH and 1 drop of 0.5-*M* hydroxylamine sulfate. A white or gray to black precipitate shows the presence of mercury.

4. **Residue:** AgCl. Add 4 drops of 4-*N* NH_4OH, and then 10 drops of water. Force the solution through the filter medium into a test tube. Confirm the presence of Ag^+ by one of the following tests:

a. Add 1 drop of phenolphthalein indicator; then add 6-*N* HCl drop by drop, until the indicator becomes colorless. If silver is present, a white precipitate will be obtained.

b. Add 1 drop of 1-*N* NH_4I. Place the tube in the hot water bath. A yellowish-white precipitate shows the presence of silver.

c. Add 1 drop of formalin and 1 or 2 drops of 4-*N* NaOH. A gray to black precipitate (Ag°) shows the presence of silver. Warming the solution in the hot water bath increases the rate of the reaction.

---

5. **Filtrate** from 1: a. For *general knowns and unknowns* this filtrate contains Groups II through V. Continue the analysis with Procedure 7, p. 173.

b. For *known and unknown solutions containing only Group I*, divide the filtrate into two parts. Test one part for mercury (Hg^{++}) by Procedure 3. Test the other part for lead (Pb^{++}) with Procedure 6.

---

6. **Filtrate** from 1: Pb^{++}. Add 2 drops of 6-*N* CH_3COONH_4 and 1 drop of 0.5-*M* K_2CrO_4. A yellow precipitate shows the presence of lead.

CHEMICAL REACTIONS IN THE ANALYSIS OF GROUP I

Procedure	Equations	Purpose—Discussion
1. Add 6-*N* HCl to the known or unknown solution.	$Ag^+ + Cl^- \rightleftharpoons \underset{\text{white}}{\underline{AgCl}} \downarrow$ $Hg_2^{++} + 2Cl^- \rightleftharpoons \underset{\text{white}}{\underline{Hg_2Cl_2}} \downarrow$ $Pb^{++} + 2Cl^- \rightleftharpoons \underset{\text{white}}{\underline{PbCl_2}} \downarrow$	The HCl precipitates the chlorides of Group I. Avoid a large excess of HCl because of the increased solubility of AgCl and $PbCl_2$ due to the formation of the complex ions $AgCl_2^-$ and $PbCl_4^=$.
If the solids SbOCl and/or BiOCl are present in the original general unknown, they are dissolved by HCl.	*Formation* $Bi^{3+} + Cl^- + 3H_2O \rightleftharpoons$ $\underset{\text{white}}{\underline{BiOCl}} \downarrow + 2H_3O^+$ $Sb^{3+} + Cl^- + 3H_2O \rightleftharpoons$ $\underset{\text{white}}{\underline{SbOCl}} \downarrow + 2H_3O^+$ *Dissolution* $\underline{BiOCl} + 2H_3O^+ \rightleftharpoons Bi^{3+} + Cl^-$ $+ 3H_2O$ $\underline{SbOCl} + 2H_3O^+ \rightleftharpoons Sb^{3+} + Cl^-$ $+ 3H_2O$	Bi^{3+} and Sb^{3+} hydrolyze to give their slightly soluble oxychlorides or oxynitrates, but these are dissolved by HCl. Sn^{4+} also hydrolyzes to form $\underline{Sn(OH)_4} \downarrow$ which is difficultly soluble in HCl.
Wash the precipitate of AgCl, $PbCl_2$, and Hg_2Cl_2 with hot water.	——	$PbCl_2$ is much more soluble in hot water than in cold water. It is dissolved if it is present.
2. Add NaClO and HCl to AgCl and Hg_2Cl_2.	$\underline{Hg_2Cl_2} + HClO + 5Cl^- +$ $H_3O^+ \rightleftharpoons 2HgCl_4^= + 2H_2O$	AgCl is not soluble in the NaClO-HCl reagent, but Hg_2Cl_2 dissolves readily in the reagent.
3a. Add NH_4OH, NH_4I, and NaOH.	$HgCl_4^= + 2NH_3 \rightleftharpoons \underset{\text{white}}{\underline{HgNH_2Cl}} \downarrow$ $+ NH_4^+ + 3Cl^-$ $\underline{HgNH_2Cl} + 4I^- + 2H_2O \rightleftharpoons$ $HgI_4^= + Cl^- + NH_4^+ + 2OH^-$ $2HgI_4^= + NH_4^+ + 4OH^- \rightleftharpoons$ $7I^- + 3H_2O + \underset{\text{brown}}{\underline{HOHgNHHgI}} \downarrow$	The concurrent reactions are given for the formation of the brown precipitate when an acid solution of $HgCl_4^=$ is treated with NH_4OH, NH_4I, and an excess of NaOH.

Procedure	Equations	Purpose—Discussion
3b. Add NaOH and $(H_2NOH)_2H_2SO_4$.	$4HgCl_4^{=} + 2H_2NOH + 4OH^- \rightleftharpoons \underset{\text{white}}{\underline{2Hg_2Cl_2}} \downarrow + N_2O \uparrow + 12Cl^- + 5H_2O$ $2HgCl_4^{=} + 2H_2NOH + 4OH^- \rightleftharpoons \underset{\text{black}}{\underline{2Hg°}} \downarrow + N_2O \uparrow + 8Cl^- + 5H_2O$	Hydroxylamine (H_2NOH) is a good reducing agent, readily changing the mercury (II) ion (Hg^{++}) to the mercury (I) ion (Hg_2^{++}) or to free mercury (Hg°). The lead ion (Pb^{++}), if present, is not reduced to free lead.
4. Add NH_4OH to the residue.	$\underline{AgCl} + 2NH_3 \rightleftharpoons Ag(NH_3)_2^+ + Cl^-$	The NH_3 dissolves the AgCl because of the formation of the complex ion, $(Ag(NH_3)_2)^+$. The Hg_2Cl_2 was removed first to prevent the reduction of Ag^+ to free silver (Ag°). Ag° is not soluble in NH_4OH.
4a. Add phenolphthalein and HCl.	$Ag(NH_3)_2^+ + 2H_3O^+ + Cl^- \rightleftharpoons \underset{\text{white}}{\underline{AgCl}} \downarrow + 2NH_4^+ + 2H_2O$	The use of phenolphthalein enables us to make certain that the solution is acid and that a large excess of the acid is not added.
4b. Add NH_4I.	$Ag(NH_3)_2^+ + I^- \rightleftharpoons \underset{\text{yellow}}{\underline{AgI}} \downarrow + 2NH_3$	AgI is not soluble in NH_4OH.
4c. Add formalin and NaOH.	$4Ag(NH_3)_2^+ + HCHO + 6OH^- \rightleftharpoons \underset{\text{black}}{\underline{4Ag°}} \downarrow + 8NH_3 + 4H_2O + CO_3^{=}$	Formalin in the presence of a strong alkali readily reduces the silver ion (Ag^+) to free silver (Ag°). If excess NaOH is not added, the reduction takes place slowly with the formation of a silver mirror on the test tube.

CHEMICAL REACTIONS IN THE ANALYSIS OF GROUP I
(Continued)

Procedure	Equations	Purpose—Discussion
5–6. Add CH_3COONH_4 and K_2CrO_4.	$Pb^{++} + 2CH_3COO^- \rightleftharpoons Pb(CH_3COO)_2$ $Pb(CH_3COO)_2 + CrO_4^{=} \rightleftharpoons \underset{\text{yellow}}{PbCrO_4\downarrow} + 2CH_3COO^-$	The ammonium acetate decreases the concentration of H_3O^+, if the solution is acidic, and allows the precipitation of $PbCrO_4$. $Pb(CH_3COO)_2$ forms because it is a weak salt.

REVIEW QUESTIONS

1. Give a schematic outline for the analysis of Group I cations.
2. Discuss the reasons for each operation during the analysis.
3. Study the preceding list of reactions and be prepared to write equations for all those that occur in the analysis of Group I.
4. Describe the confirmatory test for each ion of Group I, stating in each case the conditions under which the reaction takes place.
5. What precipitates other than the chlorides of Group I might be present in the precipitate obtained for Group I?
6. If a precipitate forms when HCl is added to an unknown solution and then redissolves when the concentration of HCl is about 2-*M*, what may the precipitate be?
7. If a very large excess of Pb^{++} is present, some of the $PbCl_2$ formed when HCl is added may not dissolve in the hot water. What difficulty, if any, would this cause in the analysis?
8. Explain why tests are made for Pb^{++} in the analysis of Groups I and II, for mercury in Groups I and II, and for Ag^+ only in Group I.
9. After the ions of Group I are precipitated, how are they separated from one another?
10. Outline an alternate scheme for separating Group I ions from one another, and state what difficulties might be encountered.
11. Name suitable reagents for separating each of the following pairs of substances in one operation: Hg_2Cl_2—$PbCl_2$; AgCl—$PbCl_2$; Hg_2Cl_2—AgCl; $HgCl_2$—AgCl.
12. A precipitate is one of the following: AgCl, $PbCl_2$, or Hg_2Cl_2. Explain how ammonium hydroxide may be used to establish which one it is.
13. An unknown for Group I contains only Ag^+ and Pb^{++}. Write equations for the reactions by which these ions may be separated and identified. Do not write equations in which these ions do not appear.
14. Repeat Problem 13 for each of the following solutions: Ag^+ and Hg_2^{++};

Pb^{++} and Hg_2^{++}; Ag^+, Hg_2^{++}, Pb^{++}; Ag^+; Hg_2^{++}; Pb^{++}; Ag^+ and Pb^{++}.

15. What difficulties would there be if an iodide rather than a chloride were added to precipitate the ions of Group I?
16. What cation of Group I is indicated by each of the following observations:
    a. A white precipitate insoluble in hot water dissolves in HCl plus NaClO.
    b. When HCl was added to a hot solution, no precipitate formed until the solution was cooled.
    c. A chloride precipitate did not dissolve in hot water but did dissolve in ammonia.
17. If Ba^{++} instead of Pb^{++} had been added to the unknown solution for Group I cations, would the procedure for *Group I only* indicate the presence of Pb^{++}? Explain. Suggest a modified procedure for testing for Pb^{++} (see the analysis for Group II) that would distinguish between Ba^{++} and Pb^{++}.
18. Would the use of Na_2HPO_4 be satisfactory for a confirmatory test for Pb^{++}? Why or why not?
19. A white precipitate obtained when HCl was added to a solution of Group I was insoluble in excess acid, hot water, and NH_3. What might it be?
20. Write equations for the oxidation of Hg_2^{++} to Hg^{++} by oxygen of the air. How might this influence an analysis for the ions of Group I?
21. What ion of Group I would be indicated by the following behavior:
    a. An ion whose chloride turns black when ammonia is added.
    b. An ion whose chromate dissolves in ammonia but not in sodium hydroxide.
    c. An ion whose chromate is soluble in sodium hydroxide.
    d. An ion whose chloride does not dissolve on the addition of ammonia or hot water.
    e. An ion whose chloride dissolves in HCl plus HClO but not in hot water.
    f. An ion whose phosphate is insoluble in acetic acid and whose sulfate is soluble in ammonium acetate.
    g. An ion whose iodide is not soluble in excess KI but is soluble in $Na_2S_2O_3$.

REVIEW QUESTIONS ON THE THEORY OF GROUP I ANALYSIS *

1. Illustrate the application of the solubility product principle to the precipitation of Group I chlorides.
2. Show by applying the solubility product principle or Le Chatelier's principle that excess chloride ion decreases the solubility of AgCl.
3. By what factor does the common ion effect of 0.3-*M* Cl^- decrease the solubility of AgCl? Of $PbCl_2$?
4. What is the effect of a large excess of Cl^- on the solubility of AgCl or $PbCl_2$? Write equations to illustrate.
5. Write equations to show how Hg_2Cl_2 may be dissolved. Will nitric acid dissolve Hg_2Cl_2? Why or why not? Will aqua regia dissolve it? Explain.

* NOTE TO INSTRUCTOR: If the students have not had a reasonably good treatment of ionic equilibria in general chemistry it may be advantageous to omit certain of these questions and problems until the relevant theories have been discussed.

6. Describe suitable confirmatory tests for Hg_2^{++} and write the equations for the reactions.
7. What complex ions are involved in Nessler's test for mercury?
8. Write equations for the dissolution of AgCl by an aqueous solution of NH_3.
9. Apply the expression for the instability constant of $Ag(NH_3)_2^+$ to calculating the concentration of Ag^+ that can be present when the concentration of NH_3 is 1-*M*. By what factor is this smaller than the concentration of Ag^+ in a saturated solution of AgCl?
10. How can AgCl be reprecipitated from a solution containing $Ag(NH_3)_2^+$?
11. By what factor is the concentration of Ag^+ in a solution that is 1-*M* to NH_3 and 0.01-*M* to $Ag(NH_3)_2^+$ greater than its concentration in a saturated solution of AgI containing 0.1-*M* I^-?
12. Write equations for the dissolution of AgI by NaCN. By what factor is the concentration of Ag^+ in a saturated solution of AgI greater than its concentration in a solution that is 0.01-*M* with respect to $Ag(CN)_2^-$ and 0.1-*M* to CN^-?
13. Discuss the equilibria involved in the confirmatory test for lead.

PROBLEMS

1. Calculate the molar solubility of AgCl, $PbCl_2$, and Hg_2Cl_2 from their respective solubility product constants (Appendix H). How many milligrams of each cation will be present in 1 ml. of each solution?
2. The solubility of AgCl is 0.19 mg. per 100 ml. of solution. Calculate the solubility product constant.
3. What concentration of Cl^- is required to form a precipitate of AgCl in a solution that is 0.01-*M* to Ag^+?
4. What concentration of Ag^+ is required to form a precipitate of AgCl in a solution that is 0.1-*M* to Cl^-?
5. To what volume must 1 drop of 0.1-*M* $AgNO_3$ be diluted before 1 ml. of the solution just fails to form a precipitate with 1 drop of 6-*M* HCl?
6. What is the solubility of AgCl in 0.05-*M* NaCl? By what factor does the common ion effect of 0.05-*M* Cl^- reduce the molar solubility of AgCl as compared to its solubility in water?
7. Repeat the calculations in Problem 6 for $PbCl_2$ in 0.05-*M* NaCl.
8. If Cl^- is added to a solution of the cations of Group I until its concentration is 0.1-*M*, what concentration of each cation is left in solution? If the volume of the solution is 2 ml., how many micrograms of each cation remain unprecipitated?
9. Calculate the concentration of Pb^{++} required to form a precipitate when the Cl^- concentration is 0.01-*M*. To how many mg./ml. of Pb^{++} does this correspond?
10. In a solution containing Ag^+ and Pb^{++}, the concentration of Pb^{++} is 10 mg./ml. If Cl^- is added to precipitate the chlorides, what is the concentration of Ag^+ when $PbCl_2$ begins to precipitate?
11. a. Calculate the concentration of Ag^+ in a 0.01-*M* solution of $Ag(NH_3)_2Cl$.
    b. If the solution is made 0.1-*M* to NH_3, calculate the concentration of Ag^+.

c. How many micrograms of Ag^+ are present in 1 ml. of the two preceding solutions?

12. What concentration of I^- will be required to start the precipitation of AgI from a solution with a concentration of Ag^+ equal to that calculated in 11b?

13. How many drops of 4-*M* HCl would be required to neutralize 2 ml. of a solution containing 5 mg. of Ag^+ as $Ag(NH_3)_2{}^+$ and enough NH_3 to make the solution 0.1-*M* to NH_3? How many drops of 4-*M* HCl would be required to precipitate the Ag^+ in it?

14. a. How many mg. of Pb^{++} are there in 2 ml. of a saturated solution of $PbCl_2$ at 25° and 100° C.?

b. If the solutions are 0.3-*M* to Cl^-, calculate the mg. of Pb^{++} in 2 ml. of solution at 25° and 100° C.

15. What weight of $PbCrO_4$ forms when 5 drops of a lead nitrate test solution (10 mg. Pb^{++} per ml.) is reacted with a solution of ammonium acetate and excess K_2CrO_4?

16. a. How many drops (0.05 ml. each) of 4-*M* NH_3 will be required to dissolve 10 mg. of AgCl suspended in 2 ml. of water and make the resulting solution 0.2-*M* to NH_3?

b. How many drops of 1-*M* HCl will be required to react with the NH_3 and $Ag(NH_3)_2Cl$ in the solution in a?

17. An increase in the concentration of HCl in a solution decreases the solubility of $PbCl_2$ in accordance with the common ion effect of Cl^-; but when the concentration of HCl becomes higher than about 1-*M*, the solubility of $PbCl_2$ increases because of the formation of $PbCl_4{}^{--}$. How many drops of 4-*M* HCl must be added to 2 ml. of a saturated solution of $PbCl_2$ to reduce the solubility of $PbCl_2$ to a minimum?

CHAPTER 9

PRELIMINARY EXPERIMENTS AND REACTIONS FOR GROUP II CATIONS *

IONS OF GROUP II, DIVISION A

Test Solution †	Ion	Concentration (mg./ml.)
0.1-*M* Lead nitrate	Pb^{++}	20.7
0.1-*M* Bismuth (III) nitrate	Bi^{3+}	20.9
0.1-*M* Copper (II) nitrate	Cu^{++}	6.4
0.1-*M* Cadmium nitrate	Cd^{++}	11.2

† If desired, test solutions may be prepared to contain 10 mg. of cation per ml. (Appendix C).

The Lead Ion, Pb^{++}

Pb-1. Review Experiments Pb-1 and Pb-2 in the Preliminary Experiments for Group I (p. 113).

Pb-2. Precipitation of PbS. To 1 ml. of water add 1 drop of the lead nitrate test solution. To this solution add 1 drop of malachite green indicator. Note the color. Refer to the properties of the indicator (p. 159) and state whether the H_3O^+ concentration is above or below 0.2- to 0.3-*M*. To this solution add 1 drop of thymol blue indicator and then add 1-*N* HCl drop by drop, until the solution has a distinct reddish color ($[H_3O^+]$ = 0.2- to 0.3-*M*). About 5 drops will be required. To this reddish solution add 3 drops of a 5% solution of thioacetamide. Set the test tube in a hot (boiling) water bath and fit it tightly with a rubber-tipped filter tube which has a loose plug of cotton or glass fiber in its tapered end (Fig. 4.20). Fill the filter tube about three-quarters full of water. Allow the assembly to remain in the boiling water for 5 minutes and note whether or not a precipitate has formed. Now force the water from the filter tube into the solution containing the lead. Note the formation of a black precipitate. Heat the mixture for another 2 minutes in the boiling water

* Study the discussion of the Procedures for Group II (pp. 157 ff.) and the chemical reactions in the analysis of Group II (pp. 176 ff.) before doing these Preliminary Experiments.

bath. Write the equation for the reaction. Filter off the precipitate through a cotton filter medium.

Test the filtrate for complete precipitation by adding 2 drops of 4-*N* NH_4OH and 1 drop of thioacetamide. If more PbS forms, the bath was not hot enough, the solution was not left in the bath long enough, or the acidity was too high.

Repeat the precipitation using 2-4 dinitrophenol indicator to adjust the acidity of the solution (p. 159).

Pb-3. Test for the Solubility of PbS in Alkaline Sulfide Solutions. To the precipitate on the filter medium add 5 drops of 4-*N* NaOH and 1 drop of thioacetamide. Place the filter tube in a test tube and set the assembly in the hot water bath until the $NaOH\text{-}CH_3CS \cdot NH_2$ solution passes through the precipitate and the filter medium. Has the precipitate dissolved? Wash any undissolved precipitate with water. Compare this result with the action of alkaline sulfide solution on the other sulfides of Group II.

Pb-4. Dissolution of PbS by HNO_3. To the undissolved precipitate add 10 drops of 4-*N* HNO_3. Place the filter tube in a test tube and set the assembly in the hot water bath. Allow the nitric acid solution to pass through the filter medium. Did the precipitate dissolve? Write the equation for the reaction.

Pb-5. Precipitation of $PbSO_4$. Transfer the lead nitrate solution from the test tube in Pb-4 to an evaporation test tube. To this tube add 4 drops of 4-*N* H_2SO_4 and evaporate the solution until SO_3 fumes are evolved. Cool the tube, and then add 1 ml. of water. Loosen the residue from the sides of the tube with a rubber policeman. Did the residue dissolve? What is the residue? Filter it off.

Pb-6. Dissolution of $PbSO_4$ and Precipitation of $PbCrO_4$. To the residue on the filter medium from Pb-5 add a few drops of 1-*N* CH_3COONH_4 and a few drops of water. Force the solution through the filter medium into a test tube. To the solution add 1 drop of 0.5-*M* K_2CrO_4. Note the color of the precipitate. Write equations for the action of CH_3COONH_4 on $PbSO_4$, and for the formation of the yellow precipitate, $PbCrO_4$. This reaction is used as a confirmatory test for Pb^{++}.

The Bismuth Ion, Bi^{3+}

Bi-1. Hydrolysis of $Bi(NO_3)_3$ and Precipitation of Bi_2S_3. To 1 ml. of water add 1 drop of the bismuth nitrate test solution. If a precipitate forms, name the compound and write the equation for the reaction. To the tube containing the bismuth nitrate solution add 1 drop of malachite green indicator. Note the color of the solution. Refer to the properties of this indicator (p. 159) and state whether the H_3O^+ concentration is above or below 0.2- to 0.3-*N*. To this solution add 1-*N* NH_4OH until a blue-green color is obtained. Is a precipitate formed? If so, write the equation for its formation. Add 1 drop of thymol blue indicator to the tube and then add 1-*N* HCl until the solution has a distinct reddish color ($[H_3O^+]$ = 0.2- to 0.3-*M*). (NOTE: Some of the $Bi(OH)_3$ may not dissolve.) To the solution add 3 drops of thioacetamide. Fit the test tube with a filter tube containing water (Fig. 4.20) and place the assembly in the hot water bath. What is the color of the precipitate? Write the equation for the reaction. Force the water from the filter tube into the solution containing the bismuth. Filter off the precipitate.

Bi-2. Dissolution of Bi_2S_3 by HNO_3. (Bi_2S_3, like PbS, CuS, and CdS, is not soluble in $NaOH\text{-}CH_3CS\cdot NH_2$ solution.) To the precipitate from Bi-1 add 10 drops of 4-*N* HNO_3. Place the filter tube in a test tube and set the assembly in the hot water bath. Allow the nitric acid solution to pass through the filter medium. Did the precipitate dissolve? Write the equation for the reaction.

Bi-3. Precipitation of $Bi(OH)_3$ and Solubility in Excess NH_4OH. Transfer the solution from Bi-2 to an evaporation test tube, add 4 drops of 4-*N* H_2SO_4, and evaporate the solution until SO_3 fumes are evolved. Cool the tube, and then add 1 ml. of water. Did the residue dissolve? To the solution of $Bi_2(SO_4)_3$ add 2 drops of 15-*N* NH_4OH. Did a precipitate form? Write the equation for the reaction. (Compare this result with that for Cu-4, Cd-3, and Pb-5.) Filter off the precipitate and wash it with water.

Bi-4. Confirmatory Tests. Reaction of $Bi(OH)_3$ with Sn^{++} and with HCHO. To the precipitate on the filter medium from Bi-3 add 3 drops of 4-*N* NaOH and 1 drop of tin (II) chloride. Note the color of this "spot" test and write the equation for the reaction.

Prepare another precipitate of $Bi(OH)_3$ by adding 1 drop of the bismuth nitrate test solution to 1 ml. of water and then 2 drops of 4-*N* NH_4OH. Filter the solution and add 3 drops of 4-*N* NaOH and 1 drop of formaldehyde solution to the $Bi(OH)_3$ on the filter. Warming the mixture in a hot water bath speeds up the reduction of the Bi^{3+} to Bi°. Describe the result and write an equation for the reaction.

Bi-5. Another Confirmatory Test. Reaction of $Bi(OH)_3$ with KI-Antipyrine Reagent. Prepare another precipitate of $Bi(OH)_3$, as in Bi-4.

Add 1 or 2 drops of KI-antipyrine reagent to the $Bi(OH)_3$ on the filter medium and then acidify the mixture with 1 or 2 drops of 4-*N* CH_3COOH. Describe the color of the product.

The Copper (II) Ion, Cu^{++}

Cu-1. Precipitation of CuS. To 1 ml. of water add 1 drop of the copper nitrate test solution. To this solution add 1 drop of malachite green indicator. Note the color of the solution. Refer to the properties of this indicator (p. 159) and state whether the H_3O^+ concentration is above or below 0.2- to 0.3-*M*. To this solution add 1 drop of thymol blue indicator and then add 1-*N* HCl drop by drop, until the solution has a distinct reddish color ($[H_3O^+]$ = 0.2- to 0.3-*M*). Add 4 drops of a 5% solution of thioacetamide to this reddish solution. Fit the test tube with a filter tube containing water (Fig. 4.20) and place the assembly in the hot water bath. Note the formation of a white precipitate that changes color with the formation of a black precipitate. Write the equations for the reactions. After the assembly has been in the hot water bath for 5 minutes or longer, force the water from the filter tube into the solution containing the CuS precipitate. Filter off the precipitate and wash it with water.

Cu-2. Test for Solubility of CuS in Alkaline Sulfide Solution. To the precipitate on the filter medium add 5 drops of 4-*N* NaOH and 1 drop of thioacetamide. Place the filter tube in a test tube and set the assembly in the hot water bath. Allow the NaOH-$CH_3CS \cdot NH_2$ solution to pass slowly through the precipitate. Wash the undissolved precipitate with water.

Cu-3. Dissolution of CuS by HNO_3. To the undissolved precipitate from Cu-2 add 10 drops of 4-*N* HNO_3. Place the filter tube in a test tube and set the assembly in the hot water bath. Allow the nitric acid solution to pass through the filter medium. Did the precipitate dissolve? Write the equation for the reaction.

Cu-4. Reaction of Cu^{++} with NH_4OH and Dissolution of CuS by KCN. Transfer the copper (II) nitrate solution from the test tube in Cu-3 to an evaporation test tube. To this tube add 4 drops of 4-*N* H_2SO_4 and evaporate the solution until SO_3 fumes are evolved. Cool the tube, and then add 1 ml. of water. Did the residue dissolve? (See Pb-5.) Add 2 drops of 15-*N* NH_4OH to the solution of $CuSO_4$. What is the color of the solution? Write the equation for the reaction. To this solution add 1 drop of thioacetamide and place the tube in the hot water bath. Note the formation of a black precipitate. Write the equation for the reaction. Add 1 or 2 drops of 1-*N* KCN to the tube containing the black precipitate. Did the black precipitate dissolve? Write the equation for the reaction.

The Cadmium Ion, Cd^{++}

Cd-1. Precipitation of CdS. To 1 ml. of water add 1 drop of the cadmium nitrate test solution, and then add 1 drop of malachite green indicator. Note the color of the solution. Refer to the properties of this indicator (p. 159) and state whether the concentration of H_3O^+ is above or below 0.2- to 0.3-*M*. To this solution add 1 drop of thymol blue indicator and then add 1-*N* HCl drop by drop, until the solution has a distinct reddish color ($[H_3O^+]$ = 0.2- to 0.3-*M*). To this solution add 3 drops of thioacetamide. Fit the test tube with a filter tube containing water (Fig. 4.20), and place the assembly in the hot water bath for 5 minutes; note whether a precipitate has formed. Now force the water from the water-sealed filter tube into the solution containing the cadmium. Note the formation of a yellow precipitate and write the equation for the reaction. (Sometimes a reddish-colored precipitate forms in the solution before the dilution.) Filter off the precipitate.

Repeat the precipitation using 2-4 dinitrophenol indicator to adjust the acidity of the solution (p. 159).

Cd-2. Dissolution of CdS by HNO_3. (CdS, like PbS, Bi_2S_3, and CuS, is not soluble in NaOH-$CH_3CS \cdot NH_2$ solution.) To the precipitate from Cd-1 add 10 drops of 4-*N* HNO_3. Place the filter tube in a test tube, set the assembly in the hot water bath, and allow the nitric acid solution to pass through the filter medium. Did the precipitate dissolve? Write the equation for the reaction.

Cd-3. Solubility of $CdSO_4$, Reaction of Cd^{++} with NH_4OH, and Test for Reaction of CdS with KCN. Transfer the solution from Cd-2 to an evaporation test tube, add 4 drops of 4-*N* H_2SO_4, and evaporate the solution until SO_3 fumes are evolved. Cool the tube and add 1 ml. of water. Did the residue dissolve? (Compare with Cu-4, Bi-3, and Pb-5.) Add 2 drops of 15-*N* NH_4OH to the solution of $CdSO_4$. What is the color of the solution? (Compare with Cu-4.) Write the equation for the reaction. Add 1 drop of thioacetamide to this solution and place the tube in the hot water bath. What is the color of the precipitate? Write the equation for the reaction. To the tube containing the precipitate add 1 or 2 drops of 1-*N* KCN. Did the precipitate dissolve? (Compare this with Cu-4.)

IONS OF GROUP II, DIVISION B

Test Solution *	Ion	Concentration (mg./ml.)
0.1-*M* Antimony (III) chloride	Sb^{3+}	12.2
0.1-*M* Tin (II) or (IV) chloride	Sn^{++} or Sn^{4+}	12.0
0.1-*M* Sodium arsenate	AsO_4^{3-}	13.9
0.1-*M* Mercury (II) nitrate	Hg^{++}	20.1

* If desired, test solutions may be prepared to contain 10 mg. of cation per ml. (Appendix C).

The Antimony Ion, Sb^{3+}

Sb-1. Hydrolysis of Sb^{3+} and Precipitation of Sb_2S_3. To 1 ml. of water add 1 drop of the antimony chloride test solution. Did a white precipitate form? If so, write the equation for the reaction. To this solution, with or without the precipitate, add 1 drop of malachite green indicator. Refer to the properties of this indicator (p. 159) and state whether the concentration of H_3O^+ is above or below 0.2- to 0.3-*M*. To this solution add 1-*N* NH_4OH drop by drop, until a blue-green color is obtained. Place the tube in the hot water bath. Did the precipitate dissolve? Write the equation for the reaction. To this solution add 1 drop of thymol blue indicator, and then add 1-*N* HCl drop by drop, until the solution has a distinct reddish color ($[H_3O^+] = 0.2$- to 0.3-*M*). To this solution add 3 drops of a 5% solution of thioacetamide. Fit the test tube with a filter tube containing water (Fig. 4.20), and place the assembly in the hot water bath. Note the color of the precipitate and write the equation for the reaction. Filter off the precipitate and wash it with water.

Repeat the precipitation using 2-4 dinitrophenol to adjust the acidity of the solution (p. 159).

Sb-2. Dissolution of Sb_2S_3 by Alkaline Sulfide Solutions. To the precipitate on the filter medium add 5 drops of 4-*N* NaOH and 1 drop of thioacetamide. Place the filter tube in a test tube and set the assembly in the hot water bath. Did the precipitate dissolve? Write the equation for the reaction. Wash the filter medium with a little water, forcing the solution into the test tube.

Sb-3. Reprecipitation of Sb_2S_3 from SbS_3^{3-} by HCl. To the solution in the test tube add 1 drop of bromcresol green indicator. To this solution add 6-*N* HCl until the indicator has turned yellow (pH about 4) and an orange-yellow precipitate has formed. Write the equation for the reaction. Filter off the precipitate. (Bromcresol green, yellow — pH = 4.0 : green — pH = 5.6.)

Sb-4. Dissolution of Sb_2S_3 by HCl. To the precipitate on the filter medium from Sb-3 add 10 drops of 6-*N* HCl. Place the filter tube in a test tube and set the assembly in the hot water bath. Allow the HCl solution to pass slowly through the filter medium. Did the precipitate dissolve? (NOTE: If the precipitate has not dissolved completely, repass the hot HCl solution through the filter medium.) Write the equation for the reaction. Wash the filter medium with about 10 drops of water.

Sb-5. Confirmatory Test. Reprecipitation of Sb_2S_3. Transfer the solution from Sb-4 to an evaporation test tube and evaporate it to incipient dryness. To the residue in the evaporation test tube add 1 drop of 6-*N* HCl and 1 ml. of water. Transfer the solution from the evaporation test tube to the smaller test tube, add 1 drop of thioacetamide, and place the tube in the hot water bath for 1 minute or longer. Note the color of the precipitate and write the equation for the reaction.

The Tin Ions, Sn^{++} and Sn^{4+}

Sn-1. Precipitation of SnS or SnS_2. To 1 ml. of water add 1 drop of the tin chloride test solution. To this solution add 1 drop of the malachite green indicator. Note the color of the solution. From the properties of this indicator (p. 159), state whether the concentration of H_3O^+ is above or below 0.2- to 0.3-*M*. If the color of the solution is yellow, add 1-*N* NH_4OH until the color of the indicator changes to a blue-green with the formation of a precipitate. Write the equation for the reaction. To this solution add 1 drop of thymol blue and then add 1-*N* HCl until a distinct reddish color appears. ($[H_3O^+]$ = 0.2- to 0.3-*M*.) Did the precipitate dissolve? Write the equation for the reaction. To this solution add 3 drops of a solution of thioacetamide. Fit the test tube with a filter tube containing water (Fig. 4.20) and place the assembly in the hot water bath. Allow it to remain there for about 5 minutes. Note the color of the precipitate and write the equation for the reaction. (NOTE: SnS is brown in color; SnS_2 has a yellow color. Adsorption of the indicator by SnS_2 may change its color somewhat.) Filter off the precipitate and wash it with water.

Repeat the precipitation using 2-4 dinitrophenol to adjust the acidity of the solution (p. 159).

Sn-2. Dissolution of the Sulfides of Tin by Alkaline Sulfide Solutions. Add 10 drops of 4-*N* NaOH and 1 drop of thioacetamide to the precipitate on the filter medium from Sn-1. Place the filter tube in a test tube and set the assembly in the hot water bath; allow the solution to become hot and to pass slowly through the filter medium. Did the precipitate dissolve? Write the equation for the reaction. Add 1 drop of bromcresol green to the solution in the test tube. (NOTE: If SnS_2^{--} is present, the indicator will become colorless; if SnS_3^{--} is present, the indicator will have a blue-green color.) To the colorless or blue-green solution add 6-*N* HCl until a precipitate is formed, or until the blue-green solution becomes yellow (pH about 4). Note the color of the precipitate and write the equation for the reaction. Place the tube in the hot water bath for 1 minute or longer. Filter off the precipitate.

Sn-3. Dissolution of the Tin Sulfides by HCl. Add 10 drops of 6-*N* HCl to the precipitate on the filter medium from Sn-2. Place the filter tube in a test tube and set the assembly in the hot water bath; allow the HCl solution to become hot and to pass slowly through the filter medium. Did the precipitate dissolve? Write the equation for the reaction.

Sn-4. Confirmatory Test for Tin. Reaction with m-Nitro-phenyl-arsonic Acid. Transfer the solution from Sn-3 to an evaporation test tube and evaporate it to incipient dryness. To the residue add 1 drop of 6-*N* HCl and 1 ml. of water. Transfer the solution from the evaporation test tube to a smaller test tube and add 1 drop of malachite green indicator and 5 drops of m-nitro-phenyl-arsonic acid. Place the tube in the hot water bath. Note the color of the precipitate.

The Arsenate Ion, AsO_4^{3-}

As-1. Precipitation of As_2S_3. To 1 ml. of water add 1 drop of the arsenate test solution. To this solution add 1 drop of malachite green indicator. Note the color of the solution, and by reference to the properties of this indicator state whether the concentration of H_3O^+ is above or below 0.2- to 0.3-*M*. To this solution add 1 drop of thymol blue indicator and then add 1-*N* HCl drop by drop, until the solution has a distinct reddish color. To this solution add 3 drops of a 5% solution of thioacetamide. Fit the test tube with a filter tube containing water (Fig. 4.20), and place the assembly in the hot water bath. Note the colors of the precipitates that form. The white precipitate formed first is free sulfur. The final yellow precipitate is As_2S_3. Write equations for these reactions. Allow the assembly to remain in the hot water bath for 5 minutes or longer. Filter off the precipitate and wash it with water.

Repeat the precipitation using 2-4 dinitrophenol indicator to adjust the acidity of the solution.

As-2. Dissolution of As_2S_3 by Alkaline Sulfide Solutions. Add 5 drops of 4-*N* NaOH and 1 drop of thioacetamide to the precipitate on the filter medium from As-1. (NOTE: The As_2S_3 precipitate dissolves readily in the $NaOH\text{-}CH_3CS \cdot NH_2$ solution.) Write the equation for the reaction. Force the solution into a test tube and wash the filter medium with a little water.

As-3. Precipitation of As_2S_3 from Solutions of AsS_3^{3-}. To the test tube add 1 drop of bromcresol green indicator; then add 6-*N* HCl until the solution becomes yellow (pH about 4) and a precipitate forms. Place the test tube in the hot water bath for 1 minute or longer. Write the equation for the reaction. Filter off the precipitate.

As-4. Test for Solubility of As_2S_3 in HCl and in H_2O_2. Add 5 drops of 6-*N* HCl to the precipitate on the filter medium from As-3. Place the filter tube in a test tube and set the assembly in the hot water bath. After the solution is hot, wash the precipitate with water. Add 5 drops of 4-*N* NH_4OH and 1 drop of H_2O_2 to the precipitate on the filter medium. Did the precipitate dissolve? Write the equation for the reaction.

As-5. Confirmatory Test. Formation of NH_4MgAsO_4. To the solution from As-4 add 4 drops of magnesium mixture reagent. Place the tube in the hot water bath. Note the formation of a white precipitate. Write the equation for the reaction. Filter off the precipitate and wash it with water.

As-6. Confirmatory Test. Reaction with Ammonium Molybdate. Add 5 drops of 1-*N* $(NH_4)_2MoO_4$ to a test tube. Place the filter tube from As-5 in a test tube and add 10 drops of 4-*N* HNO_3 to the filter tube. Force the acid through the filter medium into the test tube. Place the test tube in the hot water bath and allow it to remain there for several minutes. Note the formation of a yellow crystalline precipitate. Write the equation for the reaction. (NOTE: The crystalline precipitate has the formula $(NH_4)_2AsO_4 \cdot 12MoO_3$.)

The Mercury (II) Ion, Hg^{++}

Hg-1. Precipitation of HgS. To 1 ml. of water add 1 drop of the mercuric nitrate test solution, and then add 1 drop of malachite green indicator. Note the color of the solution and by reference to the properties of this indicator (p. 159) state whether the concentration of H_3O^+ is above or below 0.2- to 0.3-*M*. Add 1 drop of thymol blue indicator to this solution and then add 1-*N* HCl drop by drop, until the solution has a distinct reddish color. To this solution add 3 drops of a 5% solution of thioacetamide. Fit the test tube with a filter tube containing water (Fig. 4.20) and place the assembly in the hot water bath. Allow it to remain there for 1 or 2 minutes. Note the color of the precipitate and write the equation for the reaction. Filter off the precipitate and wash it with water.

Hg-2. Dissolution of HgS by Alkaline Sulfide Solutions. Add 5 drops of 4-*N* NaOH and 1 drop of thioacetamide to the precipitate on the filter medium. Place the filter tube in a test tube and set the assembly in the hot water bath. Allow the tubes to become hot and let the NaOH-$CH_3CS \cdot NH_2$ pass slowly through the filter medium. Has the precipitate dissolved? Write the equation for the reaction. (NOTE: If the filter medium was not packed tightly, the NaOH-$CH_3CS \cdot NH_2$ solution may pass through the medium before it has become hot and acted on the precipitate. In this case, return the solution from the test tube to the filter tube, and allow it to pass through the filter medium again.) Wash the filter with about 10 drops of water.

Hg-3. Precipitation of HgS from Solutions of HgS_2^{--}. Add 1 drop of bromcresol green indicator to the test tube containing the HgS_2^{--} solution. Then add 6-*N* HCl until the indicator has turned yellow and a black precipitate has formed. Write the equation for the reaction. Filter off the precipitate. (Bromcresol green, yellow — pH = 4.0 : green — pH = 5.6.)

Hg-4. Test for Solubility of HgS in HCl. To the precipitate on the filter medium add 10 drops of 6-*N* HCl. Place the filter tube in a test tube and set the assembly in the hot water bath; allow the HCl solution to pass through the precipitate. Has the precipitate dissolved?

Hg-5. Dissolution of HgS and Confirmatory Test for Hg^{++}. To the precipitate from Hg-4 add 2 drops of 5% NaClO and 2 or 3 drops of 1-*N* HCl. Place the filter tube in a test tube and set the assembly in the hot water bath. Did the precipitate dissolve? Write the equation for the reaction. To the test tube containing the Hg^{++} solution add 1 drop of 15-*N* NH_4OH, 1 drop of 1-*N* NH_4I, and from 2 to 5 drops of 4-*N* NaOH. What is the color of the precipitate? Write the equation for the reaction. (See Procedure 3, Group I, page 129.)

SUMMARY OF REACTIONS OF GROUP II CATIONS

Reagents	Bismuth—$Bi(NO_3)_3$	Copper—$Cu(NO_3)_2$	Cadmium—$Cd(NO_3)_2$
Acids	Metal $Bi + 3NO_3^- + 6H_3O^+ \rightleftharpoons Bi^{3+} + 3NO_2\uparrow + 9H_2O$ Bi is also dissolved by aqua regia, hot concd. H_2SO_4, but not by HCl or other nonoxidizing acids.	Metal $3Cu + 2NO_3^- + 8H_3O^+ \rightleftharpoons 3Cu^{++} + 2NO\uparrow + 12H_2O$ $Cu + H_2SO_4 + 2H_3O^+ \rightleftharpoons Cu^{++} + SO_2\uparrow + 4H_2O$ Cu is not dissolved by HCl or other nonoxidizing acids.	Metal $Cd + 2H_3O^+ \rightleftharpoons Cd^{++} + H_2\uparrow + 2H_2O$ $3Cd + 2NO_3^- + 8H_3O^+ \rightleftharpoons 3Cd^{++} + 2NO\uparrow + 12H_2O$ Cd is soluble in nonoxidizing acids as well as in oxidizing acids.
Precipitants	Insoluble compounds: Bi_2S_3, $BiPO_4$, $Bi(OH)_3$, $Bi_2(C_2O_4)_3$, $Bi_2(CrO_4)_3$, $Bi(IO_3)_3$, $Bi_2(CO_3)_3$, BiOCl, $BiONO_3$, BiOI, $(BiO)_2CrO_4$.	Insoluble cuprous compounds: CuCl, CuBr, CuI, CuSCN, CuCN, Cu_2S, Cu_2O, etc. Cupric compounds: CuS, $Cu_2Fe(CN)_6$, $Cu_3[Fe(CN)_6]_2$, $Cu(OH)_2$, $CuCO_3$, $CuCrO_4$, CuC_2O_4, $Cu_3(PO_4)_2$, $Cu(IO_3)_2$.	Insoluble salts: CdS, $Cd(OH)_2$, $CdCO_3$, CdC_2O_4, $CdCrO_4$, $Cd_2Fe(CN)_6$, $Cd_3(PO_4)_2$, $CdSO_3$.
Excess reagent	Complex ions: BiO^+, $BiCl_4^-$ in concd. HCl, $Bi(NO_3)_4^-$ in concd. HNO_3.	Complex ions: $Cu(CN)_4^{3-}$, $CuCl_2^-$, $Cu(NH_3)_2^+$, $Cu(NH_3)_4^{++}$.	Complex ions: $Cd(NH_3)_4^{++}$, $Cd(CN)_4^=$, $CdCl_4^=$, $CdBr_4^=$, $CdI_4^=$.
H_2S	$2Bi^{3+} + 3S^= \rightleftharpoons \underset{\text{brown}}{\underline{Bi_2S_3}}\downarrow$ Bi_2S_3 is soluble in hot 4-*N* HNO_3 and in concd. HCl, with the formation of $Bi^{3+} + S$ and $BiCl_4^- + H_2S$ respectively. The precipitate is not soluble in Na_2S, NaOH, or dilute acids.	$Cu^{++} + S^= \rightleftharpoons \underset{\text{black}}{\underline{CuS}}\downarrow$ CuS is soluble in hot 4-*N* HNO_3, concd. HCl, and KCN solution, with the formation of $Cu^{++} + S$, $Cu^{++} + H_2S$, and $Cu(CN)_4^{3-} + S^= + CNO^-$ respectively. CuS is not soluble in NaOH or Na_2S.	$Cd^{++} + S^= \rightleftharpoons \underset{\text{yellow}}{\underline{CdS}}\downarrow$ CdS is soluble in 4-*N* HNO_3, concd. HCl, and concentrated solutions of halides, with the formation of $Cd^{++} + S$, $CdCl_2 + H_2S$, and $CdI_4^= + S^=$ respectively. CdS is not soluble in solutions of KCN, NaOH, or Na_2S.

NH_4OH	$Bi^{3+} + 3NH_3 + 3H_2O \rightleftharpoons \underset{\text{white}}{\underline{Bi(OH)_3}}\downarrow + 3NH_4^+$ $BiO^+ + NH_3 + H_2O \rightleftharpoons \underset{\text{white}}{\underline{BiOOH}}\downarrow + NH_4^+$ The precipitates do not dissolve in excess NH_4OH. NH_4^+ does not prevent the formation of the precipitates. They are soluble in HNO_3 or warm HCl. $Bi(OH)_3$ is reduced by sodium stannite to Bi (black).	$Cu^{++} + NO_3^- + NH_3 + H_2O \rightleftharpoons \underset{\text{bluish-green}}{\underline{Cu(OH)NO_3}}\downarrow + NH_4^+$ $Cu(OH)NO_3 + 4NH_3 \rightleftharpoons \underset{\text{deep blue}}{\underline{Cu(NH_3)_4^{++}}} + OH^- + NO_3^-$ Excess NH_4OH dissolves the precipitate. NH_4^+ prevents its formation.	$Cd^{++} + 2NH_3 + 2H_2O \rightleftharpoons \underset{\text{white}}{\underline{Cd(OH)_2}}\downarrow + 2NH_4^+$ $Cd(OH)_2 + 4NH_3 \rightleftharpoons Cd(NH_3)_4^{++} + 2OH^-$ Excess NH_4OH dissolves $Cd(OH)_2$. NH_4^+ prevents its formation.
NaOH	$Bi^{3+} + 3OH^- \rightleftharpoons \underset{\text{white}}{\underline{Bi(OH)_3}}\downarrow$ $BiO^+ + OH^- \rightleftharpoons \underset{\text{white}}{\underline{BiOOH}}\downarrow$ The precipitates are not soluble in excess NaOH.	$Cu^{++} + 2OH^- \rightleftharpoons \underset{\text{blue}}{\underline{Cu(OH)_2}}\downarrow$ $Cu(OH)_2$ is not soluble in excess NaOH but decomposes to black CuO when heated.	$Cd^{++} + 2OH^- \rightleftharpoons \underset{\text{white}}{\underline{Cd(OH)_2}}\downarrow$ $Cd(OH)_2$ is not soluble in excess NaOH.
Na_2CO_3	$2Bi^{3+} + 3CO_3^= \rightleftharpoons \underset{\text{white}}{\underline{Bi_2(CO_3)_3}}\downarrow$ $2BiO^+ + CO_3^= \rightleftharpoons \underset{\text{white}}{\underline{(BiO)_2CO_3}}\downarrow$ The precipitates are not soluble in excess Na_2CO_3. They dissolve in dilute HNO_3.	$2Cu^{++} + CO_3^= + 2OH^- \rightleftharpoons \underset{\text{blue}}{\underline{CuCO_3 \cdot Cu(OH)_2}}\downarrow$ Insoluble in excess reagent, but forms CuO when boiled. The precipitate dissolves in solutions of NH_4OH, KCN, and in acids.	$Cd^{++} + CO_3^= \rightleftharpoons \underset{\text{white}}{\underline{CdCO_3}}\downarrow$ $CdCO_3$ is insoluble in excess reagent but dissolves in solutions of NH_4OH, KCN, and in acids.

SUMMARY OF REACTIONS OF GROUP II CATIONS (*Continued*)

Reagents	Bismuth—$Bi(NO_3)_3$	Copper—$Cu(NO_3)_2$	Cadmium—$Cd(NO_3)_2$
K_2CrO_4	$2Bi^{3+} + 3CrO_4^{=} \rightleftharpoons \underline{Bi_2(CrO_4)_3}\downarrow$ (yellow) $2BiO^{+} + CrO_4^{=} \rightleftharpoons \underline{(BiO)_2CrO_4}\downarrow$ (yellow) The precipitate is soluble in dilute HNO_3, but not in solutions of NaOH (cf. $PbCrO_4$).	$Cu^{++} + CrO_4^{=} \rightleftharpoons \underline{CuCrO_4}\downarrow$ (brownish-red) The precipitate is soluble in NH_4OH, KCN, and dilute acids, but not in solutions of NaOH (cf. $PbCrO_4$).	$Cd^{++} + CrO_4^{=} \rightleftharpoons \underline{CdCrO_4}\downarrow$ (yellow) The precipitate is soluble in NH_4OH, KCN, and dilute acids, but not in solutions of NaOH (cf. $PbCrO_4$).
$K_4Fe(CN)_6$	$4Bi^{3+} + 3Fe(CN)_6^{4-} \rightleftharpoons \underline{Bi_4[Fe(CN)_6]_3}\downarrow$ (yellowish-white) The precipitate is soluble in excess HNO_3 or HCl.	$2Cu^{++} + Fe(CN)_6^{4-} \rightleftharpoons \underline{Cu_2Fe(CN)_6}\downarrow$ (reddish-brown) The precipitate is insoluble in CH_3COOH or very dilute HNO_3, but is soluble in NH_4OH.	$2Cd^{++} + Fe(CN)_6^{4-} \rightleftharpoons \underline{Cd_2Fe(CN)_6}\downarrow$ (white) The precipitate is soluble in dilute HNO_3 or HCl and concd. NH_4OH, but not in CH_3COOH.
NaOH + $SnCl_2$	$\underline{2Bi(OH)_3} + 3Sn(OH)_4^{=} \rightleftharpoons \underline{2Bi}\downarrow + 3Sn(OH)_6^{=}$ (black) Excess NaOH is required.	$\underline{2Cu(OH)_2} + Sn(OH)_4^{=} + 2Cl^{-} \rightleftharpoons \underline{2CuCl}\downarrow + Sn(OH)_6^{=} + 2OH^{-}$ (white) This reaction takes place only in concentrated solutions.	$Cd^{++} + 2OH^{-} \rightleftharpoons \underline{Cd(OH)_2}\downarrow$ (white) $Cd(OH)_2$ is not reduced by $Sn(OH)_4^{=}$.
H_2O	$\underline{Bi(NO_3)_3} \rightleftharpoons Bi^{3+} + 3NO_3^{-}$ $Bi^{3+} + 3NO_3^{-} + 3H_2O \rightleftharpoons \underline{BiONO_3}\downarrow + 2H_3O^{+} + 2NO_3^{-}$ (white) Most soluble bismuth salts are hydrolyzed. The products are soluble in strong acids but not in tartaric acid (cf. antimony).	$Cu(NO_3)_2$ is hydrolyzed to a small extent to form an acid solution, but no precipitate forms.	Very little hydrolysis occurs.

Reagents	Mercury Mercuric Salts—$Hg(NO_3)_2$	Antimony Antimonous Salts—$SbCl_3$	Antimony Antimonic Salts—$SbCl_5$
Acids	Metal $\underline{Hg} + \underset{excess}{2NO_3^-} + 4H_3O^+ \rightleftharpoons$ $Hg^{++} + 2NO_2\uparrow + 6H_2O$ $\underline{3Hg} + \underset{aqua\ regia}{2NO_3^- + 12Cl^-} + 8H_3O^+ \rightleftharpoons$ $3HgCl_4^= + 2NO\uparrow + 12H_2O$ Mercury is also dissolved by excess hot concd. H_2SO_4 and by HClO (cf. Hg_2^{++}).	Metal $\underline{2Sb} + 2NO_3^- + 2H_3O^+ \rightleftharpoons$ $\underset{white}{\underline{Sb_2O_3}}\downarrow + 2NO\uparrow + 3H_2O$ $\underline{Sb_2O_3} + 2C_4H_4O_6^= + 2H_3O^+ \rightleftharpoons$ $2[(SbO)C_4H_4O_6]^- + 3H_2O$ Sb_2O_3 which is formed by reaction of Sb with dilute HNO_3 is dissolved by tartaric acid to form the complex antimonyl tartrate ion. Sb_2O_3 also dissolves in HCl, $H_2C_2O_4$, and in alkali hydroxides to form $SbCl_4^-$, $[(SbO)C_2O_4]^-$, and $Sb(OH)_4^-$ or SbO_2^- respectively.	Metal $\underline{2Sb} + 10NO_3^- + 10H_3O^+ \rightleftharpoons$ $\underset{white}{\underline{Sb_2O_5}}\downarrow + 10NO_2\uparrow + 15H_2O$ $\underline{Sb} + 5NO_3^- + 6Cl^- + 10H_3O^+ \rightleftharpoons$ $SbCl_6^- + 5NO_2\uparrow + 15H_2O$ With concd. HCl plus HNO_3 no white precipitate of Sb_2O_5 is formed. Sb_2O_5 is soluble in concd. HCl, tartaric acid, and alkali hydroxides, with the formation of $SbCl_6^-$, $[(SbO_2)C_4H_4O_6]^-$, $Sb(OH)_6^-$, or SbO_4^{3-} respectively.
Precipitants	Insoluble salts: HgS, HgO, HgI_2, $Hg(SCN)_2$, $HgSO_4$, $Hg(NH_2)Cl$, $HgCrO_4$, $HgCO_3$, HgC_2O_4, $Hg_2Fe(CN)_6$, HOHgNHHgI, $HgCl_2\cdot HgS$.	Insoluble salts: Sb_2S_3, Sb_2O_3, $Sb(OH)_3$, SbOOH, SbOCl, $Sb_2(SO_4)_3$.	Insoluble salts: Sb_2S_5, Sb_2O_5, H_3SbO_4, SbO_2Cl, $NaSb(OH)_6$.
Excess reagent	Complex ions: $Hg(CN)_4^=$, $HgI_4^=$, $Hg(SCN)_4^=$, $HgBr_4^=$, $HgCl_4^=$, $HgS_2^=$.	Complex ions: $Sb(OH)_4^-$ or SbO_2^-, SbO^+, $SbCl_4^-$, SbS_2^-, $[(SbO)C_4H_4O_6]^-$, $[(SbO)C_2O_4]^-$.	Complex ions: $Sb(OH)_6^-$ or SbO_3^-, SbO_4^{3-}, SbO_2^+, $SbCl_6^-$, SbS_4^{3-}, $[(SbO_2)C_4H_4O_6]^-$.

SUMMARY OF REACTIONS OF GROUP II CATIONS (*Continued*)

Reagents	Mercury Mercuric Salts—$Hg(NO_3)_2$	Antimony Antimonous Salts—$SbCl_3$	Antimony Antimonic Salts—$SbCl_5$
H_2S	$Hg^{++} + S^{=} \rightleftharpoons \underset{\text{black}}{\underline{HgS}} \downarrow$ HgS is insoluble in HNO_3, but it dissolves in HCl + HNO_3 or HCl + NaClO, with the formation of $HgCl_4^{=}$ + S. It does not dissolve in NaOH or $(NH_4)_2S$, but does dissolve in Na_2S, with the formation of $HgS_2^{=}$. HgS is reprecipitated by addition of acid to a solution of $HgS_2^{=}$.	$2Sb^{3+} + 3S^{=} \rightleftharpoons \underset{\text{orange}}{\underline{Sb_2S_3}} \downarrow$ Sb_2S_3 is soluble in hot 6-*N* HCl, 4-*N* HNO_3, $(NH_4)_2S$, NaOH, and Na_2S, with the formation of $SbCl_4^-$, Sb^{3+} + S, SbS_2^-, $Sb(OH)_4^-$ + SbS_2^-, and SbS_2^- respectively. Sb_2S_3 is reprecipitated from a solution of SbS_2^- by the addition of an acid.	$2SbCl_6^- + 5S^{=} \rightleftharpoons \underset{\text{orange}}{\underline{Sb_2S_5}} \downarrow + 12Cl^-$ Sb_2S_5 is soluble in hot 6-*N* HCl, 4-*N* HNO_3, $(NH_4)_2S$, NaOH, and Na_2S, with the formation of $SbCl_6^-$, $H_2SbO_4^-$ + S, SbS_4^{3-}, SbS_4^{3-} + SbO_3S^{3-}, and SbS_4^{3-} respectively. Sb_2S_5 is reprecipitated from a solution of SbS_4^{3-} by the addition of an acid.
NH_4OH	$Hg^{++} + NO_3^- + NH_3 + H_2O \rightleftharpoons \underset{\text{white}}{\underline{HgNH_2NO_3}} \downarrow + H_3O^+$ The precipitate is insoluble in excess NH_4OH, and is only slightly soluble in acids.	$Sb^{3+} + 3NH_3 + 3H_2O \rightleftharpoons 3NH_4^+ + \underline{Sb(OH)_3} \downarrow$ or $\underline{H_3SbO_3}$ $SbO^+ + NH_3 + H_2O \rightleftharpoons NH_4^+ + \underline{(SbO)OH} \downarrow$ or $\underline{HSbO_2}$ $Sb(OH)_3$ gradually changes to meta antimonous acid, $HSbO_2$, and then to Sb_2O_3. The precipitates are insoluble in excess NH_4OH, but dissolve in solutions of NaOH, Na_2CO_3, and HCl.	$SbCl_6^- + 5NH_3 + 6H_2O \rightleftharpoons \underset{\text{white}}{\underline{HSb(OH)_6}} \downarrow + 6Cl^- + 5NH_4^+$ $SbO_2^+ + NH_3 + H_2O \rightleftharpoons NH_4^+ + \underline{(SbO_2)OH} \downarrow$ or $\underline{HSbO_3}$ $\underline{HSbO_3} \xrightarrow{H_2O} \underline{H_3SbO_4} \xrightarrow{2H_2O} \underline{HSb(OH)_6}$ Antimonic acid is only slightly soluble in water and in excess NH_4OH. It dissolves readily in solutions of NaOH, Na_2CO_3, or HCl.
NaOH	$Hg^{++} + 2OH^- \rightleftharpoons \underset{\text{yellow}}{\underline{HgO}} \downarrow + H_2O$ HgO is soluble in warm dilute acids but not in excess alkali hydroxide.	$Sb^{3+} + 3OH^- \rightleftharpoons \underline{Sb(OH)_3} \downarrow$ or $\underline{H_3SbO_3}$ $SbO^+ + OH^- \rightleftharpoons \underline{SbO(OH)} \downarrow$ or $\underline{HSbO_2}$ (See NH_4OH.)	$SbCl_6^- + 5OH^- + H_2O \rightleftharpoons \underline{HSb(OH)_6} \downarrow + 6Cl^-$ $SbO_2^+ + OH^- \rightleftharpoons \underline{(SbO_2)OH} \downarrow$ (See NH_4OH.)

Na_2CO_3	$4Hg^{++} + CO_3^{=} + 6OH^- \rightleftharpoons \underset{\text{reddish-brown}}{\underline{HgCO_3 \cdot 3HgO}} + 3H_2O$ The solid decomposes to HgO and CO_2 when heated.	(Same as for NaOH.)	(Same as for NaOH.)
K_2CrO_4	$Hg^{++} + CrO_4^{=} \rightleftharpoons \underset{\text{reddish-yellow}}{\underline{HgCrO}} \downarrow$ $HgCrO_4$ dissolves in acids.	—	—
$SnCl_2$	$2Hg^{++} + Sn^{++} + 8Cl^- \rightleftharpoons \underset{\text{white}}{\underline{Hg_2Cl_2}} \downarrow + SnCl_6^{=}$ $\underline{Hg_2Cl_2} + Sn^{++} + 4Cl^- \rightleftharpoons \underset{\text{black}}{\underline{2Hg}} \downarrow + SnCl_6^{=}$ The mixture of Hg_2Cl_2 and Hg obtained with excess $SnCl_2$ is gray.	—	—
Zn, Sn, Al, Fe, or Mg in acid solution	$Hg^{++} + \underline{Fe} \rightleftharpoons \underset{\text{black}}{\underline{Hg}} \downarrow + Fe^{++}$ Cu also displaces Hg^{++}, which then amalgamates with the excess Cu ("penny test"). Cu should be cleaned first with dilute HNO_3.	$2Sb^{3+} + \underline{3Fe} \rightleftharpoons \underset{\text{black}}{\underline{2Sb}} \downarrow + 3Fe^{++}$ The flaky black precipitate of Sb is not soluble in dilute HCl but is soluble in dilute HNO_3 + tartaric acid (cf. arsenic).	$3SbCl_6^- + \underline{5Fe} \rightleftharpoons \underset{\text{black}}{\underline{3Sb}} \downarrow + 5Fe^{3+} + 18Cl^-$ With Sn plus Pt foil a black deposit of Sb is formed on the Pt.
H_2O	$\underline{Hg(NO_3)_2} \rightleftharpoons Hg^{++} + 2NO_3^-$ $Hg^{++} + 2NO_3^- + 2H_2O \rightleftharpoons \underset{\text{white}}{\underline{Hg(OH)NO_3}} \downarrow + H_3O^+ + NO_3^-$ A small excess of acid prevents hydrolysis.	$SbCl_3 + 3H_2O \rightleftharpoons \underset{\text{white}}{\underline{SbOCl}} \downarrow + 2H_3O^+ + 2Cl^-$ Most antimonous salts hydrolyze. Excess HCl or tartaric acid dissolves the precipitate. H_2S converts it to Sb_2S_3.	$SbCl_5 + 6H_2O \rightleftharpoons \underset{\text{white}}{\underline{SbO_2Cl}} \downarrow + 4H_3O^+ + 4Cl^-$ Excess HCl or tartaric acid dissolves the precipitate. H_2S converts it to Sb_2S_5.

SUMMARY OF REACTIONS OF GROUP II CATIONS (*Continued*)

Reagents	Arsenic		Tin	
	Arsenious Compounds—Arsenites $NaAsO_2$	Arsenic Compounds—Arsenates Na_3AsO_4	Stannous Salts $SnCl_2$	Stannic Salts $SnCl_4$
Acids	Metal $As + NO_3^- + H_3O^+ \rightleftharpoons HAsO_2 + NO\uparrow + H_2O$ Arsenic is dissolved by dilute HNO_3, with the formation of arsenious acid. Concd. H_2SO_4 forms As_2O_3.	$As + 5NO_3^- + 4H_3O^+ \rightleftharpoons H_2AsO_4^- + 5NO_2\uparrow + 5H_2O$ $2As + 5ClO^- + 6OH^- \rightleftharpoons 2AsO_4^{3-} + 5Cl^- + 3H_2O$ Concd. HNO_3, aqua regia, $NaClO$, Na_2O_2, and hot concd. KOH dissolve As, with the formation of arsenates.	Metal $Sn + 2H_3O^+ \rightleftharpoons Sn^{++} + H_2\uparrow + 2H_2O$ Sn dissolves in HCl, dilute HNO_3, and KOH, with the formation of $Sn^{++} + H_2$, $Sn^{++} + NH_4^+$, and $Sn(OH)_4^= + H_2$ respectively.	$Sn + 4NO_3^- + 4H_3O^+ \rightleftharpoons \underset{\text{white}}{\underline{H_2SnO_3}}\downarrow + 4NO_2\uparrow + 5H_2O$ Concd. HNO_3 forms insoluble metastannic acid, and aqua regia forms $SnCl_6^=$.
Precipitants	Insoluble compounds: As_2S_3, As_2O_3, Ag_3AsO_3, $Hg_3(AsO_3)_2$, $Mg_3(AsO_3)_2$, $Pb(AsO_2)_2$.	Insoluble compounds: As_2S_5, Ag_3AsO_4, $MgNH_4AsO_4$, Hg_3AsO_4, $Hg_3(AsO_4)_2$, $Cu_3(AsO_4)_2$, $Ba_3(AsO_4)_2$, $Ca_3(AsO_4)_2$, $(NH_4)_3AsO_4(MoO_3)_{12}$.	Insoluble compounds: SnS, $Sn(OH)_2$, $Sn_3(PO_4)_2$, $Sn_2Fe(CN)_6$, $Sn_3[Fe(CN)_6]_2$.	Insoluble compounds: SnS_2, $Sn(OH)_4$, $H_2SnO_3(SnO_2 \cdot xH_2O)$, $SnFe(CN)_6$.
Excess reagent	Complex ions: AsO_2^- (meta), AsO_3^{3-} (ortho), AsS_2^-, AsS_3^{3-}, $AsCl_4^-$.	Complex ions: AsO_3^- (meta), AsO_4^{3-} (ortho), AsO_3S^{3-}, AsS_4^{3-}, $AsCl_6^-$.	Complex ions: $Sn(OH)_4^=$ or $SnO_2^=$, $SnCl_4^=$.	Complex ions: $Sn(OH)_6^=$ or $SnO_3^=$, $SnS_3^=$, $SnCl_6^=$, $Sn(C_2O_4)_3^=$.

H_2S	$2As^{3+} + 3S^{=} \rightleftharpoons \underset{\text{yellow}}{\underline{As_2S_3}} \downarrow$ $2HAsO_2 + 3H_2S \rightleftharpoons \underset{\text{yellow}}{\underline{As_2S_3}} \downarrow + 4H_2O$ As_2S_3 is not precipitated from alkaline solutions. It is soluble in solutions of NH_4OH, $NaOH$, Na_2S, concd. HNO_3, and $HClO$, with the formation of $AsO_2^- + AsS_2^-$, $AsO_2^- + AsS_2^-$, AsS_2^-, $H_2AsO_4^- + S$, and $H_2AsO_4^- + S$ respectively. As_2S_3 is not soluble in concd. HCl. The sulfides of arsenic are reprecipitated when solutions of their thio-ions are acidified.	$2H_2AsO_4^- + 5H_2S + 2H_3O^+ \rightleftharpoons \underset{\text{yellow}}{\underline{As_2S_5}} \downarrow + 10H_2O$ $H_2AsO_4^- + H_2S \rightleftharpoons H_2AsO_3S^- + H_2O$ $H_2AsO_3S^- + H_3O^+ \rightleftharpoons HAsO_2 + 2H_2O + \underline{S} \downarrow$ $2HAsO_2 + 3H_2S \rightleftharpoons As_2S_3 + 4H_2O$ In concd. HCl solution As_2S_5 is formed very slowly. In more dilute acid solution $H_2AsO_4^-$ is reduced to $HAsO_2$, and a mixture of As_2S_5, As_2S_3, and S is obtained. As_2S_5 is soluble in solutions of NH_4OH, $NaOH$, Na_2S, concd. HNO_3, and $HClO$ with the formation of $AsS_4^{3-} + AsO_3S^{3-}$, $AsS_4^{3-} + AsO_3S^{3-}$, AsS_4^{3-}, $H_2AsO_4^- + S$, and $H_2AsO_4^- + S$. As_2S_5 is not soluble in concd. HCl.	$Sn^{++} + S^{=} \rightleftharpoons \underset{\text{brown}}{\underline{SnS}} \downarrow$ SnS precipitates in 0.3-*N* HCl, but is dissolved by hot 6-*N* HCl. SnS is not soluble in solutions of NH_4OH, $NaOH$, or Na_2S. It is oxidized to SnS_2 and dissolved as $SnS_3^{=}$ by Na_2S_2.	$SnCl_6^{=} + 2S^{=} \rightleftharpoons \underset{\text{yellow}}{\underline{SnS_2}} \downarrow + 6Cl^-$ SnS_2 precipitates from 0.3-*N* HCl but is dissolved by hot 6-*N* HCl. It is soluble in solutions of NaOH and in Na_2S, with the formation of $Sn(OH)_6^{=} + SnS_3^{=}$ and $SnS_3^{=}$ respectively. Solutions of $C_2O_4^{=}$ dissolve SnS_2 or prevent the formation of SnS_2 (distinction from Sb^{3+}). SnS_2 is reprecipitated when solutions of $SnS_3^{=}$ are acidified.

SUMMARY OF REACTIONS OF GROUP II CATIONS (*Continued*)

Reagents	Arsenic		Tin	
	Arsenious Compounds—Arsenites $NaAsO_2$	Arsenic Compounds—Arsenates Na_3AsO_4	Stannous Compounds $SnCl_2$	Stannic Compounds $SnCl_4$
NH_4OH	—	—	$Sn^{++} + 2NH_3 + 2H_2O \rightleftharpoons \underset{\text{white}}{\underline{Sn(OH)_2}} \downarrow + 2NH_4^+$ The precipitate is insoluble in excess NH_4OH but dissolves in acids and alkali hydroxides.	$SnCl_6^= + 4NH_3 + 4H_2O \rightleftharpoons \underset{\text{white}}{\underline{Sn(OH)_4}} \downarrow + 4NH_4^+ + 6Cl^-$ The precipitate is soluble in HCl and alkali hydroxides.
NaOH	—	—	$Sn^{++} + 2OH^- \rightleftharpoons \underset{\text{white}}{\underline{Sn(OH)_2}} \downarrow$ $\underline{Sn(OH)_2} + 2OH^- \rightleftharpoons Sn(OH)_4^= \text{ or } SnO_2^= + 2H_2O$ The precipitate dissolves in excess NaOH, with the formation of the stannite ion.	$SnCl_6^= + 4OH^- \rightleftharpoons \underset{\text{white}}{\underline{Sn(OH)_4}} \downarrow + 6Cl^-$ $\underline{Sn(OH)_4} + 2OH^- \rightleftharpoons Sn(OH)_6^= \text{ or } SnO_3^= + 3H_2O$ The precipitate is soluble in excess NaOH or in HCl.

$HgCl_2$	—	—	$Sn^{++} + 2Hg^{++} + 8Cl^- \rightleftharpoons \underset{\text{white}}{\underline{Hg_2Cl_2}} \downarrow + SnCl_6^=$ $Sn^{++} + \underline{Hg_2Cl_2} + 4Cl^- \rightleftharpoons \underset{\text{black}}{\underline{2Hg}} \downarrow + SnCl_6^=$ The white precipitate first formed turns gray with excess Sn^{++}.	$SnCl_6^=$ does not react with $HgCl_2$, but it may be reduced to Sn^{++} with Fe, Cu, Sb, etc., and then treated with $HgCl_2$.
$AgNO_3$	$AsO_2^- + 3H_2O \rightleftharpoons AsO_3^{3-} + 2H_3O^+$ $3Ag^+ + AsO_3^{3-} \rightleftharpoons \underset{\text{yellowish-white}}{\underline{Ag_3AsO_3}} \downarrow$ The precipitate is insoluble in dilute acetic acid, but is dissolved by dilute HNO_3 or NH_4OH.	$3Ag^+ + AsO_4^{3-} \rightleftharpoons \underset{\text{reddish-brown}}{\underline{Ag_3AsO_4}} \downarrow$ The precipitate is soluble in dilute HNO_3 or NH_4OH, but is not soluble in dilute acetic acid.	—	—
Magnesium mixture: $Mg(NO_3)_2$, NH_4NO_3, NH_4OH	No precipitate.	$Mg^{++} + NH_4^+ + AsO_4^{3-} \rightleftharpoons \underset{\text{white}}{\underline{MgNH_4AsO_4}} \downarrow$ The precipitate is soluble in dilute acetic acid.	—	—

SUMMARY OF REACTIONS OF GROUP II CATIONS (*Continued*)

<table>
<tr><th rowspan="2">Reagents</th><th colspan="2">Arsenic</th></tr>
<tr><th>Arsenious Compounds—Arsenites—$NaAsO_2$</th><th>Arsenic Compounds—Arsenates—Na_3AsO_4</th></tr>
<tr><td rowspan="4">Special tests for arsenates or arsenites</td><td colspan="2">The Marsh Test.
$HAsO_2 + 3Zn + 6H_3O^+ \rightleftharpoons AsH_3\uparrow + 3Zn^{++} + 8H_2O$. The AsH_3 is carried through a hot tube by $H_2(Zn + 2H_3O^+ \rightleftharpoons Zn^{++} + H_2\uparrow + 2H_2O)$ where decomposition takes place ($2AsH_3 \rightleftharpoons 2As\downarrow + 3H_2\uparrow$). SbH_3 is also formed and decomposed, but As is soluble in NaBrO whereas Sb is not. If NaOH is used in place of H_2SO_4, SbH_3 is not formed (Fleitmann's Test).</td></tr>
<tr><td colspan="2">The Gutzeit Test.
$HAsO_2 + 3Zn + 6H_3O^+ \rightleftharpoons AsH_3\uparrow + 3Zn^{++} + 8H_2O$. The AsH_3 rises in the test tube in which the reaction is carried out and reacts with $AgNO_3$ which is placed on filter paper over the mouth of the tube. $AsH_3 + 6Ag^+ + 3NO_3^- + 3H_2O \rightleftharpoons \underset{\text{yellow}}{\underline{Ag_3As\cdot 3AgNO_3}}\downarrow + 3H_3O^+$. The yellow compound decomposes: $Ag_3As\cdot 3AgNO_3 + 5H_2O \rightleftharpoons \underset{\text{black}}{\underline{6Ag}}\downarrow + HAsO_2 + 3H_3O^+ + 3NO_3^-$. SbH_3, PH_3, and H_2S also stain the paper.</td></tr>
<tr><td colspan="2">The Bettendorf Test.
In 12-N HCl, $SnCl_2$ reduces $HAsO_2$ to As. ($2HAsO_2 + 3Sn^{++} + 18Cl^- + 6H_3O^+ \rightleftharpoons \underset{\text{black or brown}}{\underline{2As}}\downarrow + 10H_2O + 3SnCl_6^{=}$.) Sb does not give this test, but compounds of Hg and Ag must be absent.</td></tr>
<tr><td colspan="2">The Reinsch Test.
When a bright piece of Cu is placed in an HCl solution of an arsenic compound, As is displaced, forming gray Cu_5As_2. When the solid is heated, As_2O_3 forms and sublimes.</td></tr>
</table>

CHAPTER 10

ANALYSIS OF GROUP II CATIONS

DISCUSSION OF THE PROCEDURE

The cations of Group II are those that form sulfides insoluble in 0.2- to 0.3-M H_3O^+ solution, after Group I has been removed. This concentration of H_3O^+ is sufficient to prevent the precipitation of the sulfides of Group III (FeS, MnS, NiS, CoS) by either H_2S gas or CH_3CSNH_2. Actually ZnS, the least soluble of the Group III sulfides, will not precipitate with H_2S gas from solutions in which the H_3O^+ concentration is as low as 0.1-M. When CH_3CSNH_2 is used, ZnS will not precipitate readily from 0.05-M H_3O^+ solutions because of the low rate of hydrolysis of CH_3CSNH_2 to H_2S. In order to precipitate arsenic completely as its sulfide, the concentration of H_3O^+ must be at least 0.2- to 0.3-M; but in order to precipitate PbS, CdS, and SnS completely, the final concentration of H_3O^+ should be about 0.1-M. Consequently the proper adjustment of the pH of the solution for the precipitation of Group II sulfides is important. Complete precipitation with CH_3CSNH_2 is achieved by precipitation from 0.2- to 0.3-M H_3O^+ first. The rate of hydrolysis is reasonably rapid under these conditions. The solution is then diluted to about 0.1-M H_3O^+ for the final period of precipitation. *It is necessary to carry out these precipitations in a hot (boiling) water bath, for otherwise the hydrolysis of CH_3CSNH_2 will be too slow and precipitation will not be complete.* It is also important that the solutions be left in the boiling water bath for the full time specified in the Procedures.

Adjustment of pH for Precipitation of Group II Cations

The concentration of H_3O^+ may be adjusted by either of the following methods.

1. The filtrate from Group I (or the Group II known or unknown) is evaporated to incipient dryness (still moist). To the residue 5 drops of 1-N HCl are added and the solution is diluted to 1 ml. with water. Since 1 drop is 0.05 ml., there is present in the 1 ml. of solution about (0.25)(1) = 0.25 m. mole of HCl; hence the concentration of H_3O^+ is 0.25 m. mole/ml., or 0.25-M.

SCHEMATIC OUTLINE OF THE PROCEDURE

<table>
<tr><td colspan="7">7. Filtrate from Group I: Pb^{++}, Bi^{3+}, Cu^{++}, Cd^{++}, Hg^{++}, As^{3+}, (As^{5+}), Sb^{3+}, (Sb^{5+}), Sn^{++}, (Sn^{4+}) + Groups III–V for general unknowns
Adjust to 0.2- to 0.3-M H_3O^+. Add CH_3CSNH_2. Heat.</td></tr>
<tr><td colspan="5">8. Precipitate: PbS, Bi_2S_3, CuS, CdS, HgS, As_2S_3, Sb_2S_3, SnS(SnS_2)
Add NaOH + CH_3CSNH_2.</td><td colspan="2">21. Filtrate: Groups III–V.</td></tr>
<tr><td colspan="3">9. Residue (Div. A): PbS, Bi_2S_3, CuS, CdS
Dissolve in HNO_3. Evaporate with H_2SO_4. Add H_2O.</td><td colspan="4">14. Dissolved sulfides (Div. B): $HgS_2^{=}$, AsS_3^{3-}, SbS_3^{3-}, $SnS_3^{=}$, $SnOS^{=}$.
Add HCl.</td></tr>
<tr><td rowspan="3">10. Residue: $PbSO_4$
Add
CH_3COONH_4.
Add K_2CrO_4.
Yellow ppt.:
$PbCrO_4$</td><td colspan="2">11. Filtrate: Bi^{3+}, Cu^{++}, Cd^{++}
Add NH_4OH.</td><td colspan="2">15. Precipitate: HgS, As_2S_3, Sb_2S_3, SnS_2, SnS
Add 6-N HCl.</td><td colspan="2">Filtrate: Discard filtrate from 14.</td></tr>
<tr><td rowspan="2">12. Precipitate:
$Bi(OH)_3$
a. Add NaOH and $SnCl_2$.
Black ppt.:
Bi
b. Add KI^- antipyrine + CH_3COOH.
Reddish-orange ppt.</td><td rowspan="2">13. Filtrate:
$Cu(NH_3)_4^{++}$
$Cd(NH_3)_4^{++}$
Add
CH_3CSNH_2.
Black ppt.:
CuS
Yellow ppt.:
CdS
If black, add KCN. CuS dissolves, CdS remains.</td><td colspan="2">16. Undissolved sulfides: HgS, As_2S_3.
Add NH_4OH + H_2O_2.</td><td colspan="2">19. Filtrate from 15: $SnCl_6^{=}$, $SbCl_4^{-}$.
Evaporate. Add HCl. Divide.</td></tr>
<tr><td>17. Residue: HgS
Add HCl + NaClO.
a. Add NH_4OH + NH_4I + NaOH.
Brown ppt.:
HOHgNHHgI
b. Add NaOH + $(H_2NOH)_2H_2SO_4$.
White to black ppt.:
Hg_2Cl_2 or Hg</td><td>18. Filtrate: AsO_4^{3-}
a. Add NH_4OH + $Mg(NO_3)_2$ mixture.
White ppt.:
$MgNH_4AsO_4$
b. Add $(NH_4)_2MoO_4$.
Yellow ppt.:
$(NH_4)_3AsO_4 \cdot 12MoO_3$</td><td>20a. Add malachite green and m-nitrophenylarsonic acid.
Green ppt.</td><td>20b. Add
$(NH_4)_2C_2O_4$
+
CH_3CSNH_2.
Reddish-orange ppt.:
Sb_2S_3</td></tr>
<tr><td>Lead</td><td>Bismuth</td><td>Copper-Cadmium</td><td>Mercury</td><td>Arsenic</td><td>Tin</td><td>Antimony</td></tr>
</table>

2. Indicators instead of the evaporation procedure just described may be used to adjust the concentration of H_3O^+. To the filtrate from Group I (or the Group II known or unknown) is added 1 drop of malachite green indicator. If the concentration of H_3O^+ is near 0.6-*M* or greater, the solution will have a faint yellow color. This indicates that the acid concentration is too high; a blue solution indicates that it is too low. To reduce the acid concentration, 1-*N* NH_4OH is added drop by drop, until the color is blue-green. Next 1 drop of thymol blue indicator is added, and then 1-*N* HCl drop by drop, until a reddish color can be seen in the solution when the tube is held over a piece of white paper. The H_3O^+ concentration is about 0.2-*M* when this color is obtained with the mixed indicators, and the sulfides can be precipitated as outlined in the Procedures. Any precipitate formed during the adjustment of the acidity may be disregarded because it will be transposed to the sulfides.

The malachite green may be adsorbed on the sulfides but this will not be noticeable in the dark-colored ones. In the absence of the dark-colored sulfides, the light-colored ones, such as SnS_2, As_2S_3, and Sb_2S_3, will be somewhat discolored. Since no definite conclusions should be drawn from the colors of the sulfides alone, this will not interfere with the analysis. The confirmatory tests from which the final conclusions are drawn regarding the presence or absence of the ions are not affected by the indicators.

If it is desired to avoid this coloration of the sulfide precipitates, 2-4-dinitrophenol (colorless — 2.6 : 4.4 — yellow) may be used in the following way. One drop of the indicator is added. If the solution is colorless, 1-*N* NH_4OH is added until the solution just turns yellow (pH = 3 to 4). Then 1-*N* HCl is added drop by drop, until the solution is again just colorless. This adjusts the pH of the solution to about 3 so that the concentration of H_3O^+ is about 0.001-*M*. Four to 5 drops of 1-*N* HCl is then added for each milliliter of solution to give a final concentration of 0.2- to 0.25-*M* for H_3O^+.

The color changes and pH ranges of the two indicators used in adjusting the acidity are as follows: *

Malachite green
  Acid range
    (H_3O^+) : yellow 0.6-*M* — 0.02-*M* blue-green
      pH : yellow 0.2 — 1.8 blue-green
Thymol blue
    (H_3O^+) : red 0.05-*M* — 0.002-*M* yellow
      pH : red 1.3 — 2.8 yellow

* A more complete list of the color changes and pH ranges of indicators is given in Appendix L.

Malachite green
Alkaline range
(OH^-) : blue-green 0.0025-*M* — 0.1-*M* colorless
pH : blue-green 11.4 — 13.0 colorless
Thymol blue
(OH^-) : yellow 10^{-6}-*M* — 4×10^{-5}-*M* blue
pH : yellow 8.0 — 9.6 blue

In a mixture of malachite green and thymol blue indicators, a red color does not show distinctly until the concentration of H_3O^+ is approximately 0.2-*M*.

PRECIPITATION AND DISSOLUTION OF SULFIDES

Conditions for the Precipitation of a Sulfide

According to the solubility product principle, a sulfide, such as PbS, is precipitated if the product of the molar concentrations of the ions exceeds the solubility product constant. That is, precipitation occurs if

$$[Pb^{++}][S^{--}] > K_{PbS}$$

Similarly, PbS is dissolved or prevented from forming if

$$[Pb^{++}][S^{--}] < K_{PbS}$$

Since the concentration of the cations is usually about 0.01 gram-ion, the concentration of the sulfide ion needed to cause the precipitation of PbS, for example, is

$$[S^{--}] = \frac{K_{PbS}}{0.01} = \frac{1 \times 10^{-29}}{0.01} = 1 \times 10^{-27}$$

This means that the sulfide ion concentration must be controlled in order to precipitate the sulfides selectively.

Sulfide Ion Concentrations in Solutions of H_2S

In a solution of H_2S obtained by passing H_2S into water or by hydrolyzing CH_3CSNH_2, the following equilibria exist:

1. Primary:

$$H_2S + H_2O \rightleftharpoons H_3O^+ + HS^-; \quad \frac{[H_3O^+][HS^-]}{[H_2S]} = K_{H_2S} = 1.2 \times 10^{-7}$$

2. Secondary:

$$HS^- + H_2O \rightleftharpoons H_3O^+ + S^{--}; \quad \frac{[H_3O^+][S^{--}]}{[HS^-]} = K_{HS^-} = 1.0 \times 10^{-15}$$

The very small value of the secondary ionization constant (1.0×10^{-15}) compared to that of the primary ionization constant (1.2×10^{-7}) shows that the ionization of H_2S into H_3O^+ and HS^- is much greater than that of HS^- into

H_3O^+ and S^{--}. Consequently, only a *very small* part of the H_3O^+ in a solution of H_2S is derived from the secondary ionization of H_2S. As a first approximation, then, the concentration of H_3O^+ in a solution containing *only hydrogen sulfide* is very nearly equal to the concentration of HS^-. Now, since these two concentrations are very nearly equal, $[H_3O^+]$ and $[HS^-]$ cancel in the expression for K_{HS^-}, with the result that

$$[S^{--}] = K_{HS^-} = 1.0 \times 10^{-15}$$

That is, the concentration of the sulfide ion in a solution containing *only H_2S* in any appreciable concentration is very nearly equal to the secondary ionization constant.

The situation is quite different, however, when the H_3O^+ concentration is changed by the addition of an acid or a base. Multiplying the equation for K_{H_2S} by the one for K_{HS^-} gives:

$$\left(\frac{[H_3O^+][HS^-]}{[H_2S]}\right)\left(\frac{[H_3O^+][S^{--}]}{[HS^-]}\right) = \frac{[H_3O^+]^2[S^{--}]}{[H_2S]} = (K_{H_2S})(K_{HS^-})$$
$$= (1.2 \times 10^{-7})(1.0 \times 10^{-15}) = 1.2 \times 10^{-22}$$

If the concentration of H_3O^+ and of H_2S is known, the concentration of S^{--} can be calculated. In qualitative analysis, the solution is usually saturated with H_2S so that its concentration is about 0.1-*M*. When this value is substituted in the above equation,

$$\frac{[H_3O^+]^2[S^{--}]}{0.1} = 1.2 \times 10^{-22}, \text{ or } [H_3O^+]^2[S^{--}] = 1.2 \times 10^{-23}$$

This equation shows that the sulfide ion concentration in a solution saturated with H_2S varies inversely as the square of the concentration of H_3O^+:

$$[S^{--}] = \frac{1.2 \times 10^{-23}}{[H_3O^+]^2}$$

That is, a fourfold increase in H_3O^+ concentration causes a sixteenfold decrease in the concentration of S^{--}. The presence of 0.1-*M* H_3O^+ reduces the concentration of S^{--} from 1.0×10^{-15}-*M*, in a solution containing only H_2S, to 1.2×10^{-21}-*M*. This is about a millionfold decrease in the concentration of the sulfide ion. From this it can be seen that the pH of a solution may be used to control the sulfide ion concentration over wide ranges, and this in turn determines which sulfides will precipitate from the solution.

Acidity Conditions for the Precipitation of the Sulfides

The acidity conditions under which the sulfides of the cations are precipitated are summarized in Table 10.1. These conditions apply to the use of H_2S gas. When thioacetamide, CH_3CSNH_2, is used, the conditions are changed somewhat, owing to its slow hydrolysis in neutral and dilute acid solutions. The hydrolysis is more rapid in stronger acid solutions and in alkaline solu-

TABLE 10.1. Acidity Conditions for the Precipitation of the Sulfides

Sulfides	Conditions for Precipitation with H_2S
Na_2S, K_2S, $(NH_4)_2S$	Soluble. Not precipitated in aqueous solution.
MgS, CaS, SrS, BaS	Soluble. Not precipitated in aqueous solution.
Al_2S_3, Cr_2S_3	Hydrolyze completely. Not precipitated in aqueous solution.
MnS	Precipitated only in alkaline or very dilute acid solution.
FeS, CoS, NiS	Precipitated in alkaline solution or in CH_3COOH-CH_3COONa buffer solutions, but not in dilute (4-*M*) CH_3COOH solutions.
ZnS	Precipitated in dilute CH_3COOH but not in 0.3-*N* HCl.
SnS, Bi_2S_3, CdS, PbS	Precipitated in 0.3-*N* HCl, but not in 3-*N* HCl.
SnS_2, CuS, Sb_2S_3	Precipitated in 3-*N* HCl, but not in 12-*N* HCl.
HgS	Precipitated in 6-*N* HCl, but not in 12-*N* HCl.
As_2S_3	Precipitated in 12-*N* HCl.

tions so that the conditions are more nearly like those for H_2S gas. For the complete precipitation of SnS, CdS, and PbS, for example, the concentration of H_3O^+ should be about 0.1-*M* instead of 0.3-*M*. This causes no difficulties because ZnS is not readily precipitated from dilute acid solutions such as 4-*N* CH_3COOH or 0.05-*N* HCl by CH_3CSNH_2. Actually the fact that ZnS is not readily precipitated with CH_3CSNH_2 under acidity conditions where the sulfide precipitates with H_2S gas is an advantage because it decreases the co-precipitation and post-precipitation of ZnS with Group II sulfides.

Conditions for the Separation of Group II from Group III

In order to separate Groups II and III, the H_3O^+ concentration must be such that the sulfide ion concentration will be large enough to cause the precipitation of the most soluble sulfide of Group II (PbS or CdS), and small enough to prevent the precipitation of the least soluble sulfide of Group III (ZnS). That is,

$$[Pb^{++}][S^{--}] > 1 \times 10^{-29}$$
$$[Zn^{++}][S^{--}] < 1 \times 10^{-23}$$

Separation of an ion from solution usually is sufficiently complete if its concentration is reduced to at least 0.0001-*M*. The maximum concentration of Zn^{++} ordinarily encountered is 0.1-*M*. Hence

for PbS, $(0.0001)[S^{--}] > 1 \times 10^{-29}$, or $[S^{--}] > 1 \times 10^{-25}$
for ZnS, $(0.1)[S^{--}] < 1 \times 10^{-23}$, or $[S^{--}] < 1 \times 10^{-22}$

That is, the sulfide ion concentration should be maintained between 1×10^{-22}-*M* and 1×10^{-25}-*M*. The higher it can be maintained without precipitating ZnS, the more complete will be the precipitation of PbS. The concentration of the hydronium ion required to reduce the sulfide ion concentration to 1×10^{-22} gram ion is calculated as follows:

$$[H_3O^+]^2[S^{--}] = 1.2 \times 10^{-23}$$

or

$$[H_3O^+]^2[1 \times 10^{-22}] = 1.2 \times 10^{-23}$$

Then

$$[H_3O^+]^2 = \frac{1.2 \times 10^{-23}}{1 \times 10^{-22}} = 0.12$$

$$[H_3O^+] = \sqrt{0.12} = 0.35$$

Therefore, the concentration of the hydronium ion must be maintained at about 0.3-M in order to prevent the precipitation of the sulfides of the ions of Group III (Fe^{++}, Mn^{++}, Zn^{++}, Co^{++}, Ni^{++}). This concentration allows almost complete precipitation of the sulfides of the cations of Group II (As^{3+}, Sb^{3+}, Sn^{++}, Pb^{++}, Cu^{++}, Cd^{++}, Bi^{3+}, Hg^{++}). The concentration of Pb^{++} which remains in solution is

$$[Pb^{++}](1 \times 10^{-22}) = 1 \times 10^{-29}$$

or

$$[Pb^{++}] = \frac{1 \times 10^{-29}}{1 \times 10^{-22}} = 1 \times 10^{-7} \text{ mole/liter}$$

or

$$0.02\mu g.\ Pb^{++}/ml.$$

The precipitation of CdS also requires a concentration of H_3O^+ not larger than 0.3-M. In fact, it is more difficult to obtain analytically complete precipitation of CdS than of PbS. In equal molar solutions of cadmium salts and lead salts that contain Cl^-, the concentration of Cd^{++} is less than the concentration of Pb^{++} because $CdCl_2$ is a weak salt.

As pointed out previously, it is necessary to reduce the H_3O^+ concentration to about 0.1-M to obtain complete precipitation of PbS and CdS with CH_3CSNH_2. A simple dilution technique is used in the Procedures to precipitate the sulfides first at 0.2- to 0.3-M in order to insure complete precipitation of arsenic, and then at 0.1-M H_3O^+ to insure complete precipitation of tin, lead, and cadmium.

Acidity Requirements for the Precipitation of As_2S_3

The reason that arsenic sulfide precipitates more readily from high H_3O^+ concentrations (0.3-M and above) than from lower acid concentrations can be seen from the following equilibria:

$$As^{3+} + \boxed{\begin{matrix}3OH^- \\ 3H_3O^+\end{matrix}} \rightleftharpoons As(OH)_3 \rightleftharpoons \underset{\substack{\text{Ortho-}\\\text{arsenious}\\\text{acid}}}{H_3AsO_3} \rightleftharpoons \underset{\substack{\text{Meta-}\\\text{arsenious}\\\text{acid}}}{HAsO_2} + H_2O \rightleftharpoons \boxed{\begin{matrix}H_3O^+ \\ OH^-\end{matrix}} + AsO_2^-$$

$$3OH^- + 3H_3O^+ \rightleftharpoons 6H_2O \qquad H_3O^+ + OH^- \rightleftharpoons 2H_2O$$

The oxyacids or hydroxides of arsenic, antimony, and tin are considered to be amphoteric substances, but more acidic than basic in character. An increase in acidity shifts the above equilibria in a direction that favors the formation of As^{3+}, and a decrease in acidity favors the formation of AsO_2^-. Consequently, in changing to a moderately acid solution, the increase in the concentration of As^{3+} more than compensates for the decrease in the concentration of S^{--} so that the ion concentration product $[As^{3+}]^2[S^{--}]^3$ exceeds the value of $K_{As_2S_3}$ and precipitation occurs. That is, in an acid solution

$$[As^{3+}]^2[S^{--}]^3 > K_{As_2S_3}$$

while in an alkaline solution the concentration of As^{3+} is so low, because of the formation of AsO_2^-, that

$$[As^{3+}]^2[S^{--}]^3 < K_{As_2S_3}$$

and a precipitate does not form. If the arsenic is present as an arsenate (AsO_4^{3-}), it is first reduced by the H_2S to the arsenite (AsO_2^- or AsO_3^{3-}), which then reacts with the H_2S. An increase in acidity favors this reduction. The addition of NH_4I also speeds up the reduction because of the catalytic action of I^-.

Mechanism of the Precipitation of the Sulfides

The concentration of the sulfide ions in 0.3-*M* H_3O^+ is 1.3×10^{-22} gram ions per liter. Since there are 6.02×10^{23} ions in 1 gram-ion weight, only about 80 ions are present in 1 liter of solution. This is less than an average of 1 sulfide ion per ml., yet practically all the Pb^{++} is precipitated immediately when H_2S is passed into the solution. Hence, the mechanism by which the precipitate is formed must not be the simple union of Pb^{++} and S^{--}. There is present in a hydrogen sulfide solution containing 0.3-*N* HCl a comparatively high concentration of HS^- relative to the low concentration of S^{--}. Thus,

$$\frac{[H_3O^+][HS^-]}{[H_2S]} = 1.2 \times 10^{-7}, \text{ and } [HS^-] = \frac{(0.1)(1.2 \times 10^{-7})}{(0.3)}$$
$$= 4 \times 10^{-8} \text{ mole/liter}$$

It is reasonable therefore to assume a mechanism which involves the formation of an intermediate compound, $Pb(HS)_2$, as shown by the following reactions:

$$Pb^{++} + 2HS^- \rightleftharpoons \underline{Pb(HS)_2}\downarrow \rightleftharpoons \underline{PbS}\downarrow + H_2S\uparrow$$

or probably

$$Pb(H_2O)_4^{++} + 2H_2S \rightleftharpoons [(H_2O)_2Pb(H_2S)_2]^{++} + 2H_2O \rightleftharpoons$$
$$\underline{(H_2O)_2Pb(HS)_2}\downarrow + 2H_3O^+$$
$$\rightleftharpoons \underline{PbS}\downarrow + H_2S\uparrow + 2H_2O$$

There is also the possibility of reactions such as

$$Pb^{++} + HS^- + H_2O \rightleftharpoons \underline{PbS}\downarrow + H_3O^+$$

Reaction rate studies would be needed to determine which of these might be the mechanism. Whatever it is, equilibrium is finally established between Pb^{++} and S^{--}

$$\underline{PbS} \rightleftharpoons Pb^{++} + S^{--}$$

Hence, the final equilibrium behaves as though the reaction takes place between the two ions regardless of the indirect reaction that may occur or whether intermediate compounds are formed. Equilibrium is concerned only with the final result and not with the mechanism by which the result is obtained. Therefore, the solubility product principle is valid provided the system is in equilibrium and the correct values for the solubility product constants are known.

Solubility of Sulfides in Water

When a sulfide, such as PbS, is added to water, it dissolves until the ion concentration product $[Pb^{++}][S^{--}]$ is equal to the solubility product constant K_{PbS}. It must be remembered, however, that the sulfide ion hydrolyzes and this reduces its concentration so that in such a solution $[Pb^{++}]$ is equal not to $[S^{--}]$ but to $[HS^-] + [S^{--}]$. This may be formulated as follows:

$$\begin{array}{l} \underline{PbS} \rightleftharpoons Pb^{++} + \boxed{\begin{array}{c} S^{--} \\ + \\ H_2O \end{array}} \rightleftharpoons HS^- + OH^- \end{array}$$

This effect, as well as the tendency for Pb^{++} to form $Pb(OH)^+$, tends to increase the solubility of PbS. Actually, a calculation of the solubility of PbS, the hydrolysis of S^{--} being neglected, gives

$$[Pb^{++}][S^{--}] = 1 \times 10^{-29}, \text{ or solubility } = 3 \times 10^{-15} \text{ mole/liter}$$

However, when the hydrolysis of S^{--} is considered, the calculated solubility is about 3.2×10^{-11} mole/liter. This is about 10,000 times larger than that obtained when the hydrolysis of S^{--} is neglected, as shown by the following considerations.

In 0.1-*M* solution the extent of the hydrolysis of sulfide ion is about 99 percent. In more dilute solutions the hydrolysis reaction is even more complete since $[OH^-] = \sqrt{C_s K_h} = \sqrt{C_S \dfrac{K_w}{K_{HS^-}}}$ and the fraction α hydrolyzed is $[OH^-]/C_s$ or $\alpha = \sqrt{\dfrac{K_h}{C_s}}$. Consequently, $[Pb^{++}]$ is very nearly equal to $[HS^-]$.

In the saturated solution at equilibrium, the following expressions must be satisfied simultaneously:

$$PbS \rightleftharpoons Pb^{++} + S^{--};\ [Pb^{++}][S^{--}] = 1 \times 10^{-29}$$

$$H_2O + S^{--} \rightleftharpoons HS^- + OH^-;\ \frac{[HS^-][OH^-]}{[S^{--}]} = \frac{K_w}{K_{HS^-}} = \frac{1 \times 10^{-14}}{1 \times 10^{-15}} = 10$$

Substitution of $[S^{--}] = \dfrac{1 \times 10^{-29}}{[Pb^{++}]}$ from the first equation into the second gives

$$\frac{[HS^-][OH^-]}{\dfrac{1 \times 10^{-29}}{[Pb^{++}]}} = 10$$

or

$$[Pb^{++}][HS^-][OH^-] = 1 \times 10^{-28}$$

If the hydrolysis of S^{--} were the only source of OH^-, then $[OH^-]$ and $[HS^-]$ would be very nearly equal. But $[OH^-]$ also results from the ionization of water. In fact, the concentration of OH^- arising from the ionization of water is much greater (1×10^{-7} mole/liter) than that from the hydrolysis of S^{--} (about 10^{-11} mole/liter) because the solubility of PbS is very low. Consequently, very nearly,

$$[Pb^{++}] = [HS^-] = x$$

and

$$[OH^-] = 1 \times 10^{-7}$$

Substitution into the above expression gives

$$(x)(x)(1 \times 10^{-7}) = 1 \times 10^{-28}$$

or

$$x = [Pb^{++}] = [HS^-] = \sqrt{\frac{1 \times 10^{-28}}{1 \times 10^{-7}}}$$

$$= \sqrt{1 \times 10^{-21}} = 3.2 \times 10^{-11} \text{ mole/liter}$$

This value is the molar solubility of PbS because for each mole of PbS that dissolves, one mole of Pb^{++} is obtained.

According to the above calculations, the concentration of Pb^{++} in the saturated solution of PbS is 3.2×10^{-11} and that of S^{--} is 3.2×10^{-19} since $[Pb^{++}][S^{--}]$ must be equal to 1×10^{-29}. In other words the concentrations of Pb^{++} and S^{--} are not equal because of the extensive hydrolysis of one of the ions. For salts like AgCl the ions are not highly hydrolyzed and $[Ag^+]$ is very nearly equal to $[Cl^-]$ so that the usual calculation of its solubility is somewhat more valid.

Separation of the Sulfides of Division B from Those of Division A

This separation is based on the tendency of As_2S_3, Sb_2S_3, SnS, SnS_2, and HgS to form soluble complex sulfides in alkaline sulfide solutions. CuS, PbS, Bi_2S_3, and CdS do not form these complex ions.

The tendency of the sulfides as well as the oxides or hydroxides of arsenic, antimony, and tin to dissolve in acid or alkali is related to their amphoteric properties. Thus, in a solution of NaOH,

$$\underline{As_2O_3} + 2OH^- \rightleftharpoons 2AsO_2^- + H_2O$$
(Arsenite ion)

$$\underline{Sb(OH)_3} + OH^- \rightleftharpoons Sb(OH)_4^- \text{ (Antimonite ion)}$$
or
$$\rightarrow SbO_2^- + 2H_2O$$

$$\underline{Sn(OH)_2} + 2OH^- \rightleftharpoons Sn(OH)_4^{--} \text{ (Stannite ion)}$$
or
$$\rightarrow SnO_2^{--} + 2H_2O$$

These substances also dissolve in excess hydrochloric acid on account of their tendency to form complex halides and by reason of their slight basic nature. Thus,

$$\underline{As_2O_3} + 6H_3O^+ + 8Cl^- \rightleftharpoons 2AsCl_4^- + 9H_2O$$

$$\underline{Sb(OH)_3} + 3H_3O^+ + 4Cl^- \rightleftharpoons SbCl_4^- + 6H_2O$$

$$\underline{Sn(OH)_2} + 2H_3O^+ + 4Cl^- \rightleftharpoons SnCl_4^{--} + 4H_2O$$

In a similar way the sulfides of arsenic and antimony are dissolved by excess NaOH or HCl:

$$\underline{As_2S_3} + 3OH^- \rightleftharpoons 2AsOS^- + HS^- + H_2O$$

$$\underline{Sb_2S_3} + 3OH^- \rightleftharpoons 2SbOS^- + HS^- + H_2O$$

$$\underline{As_2S_3} + 6H_3O^+ + 8Cl^- \rightleftharpoons 2AsCl_4^- + 3H_2S\uparrow + 6H_2O$$

$$\underline{Sb_2S_3} + 6H_3O^+ + 8Cl^- \rightleftharpoons 2SbCl_4^- + 3H_2S\uparrow + 6H_2O$$

Here again the tendency of As_2S_3 and Sb_2S_3 to dissolve in HCl is due to the formation of the complex ions and the weak acid H_2S as well as to the basic properties of the sulfides. If an alkali sulfide is used in place of an alkali hydroxide, the reactions that take place in the case of the sulfides of antimony are as follows:

$$\underline{Sb_2S_3} + 8HS^- \rightleftharpoons 2Sb(HS)_4^- + 3S^{--}$$
or
$$\rightleftharpoons 2SbS_2^- + 4H_2S$$

and

$$\underline{Sb_2S_3} + S^{--} \rightleftharpoons 2SbS_2^-$$
(Thioantimonite ion)

The sulfides of these elements in the higher states of valence are also dissolved by alkali hydroxides and sulfides. For example,

$$\underline{Sb_2S_5} + 6OH^- \rightleftharpoons SbS_4^{3-} + SbO_3S^{3-} + 3H_2O$$

$$\underline{Sb_2S_5} + 3S^{--} \rightleftharpoons 2SbS_4^{3-}$$
(Thioantimonate ion)

The reactions of the sulfides of the other ions are as follows:

$$As_2S_3 + 3S^{--} \rightleftharpoons \underset{\text{(Thioarsenite ion)}}{2AsS_3^{3-}}$$

$$As_2S_5 + 3S^{--} \rightleftharpoons \underset{\text{(Thioarsenate ion)}}{2AsS_4^{3-}}$$

$$HgS + S^{--} \rightleftharpoons \underset{\text{(Thiomercurate ion)}}{HgS_2^{--}}$$

$$SnS_2 + 2S^{--} \rightleftharpoons \underset{\text{(Thiostannate ion)}}{SnS_3^{--}}$$

$$SnS + 2OH^- \rightleftharpoons SnOS^{--} + H_2O$$

Other Reagents for the Separation of Group II Sulfides into Division A and Division B

A relatively high concentration of S^{--} is needed to dissolve HgS. The presence of a high concentration of OH^- reduces the extent of hydrolysis of the sulfide ion and insures the dissolution of HgS:

$$S^{--} + H_2O \rightleftharpoons HS^- + OH^-$$

In some schemes of qualitative analysis, ammonium sulfide or ammonium polysulfide reagent with a relatively low concentration of OH^-, and consequently a low concentration of S^{--}, is used. In this case, HgS does not dissolve and Hg^{++} will be in Division A of Group II.

The rather high concentrations of S^{--} that are present in solutions of Na_2S and NaOH apparently prevent the dissolution of SnS. On the other hand, SnS_2 is readily soluble in such reagents. When the sulfides of Group II are separated into Divisions A and B with a reagent consisting of Na_2S and NaOH, a small amount of free sulfur is added. The sulfur dissolves in the solution to form polysulfide ions (S_x^{--}). The yellow solution is often called "yellow sodium sulfide" to distinguish it from "colorless sodium sulfide" solution (Na_2S + NaOH without excess sulfur). The exact composition of the solution is not known, but the simplest of the polysulfide ions results from the combination of one sulfide ion with one sulfur atom:

$$S^{--} + S \rightleftharpoons S_2^{--}, \text{ or } :\overset{..}{\underset{..}{S}}:^{--} + \overset{..}{\underset{..}{S}}: \rightleftharpoons :\overset{..}{\underset{..}{S}}:\overset{..}{\underset{..}{S}}:^{--}$$

The disulfide ion is an oxidizing agent because of the tendency of this ion to take two electrons from some other substance and become two sulfide ions. The presence of this oxidizing agent is not needed except that SnS must be converted to SnS_2 before a complex sulfide ion will form. Thus,

$$SnS + S_2^{--} \rightleftharpoons \cancel{SnS_2} + \cancel{S}^{--}$$
$$\cancel{SnS_2} + \cancel{S}^{--} \rightleftharpoons SnS_3^{--}$$
$$\overline{SnS + S_2^{--} \rightleftharpoons SnS_3^{--}}$$

In a similar way As_2S_3 and Sb_2S_3 are oxidized to As_2S_5 and Sb_2S_5. These sulfides are then dissolved by an excess of the sulfide ion. For example,

$$As_2S_5 + 3S^{--} \rightleftharpoons 2AsS_4^{3-}$$

Only a small amount of free sulfur is used to prepare the reagent because an excess of the polysulfide tends to dissolve some of the CuS and also results in the formation of a white, finely divided precipitate of free sulfur when the solution is acidified later in the procedure.

$$S_2^{--} + 2H_3O^+ \rightleftharpoons \underline{S}\downarrow + H_2S\uparrow + 2H_2O$$

The following tabulation summarizes the solubility of the sulfides of Group II, Division B, in various reagents.

Reagent	Sulfides Dissolved	Sulfides Not Dissolved
NH_4OH	As_2S_3, As_2S_5, Sb_2S_3, Sb_2S_5	SnS, SnS_2, HgS
$(NH_4)_2S$	As_2S_3, As_2S_5, Sb_2S_3, Sb_2S_5, SnS_2	SnS, HgS
$(NH_4)_2S_2$	As_2S_3, As_2S_5, Sb_2S_3, Sb_2S_5, SnS, SnS_2	HgS
NaOH	As_2S_3, As_2S_5, Sb_2S_3, Sb_2S_5, SnS, SnS_2	HgS
Na_2S + NaOH	As_2S_3, As_2S_5, Sb_2S_3, Sb_2S_5, SnS_2, HgS	SnS
Na_2S_2 + NaOH	As_2S_3, As_2S_5, Sb_2S_3, Sb_2S_5, SnS, SnS_2, HgS	
CH_3CSNH_2 + NaOH	As_2S_3, As_2S_5, Sb_2S_3, Sb_2S_5, SnS, SnS_2, HgS	

Reprecipitation of the Sulfides

To obtain the sulfides from the solution containing the complex sulfide it is necessary to increase the concentration of the cations to a value such that, for example,

$$[As^{3+}]^2[S^{--}]^3 > K_{As_2S_3}$$

This is done by increasing the extent of the dissociation of the complex ions:

$$AsS_3^{3-} \rightleftharpoons As^{3+} + \boxed{\begin{array}{c} 3S^{--} \\ + \\ 6H_3O^+ \end{array}} \rightleftharpoons 3H_2S\uparrow + 6H_2O$$

The addition of an acid displaces the equilibria in the direction of an increased concentration of As^{3+} because of the formation and escape of H_2S. The concentration of the cation increases to such an extent that, for example,

$$[As^{3+}]^2[S^{--}]^3 > K_{As_2S_3}$$

and reprecipitation of the sulfides occurs. Since a large excess of acid will dissolve SnS and some Sb_2S_3, an indicator is used to determine when the proper amount of acid has been added. One advantage in using thioacetamide as a source of sulfide is that large amounts of free sulfur do not form as in the case of the polysulfide reagents used previously. It must be emphasized that all the sulfide reactions that use thioacetamide must be carried out at elevated temperatures by placing the test tubes in a hot (boiling) water bath. This is done to increase the rate of the hydrolysis of CH_3CSNH_2 and also the rate of the other reactions.

Separation of Sb_2S_3, SnS, and SnS_2 from As_2S_3 and HgS

The order in which these sulfides dissolve as the H_3O^+ concentration is increased is:

$$SnS, SnS_2, Sb_2S_3, HgS, As_2S_3$$

To dissolve SnS, SnS_2, and Sb_2S_3 and leave HgS and As_2S_3 undissolved, the concentration of S^{--} must be such that

$$[Sb^{3+}]^2[S^{--}]^3 < K_{Sb_2S_3}, \text{ and } [Hg^{++}][S^{--}] > K_{HgS}$$

Increasing the concentration of H_3O^+ to 6-*M* reduces the concentration of S^{--} to

$$(6)^2[S^{--}] = 1.2 \times 10^{-23}, \text{ or } [S^{--}] = 3.3 \times 10^{-25}$$

This value of S^{--} is sufficiently small to cause dissolution of the SnS and some of the SnS_2 and Sb_2S_3. However, before appreciable quantities have dissolved, the increased concentration of the cations will make the ion concentration product again equal to $K_{s.p.}$.

$$[Sb^{3+}]^2[S^{--}]^3 = K_{Sb_2S_3}$$

The system is then in equilibrium and the precipitate does not dissolve further. If 6-*M* perchloric acid is used, both SnS_2 and Sb_2S_3 remain undissolved. However, when 6-*M* HCl is used, the concentration of the cations is reduced because of the formation of the complex ions $SnCl_6^{--}$ and $SbCl_4^-$, so that more of the sulfides are dissolved. Perchlorate ions do not readily form complex ions. Actually the SnS_2 will dissolve after a long time in 6-*N* HCl at room temperature, but Sb_2S_3 requires a higher temperature.

If the temperature of the solution is increased, the H_2S becomes less soluble and escapes, thereby shifting the following equilibria to the right:

$$H_3O^+ + S^{--} \rightleftharpoons HS^- + H_2O$$
$$H_3O^+ + HS^- \rightleftharpoons H_2S\uparrow + H_2O$$

The formation of the complex ion $SbCl_4^-$ aids in bringing about the dissolution of the Sb_2S_3 precipitate because the formation of this ion reduces the concentration of Sb^{3+}. Similar equations can be written for SnS_2. An elevated temperature is needed for its dissolution because the reaction is slow at room temperature.

Separation of As_2S_3 from HgS

If the concentration of the sulfide ion in a saturated solution of a sulfide is of the order of 1×10^{-25} or less, it is not possible to dissolve the sulfides with H_3O^+. This is true because $[H_3O^+]^2[S^{--}]$ does not exceed $K_{s.p.}$ for H_2S, and equilibrium is established before the sulfides are dissolved and no further reduction of the concentration of S^{--} occurs.

In order to dissolve sulfides that are as insoluble as As_2S_3 and HgS, it is necessary to reduce the concentration of the sulfide ion by oxidation or the concentration of the cation by the formation of complex ions. Frequently both are done. In separating As_2S_3 from HgS advantage is taken of the amphoteric properties of As_2S_3 and the tendency of As^{3+} to form complex oxy-ions and thio-ions such as AsO_2^- and $AsOS^-$ which can be oxidized to AsO_4^{3-} with H_2O_2. The two sulfides are treated with ammonium hydroxide and hydrogen peroxide. The overall reaction of OH^- ions in the NH_4OH solution with As_2S_3 is

$$As_2S_3 + 3OH^- \rightleftharpoons 2AsOS^- + HS^- + H_2O$$

The hydrogen peroxide then oxidizes the HS^- to SO_4^{--} and the $AsOS^-$ to AsO_4^{3-}. HgS is not dissolved by this treatment because the sulfide ion concentration in equilibrium with it is too small to be appreciably oxidized by H_2O_2.

Dissolution of HgS

In order to dissolve HgS it is necessary to reduce the concentration of both Hg^{++} and S^{--}. This is done in the Procedures by means of a mixture of NaClO and HCl (HClO + HCl). The HClO oxidizes S^{--} to free sulfur and Cl^- unites with Hg^{++} to form $HgCl_4^{--}$. The reaction may be formulated as follows to show the effect of these two reactions:

$$\begin{array}{rcccc} \underline{HgS} \rightleftharpoons & \boxed{Hg^{++}} & + & & \boxed{S^{--}} \\ 4HCl + 4H_2O \rightleftharpoons & \boxed{4Cl^-} & + & 3H_3O^+ + & \boxed{H_3O^+} \\ HClO \rightarrow & \uparrow\downarrow & & & \boxed{HClO} \\ & HgCl_4^{--} & & & \rightleftharpoons Cl^- + \underline{S}\downarrow + 2H_2O \end{array}$$

The overall reaction is

$$\underline{HgS} + 3Cl^- + HClO + H_3O^+ \rightleftharpoons HgCl_4^{--} + \underline{S}\downarrow + 2H_2O$$

The equilibria are shifted to the right and the concentrations of Hg^{++} and S^{--} are reduced to such an extent that

$$[Hg^{++}][S^{--}] < K_{s.p.}$$

Aqua regia could also be used to dissolve HgS.

Dissolution of Other Sulfides by Oxidation

The sulfides of Pb^{++}, Bi^{3+}, Cu^{++}, and Cd^{++} are dissolved in 4-*N* HNO_3 rather than in concentrated hydrochloric acid because the Cl^- might form a precipitate with Pb^{++}. By oxidizing the sulfide ion with nitric acid the ion product for these sulfides becomes less than their respective solubility product constants and the precipitates dissolve. Thus, PbS dissolves because

$$[Pb^{++}][S^{--}] < K_{s.p.}$$

The overall reaction is

$$3PbS + 2NO_3^- + 8H_3O^+ \rightleftharpoons 3Pb^{++} + 2NO + \underline{3S} + 12H_2O$$

Evaporation of the nitric acid solution of these ions with H_2SO_4 results in the formation of $PbSO_4$ which is somewhat soluble in hot concentrated H_2SO_4 because of the formation of $Pb(HSO_4)_2$. Dilution of this solution with water allows the precipitation of $PbSO_4$. After filtration, this precipitate can be dissolved readily by CH_3COONH_4 because of the formation of the slightly ionized molecule $Pb(CH_3COO)_2$. The formation of this molecule reduces the concentration of Pb^{++} to such an extent that the ion concentration product $[Pb^{++}][SO_4^{--}]$ is less than K_{PbSO_4} and the precipitate dissolves. However, even though the concentration of Pb^{++} is small in a solution of lead acetate, it is large enough to permit the precipitation of $PbCrO_4$. Addition of CrO_4^{--} to the solution causes the ion concentration product $[Pb^{++}][CrO_4^{--}]$ to become greater than K_{PbCrO_4} and a precipitate forms. It is important that the acidity of the solution not be too high, for otherwise much of the CrO_4^{--} will be converted to $Cr_2O_7^{--}$:

$$2CrO_4^{--} + 2H_3O^+ \rightleftharpoons 2HCrO_4^- + 2H_2O \rightleftharpoons Cr_2O_7^{--} + 3H_2O$$

The concentration of CrO_4^{--} will then be so low that the ion concentration product will not exceed the solubility product constant for $PbCrO_4$ and a precipitate will not form. Ammonium acetate used in dissolving the $PbSO_4$ acts as a buffer to prevent the possibility of the solution being too acidic.

Dissolution of CuS by CN^- in the Test for Cu^{++}

In the test for copper (Procedure 13), CuS and CdS are precipitated from an ammoniacal solution. Addition of KCN dissolves the black CuS but not the yellow CdS (see p. 179). The reaction with CuS may be formulated as follows:

$$\begin{array}{lll} \underline{2CuS} \rightleftharpoons & \boxed{2Cu^{++}} + 2S^{--} & \\ & \quad + & \\ & 9CN^- + 2OH^- & \rightleftharpoons 2Cu(CN)_4^{3-} + CNO^- + H_2O \end{array}$$

Cu^{++} is reduced to Cu^+ which then reacts with excess CN^- to form the very stable complex ion $Cu(CN)_4^{3-}$. The above reaction reduces the concentration of Cu^{++} so that the ion concentration product $[Cu^{++}][S^{--}]$ is much less than K_{CuS} and the precipitate dissolves.

Even though the complex $Cd(CN)_4^{--}$ ion is relatively stable, as shown by the expression for its instability constant,

$$\frac{[Cd^{++}][CN^-]^4}{[Cd(CN)_4^-]} = 1.4 \times 10^{-17}$$

the concentration of Cd^{++} is not reduced sufficiently to make

$$[Cd^{++}][S^{--}] < 1.4 \times 10^{-28}$$

and CdS does not dissolve appreciably. On the other hand, the concentration of Cu^+ resulting from the dissociation of $Cu(CN)_4^{3-}$ is so low that the ion concentration product $[Cu^+]^2[S^{--}]$ remains less than K_{Cu_2S} and a precipitate of Cu_2S does not form even though the concentration of S^{--} is high.

LABORATORY WORK—ANALYSIS OF KNOWN AND UNKNOWN SOLUTIONS

1. Obtain from the storeroom a known solution that contains all the ions of Group II. If a precipitate is present, shake the solution so that a representative sample is obtained. Add 5 drops of the solution to 1 ml. of water and analyze it according to the Procedures for Group II.

2. (Optional.) Request a student to prepare an unknown from the test solutions. Analyze it in accordance with the Procedures for Group II. (Preparation of the unknown: To 1 ml. of water add 2 drops of any four or five different test solutions for the ions of Group II.)

3. Obtain Unknown No. 2 from the storeroom and analyze it according to the Procedures for Group II. Use 5 drops of the unknown in 1 ml. of water for the analysis. Make certain that a representative sample is obtained by shaking the solution if a precipitate is present. Follow the directions carefully with respect to adjusting the pH and also with respect to the time and temperature of the sulfide precipitations. After the analysis is completed, report the results on an Unknown Report Blank, indicating, if requested by the instructor, the approximate concentration of each ion in the unknown solution (0.1, 1, or 5 mg./ml.).

PROCEDURES FOR THE ANALYSIS OF GROUP II

Analysis of Group II, Known or Unknown. Follow Procedures 7 through 20. Use 5 drops of the solution in 1 ml. of water.

Analysis of a General Unknown. The solution at this point is the filtrate from Group I, Procedure 5, and it may contain the ions of Groups II, III, IV, and V. Read the Discussion of the Procedure for the analysis of Group II (p. 157) before proceeding with the analysis.

---

7. **Filtrate from Group I or Group II, Known or Unknown:** Evaporate the solution to incipient dryness (still moist), add 5 drops of 1-*N* HCl and dilute to 1 ml. with water, or adjust the H_3O^+ concentration to about 0.2- to 0.3-*N* by means of indicators (p. 159). To this solution add 5 drops of a 5% solution of thioacetamide. Set the tube in a hot (boiling) water bath and fit it tightly with a rubber-tipped filter tube that has a loose plug of cotton or glass fiber in its tapered end (Fig. 4.20). Fill the filter tube about three-fourths full of water. Note the time and allow the assembly to remain in the *boiling* water bath for *5 minutes* or longer. Force the water from the filter tube into the test tube and allow the solution to remain in the boiling water for *2 minutes* or longer (time it). Filter the solution containing the precipitate through a cotton filter medium. Wash the precipitate on the filter medium with 1 ml. of water to which 1 drop of 1-*N* HCl has been added. Allow 4 or 5 drops of this acid wash solution to run into the filtrate and discard the remainder of the wash solution.

---

21. **Filtrate:** Groups III, IV, and V.

8. **Precipitate:** PbS, Bi_2S_3, CuS, CdS, HgS, As_2S_3, Sb_2S_3, and SnS(SnS_2). Place the filter tube containing the precipitate in a test tube and to the filter tube add 10 drops of 4-*N* NaOH and 1 drop of thioacetamide. Stir the precipitate with a microstirring rod and place the assembly in the hot water bath. The NaOH-thioacetamide solution should be allowed to pass slowly through the precipitate in order to dissolve completely the sulfides of Division B (HgS, As_2S_3, Sb_2S_3, SnS, and SnS_2). After the NaOH-thioacetamide solution has passed through the filter medium, add 10 drops more of 4-*N* NaOH and 1 drop of thioacetamide to the undissolved sulfides in the filter tube, and again permit this solution to pass slowly through the filter medium while the test tube is heated in the hot water bath. Remove the filter tube containing the undissolved sulfides of Division A (PbS, Bi_2S_3, CuS, and CdS) from the test tube and wash the precipitate with 1 to 2 ml. of water to which a few drops of 1-*N* NH_4NO_3 have been added. Discard this wash solution. Reserve the solution of the dissolved sulfides (Division B) for analysis by means of Procedure 14.

9. **Undissolved Sulfides (Division A):** PbS, Bi_2S_3, CuS, and CdS. Put 2 ml. of water in an evaporation test tube (Fig. 4.17). In this tube place the filter tube which contains the undissolved sulfides and add to the filter tube 1 ml. of 4-*N* HNO_3. Carefully bring the water in the evaporation test tube to boiling and boil it until the sulfides dissolve. Force the HNO_3 solution into the evaporation test tube if it has not passed through the filter medium. Wash the filter medium with about 10 drops of water. Add this wash water to the HNO_3 solution in the evaporation test tube. To this solution add 5 drops of 4-*N* H_2SO_4 and evaporate the solution until *SO_3 fumes* are evolved. Allow the tube to cool, and then add 1 ml. of water. Warm the water and loosen the residue with a rubber policeman (Fig. 4.18). Filter off any undissolved residue ($PbSO_4$) and wash it with a little water (10 drops).

10. **Residue:** $PbSO_4$. To the residue on the filter medium add 5 drops of 1-*N* CH_3COONH_4. Force the solution into a test tube and wash the filter medium with about 10 drops of water. To the filtrate add 1 drop of 0.5-*M* K_2CrO_4. A yellow precipitate confirms the presence of lead.

11. **Filtrate:** Bi^{3+}, Cu^{++}, and Cd^{++}. Drop by drop, add an excess of 15-*N* NH_4OH. (NOTE: The solution should smell strongly of NH_3. From 3 to 5 drops will be required.) Filter off the precipitate and wash the filter medium with about 10 drops of water.

12. **Precipitate:** $Bi(OH)_3$. Confirm the presence of bismuth by one of the following tests:

a. Add 3 drops of 4-*N* NaOH and 1 drop of 1-*N* tin (II) chloride. A black precipitate shows the presence of bismuth.

b. Add 2 or 3 drops of antipyrine-potassium iodide reagent and 1 drop of 4-*N* CH_3COOH. There will be a deep reddish-orange color on the filter if bismuth is present.

13. **Filtrate:** $Cu(NH_3)_4^{++}$ and $Cd(NH_3)_4^{++}$. Add to this filtrate 1 drop of thioacetamide and place the tube in the hot water bath. If copper is present, a black precipitate (CuS) will form. This confirms the presence of copper.

To this mixture add 1 or 2 drops of 1-*N* KCN. If only copper is present, the CuS will dissolve and a clear solution will be obtained. If cadmium is present, a yellow precipitate will remain in the solution after the addition of KCN. This confirms the presence of cadmium. (NOTE: If a black precipitate is not obtained on the addition of thioacetamide, cadmium will be precipitated as a yellow sulfide and KCN need not be added.)

14. **Dissolved Sulfides (Division B):** The filtrate contains the thio-ions, HgS_2^{--}, AsS_3^{3-}, SbS_3^{3-}, SnS_3^{--}, and $SnOS^{--}$. To the filtrate add 1 drop of bromcresol green indicator, and then 6-*N* HCl drop by drop, until the green color of the indicator changes to yellow (pH approximately 4), or until a precipitate is obtained. Place the tube in the hot water bath for 1 or 2 minutes. Filter off the precipitate through a *glass fiber filter medium.* Discard the filtrate. (NOTE: The filtrate may have a murky appearance. This is due to finely divided sulfur and may be disregarded.) Wash the precipitate with about 1 ml. of water to which a drop of 1-*N* HCl is added.

15. **Precipitate:** HgS, As_2S_3, Sb_2S_3, and SnS_2. Place the filter tube containing the precipitated sulfides in a clean test tube and place the assembly in the hot water bath. Add to the precipitate 1 ml. of 6-*N* HCl and stir with a micro stirring rod. Allow the acid to pass slowly through the precipitate. After the acid has passed through, add 1 ml. more of the 6-*N* HCl to the undissolved sulfides and allow the acid to pass slowly through the filter medium. (NOTE: The sulfides of antimony and tin dissolve in hot 6-*N* HCl, but the sulfides of arsenic and mercury are not soluble in 6-*N* HCl. If the HCl is not hot and if it passes through the filter tube too rapidly, some of the SnS_2 and Sb_2S_3 may not be dissolved.) Keep the HCl solution for Procedure 19.

16. **Undissolved Sulfides:** HgS—black, As_2S_3—yellow. Wash the sulfides with 2 ml. of water. Discard the wash water. Add to the sulfides 10 drops of 4-*N* NH_4OH and 3 drops of 3% H_2O_2. Place the filter tube in a test tube and set the assembly in the hot water bath. Stir the sulfides with a micro stirring rod, and then force the NH_4OH-H_2O_2 solution into the test tube. Add 1 ml. of water to the filter tube and force this wash water into the test tube containing the NH_4OH-H_2O_2 solution.

17. **Undissolved Sulfide:** HgS. To the black precipitate on the filter medium add 5 drops of 5% NaClO and 1 drop of 6-*N* HCl. Stir the precipitate. Add 1 ml. of water to the filter tube and force the solution into a clean test tube. Confirm the presence of mercury by one of the following tests:

a. Add 1 drop of 15-*N* NH_4OH, 1 drop of 1-*N* NH_4I, and 3 to 5 drops of 4-*N* NaOH. A brown precipitate shows the presence of mercury. (See Group I, 3.)

b. Add 2 drops of 4-*N* NaOH and 1 drop of 0.5-*M* hydroxylamine sulfate. A white or gray to black precipitate shows the presence of mercury.

18. **Filtrate:** AsO_4^{3-}. Add 1 drop of 15-*N* NH_4OH and 3 drops of the magnesium nitrate mixture. A white precipitate indicates the presence of arsenic. Warm the test tube in the hot water bath and filter off the precipitate. To a test tube add 5 drops of the ammonium molybdate solution. Place the filter tube containing the NH_4MgAsO_4 precipitate in the test tube containing the molybdate solution, and then add 10 drops of 4-*N* HNO_3 to the filter tube. Force the HNO_3 solution into the test tube. Place the test tube in the hot water bath for several minutes. A yellow precipitate confirms the presence of arsenic.

19. **HCl Solution from 15:** $SnCl_6^{--}$ and $SbCl_4^{-}$. Evaporate the HCl solution to incipient dryness (still moist). To the residue add 2 drops of 6-*N* HCl and 2 ml. of water. Divide the solution into two parts, and test for tin and antimony by means of Procedure 20.

20. a. **Confirmatory Test for Sn^{4+}:** To one part of the solution from 19 add 1 drop of malachite green indicator and 5 drops of m-nitro-phenyl-arsonic acid ($NO_2C_6H_4 \cdot AsO(OH)_2$). Place the tube in the hot water bath. If tin is present a green precipitate will form.

b. **Confirmatory Test for Sb^{3+}:** To the other part of the solution from 19 add 4 drops of 0.5-*N* $(NH_4)_2C_2O_4$ and 1 drop of thioacetamide. Place the tube in the hot water bath for 1 or 2 minutes. If antimony is present a reddish-orange precipitate will form. (NOTE: If both tin and antimony are present, the reddish-orange precipitate may turn dark after from 5 to 10 minutes in the hot water bath. If only tin is present, a yellow precipitate of SnS_2 or a brown precipitate of SnS may form in the solution in 5 to 10 minutes. The reddish-orange precipitate of Sb_2S_3 forms within 1 or 2 minutes.)

Procedure	Equations	Purpose—Discussion
7. Adjust $[H_3O^+]$ to about 0.2- to 0.3-M. Add thioacetamide and heat in a boiling water bath.	$CH_3CSNH_2 + 2H_2O \rightleftharpoons CH_3COO^- + NH_4^+ + H_2S$ $Pb^{++} + H_2S + 2H_2O \rightleftharpoons PbS\downarrow + 2H_3O^+$ black $2Bi^{3+} + 3H_2S + 6H_2O \rightleftharpoons Bi_2S_3\downarrow + 6H_3O^+$ brown $Cu^{++} + H_2S + 2H_2O \rightleftharpoons CuS\downarrow + 2H_3O^+$ black $2Cu^+ + H_2S + 2H_2O \rightleftharpoons Cu_2S\downarrow + 2H_3O^+$ black $Cd^{++} + H_2S + 2H_2O \rightleftharpoons CdS\downarrow + 2H_3O^+$ yellow $2Sb^{3+} + 3H_2S + 6H_2O \rightleftharpoons Sb_2S_3\downarrow + 6H_3O^+$ orange $Sn^{++} + H_2S + 2H_2O \rightleftharpoons SnS\downarrow + 2H_3O^+$ brown $Sn^{4+} + 2H_2S + 4H_2O \rightleftharpoons SnS_2\downarrow + 4H_3O^+$ yellow $AsO_4^{3-} + H_2S \rightleftharpoons AsO_3^{3-} + S^\circ\downarrow + H_2O$ $2AsO_3^{3-} + 3H_2S + 6H_3O^+ \rightleftharpoons As_2S_3\downarrow + 12H_2O$ yellow $Hg^{++} + H_2S + 2H_2O \rightleftharpoons HgS\downarrow + 2H_3O^+$ black *Group III* $2Fe^{3+} + H_2S + 2H_2O \rightleftharpoons 2Fe^{++} + S^\circ\downarrow + 2H_3O^+$ white	The reddish color of the malachite green-thymol blue indicators shows that the concentration of H_3O^+ is about 0.2-N. This concentration adjusts the $S^=$ to a value that allows the precipitation of Group II and prevents the precipitation of Group III. The white oxysalts of Bi^{3+} and Sb^{3+} or the hydroxide of Sn^{4+} may form during the adjustment of the acidity. They are converted to sulfides. The indicators may be adsorbed by some of the precipitates and impart a color to them different from the true colors of the sulfides. These imparted colors are disregarded since they do not interfere with the reactions for the separation and identification of the ions. The rate of precipitation of the sulfides depends on their solubility, the concentration of $S^=$, the temperature of the water bath, and the H_3O^+ concentration. The $S^=$ reacts with the cations as it is hydrolyzed from thioacetamide. The least soluble sulfides are precipitated first; and the more soluble sulfides, such as PbS, CdS, SnS, and SnS_2, are precipitated later, and then completely only after the H_3O^+ has been reduced to about 0.1-N. Sufficient $S^=$ for the complete precipitation of the ions of Group II requires from 5 to 10 minutes, depending on the amount and nature of the ions present. When sufficient $S^=$ has been produced to precipitate as sulfides the ions in the solution, bubbles of H_2S will form at the surface of the solution.
Force the water from the water-sealed filter tube into the test tube.	$Pb^{++} + H_2S + 2H_2O \rightleftharpoons PbS\downarrow + 2H_3O^+$ black $Cd^{++} + H_2S + 2H_2O \rightleftharpoons CdS\downarrow + 2H_3O^+$ yellow	

Procedure	Equations	Purpose—Discussion
	$Sn^{++} + H_2S + 2H_2O \rightleftharpoons SnS\downarrow + 2H_3O^+$ $\underline{\text{SnS}}$ brown	The water-sealed filter tube is used to conserve any evolved H_2S and to prevent the escape of the gas into the atmosphere. In the absence of Group II, a small white precipitate may be obtained as the result of the oxidation of H_2S to S by Fe^{3+} or other oxidants. When the sulfides are precipitated, the concentration of H_3O^+ increases, as is shown by the equations. Hence, the water from the water-sealed filter tube is added to the solution to reduce the H_3O^+ concentration to about 0.1-*N*. At this H_3O^+ concentration, CdS, PbS, and SnS are precipitated more completely. The sulfides should be filtered off without delay to diminish the post-precipitation of ZnS. The sulfides are washed with dilute HCl to prevent peptization.
8. Add 4-*N* NaOH and thioacetamide to the sulfides on the filter medium.	PbS, CdS, Bi_2S_3, and CuS are not soluble in a solution of $NaOH\text{-}CH_3CSNH_2$. $CH_3CSNH_2 + 3OH^- \rightleftharpoons S^= + CH_3COO^- + NH_3 + H_2O$ $\underline{HgS} + S^= \rightleftharpoons HgS_2^=$ $\underline{As_2S_3} + 3S^= \rightleftharpoons 2AsS_3^{3-}$ $\underline{Sb_2S_3} + 3S^= \rightleftharpoons 2SbS_3^{3-}$ $\underline{SnS_2} + 2S^= \rightleftharpoons SnS_4^{4-}$ $\underline{SnS} + 2OH^- \rightleftharpoons SnOS^= + H_2O$	The sulfides of mercury, arsenic, antimony, and tin may be considered amphoteric substances. The sulfides of arsenic, antimony, and tin (IV) are easily dissolved by a moderate excess of $S^=$. However, a high concentration of $S^=$ is required to convert HgS to $HgS_2^=$. The presence of a high concentration of OH^- favors markedly the increase of the $S^=$ concentration. $(H_2S + 2OH^- \rightleftharpoons S^= + 2H_2O)$ The SnS is probably complexed to $SnOS^=$ by the high concentration of OH^-. The amount of CuS dissolved is negligible. The undissolved sulfides are washed with water containing NH_4NO_3 to prevent peptization.

CHEMICAL REACTIONS IN THE ANALYSIS OF GROUP II

(Continued)

Procedure	Equations	Purpose—Discussion
9. Add 4-*N* HNO_3 to the undissolved sulfides, and heat.	$3PbS + 2NO_3^- + 8H_3O^+ \rightleftharpoons 3Pb^{++} + 3S^\circ + 2NO\uparrow + 12H_2O$ $Bi_2S_3 + 2NO_3^- + 8H_3O^+ \rightleftharpoons 2Bi^{3+} + 3S^\circ + 2NO\uparrow + 12H_2O$ $3CdS + 2NO_3^- + 8H_3O^+ \rightleftharpoons 3Cd^{++} + 3S^\circ + 2NO\uparrow + 12H_2O$ $3CuS + 2NO_3^- + 8H_3O^+ \rightleftharpoons 3Cu^{++} + 3S^\circ + 2NO\uparrow + 12H_2O$	The dissolution of the sulfides is more rapid and complete at elevated temperatures. The residue of sulfur which remains on the filter medium may enclose a small amount of the sulfides.
Add H_2SO_4 and evaporate to SO_3 fumes.	$Pb^{++} + SO_4^= \rightleftharpoons PbSO_4\downarrow$ (white) $2NO_3^- + H_2SO_4 \overset{heat}{\rightleftharpoons} SO_4^= + 2HNO_3\uparrow$ $2Cl^- + H_2SO_4 \overset{heat}{\rightleftharpoons} SO_4^= + 2HCl\uparrow$ $H_2SO_4 \overset{heat}{\rightleftharpoons} H_2O\uparrow + SO_3\uparrow$ $PbSO_4 + H_2SO_4 \rightleftharpoons Pb^{++} + 2HSO_4^-$	It is necessary to evaporate to white fumes of SO_3 in order to remove Cl^- and NO_3^-. These ions increase the solubility of $PbSO_4$. Do not mistake the fumes of HNO_3 for the *dense* white fumes of SO_3.
Add water.	$Pb^{++} + HSO_4^- + H_2O \rightleftharpoons PbSO_4\downarrow + H_3O^+ + HSO_4^-$	Addition of too much water may cause the precipitation of $(BiO)_2SO_4$.
10. Add CH_3COONH_4 to the $PbSO_4$.	$PbSO_4 + 2CH_3COO^- \rightleftharpoons Pb(CH_3COO)_2 + SO_4^=$	$PbSO_4$ dissolves because of the formation of the weak salt $Pb(CH_3COO)_2$.
Add K_2CrO_4 to the filtrate.	$Pb(CH_3COO)_2 + CrO_4^= \rightleftharpoons PbCrO_4\downarrow + 2CH_3COO^-$	$PbCrO_4$ is less soluble than $PbSO_4$, and is not dissolved in an acetate solution.
11. Add NH_4OH to Bi^{3+}, Cu^{++}, and Cd^{++}.	$Bi^{3+} + 3NH_3 + 3H_2O \rightleftharpoons Bi(OH)_3\downarrow + 3NH_4^+$ (white) $Cu^{++} + 4NH_3 \rightleftharpoons Cu(NH_3)_4^{++}$ (blue) $Cd^{++} + 4NH_3 \rightleftharpoons Cd(NH_3)_4^{++}$ (colorless)	A small amount of NH_4OH precipitates the hydroxides of all three ions, but $Cu(OH)_2$ and $Cd(OH)_2$ dissolve in excess NH_4OH because of the formation of the complex ammines. A blue color shows the presence of Cu^{++}. $Bi(OH)_3$ is sometimes translucent and difficult to see. Therefore a confirmatory test should always be made.

Procedure	Equations	Purpose—Discussion
12a. Add $SnCl_2$ and NaOH to the $Bi(OH)_3$.	$Sn^{++} + 2OH^- \rightleftharpoons \underset{\text{white}}{\underline{Sn(OH)_2}} \downarrow$ $\underline{Sn(OH)_2} + 2OH^- \rightleftharpoons Sn(OH)_4^=$ $2Bi(OH)_3 + 3Sn(OH)_4^= \rightleftharpoons \underset{\text{black}}{\underline{2Bi}} \downarrow + 3Sn(OH)_6^=$	NH_4^+ interferes with the formation of $Sn(OH)_4^=$. Therefore the $Bi(OH)_3$ should be washed well. It is necessary to use excess NaOH, for otherwise only a white precipitate of $Sn(OH)_2$ is obtained. A solution of $Sn(OH)_2$ slowly turns dark because of self-oxidation-reduction in which Sn is formed. $Bi(OH)_3$ turns black immediately. The tin must be in the Sn^{++} oxidation state to obtain the reduction of Bi^{3+} to Bi°.
12b. To the $Bi(OH)_3$ add KI-antipyrine and then CH_3COOH.	Forms an orange double salt, HI (antipyrine) BiI_3.	If Pb^{++} and Hg^{++} have not been completely removed, a yellow to red iodide precipitate may give a false indication of the presence of Bi^{3+}.
13. To the ammoniacal solution add 1 drop of thioacetamide. Place the tube in the hot water bath. If a black precipitate was obtained, add 1 or 2 drops of 1-*N* KCN.	$Cu^{++} + CH_3CSNH_2 + 2OH^- \rightleftharpoons \underset{\text{black}}{\underline{CuS}} \downarrow + CH_3COO^- + NH_4^+$ $Cd^{++} + CH_3CSNH_2 + 2OH^- \rightleftharpoons \underset{\text{yellow}}{\underline{CdS}} \downarrow + CH_3COO^- + NH_4^+$ $\underline{CdS} + KCN \rightleftharpoons$ no reaction $\underset{\text{black}}{\underline{2CuS}} + 9CN^- + 2OH^- \rightleftharpoons 2S^= + \underset{\text{colorless}}{2Cu(CN)_4^{3-}} + CNO^- + H_2O$	A black precipitate is quickly formed when copper is present. In the absence of copper, the precipitate will be yellow if cadmium is present. The addition of KCN dissolves the black CuS precipitate but not the yellow CdS precipitate if present. Bi_2S_3, black, is not soluble in a KCN solution. Therefore filtrate 11 must be made alkaline to remove Bi^{3+} as $Bi(OH)_3$. If both Cu^{++} and Cd^{++} are present, the precipitate remaining after the addition of KCN may have an orange tint. This tint is probably due to a little adsorbed CuS on the yellow CdS.

Procedure	Equations	Purpose—Discussion
14. Add bromcresol green indicator and 6-*N* HCl to $HgS_2^=$, AsS_3^{3-}, SbS_3^{3-}, $SnS_3^=$, and $SnOS^=$ solution. Put the tube in the hot water bath for 1 or 2 minutes.	$HgS_2^= + 2H_3O^+ \rightleftharpoons \underset{\text{black}}{HgS} \downarrow + H_2S \uparrow + 2H_2O$ $2AsS_3^{3-} + 6H_3O^+ \rightleftharpoons \underset{\text{yellow}}{As_2S_3} \downarrow + 3H_2S \uparrow + 6H_2O$ $2SbS_3^{3-} + 6H_3O^+ \rightleftharpoons \underset{\text{orange}}{Sb_2S_3} \downarrow + 3H_2S \uparrow + 6H_2O$ $SnS_3^= + 2H_3O^+ \rightleftharpoons \underset{\text{yellow}}{SnS_2} \downarrow + H_2S \uparrow + 2H_2O$ $SnOS^= + 2H_3O^+ \rightleftharpoons \underset{\text{brown}}{SnS} \downarrow + 3H_2O$	The presence of the indicator insures the complete acidification of the solution. This is required for the reprecipitation of the sulfides. Too much acid is avoided because it may dissolve SnS_2. If the ions of Division B are absent, the solution at a pH of 4 will become yellow and a little S° (white) may precipitate. This precipitated sulfur remains suspended in the solution in finely divided form. On the other hand, if the sulfides of Division B are present, the precipitate will coagulate and settle to the bottom of the tube when the solution is heated in the water bath.
15. Heat HgS, As_2S_3, Sb_2S_3, SnS_2, and SnS with 6-*N* HCl.	$\underline{Sb_2S_3} + 8Cl^- + 6H_3O^+ \rightleftharpoons 2SbCl_4^- + 3H_2S \uparrow + 6H_2O$ $\underline{SnS_2} + 6Cl^- + 4H_3O^+ \rightleftharpoons SnCl_6^= + 2H_2S \uparrow + 4H_2O$ $\underline{2SnS} + O_2 + 12Cl^- + 8H_3O^+ \rightleftharpoons 2SnCl_6^= + 2H_2S \uparrow + 10H_2O$ $\underline{SnS} + 2H_3O^+ \rightleftharpoons Sn^{++} + H_2S \uparrow + 2H_2O$	Hot 6-*N* HCl dissolves Sb_2S_3, SnS_2, and SnS. The Sn^{++} may be oxidized to Sn^{4+} by the free oxygen in the solution. No detectable amount of As_2S_3 or HgS is soluble in hot 6-*N* HCl.
16. To the undissolved HgS and As_2S_3, add NH_4OH and H_2O_2.	$\underline{As_2S_3} + 14H_2O_2 + 12OH^- \rightleftharpoons 2AsO_4^{3-} + 3SO_4^= + 20H_2O$	The HgS-As_2S_3 residue should be washed thoroughly because Cl^- in the presence of H_2O_2 increases the solubility of HgS. The As_2S_3 dissolves readily in NH_4OH. The As^{3+} is oxidized to As^{5+}, (AsO_4^{3-}), and the $S^=$ is oxidized to S^{6+}, ($SO_4^=$), by H_2O_2 in an alkaline medium.

CHEMICAL REACTIONS IN THE ANALYSIS OF GROUP II
(Continued)

Procedure	Equations	Purpose—Discussion
17. Add NaClO and HCl to the black residue, HgS.	$\underline{HgS} + 3Cl^- + HClO + H_3O^+ \rightleftharpoons HgCl_4^= + \underline{S}\downarrow + 2H_2O$	The residue dissolves because the $S^=$ is oxidized to $\underline{S}°$ and the Hg^{++} is complexed to $HgCl_4^=$.
17a. Add NH_4OH, NH_4I, and excess NaOH.	$2HgCl_4^= + NH_4^+ + I^- + 4OH^- \rightleftharpoons \underset{\text{brown}}{\underline{HOHgNHHgI}}\downarrow + 3H_2O + 8Cl^-$	See reactions under 3a (p. 130).
17b. Add NaOH and $(H_2NOH)_2H_2SO_4$.	See 3b (p. 131).	See 3b (p. 131).
18. Add magnesium nitrate mixture to AsO_4^{3-}. Dissolve NH_4MgAsO_4 in HNO_3. Add the solution to ammonium molybdate.	$AsO_4^{3-} + NH_4^+ + Mg^{++} \rightleftharpoons \underset{\text{white}}{\underline{NH_4MgAsO_4}}\downarrow$ $\underline{NH_4MgAsO_4} + 2H_3O^+ \rightleftharpoons Mg^{++} + NH_4^+ + H_2AsO_4^- + 2H_2O$ $H_2AsO_4^- + 3NH_4^+ + 12MoO_4^= + 22H_3O^+ \rightleftharpoons \underset{\text{yellow crystals}}{\underline{(NH_4)_3AsO_4 \cdot 12MoO_3}}\downarrow + 34H_2O$	Magnesium nitrate mixture is composed of $Mg(NO_3)_2$, NH_4NO_3, and NH_4OH in such proportions that Mg^{++} does not precipitate as $Mg(OH)_2$. PO_4^{3-} forms a similar precipitate (NH_4MgPO_4) with the mixture. NH_4MgAsO_4 is easily dissolved by an acid, but in a strongly acid solution the AsO_4^{3-} forms a yellow precipitate with ammonium molybdate. The formation of the yellow precipitate is favored by heating the solution in the hot water bath. PO_4^{3-} forms a similar precipitate with the reagent.
19. Evaporate the solution of $SnCl_6^=$ and $SbCl_4^-$ to incipient dryness. Add HCl and water.	See 15.	A large amount of acid decreases the sensitivity of the tests for antimony and tin. The proper amount of acid is obtained by evaporating the solution to incipient dryness, and then adding a sufficient quantity of acid to hold $SnCl_6^=$ and SbO^- in solution. The $S^=$ is also expelled.

CHEMICAL REACTIONS IN THE ANALYSIS OF GROUP II
(Continued)

Procedure	Equations	Purpose—Discussion
20a. Add 1 drop of malachite green indicator and m-nitro-phenyl-arsonic acid. Place the tube in the hot water bath.	The equation for the reaction has not been determined as the formula for the precipitate is not known.	β-$Sn(OH)_4$ forms with m-nitro-phenyl-arsonic acid a white precipitate which, however, gives a green "lake" in the presence of malachite green indicator. A precipitate forms if antimony is present, but the antimony precipitate dissolves readily in a hot solution, whereas a hot solution favors a flocculent precipitate of tin.
20b. Add $(NH_4)_2C_2O_4$ and thioacetamide. Warm the solution in the water bath.	$2SbCl_4^- + 3CH_3CSNH_2 + 12H_2O \rightleftharpoons \underset{\text{orange}}{Sb_2S_3}\downarrow + 3NH_4^+ + 8Cl^- + 3CH_3COO^- + 6H_3O^+$	The orange precipitate, Sb_2S_3, forms quickly in an acid solution containing the oxalate ion ($C_2O_4^=$), whereas no precipitate is given with tin (IV). The tin is complexed or forms a weak salt with the oxalate ion. If the solution remains in the hot water for some time, a yellow precipitate of SnS_2 may form. If it stays longer, brown SnS may form. The tin reactions are slow; the antimony reaction is fast.

REVIEW QUESTIONS

1. Reproduce the schematic outline for the analysis of Group II cations.
2. Discuss the reasons for each operation in the analysis for Group II cations.
3. Study the reactions at the end of the chapter and be prepared to write equations for all those that occur during the analysis of Group II cations.
4. Describe the confirmatory test for each cation of Group II, stating in each case the conditions under which the reactions take place.
5. Give the formulas and colors of the sulfides of Group II cations.
6. For each cation, list the formulas and colors of the precipitates, other than the sulfides, encountered in the analysis of Group II.
7. List the formulas of the complex ions encountered in the analysis of Group II.
8. Discuss the acidity conditions required for the precipitation of Group II sulfides.
9. If the final acidity is too low while Group II sulfides are being precipitated, which sulfide of Group III is most likely to be found with Group II?

10. If the final acidity is too high while Group II sulfides are being precipitated, which sulfides of Group II may not be precipitated?
11. As thioacetamide hydrolyzes to form H_2S, the concentration of S^{--} gradually builds up. List the following sulfides in the order in which they will precipitate: CuS, CdS, PbS, HgS.
12. State the conditions necessary for complete precipitation of the sulfides when thioacetamide is used.
13. Why do sulfides precipitate more readily in hot than in cold solutions?
14. Discuss two methods for adjusting the concentration of H_3O^+ to the value required for the precipitation of Group II sulfides.
15. In what way might certain indicators affect the color of the lighter-colored sulfides? Is this a serious difficulty in the analysis? What indicator might be used to avoid this discoloration?
16. List the sulfides of Group II that are dissolved by NaOH plus S^{--}. Write the equations for the reactions and state which of the sulfides dissolves least readily.
17. Which sulfides of Group II are insoluble in the following reagents: 3-*N* HCl, 12-*N* HCl, 4-*N* HNO_3?
18. Write the equations for the reactions that occur when HgS is dissolved by HCl plus HClO, and by aqua regia.
19. Explain why $PbSO_4$ dissolves in hot concentrated H_2SO_4 but is reprecipitated when water is added. Write equations for the reactions.
20. If $(BiO)_2SO_4$ formed with $PbSO_4$ because of the addition of too much water in Procedure 9, describe at least two ways of separating them.
21. Why is $PbSO_4$ readily soluble in a solution of CH_3COONH_4? Would it be as soluble in a solution of CH_3COOH of the same concentration? Why or why not?
22. What ions other than Pb^{++} form insoluble chromates? Is there any reason to expect them at this point in the analysis? Why or why not?
23. If Pb^{++} is not found in Group I, can a test for it be omitted in Group II? Explain your answer.
24. Which ions of Group II form complexes with NH_3? What application is made of this tendency in analyzing for Group II?
25. Write equations for the reactions of the hydroxides of the ions of Group II that dissolve in excess NaOH.
26. Describe at least two ways of reducing Bi^{3+} to Bi°.
27. If Bi^{3+} is not completely removed as $Bi(OH)_3$ in Procedure 11, what difficulty might there be in confirmatory tests for Cu^{++} and Cd^{++}?
28. Refer to the summary of reactions in Chapter 9 and explain how $K_4Fe(CN)_6$ could be used to test for Cu^{++} in the presence of Cd^{++}.
29. When the sulfides of Division B are reprecipitated, why is it desirable to keep the acidity of the solution from becoming too high? Explain how the pH of the solution is controlled.
30. Write equations for the reactions of the sulfides of Division B that dissolve in hot 6-*N* HCl. How are the other sulfides of Division B dissolved?
31. Describe Nessler's test for Hg^{++}. How can this test be used for ammonia? (See Procedure 35a.)

32. Describe the confirmatory tests for tin and antimony.
33. Identify the following ions of Group II:
   a. Forms a black sulfide insoluble in 6-*M* HNO_3.
   b. Forms a brown sulfide insoluble in NaOH + S^{--}.
   c. Forms a brown sulfide soluble in NaOH + S^{--}.
   d. Forms a yellow sulfide insoluble in 12-*M* HCl.
   e. Forms a black sulfide soluble in 3-*M* HCl.
34. What reagent might be used to separate the following pairs of compounds or ions: (a) Cu^{++} and Bi^{3+}; (b) Cu^{++} and Sb^{3+}; (c) Hg^{++} and Cd^{++}; (d) As_2S_3 and SnS; (e) Sb_2S_3 and CdS; (f) $PbSO_4$ and $PbCrO_4$; (g) HgS and Bi_2S_3; (h) CuS and CdS; (i) $Bi(OH)_3$ and $Sn(OH)_2$; (j) $Cu(OH)_2$ and $Pb(OH)_2$?
35. If a yellow precipitate is obtained when an unknown solution for Group II is treated with thioacetamide or H_2S, what ions are probably absent?
36. If a deep blue color and no precipitate are obtained when excess NH_3 is added to an unknown solution for Group II, what ion is known to be present and what ions are known to be absent?
37. Give a schematic outline for the separation and identification of the ions in the following solutions, but omit unnecessary steps: (a) Pb^{++}, Cd^{++}, As^{3+}; (b) Bi^{3+}, Cd^{++}, Hg^{++}; (c) As^{3+}, Sb^{3+}, Sn^{++}; (d) Pb^{++}, Bi^{3+}, Cu^{++}; (e) Cu^{++}, Cd^{++}, Hg^{++}, Sb^{3+}.
38. Write equations for the reactions by which the ions in the following unknown solutions might be separated and identified. Do not write equations for reactions that do not involve the ions.
   a. Pb^{++}, Cd^{++}, Hg^{++}.
   b. Cu^{++}, Bi^{3+}, As^{3+}.
   c. Cd^{++}, Sb^{3+}, Sn^{++}.
   d. Pb^{++}, Cu^{++}, Hg^{++}, As^{3+}.
   e. Bi^{3+}, Hg^{++}, As^{3+}.
   f. Cu^{++}, Cd^{++}, Sb^{3+}.
39. An unknown solution for Group II formed a black precipitate with thioacetamide or H_2S. The residue from treating the precipitate with NaOH and CH_3CSNH_2 was black. After treatment with HNO_3 and H_2SO_4, a white precipitate formed. The filtrate from this precipitate formed a white precipitate when excess NH_3 was added. When the NaOH CH_3CSNH_2 solution was acidified, a black precipitate insoluble in 6-*N* HCl and in NH_4OH plus H_2O_2 remained. What ions are indicated?
40. When CH_3CSNH_2 was added to a solution of an unknown for Group II, a white precipitate was formed, followed by a yellow, orange, and then a black precipitate. Treatment of the precipitate gave a filtrate (a) and a black residue (b). Residue (b) dissolved in HNO_3 but no precipitate formed on treatment with H_2SO_4. When treated with NH_3, the solution yielded a precipitate that dissolved in excess NH_3 to form a blue solution. The precipitate formed when filtrate (a) was acidified was orange-colored, but a yellow precipitate was left after treatment with 6-*M* HCl. What ions are indicated?
41. Refer to the summary of reactions in Chapter 9 and outline three tests that can be used to identify arsenic. Discuss any interferences due to the presence of antimony.

REVIEW QUESTIONS ON THE THEORY OF GROUP II ANALYSIS *

1. Discuss the principle by which the concentration of S^{--} is controlled in the precipitation of the sulfides.
2. Write the expressions for the primary and secondary ionization constants of H_2S. How many times larger is the primary than the secondary?
3. Show that the concentration of S^{--} in a solution containing *only* H_2S is very nearly equal to the secondary ionization constant of H_2S.
4. Give the formula for calculating the concentration of S^{--} when another acid is present with H_2S. Consider the case when the solution is unsaturated and when it is saturated with H_2S.
5. State the general relationship between the concentration of H_3O^+ and that of S^{--} in a solution saturated with H_2S. If the concentration of H_3O^+ is increased from 0.01- to 0.05-*M*, by what factor is the concentration of S^{--} changed?
6. Tabulate the acidity conditions for the precipitation of the sulfides of the cations.
7. On the basis of the solubility product principle, explain why 0.3-*N* HCl is used for separating the ions of Group II from those of Group III. Use numerical values in your explanation.
8. Use equilibria to explain why As_2S_3 is formed readily in solutions with relatively high concentrations of H_3O^+ even though the concentration of S^{--} is low.
9. Suggest a mechanism for the precipitation of the sulfides.
10. Show why consideration of the hydrolysis of the sulfide ion is important in calculating the solubility of a sulfide from the solubility product constant.
11. Explain in detail, using equations, the separation of As_2S_3, Sb_2S_3, SnS, and HgS from CuS, Bi_2S_3, PbS, and CdS.
12. Discuss the solvent effect of a number of reagents on the sulfides of Group II. What is the effect of excess sulfur in the reagents? Write equations to illustrate.
13. Write the equation for the reprecipitation of the sulfides from the thio-ions.
14. Why do SnS_2 and Sb_2S_3 dissolve in hot 6-*M* HCl but not in 6-*M* $HClO_4$?
15. Show by means of equations why elevated temperatures favor the reaction of Sb_2S_3 with 6-*N* HCl.
16. Explain why As_2S_3 is soluble in NH_4OH plus H_2O_2 and why HgS is not.
17. Why is oxidation often more effective than the addition of H_3O^+ in dissolving difficultly soluble sulfides? Illustrate.
18. Will HgS dissolve appreciably in concentrated HNO_3? Why or why not? What must be used to dissolve HgS? Write equations for two methods.
19. Write equations for the dissolution of PbS, Bi_2S_3, CuS, and CdS by HNO_3.
20. Why does $PbSO_4$ dissolve in CH_3COONH_4? Why does $PbCrO_4$ precipitate

* Note to instructor: See footnote, p. 133.

from an ammonium acetate solution of $PbSO_4$? By means of equations show the effect of acidity on the precipitation of $PbCrO_4$.

21. Discuss the function of CN^- in the tests for Cu^{++} and Cd^{++}. Write equations to illustrate.

PROBLEMS

1. If 2 ml. of a solution to be analyzed for Group II is 0.5-*N* to HCl, how many drops of 1-*N* NH_4OH will be required to neutralize it? If this neutral solution is to be made 0.3-*N* to HCl, how many drops of 4-*N* HCl should be used?
2. A solution contains 1 mg. of each of the following ions: Pb^{++}, Sn^{++}, As^{3+}, Hg^{++}. (a) Calculate the number of millimoles of H_2S required to precipitate these ions as their sulfides. (b) What volume of H_2S at 25° C. and 760 mm. Hg pressure is this? (c) How many milligrams of H_2S are required?
3. How many milligrams of H_2S are there in 5 ml. of water saturated with the gas (0.1-*M*)?
4. How many drops of 5% CH_3CSNH_2 will be required in Problem 2, assuming 50% hydrolysis of CH_3CSNH_2 to H_2S? (1 drop = 0.05 ml., or approximately 50 mg.)
5. If 1 ml. of 4-*N* HNO_3 is added to a precipitate consisting of 10 mg. of PbS, 10 mg. of Bi_2S_3, and 5 mg. of CdS, what percentage of the HNO_3 will be used up in the dissolution of these sulfides?
6. A solution contains 0.2 ml. of 4-*N* H_2SO_4 and 2 mg. of each of the following ions: Bi^{3+}, Cu^{++}, Cd^{++}. An excess of 15-*N* NH_4OH is added. How many drops of the 15-*N* NH_4OH will react with the acid and ions?
7. How many milligrams of As_2S_3 will be converted to $AsO_4{}^{3-}$ and $SO_4{}^{--}$ by an ammoniacal solution containing 3 drops of 3% H_2O_2?
8. Calculate the concentration of H_3O^+, HS^-, and S^{--} in a 0.01-*M* hydrogen sulfide solution.
9. In using the expression $[H_3O^+]^2[S^{--}] = 1.2 \times 10^{-23}$ for a saturated solution of H_2S in water, why can we not assume that $[S^{--}]$ is one-half the concentration of $[H_3O^+]$ as we do in the case of saturated solutions of such salts as Ag_2CrO_4?
10. Calculate the concentration of HS^- and S^{--} in a solution 0.01-*M* to H_3O^+ and saturated with H_2S.
11. How many of each of the following ions—S^{--}, HS^-, and H_3O^+—are there in 1 ml. of the solution in Problem 10?
12. Calculate the solubility of CuS from its solubility product constant without considering hydrolysis.
13. If the hydrolysis of S^{--} is considered, what is the calculated solubility of CuS?
14. Calculate the concentration of Pb^{++} in a saturated solution of $PbSO_4$ and of $PbCrO_4$. Explain why ammonium acetate dissolves $PbSO_4$ and not $PbCrO_4$.
15. Calculate the concentration of H_3O^+ required to prevent PbS from precipitating from 0.01-*M* Pb^{++}.

16. What concentration of H_3O^+ is required to prevent the precipitation of 0.001-M Zn^{++} as ZnS? What is the pH of this solution? What indicator has a color change at about this pH?

17. A solution is 0.01-M to Cu^{++}, and 0.1-M to H_3O^+. Calculate the concentration of S^{--} when Bi_2S_3 and when CuS starts to precipitate. Which of these two sulfides will form first if the concentration of S^{--} is gradually increased? (Compare Review Question 11, p. 183.)

18. What concentration of Pb^{++} will remain after H_2S has been passed through a solution containing Pb^{++} at an H_3O^+ concentration of 0.1-M?

19. Calculate the solubility of SnS in a solution that is saturated with H_2S and is 1-M to CH_3COOH.

20. Calculate the maximum concentration of Zn^{++} that can be present in the solution and not form ZnS if the concentration of H_3O^+ is 0.1-M.

21. Calculate the concentration of Cd^{++} in a 0.1-M solution of $Cd(CN)_4^{--}$. Show that CdS will precipitate when H_2S is passed into a neutral solution (pH = 7) containing this ion. Why is Cu_2S not precipitated under similar circumstances from a 0.1-M solution of $Cu(CN)_4^{3-}$?

22. On the basis of the solubility product constant, calculate the weight of HgS that will dissolve in a solution that is 6-M to H_3O^+ and saturated with H_2S.

CHAPTER 11

PRELIMINARY EXPERIMENTS AND REACTIONS FOR GROUP III CATIONS *

IONS OF GROUP III, DIVISION A

Test Solutions †	Ion	Concentration (mg./ml.)
0.1-*M* Iron (II) or (III) nitrate	Fe^{++} or Fe^{3+}	5.6
0.1-*M* Manganese (II) nitrate	Mn^{++}	5.5
0.1-*M* Nickel nitrate	Ni^{++}	5.9
0.1-*M* Cobalt nitrate	Co^{++}	5.9

† If desired, test solutions may be prepared to contain 10 mg. of cation per ml. (Appendix C).

The Iron (II), Fe^{++}, and Iron (III), Fe^{3+}, Ions

Fe-1. Precipitation of FeS. To 1 ml. of water add 1 drop of an iron nitrate solution and then add 1 drop of thymol blue indicator. Note the color of the solution. Now add 1 or 2 drops of 1-*N* HCl and note the color of the solution. Add 1 drop of a 5% solution of thioacetamide to this solution. Place the tube in the hot water bath and note whether a precipitate forms. (NOTE: If a white precipitate of S° forms, the test solution contained an iron (III) salt. If no precipitate of S° forms, the test solution contained an iron (II) salt.) Write the equation for the reaction. To the iron solution, with or without a precipitate, add 2 or 3 drops of 4-*N* NH_4OH. Note the color of the precipitate and write the equation for the reaction. Filter off the precipitate and wash it with water.

Fe-2. Dissolution of FeS and Reaction of Fe^{3+} with NaOH. Add 10 drops of 4-*N* HNO_3 to the filter tube containing the precipitate. Place the assembly in the hot water bath. Allow the solution to heat and note the dissolution of the precipitate. Write the equation for the reaction. Wash the filter medium with a small amount of water. Place the filtrate in an evaporation test tube and evaporate to incipient dryness. Add 1 ml. of water and transfer the solution to a smaller test tube. Add 4 or 5 drops of 4-*N* NaOH. Place the tube in the hot water bath and note

* Study the discussion of the Procedures for Group III (pp. 204 ff.) and the chemical reactions in the analysis of Group III (pp. 220 ff.) before doing these Preliminary Experiments.

whether the precipitate dissolves. (Compare with Al-2, Cr-2, and Zn-2.) If a precipitate remains, note its color and write an equation for its formation. Filter off any precipitate and wash it with water.

Fe-3. Confirmatory Test for Fe^{3+}. Reaction with SCN^-. To the precipitate on the filter medium add 4 or 5 drops of 4-*N* HNO_3. Did the precipitate dissolve? Write the equation for the reaction. Force the solution into the test tube and wash the filter medium with a little water. To the filtrate add 1 or 2 drops of 0.1-*N* NH_4SCN. Note the color of the solution and write the equation for the reaction.

The Manganese (II) Ion, Mn^{++}

Mn-1. Precipitation of MnS. To 1 ml. of water add 1 drop of the manganese nitrate test solution. Then add 1 drop of thymol blue indicator, 2 drops of 1-*N* HCl, and 1 drop of a 5% solution of thioacetamide. Place the tube in the hot water bath and note whether a precipitate forms. To this solution add 2 or 3 drops of 4-*N* NH_4OH. Note the color of the precipitate and write the equation for the reaction. Filter off the precipitate and wash it with a small amount of water.

Mn-2. Dissolution of MnS and Reaction of Mn^{++} with NaOH and H_2O_2. To the precipitate on the filter medium add 4 or 5 drops of 4-*N* HNO_3. Did the precipitate dissolve? Write the equation for the reaction. Force the solution into the test tube and wash the filter medium with a little water. Transfer the solution to an evaporation test tube and evaporate the solution to incipient dryness. To the residue add 1 ml. of water and transfer the solution to a smaller test tube. Add 4 or 5 drops of 4-*N* NaOH. Place the tube in the hot water bath. Note the color of the precipitate and write the equation for the reaction. (Compare with Al-2, Cr-2, Zn-2.) (NOTE: $Mn(OH)_2$ is white; MnOOH is brown.) To the tube containing the precipitate add 1 drop of 3% H_2O_2. Note the color of the precipitate and write the equation for the reaction. (NOTE: MnO_2 is black.) Filter off the precipitate and wash it with water.

Mn-3. Dissolution of MnO_2 by HNO_3 and $NaNO_2$. To the precipitate on the filter medium add 4 or 5 drops of 4-*N* HNO_3. Place the assembly in the hot water bath and allow the HNO_3 solution to pass through the precipitate. Did the precipitate dissolve? Now return the HNO_3 solution to the filter tube and add 1 drop of 1-*N* $NaNO_2$ (nitrite) solution. Did the addition of this nitrite cause the precipitate to dissolve? Write the equation for the reaction.

Mn-4. Confirmatory Test for Mn^{++}. Formation of MnO_4^-. Transfer the solution containing the manganese to an evaporation test tube and evaporate to incipient dryness. Add 5 drops of 4-*N* HNO_3 and 1 ml. of water to the residue. With a micro spatula add a small quantity (5 to 10 mg.) of solid $NaBiO_3$ (sodium bismuthate) to the solution. Note the color of the solution and write the equation for the reaction.

The Nickel Ion, Ni^{++}

Ni-1. Precipitation of NiS. To 1 ml. of water add 1 drop of the nickel nitrate test solution, then add 2 drops of 1-*N* HCl and 1 drop of a 5% solution of thioacetamide. Place the tube in the hot water bath and note whether a precipitate forms. Allow the tube to remain in the hot water bath for 2 or 3 minutes and then add 2 or 3 drops of 4-*N* NH_4OH. Note the color of the precipitate and write the equation for the reaction. Filter off the precipitate and wash it with water.

Ni-2. Dissolution of NiS and Reaction of Ni^{++} with NaOH. To the precipitate on the filter medium add 4 or 5 drops of 4-*N* HNO_3. Place the assembly in the hot water bath and allow the solution to heat and pass through the precipitate. If the precipitate did not dissolve, repass the HNO_3 solution through the precipitate until it dissolves. Wash the filter medium with a little water. Write the equation for the action of HNO_3 on NiS. Transfer the nickel solution to an evaporation test tube and evaporate to incipient dryness. Add 1 ml. of water to the residue. Transfer the solution to a small test tube, place it in the hot water bath, and add 3 or 4 drops of 4-*N* NaOH. Note the color of the precipitate and write the equation for the reaction. (Compare with Al-2, Cr-2, Zn-2.) Add a drop of 3% H_2O_2 to the solution with the precipitate. Was there a change in the color of the precipitate? (NOTE: $Ni(OH)_2$ has an apple-green color. $Ni(OH)_2$ is not changed to $Ni(OH)_3$ by H_2O_2.) Filter off the precipitate.

Ni-3. Confirmatory Test. Reaction with Dimethylglyoxime. To the precipitate on the filter medium add 3 or 4 drops of 4-*N* HNO_3 and 1 ml. of water. Force the solution into an evaporation test tube and evaporate to incipient dryness. To the residue add 1 ml. of water and 1 drop of phenolphthalein indicator, and then add 4-*N* NH_4OH drop by drop, until a faint pink color has been obtained in the solution (pH approximately 8). To this solution add 1 or 2 drops of dimethylglyoxime, and then 1 drop of 4-*N* CH_3COOH. Note the color of the precipitate.

The Cobalt Ion, Co^{++}

Co-1. Precipitation of CoS. To 1 ml. of water add 1 drop of the cobalt nitrate test solution, then add 2 drops of 1-*N* HCl and 1 drop of a 5% solution of thioacetamide. Place the tube in the hot water bath and note whether a precipitate forms. Allow the tube to remain in the hot water bath for 2 or 3 minutes and then add 3 or 4 drops of 4-*N* NH_4OH. Note the color of the precipitate and write the equation for the reaction. Filter off the precipitate and wash it with water.

Co-2. Dissolution of CoS. Reaction of Co^{++} with NaOH and H_2O_2. To the precipitate on the filter medium add 4 or 5 drops of 4-*N* HNO_3. Place the assembly in the hot water bath and allow the HNO_3 solution to pass through the precipitate. If the precipitate did not dissolve, repass the HNO_3 through the precipitate. (NOTE: NiS and CoS are not as easily dissolved in dilute HNO_3 as the hydroxides and other sulfides of Group III. They are not dissolved by dilute HCl even though they cannot be precipitated in acid solution.) Wash the filter medium with a little water. Transfer the cobalt solution to an evaporation test tube and evaporate to incipient dryness. Add 1 ml. of water to the residue. Transfer the solution to a small test tube and add 4 or 5 drops of 4-*N* NaOH. Place the tube in the hot water bath and note the color of the coagulated precipitate. Write the equation for the reaction. (Compare with Al-2, Cr-2, Zn-2.) Add 1 drop of 3% H_2O_2 to the tube containing the precipitate. Note the color of the precipitate and write the equation for the reaction. Filter off the precipitate and wash it with a little water.

Co-3. Dissolution of $Co(OH)_3$ with HNO_3 and $NaNO_2$. Confirmatory Test for Co^{++}. To the precipitate on the filter medium add 4 or 5 drops of 4-*N* HNO_3. Place the assembly in the hot water bath and allow the HNO_3 solution to pass through the precipitate. Did the precipitate dissolve? Return the HNO_3 solution to the filter tube and add to it 1 drop of 1-*N* $NaNO_2$ solution. Did the addition of this nitrite cause the precipitate to dissolve? (See Mn-3.) Write the equation for the reaction. Transfer the solution to an evaporation test tube and evaporate to incipient dryness. To the residue add 1 ml. of water and 1 drop of phenolphthalein indicator; then add 4-*N* NH_4OH drop by drop, until a faint pink color has been obtained in the solution (pH approximately 8). To this slightly alkaline solution add 1 or 2 drops of 2-nitroso-1-naphthol. Note the color of the precipitate. Add 1 or 2 drops of 6-*N* HCl to the solution containing the precipitate. Did the precipitate dissolve?

Co-4, Ni-4. Tests for Interference in the Confirmatory Tests for Co^{++} and Ni^{++}. To one test tube (A) add 2 ml. of water and 1 drop of the cobalt nitrate test solution. To a second test tube (B) add 2 ml. of water and 1 drop of the nickel nitrate test solution. To a third test tube (C) add 2 ml. of water and 1 drop of the nickel test solution and 1 drop of the cobalt test solution. To each of these tubes add 1 drop of phenolphthalein indicator, and then add 4-*N* NH_4OH drop by drop, until a faint pink color is obtained.

Divide the Co^{++} solution in Tube A into two parts. To one part add 1 or 2 drops of dimethylglyoxime and then 1 drop of 4-*N* CH_3COOH. To the other part add 1 or 2 drops of 2-nitroso-1-naphthol and then 1 drop of 6-*N* HCl. Place the tubes in the hot water bath. Describe the results and state whether Co^{++} reacts with dimethylglyoxime in a way that will interfere with the confirmatory test for Ni^{++}.

Divide the Ni^{++} solution in Tube B into two parts. To one part add 1 or 2 drops of dimethylglyoxime and then 1 drop of 4-*N* CH_3COOH. To the other part add 1 or 2 drops of 2-nitroso-1-naphthol and then 1 drop of 6-*N* HCl. Place the tubes in the hot water bath. Describe the results and state whether Ni^{++} reacts with 2-nitroso-1-naphthol in a way that will interfere with the confirmatory test for Co^{++}.

Divide the $Co^{++} + Ni^{++}$ solution in Tube C into two parts. To one part add 1 or 2 drops of dimethylglyoxime and then 1 drop of 4-*N* CH_3COOH. To the other part add 1 or 2 drops of 2-nitroso-1-naphthol and then 1 drop of 6-*N* HCl. Place the tubes in the hot water bath. Note the colors of the precipitates and state whether it is necessary to separate Ni^{++} and Co^{++} before applying the confirmatory tests.

IONS OF GROUP III, DIVISION B

Test Solution *	Ion	Concentration (mg./ml.)
0.1-*M* Aluminum nitrate	Al^{3+}	2.7
0.1-*M* Chromium (III) nitrate	Cr^{3+}	5.2
0.1-*M* Zinc nitrate	Zn^{++}	6.5

* If desired, test solutions may be prepared to contain 10 mg. of cation per ml. (Appendix C).

The Aluminum Ion, Al^{3+}

Al-1. Test for Reaction of Al^{3+} with S^{--} and Precipitation of $Al(OH)_3$. To 1 ml. of water add 1 drop of the aluminum nitrate test solution. Add 1 drop of thymol blue indicator to this solution, and by reference to the properties of the indicator state whether the pH is above or below 2. Add 1 or 2 drops of 1-*N* HCl to this solution; note the color of the solution and state its approximate pH. To this solution add 1 drop of a 5% solution of thioacetamide. Place the tube in the hot water bath and note whether a precipitate forms. To this solution add 4-*N* NH_4OH until the solution changes to yellow and then to a faint blue color. What is the approximate pH of the solution (p. 159)? Examine the contents of the tube; note that a precipitate has formed. Write the equation for the reaction. (NOTE: The precipitate is $Al(OH)_3$, not Al_2S_3. $Al(OH)_3$ is gelatinous white, like the white of an egg, and is hardly visible if only a small amount is present. If a precipitate cannot be seen, add 2 or 3 drops more of the aluminum nitrate test solution to the tube.) Filter off the precipitate and wash it with water.

Al-2. Dissolution of $Al(OH)_3$ *by NaOH.* To the precipitate on the filter medium from Al-1 add 4 or 5 drops of 4-*N* NaOH. Place the assembly in the hot water bath. Stir the precipitate with a micro stirring rod. Allow the solution to heat. Did the precipitate dissolve? Write the equation for the reaction. Force the solution through the filter medium, and wash the medium with about 10 drops of water.

Al-3. Confirmatory Test for Al^{3+}. *Formation of a Red Precipitate with Aluminon.* To the tube containing the aluminum solution from Al-2 add 1 drop of thymolphthalein. To the blue solution add 4-*N* CH_3COOH drop by drop, until the solution becomes colorless (pH approximately 9). Now add 2 drops more of 4-*N* CH_3COOH to make the solution slightly acidic. To this colorless solution add 1 drop of the aluminon reagent. Place the tube in the hot water bath for a few minutes. Observe the color of the precipitate and write the equations for the reactions. (NOTE: The precipitate is $Al(OH)_3$. It absorbs the aluminon best in a slightly acidic solution; but once the red "lake" is formed by adsorption of the dye on the $Al(OH)_3$, it is stable in ammoniacal solutions.)

Al-4. Nature of the Aluminum "Lake" with $Al(OH)_3$. To each of two test tubes add 1 ml. of water and 1 drop of the aluminum nitrate test solution. To one of these tubes add 1 drop of the aluminon reagent. Place the tubes in the hot water bath and to each tube add 1 drop of 2-*N* $(NH_4)_2CO_3$. Allow the tubes to remain in the hot water for a few minutes and note the usefulness of the "dye" in making the $Al(OH)_3$ precipitate visible.

To a third test tube add 1 ml. of water and 1 drop of aluminum nitrate test solution. Add 2 drops of 4-*N* NH_4OH and 1 drop of aluminon reagent. Set the tube in the hot water bath for about 1 minute. Why does a red "lake" not form as readily as in the other experiments, even though $Al(OH)_3$ is present? Now add 3 drops of 4-*N* CH_3COOH. What does this show about the conditions under which aluminon is adsorbed on $Al(OH)_3$? Add 1 drop of 15-*N* NH_4OH. Is the red lake stable in ammoniacal solution once it is formed in slightly acid solution?

The Chromium (III) Ion, Cr^{++}

Cr-1. Test for Reaction of Cr^{3+} with S^{--} and Precipitation of $Cr(OH)_3$. To 1 ml. of water add 1 drop of the chromium (III) nitrate test solution, and then add 1 drop of the thymol blue indicator. Note the color of the solution, and state what may be inferred about its acidity. To this solution add 1 or 2 drops of 1-*N* HCl and note the color of the solution. What is its approximate H_3O^+ concentration? Now add 1 drop of a 5% solution of thioacetamide. Place the tube in the hot water bath and note whether a precipitate forms. Add 4-*N* NH_4OH to this solution until a precipitate forms. Write the equation for the reaction. (NOTE: The precipitate is $Cr(OH)_3$, not Cr_2S_3. The color of $Cr(OH)_3$ is light green.) Filter off the precipitate and wash it with water.

Cr-2. Formation of CrO_4^{--}. To the precipitate on the filter medium from Cr-1 add 4 or 5 drops of 4-*N* NaOH and 2 to 3 drops of 3% H_2O_2. Place the assembly in the hot water bath. Stir the precipitate with a micro stirring rod. Allow the solution to heat. Did the precipitate dissolve? What is the color of the NaOH-H_2O_2 solution? Write the equation for the reaction. Force the solution through the filter medium and wash the medium with 1 ml. of water.

Cr-3. Confirmatory Test for Cr^{3+}. Precipitation of $PbCrO_4$. To the solution from Cr-2 add 1 drop of thymolphthalein indicator. Now add 4-*N* CH_3COOH until the *blue color* of the indicator is discharged, and then add 2 drops more. To the yellow solution add 1 drop of 0.1-*N* $Pb(CH_3COO)_2$. Note the color of the precipitate and write the equation for the reaction. (See Pb-4.)

The Zinc Ion, Zn^{++}

Zn-1. Precipitation of ZnS. To 1 ml. of water add 1 drop of the zinc nitrate test solution. To this solution add 1 drop of the thymol blue indicator. Note the color of the solution and state what may be inferred about its pH. To this solution add 1 or 2 drops of 1-*N* HCl and note the color of the solution. What is its approximate H_3O^+ concentration? Now add 1 drop of a 5% solution of thioacetamide. Place the tube in the hot water bath and note whether a precipitate forms. To this solu tion add 4-*N* NH_4OH until a precipitate forms. Write the equation for the reaction. Filter off the precipitate and wash it with water.

Zn-2. Dissolution of ZnS and Reaction of $Zn(OH)_2$ *with NaOH.* To the precipitate on the filter medium add 4 or 5 drops of 4-*N* HNO_3. Place the assembly in the hot water bath and allow the solution to heat. Add 1 ml. of water and force the solution into the test tube. Write the equation for the reaction. Transfer the solution from the small test tube to an evaporation test tube and evaporate to incipient (moist) dryness. To the residue add 1 ml. of water and transfer the solution from the evaporation test tube to a small test tube. Add 1 drop of thymolphthalein indicator and 4 or 5 drops of 4-*N* NaOH to the solution in the small test tube. Place the tube in the hot water bath. Write the equation for the reaction. Force the solution through the filter medium into the test tube.

Zn-3. Confirmatory Test for Zn^{++}. To the blue solution from Zn-2 add 4-*N* CH_3COOH until the solution becomes colorless; then add 2 drops more. To this solution add 1 drop of diethylaniline and 2 drops of 0.1-*N* potassium cyanoferrate (III), $K_3Fe(CN)_6$. Note the color of the precipitate. (See equations and discussion, p. 222.)

SUMMARY OF REACTIONS OF CATIONS OF GROUP III

Reagents	Aluminum—$Al(NO_3)_3$	Chromium—$Cr(NO_3)_3$	Iron: Ferrous Salts—$Fe(NH_4)_2(SO_4)_2$	Iron: Ferric Salts—$Fe(NO_3)_3$
Acids	Metal. $\underline{2Al} + 6H_3O^+ \rightleftharpoons 2Al^{3+} + 3H_2\uparrow + 6H_2O$ $\underline{2Al} + 2OH^- + 6H_2O \rightleftharpoons 2Al(OH)_4^- + 3H_2\uparrow$ Al is dissolved by HCl or NaOH. It dissolves slowly in H_2SO_4, but becomes passive in concd. HNO_3.	Metal. $\underline{2Cr} + 6H_3O^+ \rightleftharpoons 2Cr^{3+} + 3H_2\uparrow + 6H_2O$ Cr dissolves in HCl or H_2SO_4, but becomes passive and does not dissolve in concd. HNO_3.	Metal. $\underline{Fe} + 2H_3O^+ \rightleftharpoons Fe^{++} + H_2\uparrow + 2H_2O$ Fe dissolves in dilute HCl or H_2SO_4, with the formation of H_2. Cold dilute HNO_3 gives $Fe^{++} + NH_4^+$.	$\underline{Fe} + NO_3^- + 4H_3O^+ \rightleftharpoons Fe^{3+} + NO\uparrow + 6H_2O$ Hot dilute HNO_3 or hot H_2SO_4 give Fe^{3+} + NO and $Fe^{3+} + SO_2$ respectively. Cold concd. H_2SO_4 and cold concd. HNO_3 cause Fe to become passive.
Precipitants	Insoluble compounds: $Al(OH)_3$, $AlPO_4$, $Al_2(C_2O_4)_3$.	Insoluble compounds: $Cr(OH)_3$, $CrPO_4$, $PbCrO_4$, $BaCrO_4$, Ag_2CrO_4, Hg_2CrO_4, $HgCrO_4$.	Insoluble compounds: $Fe(OH)_2$, FeS, $Fe_3(PO_4)_2$, $FeCO_3$, $Fe(CN)_2$, $Fe_3[Fe(CN)_6]_2$, $Fe_2Fe(CN)_6$, $FeSO_3$.	Insoluble compounds: $Fe(OH)_3$, $FePO_4$, $FeAsO_4$, $Fe_4[Fe(CN)_6]_3$, FeF_3, $Fe_2(C_2O_4)_3$, $Fe_2(SO_3)_3$.
Excess reagent	Complex ions: $Al(OH)_4^-$ or AlO_2^-, $Al(H_2O)_6^{3+}$, $AlCl_6^{3-}$, AlF_6^{3-}. Al^{3+} forms complex ions with tartrates, glycerin, and other organic substances with OH groups.	Complex ions: $Cr(OH)_4^-$ or CrO_2^-, $Cr(H_2O)_6^{3+}$, $[Cr(H_2O)_4Cl_2]^+$, $CrCl_6^{3-}$, $Cr(NH_3)_6^{3+}$, $Cr(SCN)_6^{3-}$, $CrO_4^=$, $Cr_2O_7^=$. Cr^{3+} forms complex ions with certain organic substances which have OH groups.	Complex ions: $Fe(CN)_6^{4-}$, $Fe(NO)^{++}$.	Complex ions: $Fe(CN)_6^{3-}$, $Fe(SCN)_6^{3-}$, $FeCl_6^{3-}$, FeF_6^{3-}, $Fe(PO_4)_2^{3-}$, $Fe(C_2O_4)_2^-$. Fe^{3+} forms complex ions with certain organic substances which have OH groups.

NH_4OH	$Al^{3+} + 3NH_3 + 3H_2O \rightleftharpoons \underset{\text{white}}{\underline{Al(OH)_3}} \downarrow + 3NH_4^+$ $Al(OH)_3$ is not dissolved appreciably by excess NH_4OH. NH_4^+ does not prevent the precipitation of $Al(OH)_3$.	$Cr^{3+} + 3NH_3 + 3H_2O \rightleftharpoons \underset{\text{greenish-blue}}{\underline{Cr(OH)_3}} \downarrow + 3NH_4^+$ $Cr(OH)_3$ is slightly soluble in concentrated NH_4OH. NH_4^+ does not prevent the precipitation of $Cr(OH)_3$.	$Fe^{++} + 2NH_3 + 2H_2O \rightleftharpoons \underset{\text{white}}{\underline{Fe(OH)_2}} \downarrow + 2NH_4^+$ $Fe(OH)_2$ in the air changes in color to green and then to reddish-brown $Fe(OH)_3$. NH_4^+ prevents the precipitation of $Fe(OH)_2$.	$Fe^{3+} + 3NH_3 + 3H_2O \rightleftharpoons \underset{\text{reddish-brown}}{\underline{Fe(OH)_3}} \downarrow + 3NH_3^+$ $Fe(OH)_3$ is not dissolved by excess NH_4OH. NH_4^+ does not prevent the precipitation of $Fe(OH)_3$.
NaOH	$Al^{3+} + 3OH^- \rightleftharpoons \underset{\text{white}}{\underline{Al(OH)_3}} \downarrow$ $\underline{Al(OH)_3} + OH^- \rightleftharpoons$ $Al(OH)_4^-$ or $AlO_2^- + 2H_2O$ The precipitate dissolves readily in excess NaOH or in acids.	$Cr^{3+} + 3OH^- \rightleftharpoons \underset{\text{greenish-blue}}{\underline{Cr(OH)_3}} \downarrow$ $\underline{Cr(OH)_3} + OH^- \rightleftharpoons$ $Cr(OH)_4^-$ or $CrO_2^- + 2H_2O$ The precipitate dissolves readily in excess NaOH or in acids when freshly precipitated. H_2O_2, Na_2O_2, and NaClO oxidize $Cr(OH)_4^-$ to $CrO_4^=$.	$Fe^{++} + 2OH^- \rightleftharpoons \underset{\text{white}}{\underline{Fe(OH)_2}} \downarrow$ $Fe(OH)_2$ is readily oxidized to $Fe(OH)_3$. The precipitate is not soluble in NaOH but dissolves in acids.	$Fe^{3+} + 3OH^- \rightleftharpoons \underset{\text{reddish-brown}}{\underline{Fe(OH)_3}} \downarrow$ The precipitate is not soluble in excess NaOH, but, when freshly precipitated, it dissolves in acids.

SUMMARY OF REACTIONS OF CATIONS OF GROUP III *(Continued)*

Reagents	Aluminum—$Al(NO_3)_3$	Chromium—$Cr(NO_3)_3$	Iron	
			Ferrous Salts—$Fe(NH_4)_2(SO_4)_2$	Ferric Salts—$Fe(NO_3)_3$
$(NH_4)_2CO_3$	$H_2O + CO_3^{=} \rightleftharpoons HCO_3^- + OH^-$ $Al^{3+} + 3OH^- \rightleftharpoons \underline{Al(OH)_3} \downarrow$ $(NH_4)_2CO_3$ is appreciably hydrolyzed so that the concentration of OH^- is high enough to precipitate $Al(OH)_3$. Na_2CO_3 and $BaCO_3$ also produce a precipitate of $Al(OH)_3$.	$H_2O + CO_3^{=} \rightleftharpoons HCO_3^- + OH^-$ $Cr^{3+} + 3OH^- \rightleftharpoons \underline{Cr(OH)_3} \downarrow$ The concentration of OH^- is high enough to precipitate $Cr(OH)_3$. Na_2CO_3 and $BaCO_3$ also produce a precipitate of $Cr(OH)_3$.	$Fe^{++} + CO_3^{=} \rightleftharpoons \underset{\text{white}}{\underline{FeCO_3}} \downarrow$ The precipitate is gradually oxidized by oxygen of the air with the formation of $Fe(OH)_3$.	$H_2O + CO_3^{=} \rightleftharpoons HCO_3^- + OH^-$ $Fe^{3+} + 3OH^- \rightleftharpoons \underline{Fe(OH)_3} \downarrow$ The concentration of OH^- is high enough to precipitate $Fe(OH)_3$. CO_2 is liberated. Na_2CO_3 and $BaCO_3$ also produce a precipitate of $Fe(OH)_3$.
$(NH_4)_2S$	$H_2O + S^{=} \rightleftharpoons HS^- + OH^-$ $Al^{3+} + 3OH^- \rightleftharpoons \underline{Al(OH)_3} \downarrow$ H_2S is evolved as the $Al(OH)_3$ forms.	$H_2O + S^{=} \rightleftharpoons HS^- + OH^-$ $Cr^{3+} + 3OH^- \rightleftharpoons \underline{Cr(OH)_3} \downarrow$ H_2S is evolved as the $Cr(OH)_3$ forms.	$Fe^{++} + S^{=} \rightleftharpoons \underset{\text{black}}{\underline{FeS}} \downarrow$ FeS readily dissolves in dilute HCl or HNO_3.	$2Fe^{3+} + 3S^{=} \rightleftharpoons \underset{\text{black}}{\underline{Fe_2S_3}} \downarrow$ Fe_2S_3 dissolves in HCl, with the formation of $Fe^{++} + H_2S + S$.
Na_2HPO_4	$Al^{3+} + PO_4^{3-} \rightleftharpoons \underset{\text{white}}{\underline{AlPO_4}} \downarrow$ The hydrated gelatinous precipitate is soluble in HCl or NaOH but insoluble in CH_3COOH.	$Cr^{3+} + PO_4^{3-} \rightleftharpoons \underset{\text{violet}}{\underline{CrPO_4}} \downarrow$ The precipitate is soluble in HCl or HNO_3 but is only slightly soluble in CH_3COOH.	$3Fe^{++} + 2PO_4^{3-} \rightleftharpoons \underset{\text{bluish-white}}{\underline{Fe_3(PO_4)_2}} \downarrow$ The precipitate dissolves readily in HCl.	$Fe^{3+} + PO_4^{3-} \rightleftharpoons \underset{\text{yellowish-white}}{\underline{FePO_4}} \downarrow$ The precipitate dissolves in strong acids but not in acetic acid. Excess PO_4^{3-} dissolves the precipitate with the formation of $Fe(PO_4)_2^{3-}$.

CH_3COONa	$Al(H_2O)_6^{3+} + 3CH_3COO^- \rightleftharpoons \underline{(H_2O)_3Al(OH)_3} \downarrow + 3CH_3COOH$ The base CH_3COO^- takes protons from the acid $Al(H_2O)_6^{3+}$ and causes the formation of $Al(OH)_3$. CH_3COO^- is adsorbed by the precipitate.	CH_3COO^- does not cause the formation of $Cr(OH)_3$ in solutions of Cr^{3+} unless Al and Fe are present also.	No precipitate.	$Fe(H_2O)_6^{3+} + 3CH_3COO^- \rightleftharpoons \underline{(H_2O)_3Fe(OH)_3} \downarrow + 3CH_3COOH$ The precipitation is more rapid in hot dilute solution. A relatively large amount of CH_3COO^- is adsorbed.
$K_4Fe(CN)_6$	—	—	$2Fe^{++} + Fe(CN)_6^{4-} \rightleftharpoons \underset{\text{white}}{\underline{Fe_2Fe(CN)_6}} \downarrow$ The precipitate is a mixture of $K_2FeFe(CN)_6$ and $Fe_2Fe(CN)_6$. It slowly turns blue and is insoluble in acetic acid.	$4Fe^{3+} + 3Fe(CN)_6^{4-} \rightleftharpoons \underset{\text{Prussian blue}}{\underline{Fe_4[Fe(CN)_6]_3}} \downarrow$ The precipitate is insoluble in HCl but dissolves in $H_2C_2O_4$ and is decomposed by NaOH.
$K_3Fe(CN)_6$	—	—	$3Fe^{++} + 2Fe(CN)_6^{3-} \rightleftharpoons \underset{\text{Turnbull's blue}}{\underline{Fe_3[Fe(CN)_6]_2}} \downarrow$ The precipitate is insoluble in HCl, but is decomposed by NaOH.	The solution becomes brown, but no precipitate is obtained.
KSCN	—	—	—	$Fe^{3+} + 3SCN^- \rightleftharpoons \underset{\text{deep red}}{Fe(SCN)_3}$ $Fe(CNS)^{++}$, to $Fe(CNS)_6^{3-}$ are also formed

SUMMARY OF REACTIONS OF CATIONS OF GROUP III (*Continued*)

Reagents	Manganese—$Mn(NO_3)_2$	Zinc—$Zn(NO_3)_2$	Nickel—$Ni(NO_3)_2$	Cobalt—$Co(NO_3)_2$
Acids	Metal. $\underline{Mn} + 2H_3O^+ \rightleftharpoons$ $Mn^{++} + H_2\uparrow + 2H_2O$ Mn dissolves readily in dilute acids.	Metal. $\underline{Zn} + 2H_3O^+ \rightleftharpoons$ $Zn^{++} + H_2\uparrow + 2H_2O$ $\underline{Zn} + 2OH^- + 2H_2O \rightleftharpoons$ $Zn(OH)_4^{=} + H_2\uparrow$ Zn dissolves in NaOH and in dilute acids, especially in the presence of metals lower in the E.M.F. series. With increasing concentration of HNO_3 the following reduction products are obtained: NH_4^+, NO, NO_2. With H_2SO_4 at higher concentrations some H_2S and SO_2 is obtained.	Metal. $\underline{3Ni} + 2NO_3^- + 8H_3O^+ \rightleftharpoons$ $3Ni^{++} + 2NO\uparrow + 12H_2O$ Ni dissolves readily in dilute HNO_3, but becomes passive in concd. HNO_3. It dissolves slowly in HCl or H_2SO_4.	Metal. $\underline{3Co} + 2NO_3^- + 8H_3O^+ \rightleftharpoons$ $3Co^{++} + 2NO\uparrow + 12H_2O$ Co dissolves more readily in acids than Ni.
Precipitants	Insoluble compounds: $Mn(OH)_2$, $Mn(OH)_3$ or $MnOOH$, MnO_2, MnS, $Mn_2Fe(CN)_6$, $Mn_3[Fe(CN)_6]_2$, $MnCO_3$, MnF_2, $Mn_3(PO_4)_2$.	Insoluble compounds: ZnS, $Zn(OH)_2$, $Zn_2Fe(CN)_6$, $Zn_3[Fe(CN)_6]_2$, $ZnCO_3$, $ZnCrO_4$, $Zn(CN)_2$, ZnC_2O_4, $Zn_3(PO_4)_2$, $ZnSO_3$.	Insoluble salts: NiS, $Ni(OH)_2$, $Ni_2Fe(CN)_6$, $Ni_3[Fe(CN)_6]_2$, $Ni(CN)_2$, $NiCO_3$, NiC_2O_4, $Ni_3(PO_4)_2$, $NiSO_3$.	Insoluble salts: CoS, $Co(OH)_2$, $Co(OH)_3$, $Co_2Fe(CN)_6$, $Co_3[Fe(CN)_6]_2$, $Co(CN)_2$, $CoCO_3$, CoC_2O_4, $Co_3(PO_4)_2$, $CoSO_3$, $K_2NaCo(NO_2)_6$, $K_2AgCo(NO_2)_6$.

Excess reagent	Complex ions: $Mn(CN)_6^{4-}$, MnO_4^-, $MnF_6^{=}$.	Complex ions: $Zn(NH_3)_4^{++}$, $Zn(OH)_4^{=}$ or $ZnO_2^{=}$, $Zn(CN)_4^{=}$.	Complex ions: $Ni(NH_3)_6^{++}$, $Ni(CN)_4^{=}$, $Ni(SCN)_4^{=}$.	Complex ions: $Co(NH_3)_6^{++}$, $Co(CN)_6^{4-}$, $Co(SCN)_4^{=}$, $CoCl_4^{=}$, $Co(NH_3)_6^{3+}$, $Co(NO_2)_6^{3-}$, $Co(CN)_6^{3-}$.
NH_4OH	$Mn^{++} + 2NH_3 + 2H_2O \rightleftharpoons \underset{\text{white}}{\underline{Mn(OH)_2}} \downarrow + 2NH_4^+$ The precipitate is not soluble in excess NH_4OH, but is prevented from forming by NH_4^+. $Mn(OH)_2$ slowly oxidizes to brown MnOOH or $Mn(OH)_3$. NH_4OH + Br_2 water gives $Mn(OH)_3$. NH_4^+ does not prevent the precipitation of $Mn(OH)_3$.	$Zn^{++} + 2NH_3 + 2H_2O \rightleftharpoons \underset{\text{white}}{\underline{Zn(OH)_2}} \downarrow + 2NH_4^+$ $\underline{Zn(OH)_2} + 4NH_3 \rightleftharpoons Zn(NH_3)_4^{++} + 2OH^-$ $Zn(OH)_2$ dissolves in excess NH_4OH. Solutions containing NH_4^+ dissolve $Zn(OH)_2$ or prevent it from forming.	$Ni^{++} + NH_3 + H_2O + NO_3^- \rightleftharpoons \underset{\text{green}}{\underline{Ni(OH)NO_3}} \downarrow + NH_4^+$ $\underline{Ni(OH)NO_3} + 6NH_3 \rightleftharpoons \underset{\text{blue}}{\underline{Ni(NH_3)_6^{++}}} + NO_3^- + OH^-$ The precipitate dissolves in excess NH_4OH. Solutions containing NH_4^+ dissolve $Ni(OH)_2$ or prevent it from forming.	$Co^{++} + NH_3 + H_2O + NO_3^- \rightleftharpoons \underset{\text{blue}}{\underline{Co(OH)NO_3}} \downarrow + NH_4^+$ The precipitate is not completely dissolved by excess NH_4OH, but in the presence of NH_4Cl a pink solution of $Co(NH_3)_6^{++}$ is formed and this is rapidly oxidized to give a yellow solution and finally a red solution of $[Co(NH_3)_5Cl]^{++}$. When Co^{++} is treated with NH_4OH, NH_4Cl, and Br_2, cobalt is oxidized to the cobaltic state, but $Co(OH)_3$ is not precipitated (cf. manganese and NaOH).

SUMMARY OF REACTIONS OF CATIONS OF GROUP III (*Continued*)

Reagents	Manganese—$Mn(NO_3)_2$	Zinc—$Zn(NO_3)_2$	Nickel—$Ni(NO_3)_2$	Cobalt—$Co(NO_3)_2$
NaOH	$Mn^{++} + 2OH^- \rightleftharpoons \underset{\text{white}}{\underline{Mn(OH)_2}} \downarrow$	$Zn^{++} + 2OH^- \rightleftharpoons \underset{\text{white}}{\underline{Zn(OH)_2}} \downarrow$	$Ni^{++} + 2OH^- \rightleftharpoons \underset{\text{green}}{\underline{Ni(OH)_2}} \downarrow$	$Co^{++} + OH^- + NO_3^- \rightleftharpoons \underset{\text{blue}}{\underline{Co(OH)NO_3}} \downarrow$
	The precipitate is rapidly oxidized to brown MnOOH or $MnO_2 \cdot xH_2O$. The precipitate is not dissolved by excess NaOH.	$Zn(OH)_2 + 2OH^- \rightleftharpoons Zn(OH)_4^{=}$ or $ZnO_2^{=} + 2H_2O$ $Zn(OH)_2$ dissolves readily in excess NaOH (cf. aluminum and chromium).	$Ni(OH)_2$ is soluble in solutions of NH_4OH, ammonium salts, or acids. It is oxidized to $Ni(OH)_3$ by Br_2 in the presence of NaOH. $Ni(OH)_2$ does not dissolve in excess NaOH.	$\underline{Co(OH)NO_3} + OH^- \rightleftharpoons \underset{\text{pink}}{\underline{Co(OH)_2}} \downarrow + NO_3^-$ On warming, the hydroxy-salt changes to $Co(OH)_2$ and this gradually oxidizes to brown $Co(OH)_3$. Br_2 oxidizes $Co(OH)_2$ to $Co(OH)_3$ in a solution of NaOH. $Co(OH)_2$ does not dissolve in excess NaOH.
$(NH_4)_2S$ or H_2S	$Mn^{++} + S^{=} \rightleftharpoons \underset{\text{flesh}}{\underline{MnS}} \downarrow$ MnS is soluble in dilute HCl or in CH_3COOH. It slowly turns brown as a result of oxidation.	$Zn^{++} + S^{=} \rightleftharpoons \underset{\text{white}}{\underline{ZnS}} \downarrow$ ZnS does not precipitate in 0.3-*N* HCl with H_2S, but will precipitate in dilute acetic acid. ZnS can be precipitated from solutions which contain the zincate ion, $Zn(OH)_4^{=}$.	$Ni^{++} + S^{=} \rightleftharpoons \underset{\text{black}}{\underline{NiS}} \downarrow$ NiS does not precipitate from dilute acid solutions; but after it has been precipitated in an ammoniacal solution, NiS is practically insoluble in dilute HCl. It is readily dissolved by HNO_3 or HClO.	$Co^{++} + S^{=} \rightleftharpoons \underset{\text{black}}{\underline{CoS}} \downarrow$ CoS does not precipitate from dilute acid solutions; but after it has been precipitated in an ammoniacal solution, CoS is practically insoluble in dilute HCl. It is readily dissolved by HNO_3 or HClO.

$(NH_4)_2CO_3$	$Mn^{++} + CO_3^{=} \rightleftharpoons \underset{\text{white}}{\underline{MnCO_3}} \downarrow$ The precipitate slowly turns brown, with the formation of $Mn(OH)_3$ or MnOOH. High concentrations of NH_4^+ prevent the precipitation of $MnCO_3$.	A white basic carbonate with the empirical formula $5ZnO \cdot 2CO_2 \cdot 4H_2O$ is formed. It is soluble in NH_4OH, $(NH_4)_2CO_3$, or NaOH. Some $ZnCO_3$ also forms. NH_4^+ prevents the formation of the precipitate.	A light-green basic carbonate, along with some $NiCO_3$, is formed. The precipitate is soluble in NH_4OH or $(NH_4)_2CO_3$ but not in NaOH. NH_4^+ prevents the formation of the precipitate.	A light-red basic carbonate is formed, along with some $CoCO_3$. The precipitate is soluble in NH_4OH or $(NH_4)_2CO_3$ but not in NaOH. NH_4^+ prevents the formation of the precipitate.
$K_4Fe(CN)_6$	$2Mn^{++} + Fe(CN)_6^{4-} \rightleftharpoons \underset{\text{pinkish-white}}{\underline{Mn_2Fe(CN)_6}} \downarrow$ The precipitate is slightly soluble in HCl.	$2Zn^{++} + Fe(CN)_6^{4-} \rightleftharpoons \underset{\text{white}}{\underline{Zn_2Fe(CN)_6}} \downarrow$ The precipitate is not soluble in HCl, but is soluble in NaOH.	$2Ni^{++} + Fe(CN)_6^{4-} \rightleftharpoons \underset{\text{greenish-white}}{\underline{Ni_2Fe(CN)_6}} \downarrow$ The precipitate is not soluble in HCl or in NaOH.	$2Co^{++} + Fe(CN)_6^{4-} \rightleftharpoons \underset{\text{green}}{\underline{Co_2Fe(CN)_6}} \downarrow$ The precipitate is not soluble in HCl or NaOH.
$K_3Fe(CN)_6$	$3Mn^{++} + 2Fe(CN)_6^{3-} \rightleftharpoons \underset{\text{light brown}}{\underline{Mn_3[Fe(CN)_6]_2}} \downarrow$ The precipitate is slightly soluble in HCl and insoluble in NH_4OH.	$3Zn^{++} + 2Fe(CN)_6^{3-} \rightleftharpoons \underset{\text{yellowish-white}}{\underline{Zn_3[Fe(CN)_6]_2}} \downarrow$ The precipitate is slightly soluble in HCl, and readily soluble in NaOH and NH_4OH.	$3Ni^{++} + 2Fe(CN)_6^{3-} \rightleftharpoons \underset{\text{greenish-white}}{\underline{Ni_3[Fe(CN)_6]_2}} \downarrow$ The precipitate is not soluble in HCl, but is soluble in NH_4OH.	$3Co^{++} + 2Fe(CN)_6^{3-} \rightleftharpoons \underset{\text{reddish-brown}}{\underline{Co_3[Fe(CN)_6]_2}} \downarrow$ The precipitate is not soluble in HCl or NH_4OH.

CHAPTER 12

ANALYSIS OF GROUP III CATIONS

DISCUSSION OF THE PROCEDURE FOR GROUP III

Precipitation of Group III and Separation into Divisions A and B

The ions of Group III (Fe^{++}, Mn^{++}, Co^{++}, Ni^{++}, Al^{3+}, Cr^{3+}, and Zn^{++}) are precipitated as sulfides and hydroxides from the Group II filtrate (Procedure 7) by adding NH_4OH to the filtrate until the solution is alkaline. This procedure obviates the necessity of boiling off H_2S or destroying any unhydrolyzed thioacetamide from the Group II filtrate before the solution is made ammoniacal. Owing to the low concentration of the S^{--}, the precipitate is usually obtained in a well-coagulated and easily filterable form.

The precipitate, FeS, MnS, CoS, NiS, $Al(OH)_3$, $Cr(OH)_3$, and ZnS, is dissolved in HNO_3 rather than HCl because CoS and NiS are practically insoluble in dilute HCl even though they cannot be precipitated in dilute acid (0.01-*N* HCl) solution. Apparently after these two sulfides are once formed they either change to a more insoluble form or for some reason dissolve very slowly in HCl. Because nitric acid oxidizes the S^{--} ion, these sulfides dissolve readily in hot 4-*N* HNO_3. The excess of HNO_3 is boiled off and the ions of Group III are separated into Divisions A and B by means of NaOH and H_2O_2. Division A consists of the ions of iron, manganese, cobalt, and nickel. These are precipitated from a solution containing NaOH and H_2O_2 as $Fe(OH)_3$, MnO_2, $Ni(OH)_2$, and $Co(OH)_3$. Division B consists of the ions of aluminum, chromium, and zinc. Because their hydroxides are amphoteric they dissolve in excess NaOH and the H_2O_2 oxidizes the chromium to CrO_4^{--}. The resulting solution contains the ions of Division B as $Al(OH)_4^-$, CrO_4^{--}, and $Zn(OH)_4^{--}$.

Tests for the Ions of Division B

Addition of acetic acid to the alkaline solution of the ions of Division B results in the formation of sodium acetate, which with a small excess

SCHEMATIC OUTLINE OF THE PROCEDURE

21. **Filtrate from 7:** Al^{3+}, Cr^{3+}, Zn^{++}, Fe^{++}, Mn^{++}, Co^{++}, Ni^{++} + Groups IV–V
Contains HCl, H_2S, and CH_3CSNH_2 from 7. Add NH_4OH.

25. **Filtrate:** Groups IV–V	22. **Precipitate:** $Al(OH)_3$, $Cr(OH)_3$, ZnS, FeS, MnS, CoS, NiS Add HNO_3. Evaporate. Add NaOH + H_2O_2.

23. **Filtrate (Div. B):** $Al(OH)_4^-$, $CrO_4^=$, $Zn(OH)_4^=$ Add CH_3COOH. Divide into 3 parts.			24. **Precipitate (Div. A):** $Fe(OH)_3$, MnO_2, $Ni(OH)_2$, $Co(OH)_3$ Add HNO_3 + $NaNO_2$. Add sulfamic acid and divide into 4 parts.			
a. Al^{3+} Add aluminon and $(NH_4)_2CO_3$. *Red ppt.:* $Al(OH)_3$ lake	b. $CrO_4^=$ Add $Pb(CH_3COO)_2$. *Yellow ppt.:* $PbCrO_4$	c. Zn^{++} Add $K_3Fe(CN)_6$ + diethylaniline. Yellow changing to *red ppt.*	a. Fe^{3+} Add NH_4SCN. *Red solution:* $Fe(SCN)_3$	b. Mn^{++} Add $NaBiO_3$. *Purple solution:* MnO_4^-	c. Ni^{++} Add tartaric acid, dimethylgloxime + CH_3COOH. *Scarlet ppt.*	d. Co^{++} Add tartaric acid + 2-nitroso-1-naphthol + HCl. *Purple ppt.*
Aluminum	*Chromium*	*Zinc*	*Iron*	*Manganese*	*Nickel*	*Cobalt*

of acetic acid gives a buffered solution (pH = 4 to 5) that is suitable for the confirmatory tests for these ions. The solution is divided into three parts for these tests.

One part is tested for Al^{3+} by precipitation of $Al(OH)_3$ in the presence of aluminon. Aluminum hydroxide is relatively insoluble in solutions whose pH is between 4 and 9. The hydroxide is often translucent or colloidal and is therefore difficult to see. To make the precipitate more visible and to distinguish it from silicic acid or other hydroxides, a dye such as aluminon or eriochrom-cyanin R is added to the solution. In order for the aluminon to be adsorbed by the $Al(OH)_3$ and form a red "lake," the reagent must be added to the hydroxide in a slightly acidic solution. The negatively charged dye ion is then adsorbed on the positively charged aluminum hydroxide and forms a red precipitate that is stable in dilute ammoniacal solutions. Frequently ammonium carbonate solution is added to reduce the possibility of interference from other hydroxides and to aid in the coagulation of the lake.

Addition of lead acetate to a second part of the buffered solution of the ions of Division B results in the formation of a yellow precipitate of $PbCrO_4$. If the acid concentration is too high, this precipitate will not form because CrO_4^{--} is converted to $Cr_2O_7^{--}$ in acid solution.

Zinc ion can also be confirmed in the solution without separating the ions of Division B from one another. This is done by adding $K_3Fe(CN)_6$ and diethylaniline to a third portion of the solution. The $Fe(CN)_6^{4-}$ resulting from the oxidation of the diethylaniline by $Fe(CN)_6^{3-}$ reacts with the Zn^{++} to form a rather insoluble precipitate of $Zn_2Fe(CN)_6$. This precipitate adsorbs the oxidized diethylaniline and forms a characteristic red precipitate. Apparently the insolubility of $Zn_2Fe(CN)_6$ acts as a "driving force" in the reaction of $Fe(CN)_6^{3-}$ with the diethylaniline.

Dissolution of Division A Precipitate and Tests for the Ions

Both $Fe(OH)_3$ and $Ni(OH)_2$ in the Division B precipitates dissolve readily in 4-*N* HNO_3, but MnO_2 and $Co(OH)_3$ require a small amount of a reducing ion such as NO_2^- for rapid dissolution. Any excess NO_2^- is destroyed by the addition of sulfamic acid. The resulting acid solution is then divided into four parts and tested for the ions of Group III, Division A.

Fe^{3+} forms with SCN^- a red compound, $Fe(SCN)_3$, in the nitric acid solution, and Mn^{++} is oxidized to the reddish-purple ion, MnO_4^-, by sodium bismuthate.

The other two portions of the nitric acid solution are made alkaline with ammonium hydroxide with the aid of an appropriate indicator. One part is tested for nickel with dimethylglyoxime and the other is tested for cobalt with 2-nitroso-1-naphthol. The precipitates are respectively $Ni(C_4H_7N_2O_2)_2$ and $Co[C_{10}H_6O(NO)]_3$ with the structures:

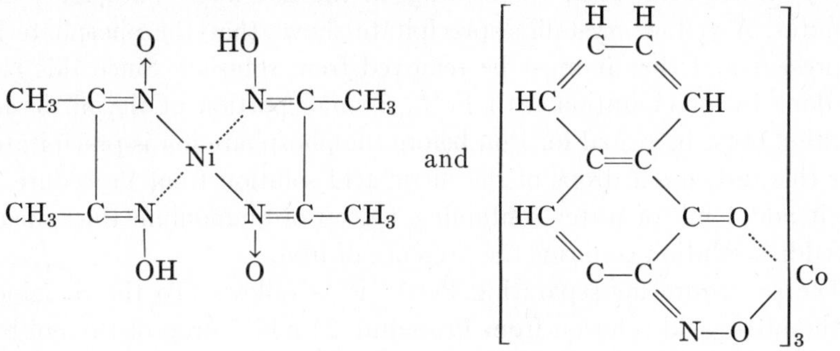

After the formation of the nickel dimethylglyoxime, acetic acid is added to make the scarlet color of the precipitate more distinctive. Once the purple-red precipitate of cobalt 2-nitroso-1-naphthol has been formed in ammoniacal solution, the addition of dilute HCl does not dissolve it, but any other precipitate that may form with cobalt is dissolved by the dilute acid.

When iron is present in the solutions to be tested for Ni^{++} and Co^{++} by the above reagents, tartaric acid is added to form a complex with Fe^{3+}. If this were not done, the addition of ammonium hydroxide would precipitate $Fe(OH)_3$, and this precipitate would interfere with the confirmatory tests for Ni^{++} and Co^{++}.

Interference of Phosphates in the Analysis

If phosphates are present in the solutions to be analyzed, there may be interference because the phosphates of Ca^{++}, Ba^{++}, Sr^{++}, or Mg^{++} may precipitate when the acid solution from Group II is made ammoniacal in Procedure 21. These phosphates will then remain with the precipitates of Division A, Procedure 24, and will be dissolved by the nitric acid. No provision is made in the Procedures for the presence of phosphates because they are seldom present in the samples used for elementary courses in qualitative analysis. (Similar interference is caused by the presence of certain other anions such as oxalate or borate.) Unless the instructor specifically states that phosphates may be present in the sample, assume that they are absent and proceed with the analysis.

However, if there is a possibility of their being present, the Procedures should be modified as outlined in the following section.

MODIFICATION OF THE PROCEDURE FOR THE PRESENCE OF PHOSPHATES. Add 2 drops of the nitric acid solution from Procedure 24 to a solution containing 5 drops of 1-*N* ammonium molybdate and 10 drops of 4-*N* nitric acid. Heat the solution in the hot water bath for 1 or 2 minutes. A yellow crystalline precipitate shows that the phosphate ion is present and that it must be removed from solution. Since this is to be done by precipitation with Fe^{3+}, a small portion of the nitric acid solution must be tested for iron before the phosphate ion is precipitated. For this test, use 2 drops of the nitric acid solution from Procedure 24. To it add 1 ml. of water containing 1 drop of ammonium thiocyanate. A reddish solution confirms the presence of iron.

The procedure for separating PO_4^{3-} is as follows. To the remainder of the nitric acid solution from Procedure 24 add 1 drop of thymol blue indicator and then 4-*N* NH_4OH drop by drop, until the solution is yellow. Now add 3 drops of 4-*N* CH_3COOH and 1 drop of 6-*N* CH_3COONH_4. The solution is now slightly acid. Under these conditions $FePO_4$ precipitates, but the phosphates of the alkaline earths do not. Add 4 or 5 drops of the ferric nitrate test solution to make certain that enough Fe^{3+} is present to precipitate all the PO_4^{3-}. Place the tube containing the $FePO_4$ precipitate in the hot water bath for 10 minutes. The hydrolysis of Fe^{3+} results in the precipitation of the relatively insoluble basic acetate of iron and thereby removes the excess Fe^{3+} as well as the PO_4^{3-}. Filter off the precipitate. The filtrate contains Mn^{++}, Co^{++}, Ni^{++}, and the alkaline earths precipitated in Procedure 24 by PO_4^{3-}. To it add 3 drops of 15-*N* NH_4OH and 5 drops of a 5% solution of thioacetamide. Place the tube in the hot water bath for 4 or 5 minutes. Filter off the precipitate and add the filtrate to the one that is to be used for the analysis of Groups IV–V. Wash the precipitate with water and dissolve it in 4-*N* nitric acid. Boil the solution to remove any H_2S which may be present, and test portions of the solution for Mn^{++}, Ni^{++}, and Co^{++} by Procedures 24b, c, d.

PRECIPITATION AND DISSOLUTION OF HYDROXIDE PRECIPITATES

Hydration and Hydrolysis of Ions

Because of strong ion-dipole interactions, most ions are probably hydrated in aqueous solutions. The extent of this interaction depends on the charge and size of the ion. Thus the smaller Na^+ ion (0.98 A) is more strongly hydrated than the larger K^+ ion (1.33 A), as is evidenced by their relative heat of hydration (115,000 calories for Na^+ compared to 96,000 for K^+), their relative speed of migration (1.6 for $Na^+\ xH_2O$ compared to 2.4 cm./hr./volt/cm. for $K^+\ xH_2O$), and the order of their exchange ability on zeolites (K^+ displaces Na^+). Likewise in the series Na^+, Mg^{++}, and Al^{3+}, the more highly charged ion combines with water more strongly than the lower-charged ions. It is not possible to determine the exact number of water molecules attached to each ion. However, for purposes of writing equations the number of water molecules is usually taken as equal to the normal coordination number of the ion or, in some cases, to the number of water molecules normally attached to the ion when it crystallizes as a salt from aqueous solutions. It should be remembered that the total number of water molecules may be greater than the coordination number. On the above basis, the complex aquo-ions of Na^+, Mg^{++}, Cu^{++}, Al^{3+} are written $Na(H_2O)_6{}^+$, $Mg(H_2O)_6{}^{++}$, $Cu(H_2O)_4{}^{++}$, $Al(H_2O)_6{}^{3+}$. Actually, in writing equations when the H_2O molecules are not involved, the simpler representation of the ions without the water molecules is used.

In some cases the combination of the water molecules markedly influences the properties of the ion as compared to the unhydrated ion. For example, in the case of $Al(H_2O)_6{}^{3+}$, the small size and high positive charge on Al^{3+} attract the oxygen of the H_2O molecule and repel the hydrogen. This weakens the oxygen-hydrogen bond to such an extent that the hydrated ion acts as a weak acid ($K_a = 1.4 \times 10^{-5}$):

$$Al(H_2O)_6{}^{3+} + H_2O \rightleftharpoons [Al(H_2O)_5OH]^{++} + H_3O^+$$

This is the equation for the **hydrolysis** of the aluminum ion. Hydrolysis of the ions of a salt on this basis is the reaction of a cation-acid or an anion-base with water. A cation-acid produces H_3O^+ ions, and an anion-base produces OH^- ions:

$$S^{--} + H_2O \rightleftharpoons HS^- + OH^-$$

The reverse of these reactions (right to left) are neutralization reactions. A reduction in the concentration of H_3O^+ by a base causes further hydrolysis of $[Al(H_2O)_5OH]^{++}$ and ultimately the precipitation of aluminum hydroxide, $Al(H_2O)_3(OH)_3$, or more simply $Al(OH)_3$.

When aluminum chloride is added to water, the solution becomes acidic because the hydrated aluminum ion hydrolyzes to give more H_3O^+ than the chloride ion hydrolyzes to give OH^-. In fact the Cl^- ion does not hydrolyze to any appreciable extent. If, however, aluminum sulfide is added to water, both ions are hydrolyzed and a precipitate of $Al(OH)_3$ is obtained:

$$\begin{array}{rcll} 2Al(H_2O)_6{}^{3+} + 6H_2O & \rightleftharpoons & \underline{2Al(H_2O)_3(OH)_3}\downarrow & + \boxed{6H_3O^+} \\ 6H_2O + 3S^{--} & \rightleftharpoons & 3H_2S\uparrow & + \boxed{6OH^-} \\ & & & \quad\ \uparrow\downarrow \\ & & & \quad 12H_2O \end{array}$$

The OH^- ions resulting from the hydrolysis of S^{--} reduce the concentration of H_3O^+, thereby causing the equilibria to be shifted to the right. If a sufficient quantity of aluminum sulfide is added, H_2S gas will be evolved and this tends to make the reaction more complete. This behavior explains why $Al(OH)_3$ rather than Al_2S_3 is obtained when ammonium sulfide (or ammonia and thioacetamide) is added to a solution containing aluminum ions.

Hydroxides, Sulfides, and Complex Ions in the Precipitation of Group III

Hydrated zinc ions react slightly with water in the same way that $Al(H_2O)_6{}^{3+}$ does:

$$Zn(H_2O)_4{}^{++} + H_2O \rightleftharpoons [Zn(H_2O)_3OH]^+ + H_3O^+$$

The ion $[Zn(H_2O)_3OH]^+$ is a weak base with a K_b of 4×10^{-5}; hence K_a for $Zn(H_2O)_4{}^{++}$ is 2.5×10^{-10}. Addition of a base causes the above equilibrium to be shifted to the right; and if $[H_3O^+]$ is reduced sufficiently, $Zn(H_2O)_2(OH)_2$, or more simply $Zn(OH)_2$, will be precipitated. This precipitate will dissolve if a sufficient concentration of $NH_4{}^+$ is present:

$$\begin{array}{l} \underline{Zn(OH)_2} \rightleftharpoons Zn^{++} + \boxed{2OH^-} \\ 2NH_4{}^+Cl^- \rightarrow 2Cl^- + \boxed{2NH_4{}^+} \\ \qquad\qquad\qquad \rightleftharpoons 2NH_3 + 2H_2O \end{array}$$

Reaction of $NH_4{}^+$ with OH^- shifts the equilibrium to the right and the precipitate dissolves. In a similar way $NH_4{}^+$ tends to cause the dissolution or prevent the formation of the hydroxides of Mn^{++}, Co^{++}, and Ni^{++}, but not those of Al^{3+}, Cr^{3+}, and Fe^{3+}.

Addition of a small amount of NH_3 to a solution of Zn^{++} causes the precipitation of $Zn(OH)_2$. Addition of more NH_3 dissolves the $Zn(OH)_2$ because of the formation of the relatively stable $Zn(NH_3)_4{}^{++}$ ion.

$$\begin{array}{l} Zn(OH)_2 \rightleftharpoons \boxed{Zn^{++}} + 2OH^- \\ \qquad\qquad\quad + \\ \qquad\qquad \boxed{4NH_3} \\ \qquad\qquad\quad \rightleftharpoons Zn(NH_3)_4{}^{++} \end{array}$$

The precipitates that form when *dilute* NH_3 is added to the ions of Groups III–V are $Fe(OH)_3$, $Al(OH)_3$, $Cr(OH)_3$, $Mn(OH)_2$, $Zn(OH)_2$, $Co(OH)_2$, $Ni(OH)_2$, and $Mg(OH)_2$. Excess NH_3 forms $Zn(NH_3)_4{}^{++}$, $Co(NH_3)_6{}^{++}$, and $Ni(NH_3)_6{}^{++}$; the corresponding hydroxides dissolve. Other hydroxides that dissolve in the presence of excess NH_3 are $Cu(OH)_2$, $Cd(OH)_2$, and AgOH, with the formation of $Cu(NH_3)_4{}^{++}$, $Cd(NH_3)_4{}^{++}$, and $Ag(NH_3)_2{}^+$. Those of $Pb(OH)_2$, $Bi(OH)_3$, $Sn(OH)_2$, $Sn(OH)_4$, and $Sb(OH)_3$ or SbOCl form with dilute NH_3 but do not dissolve in an excess of the reagent.

If $NH_4{}^+$ is also present when NH_4OH is added to Groups III–V, the concentration of OH^- is reduced to such an extent that the precipitates of $Mn(OH)_2$ and $Mg(OH)_2$ do not form. This is true because the OH^- is so low in a buffered solution of NH_3 and $NH_4{}^+$ that the ion concentration product $[Mg^{++}][OH^-]^2$ remains less than $K_{Mg(OH)_2}$ and no precipitation occurs. The same is true for $Mn(OH)_2$. Unless $NH_4{}^+$ is present when NH_4OH is added to the solution containing Groups III–V in Procedure 21, Mg^{++} will be precipitated in Group III. Ammonium ions result from the neutralization of the acid solution in the precipitation of the Group II sulfides. Consequently, if NH_4OH is added to a solution of the ions of Groups III–V in which NH_4^+ is present, the only precipitates that will be obtained are $Al(OH)_3$, $Cr(OH)_3$, $Fe(OH)_3$, and some $Mn(OH)_3$ resulting from the oxidation of Mn^{++} in alkaline solution by the oxygen of the air. Zinc, cobalt, and nickel will be in solution as their complex ammine ions, and Mn^{++} and Mg^{++} will not precipitate because the concentration of OH^- is too low.

If sulfide ions, either from H_2S gas or from the hydrolysis of CH_3CSNH_2, are present when NH_4OH is added in Procedure 21 for the precipitation of Group III ions, the only hydroxides obtained will be $Al(OH)_3$ and $Cr(OH)_3$. Ferric ion is reduced to Fe^{++}; and iron along with zinc, manganese, cobalt, and nickel precipitates as FeS, ZnS, MnS, CoS, and NiS, because their sulfides are less soluble than the corresponding hydroxides. Also the complex ions $Zn(NH_3)_4^{++}$, $Co(NH_3)_6^{++}$, and $Ni(NH_3)_6^{++}$ are not sufficiently stable to prevent $[Zn^{++}][S^{--}]$, for example, from exceeding K_{ZnS}.

According to Table 10.1, the order of decreasing solubility of the sulfides of Group III is MnS, FeS, NiS, CoS, and ZnS. In 6-*N* acetic acid solution or in about 0.05-*N* HCl, ZnS is partially precipitated by H_2S gas, but the other ions are not.

$$Zn^{++} + H_2S + 2H_2O \rightleftharpoons \underline{ZnS}\downarrow + 2H_3O^+$$

The increase in the concentration of H_3O^+ reverses the above reaction and only part of the ZnS precipitates. With thioacetamide the hydrolysis that forms H_2S proceeds so slowly that very little precipitation of ZnS is observed in a period of from 5 to 10 minutes. By using an acetic acid-acetate buffered solution, ZnS is more completely precipitated by H_2S gas because the H_3O^+ formed in the above reaction unites with the acetate ion and this prevents any appreciable increase in the acidity of the solution. However, if the acidity of the buffered solution is too low, part of the CoS and NiS may be precipitated with the ZnS.

Zinc sulfide is not normally precipitated by H_2S from a 0.01-*N* solution of Zn^{++} which is 0.1-*N* with respect to H_3O^+. However, if CuS or some other metallic sulfide is present, ZnS slowly precipitates on the surface of the sulfide. Hence, a large part of Zn^{++} may be lost in the analysis if the sulfide precipitates of Group II are allowed to remain in contact for some time with the supernatant liquid. When a foreign substance forms on the surface of a precipitate after precipitation is complete, the phenomenon is called **post-precipitation.** However, when the foreign substances are occluded or adsorbed on the precipitate as it is formed, the phenomenon is called **co-precipitation.** Some co-precipitation takes place during the precipitation of most precipitates, but it is rather extensive in the case of such precipitates as the hydroxides of Al^{3+}, Cr^{3+}, and Fe^{3+}.

The reason for the post-precipitation of a substance such as ZnS on the Group II sulfides is not known with certainty, but it is assumed to be due to the formation of a supersaturated solution of the substance that is post-precipitated. The presence of other sulfides speeds up the precipitation, because of the high concentration of sulfide ions adsorbed on their surfaces.

Such phenomena as post-precipitation and co-precipitation limit the usefulness of the solubility product principle. Uncertainty as to the true value of the solubility of such sulfides as ZnS is the most serious handicap in the quantitative application of the solubility product principle.

Any difficulties that might be encountered in the differential precipitation of ZnS and the other sulfides of Group III are circumvented in the Procedures by dissolving all the sulfides and hydroxides of the group with nitric acid. Addition of NaOH to the nitric acid solution of the ions precipitates their hydroxides first, and excess NaOH then dissolves the amphoteric hydroxides, $Al(OH)_3$ and $Zn(OH)_2$. If H_2O_2 is also added, CrO_4^{--} and MnO_2 (or H_3MnO_3) will be formed. $Co(OH)_2$ is also converted to $Co(OH)_3$. The nature of the amphoteric hydroxides of this group is considered in the following section.

Amphoteric Hydroxides of Group III

Amphoteric hydroxides possess the dual property of dissolving in both acids and bases. This property results from their tendency to either lose or gain protons, thereby acting either as acids or as bases. The following formulation illustrates these reactions:

$$\underline{Al(H_2O)_3(OH)_3}$$

$$3H_3O^+ \downarrow \qquad\qquad OH^- \downarrow$$

$$\underset{\text{Aluminum ion}}{Al(H_2O)_6^{3+}} + 3H_2O \qquad\qquad \underset{\text{Aluminate ion}}{[Al(H_2O)_2(OH)_4]^-} + H_2O$$

The water molecules may be omitted to give a simplified equation.

$$\underline{Al(OH)_3}$$

$$3H_3O^+ \downarrow \qquad\qquad OH^- \downarrow$$

$$\underset{\text{Aluminum ion}}{Al^{3+}} + 6H_2O \qquad\qquad \underset{\text{Aluminate ion}}{Al(OH)_4^-}$$

When the aluminate ion $Al(OH)_4^-$ is dehydrated it becomes AlO_2^-.

Other hydroxides of this type are $Cr(OH)_3$, $Sn(OH)_2$, $Zn(OH)_2$, and $Pb(OH)_2$. These hydroxides dissolve in excess NaOH with the formation of the complex hydroxide ions $Cr(OH)_4^-$, $Sn(OH)_4^{--}$, $Zn(OH)_4^{--}$, and $Pb(OH)_4^{--}$, respectively. Sometimes these ions are represented by the simpler formulas, AlO_2^-, CrO_2^-, $HSnO_2^-$, ZnO_2^{--}, and $HPbO_2^-$. There is some evidence, however, that $Zn(OH)_4^{--}$, for example, is more correct than ZnO_2^{--}.

In addition to the above ions, excess NaOH forms $Pb(OH)_6^{--}$, $Sn(OH)_6^{--}$, $Sb(OH)_4^-$, and $Sb(OH)_6^-$ from the corresponding oxides or hydroxides. $As(OH)_3$ or H_3AsO_3 is more acidic than basic, though it does have some amphoteric properties. When the oxidation state of arsenic or other elements is increased, the acidic nature of the corresponding hydroxides or oxides is more pronounced. Thus H_3AsO_4 (from As_2O_5 or $As(OH)_5 \rightarrow H_3AsO_4 + H_2O$) is a strong acid, whereas $As(OH)_3$ or H_3AsO_3 is a weak acid with some basic properties. In contrast to the hydroxides of arsenic and antimony, $Bi(OH)_3$ is largely basic in character and does not dissolve appreciably in NaOH solutions. In general, the oxides or hydroxides of the elements in a given family of the periodic table become less acidic (more basic) in their chemical behavior as the atomic weight increases.

Since $Cu(OH)_2$ and $Co(OH)_2$ dissolve slightly in very concentrated NaOH solutions they can be considered to have a very slight acidic character. Fused NaOH converts $Fe(OH)_3$ to $NaFeO_2$. But when $NaFeO_2$ is dissolved in water it is completely converted to NaOH and $Fe(OH)_3$.

Precipitation and Dissolution of the Amphoteric Hydroxides of Group III

When a small amount of NaOH is added to a solution of the ions of Groups III–V the following precipitates are obtained: $Fe(OH)_3$, $Al(OH)_3$, $Cr(OH)_3$, $Mn(OH)_2$, $Zn(OH)_2$, $Co(OH)_2$, $Ni(OH)_2$, $Mg(OH)_2$, and some $Sr(OH)_2$ and $Ba(OH)_2$. But, as was pointed out above, excess sodium hydroxide dissolves the amphoteric hydroxides $Al(OH)_3$, $Cr(OH)_3$, and $Zn(OH)_2$. Actually, the alkaline earth ions are separated from Group III before NaOH is added; therefore their precipitation does not concern us in this discussion.

A formulation of the precipitation and dissolution of $Al(OH)_3$ will illustrate the behavior of the three amphoteric hydroxides of Group III. When dilute NaOH is added to a solution of an aluminum salt, a precipitate of $Al(OH)_3$ forms, because

$$[Al^{3+}][OH^-]^3 > K_{s.p.}$$

Excess NaOH reacts with the precipitated hydroxide and forms the complex $Al(OH)_4^-$ ion.

$$\underline{Al(OH)_3} + OH^- \rightleftharpoons Al(OH)_4^-$$

The above reaction is reversible and any substance that will reduce the concentration of OH^- will cause the re-formation of the precipitate. Ammonium hydroxide has a sufficiently high concentration of OH^- to precipitate $Al(OH)_3$ but not to form $Al(OH)_4^-$.

The addition of an acid to an aluminate solution (a) produces a precipitate and then (b) redissolves it.

(a) $$Al(OH)_4^- + H_3O^+ \rightleftharpoons \underline{Al(OH)_3}\downarrow + 2H_2O$$

(b) $$\underline{Al(OH)_3} + 3H_3O^+ \rightleftharpoons Al^{3+} + 6H_2O$$

Similarly, the addition of a high concentration of NH_4^+ reduces the concentration of OH^- sufficiently to reprecipitate $Al(OH)_3$.

$$Al(OH)_4^- + NH_4^+ \rightleftharpoons \underline{Al(OH)_3}\downarrow + NH_3 + H_2O$$

Experiments show that precipitation of $Al(OH)_3$ is sufficiently complete if the pH of the solution is between 4 and 9. Hence, a buffered solution of NH_4Cl and NH_4OH, such as is present when Group III is precipitated, maintains the pH in this range, and the precipitation of $Al(OH)_3$ is rather complete. The OH^- is also sufficiently high for the precipitation of $Cr(OH)_3$ but not high enough to form $Cr(OH)_4^-$ or $Al(OH)_4^-$. In such a solution $Zn(OH)_2$ does not precipitate because the OH^- ion concentration is too low and the Zn^{++} unites with the NH_3 to form $Zn(NH_3)_4^{++}$.

$Al(OH)_3$, $Cr(OH)_3$, and $Fe(OH)_3$ can also be precipitated in an acetic acid-sodium acetate buffered solution at elevated temperatures. Although the solution is slightly acidic, the OH^- concentration is high enough to allow the precipitation of the hydroxides. The acetate ion in the buffered solution prevents the concentration of H_3O^+ from becoming high enough to dissolve any appreciable quantity of the $Al(OH)_3$. This may be formulated for aluminum hydroxide in the following way:

$$6H_2O \rightleftharpoons \boxed{\begin{matrix} 3OH^- \\ + \\ Al^{3+} \end{matrix}} + \boxed{\begin{matrix} 3H_3O^+ \\ + \\ 3CH_3COO^- \end{matrix}}$$

$$Al(OH)_3 \downarrow \rightleftharpoons \qquad\qquad \rightleftharpoons 3CH_3COOH + 3H_2O$$

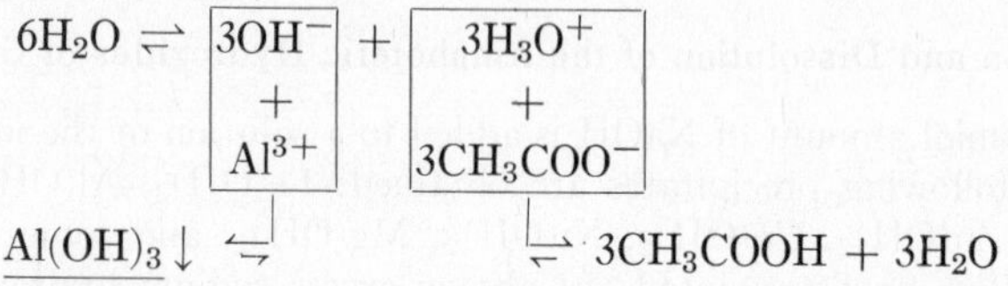

The hydroxide occludes a large amount of the acetate ion and the precipitate is frequently called "basic aluminum acetate." The precipitate is sometimes so translucent or colloidal that it is difficult to see, especially when small amounts are present. Consequently a dye that is adsorbed on the aluminum hydroxide is added to make the precipitate more visible and to increase the specificity of the test. The nature of this process is discussed in the following sections.

Colloidal Hydrous Oxides

Precipitation of hydroxides such as those of aluminum, chromium, and iron often results in the formation of a colloidal solution. The nature of the colloidal particles or **micelles** depends upon the conditions under which precipitation takes place. The formation of the particles of an aluminum hydroxide sol in a neutral or a slightly acid solution may be illustrated as follows:

(a) $\qquad Al(H_2O)_6^{3+} + H_2O \rightleftharpoons [Al(H_2O)_5OH]^{++} + H_3O^+$

(b) $\quad 2 \begin{bmatrix} H_2O & OH \\ H_2O\text{----}Al\text{----}H_2O \\ H_2O & H_2O \end{bmatrix}^{++} \rightleftharpoons \begin{bmatrix} & H & \\ H_2O\ H_2O\ O\ H_2O\ H_2O \\ Al \qquad Al \\ H_2O\ H_2O\ O\ H_2O\ H_2O \\ & H & \end{bmatrix}^{4+} + 2H_2O$

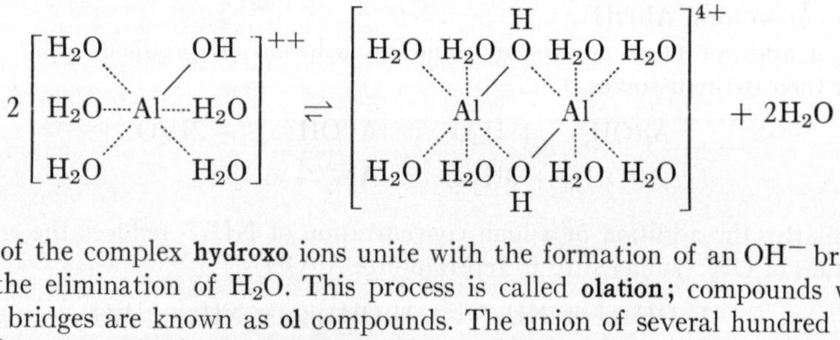

Two of the complex **hydroxo** ions unite with the formation of an OH^- bridge and the elimination of H_2O. This process is called **olation**; compounds with OH^- bridges are known as **ol** compounds. The union of several hundred ions in this way results in the formation of a colloidal particle. If the solution is not too acidic or too basic the process continues until a precipitate is formed. No definite formula can be assigned to the precipitate, but for simplicity it is written $Al(OH)_3$.

The process of olation is aided by an increase in temperature and by a decrease in the concentration of H_3O^+ to the "isoelectric point" of the hydroxide. When the concentration of H_3O^+ or OH^- is at the isoelectric point, aluminum hydroxide is least soluble and precipitates most readily. The ionization of an amphiprotic hydroxide as a base or as an acid is least at the isoelectric point; for aluminum hydroxide the isoelectric point is in a slightly alkaline solution.

In solutions more acid than the isoelectric point, part of the hydroxide is in the colloidal state. The particles are positively charged and have a great tendency to attract and react with negative ions, particularly those which have strong coordinating power. The negative ions replace OH^- and H_2O groups from the micelle. *Hence, aluminum hydroxide precipitated in acid solutions is highly contaminated with the negative ions that are present in the solution.* Increased concentration of an acid completely disperses (peptizes) the precipitated hydroxide and finally dissolves it because of two effects: (1) The hydronium ions unite with the OH^- groups to form aquo groups (H_2O); (2) the anions of the acid displace some of the OH^- groups. Disruption of ol bridges produces smaller and smaller particles until the solution contains only hydrated ions.

On the alkaline side of the isoelectric point of aluminum hydroxide, colloidal solutions are formed in which the particles are negatively charged. These par-

$$
\begin{bmatrix}
& & \text{H} & & \\
\text{H}_2\text{O} & \text{H}_2\text{O} & \text{O} & \text{H}_2\text{O} & \text{H}_2\text{O} \\
& \diagdown \, | \diagup & & \diagdown \, | \diagup & \\
& \text{Al} & & \text{Al} & \\
& \diagup | \diagdown & & \diagup | \diagdown & \\
\text{H}_2\text{O} & \text{H}_2\text{O} & \text{O} & \text{H}_2\text{O} & \text{H}_2\text{O} \\
& & \text{H} & &
\end{bmatrix}^{4+} + 6\text{OH}^- \rightleftharpoons
$$

$$
\begin{bmatrix}
& & \text{H} & & \\
\text{OH} & \text{OH} & \text{O} & \text{OH} & \text{H}_2\text{O} \\
& \diagdown \, | \diagup & & \diagdown \, | & \\
& \text{Al} & & \text{Al} & \\
& \diagup | \diagdown & & \diagup | \diagdown & \\
\text{H}_2\text{O} & \text{OH} & \text{O} & \text{OH} & \text{OH} \\
& & \text{H} & &
\end{bmatrix}^{=} + 6\text{H}_2\text{O}
$$

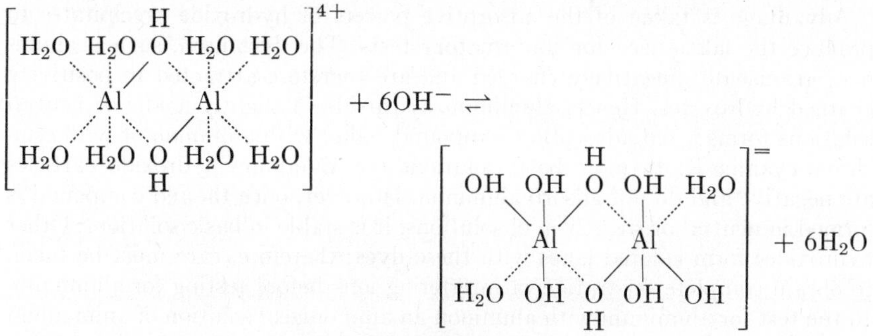

ticles have a great tendency to attract and adsorb the cations (Mn^{++}, Zn^{++}, Mg^{++}, Ni^{++}, Ca^{++}, etc.) that form slightly soluble hydroxides. *Hence, aluminum hydroxide precipitated in alkaline solutions is contaminated with cations.*

Heating a precipitate or a colloidal solution of aluminum hydroxide reduces its solubility in acids and bases, causes more complete coagulation, and reduces the extent of contamination with ions. The following formulation indicates the reason for this behavior:

$$
\begin{bmatrix}
& \text{H} & \\
& \text{O} & \\
& \diagup \quad \diagdown & \\
(\text{H}_2\text{O})_4\text{Al} & & \text{Al}(\text{H}_2\text{O})_4 \\
& \diagdown \quad \diagup & \\
& \text{O} & \\
& \text{H} &
\end{bmatrix}^{4+} + 2\text{H}_2\text{O} \rightleftharpoons
$$

$$
\begin{bmatrix}
& \text{O} & \\
& \diagup \quad \diagdown & \\
(\text{H}_2\text{O})_4\text{Al} & & \text{Al}(\text{H}_2\text{O})_4 \\
& \diagdown \quad \diagup & \\
& \text{O} &
\end{bmatrix}^{++} + 2\text{H}_3\text{O}^+
$$

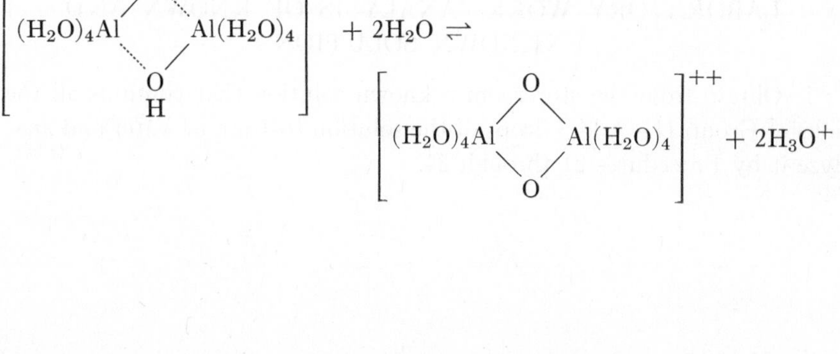

The OH^- bridges change to O^{--} bridges (called **oxo** bridges). The oxo bridges are more firmly attached to the aluminum atoms and are therefore not as easily replaced by anions. Furthermore, they do not adsorb cations as readily as do the OH^- groups.

In Procedure 21 for the precipitation of Group III, $Al(OH)_3$ and $Cr(OH)_3$ along with the sulfides of the other ions of the group are precipitated by NH_4OH in the presence of NH_4^+ and then heated in the hot water bath. This slightly alkaline solution is favorable for complete precipitation of the hydroxides. The presence of NH_4^+ reduces the OH^- concentration so that the precipitate is not highly charged negatively and this reduces the extent of the adsorption of cations. Heating the precipitate also favors its coagulation, as explained above, and further reduces the extent of the adsorption of the ions of Groups IV–V.

When aluminum hydroxide is again precipitated from the NaOH solution in Procedure 23a by the addition of acetic acid, it is necessary that the solution be slightly acidic, for otherwise the red-colored lake will not form readily with aluminon. The reason for this is given in the following section.

Formation of Lakes

Advantage is taken of the adsorptive powers of hydroxide precipitates to produce the **lakes** used for confirmatory tests. The dyes used, such as aluminon, are usually negatively charged and are therefore attracted to positively charged hydroxides. Hence, aluminum hydroxide in slightly acidic or neutral solutions forms a red adsorption compound (lake) with aluminon or with eriochrom-cyanine-R. In more basic solutions the aluminum hydroxide particles are negative and do not adsorb aluminon. However, once the red compound is formed in neutral or slightly acid solutions, it is stable in basic solutions. Other hydroxides form colored lakes with these dyes; therefore, care must be taken to obtain complete separation of interfering ions before testing for aluminum. In the test for aluminum with aluminon an ammoniacal solution of ammonium carbonate is often added because this reagent decomposes adsorption compounds with the hydroxides of Cr^{3+} and the alkaline earth ions. This reagent also changes the violet lake due to $Fe(OH)_3$ to a reddish-brown precipitate. Precipitates or colloidal particles of silicic acid (H_2SiO_3) are negative and therefore do not adsorb negatively charged dyes such as aluminon. The hydroxides of Bi^{3+}, Pb^{++}, Sb^{3+}, Sn^{4+}, and Hg^{++} form white adsorption compounds and hence do not interfere with the test.

$Mg(OH)_2$ reacts similarly and forms a blue lake with the dye *p*-nitro-benzene-azo-α-naphthol, and a red lake with titan-yellow.

LABORATORY WORK—ANALYSIS OF KNOWN AND UNKNOWN SOLUTIONS

1. Obtain from the storeroom a known solution that contains all the ions of Group III. Add 3 drops of the solution to 1 ml. of water and analyze it by Procedures 21 through 24.

2. (Optional.) Request a student to prepare an unknown solution from the test solutions for Group III ions. Analyze it by following the procedures for the analysis of Group III. (Preparation of the unknown: To 1 ml. of water add 1 drop of each of four or five different test solutions for the Group III ions.)

3. Obtain Unknown No. 3 from the storeroom and analyze it according to the Procedures for the analysis of Group III. Use 5 drops of the unknown solution in 1 ml. of water for the analysis. Report the results on an Unknown Report Blank, indicating, if requested by the instructor, the approximate concentration of each ion in the unknown solution (0.1, 1, or 5 mg./ml.).

4. Obtain Unknown No. 4 from the storeroom and analyze it by the Procedures for the analysis of Groups I, II, and III. Use 5 drops of the unknown solution in 1 ml. of water for the analysis. Report the results of the analysis on an Unknown Report Blank, indicating, if requested by the instructor, the approximate concentration of each ion in the solution (0.1, 1, or 5 mg./ml.).

In analyzing unknown solutions such as those for Group III, keep careful notes on the color of the solutions and the precipitates. Such information will be valuable in arriving at conclusions regarding the composition of the solution and in taking certain short cuts. For example, solutions of Al^{3+} and Zn^{++} are colorless; those of Fe^{3+} are yellow; of Cr^{3+}, bluish green; of Mn^{++}, faintly pink; of Ni^{++}, green; and of Co^{++}, faint red. If these colored ions are present in the solution, it will be colored. The depth of color and the hue will depend on the concentration of the ions and on the particular mixture of colored ions. For this reason, not too much can be concluded with certainty from the color.

Likewise, the color of precipitates formed during the analysis should be noted and accounted for by the final results. Some short cuts in the analysis should be obvious from certain observations. For example, if no black sulfide is obtained when Group III is precipitated in Procedure 21, iron, cobalt, and nickel are absent and nothing is gained by testing for these ions.

Analysis of Group III, Known or Unknown. Add 1 drop of 6-*N* HCl and 4 drops of 5% CH_3CSNH_2. Set the test tube in the hot water bath for about 1 minute and then continue with Procedure 21. (The composition of this solution is about the same as that of the solution obtained at this point in the analysis of a general unknown sample.)

Analysis of a General Unknown. The solution at this point is the filtrate from Group II (see Procedure 7) and contains Groups III–V. It is about 0.2- to 0.3-*N* with respect to HCl and contains CH_3CSNH_2 and some H_2S. Set the test tube in the hot water bath for about 1 minute and then continue with Procedure 21.

21. **Filtrate from Group II or Group III, Known or Unknown:** To the hot solution (see above) add 1 drop of 15-*N* NH_4OH and shake the test tube. Continue adding the 15-*N* NH_4OH drop by drop, shaking the tube after each drop is added, until 3 or more drops have been added and the solution is ammoniacal. (NOTE: Adding the NH_4OH drop by drop and shaking the tube favor the coagulation of the precipitate.) Place the tube in the hot water bath for at least 2 minutes. Filter off any precipitate that has formed, through a double-packed cotton filter medium. Wash the precipitate with about 1 ml. of water. *Reserve the filtrate for Groups IV and V.*

22. **Precipitate:** $Al(OH)_3$, $Cr(OH)_3$, ZnS, FeS, MnS, CoS, and NiS. Place the filter tube containing the precipitate in a test tube and add 1 ml. of 4-*N* HNO_3 to the filter tube. Place the assembly in the hot water bath and allow it to remain there until all the precipitate on the filter medium has dissolved. (NOTE: The precipitate on the filter medium dissolves readily when the acid in the filter tube becomes hot.) Force the solution into the test tube and wash the filter medium with a little water. Transfer the solution from the small test tube to an evaporation test tube and boil it until the volume is 1 or 2 drops (incipient dryness). Add 1 ml. of water to the evaporation test tube. Transfer the solution to a small test tube and add 1 drop of thymolphthalein indicator, and then 4-*N* NaOH until a precipitate forms, or until the solution becomes blue; now add 7 drops more of 4-*N* NaOH. To this alkaline solution add 5 drops of 3% H_2O_2. Place the tube in the hot water bath for 2 or 3 minutes, or longer. Filter off any precipitate that may have formed. Wash the precipitate first with 1 ml. of water to which has been added 1 drop of 4-*N* NaOH, and then with 1 ml. of plain water.

23. **Filtrate:** $Al(OH)_4^-$, CrO_4^{--} (yellow), $Zn(OH)_4^{--}$ (Division B). Add 4-*N* CH_3COOH drop by drop, until the bluish-green color of the indicator is discharged; then add 1 or 2 drops more. (NOTE: If CrO_4^{--} is present, the solution will have a yellow color; if there is no CrO_4^{--}, the solution will be colorless.) Divide the solution into three parts and test them as follows.

a. Al^{3+}: Add 2 drops of aluminon reagent. Shake the tube and place it in the hot water bath for a few minutes. A reddish-colored precipitate shows the presence of aluminum.

b. CrO_4^{--}: Add 1 drop of 0.1-*N* $Pb(CH_3COO)_2$. A yellow precipitate confirms the presence of chromium.

c. Zn^{++}: Add 1 drop of diethylaniline and 1 or 2 drops of potassium cyanoferrate (III), $K_3Fe(CN)_6$. Shake the tube and allow it to stand for 1 minute or longer. A reddish-colored precipitate shows the presence of zinc. (NOTE: Do not heat the solution in the hot water bath.)

24. **Precipitate from 22:** $Fe(OH)_3$, MnO_2 or (H_2MnO_3), $Ni(OH)_2$, and $Co(OH)_3$ (Division A). Place the filter tube containing the precipitate in a test tube and to the filter tube add 1 ml. of 4-*N* HNO_3 and 1 drop of 1-*N* $NaNO_2$ (sodium nitrite). Stir the precipitate with a micro stirring rod until the precipitate is dissolved. Force the solution containing the dissolved precipitate into the test tube and wash the filter medium with about 2 ml. of water. Add 2 or 3 drops of 0.5-*M* NH_2SO_3H (sulfamic acid) to the solution. Divide it into four parts and test them as follows.

a. Fe^{3+}: Add 2 or 3 drops of NH_4SCN. If iron is present, a red-colored solution will be obtained.

b. Mn^{++}: Add a small amount of solid $NaBiO_3$ with a micro spatula. If manganese is present, a reddish-purple color will be imparted to the solution. If an excess of $NaBiO_3$ has been added, a dark yellow residue will be suspended in the solution. This residue will settle, imparting a reddish-purple color to the solution. (NOTE: The residue may be filtered off. If MnO_4^- is present, the filtrate will be reddish-purple.)

c. Ni^{++}: Add 1 drop of bromthymol blue indicator and, if iron is present, 2 drops of 1-*N* tartaric acid. To this solution add 4-*N* NH_4OH drop by drop, until a blue to green color is imparted to it (pH about 8). (NOTE: If Fe^{3+} is present, the color tends toward green, whereas the indicator gives a clear blue if only Mn^{++}, Ni^{++}, or Co^{++} is present.) To this colored solution add 5 drops of dimethylglyoxime, shake the tube, and then add 1 drop of 4-*N* CH_3COOH. A scarlet-colored precipitate confirms the presence of nickel. (NOTE: If no nickel is present, the solution will be clear yellow and there will be no precipitate.)

d. Co^{++}: Add 1 drop of bromthymol blue indicator and, if iron is present, 2 drops of 1-*N* tartaric acid. To this solution add 4-*N* NH_4OH drop by drop, until a blue to green color is imparted to it. (See first note above.) To this colored solution add 3 drops of 2-nitroso-1-naphthol. Place the tube in the hot water bath for 1 or 2 minutes, and then add 1 or 2 drops of 6-*N* HCl. A purple-red precipitate confirms the presence of cobalt. (NOTE: If no cobalt is present, the solution will be yellow. If the tube is allowed to remain in the hot water bath, a yellow precipitate will form even in the absence of cobalt.)

CHEMICAL REACTIONS IN THE ANALYSIS OF GROUP III

Procedure	Equations	Purpose—Discussion
21. Add excess NH_4OH. Put the tube in the hot water bath.	$H_3O^+ + NH_3 \rightleftharpoons NH_4^+ + H_2O$ $NH_3 + H_2O \rightleftharpoons NH_4^+ + OH^-$ $CH_3CSNH_2 + 2H_3O \rightleftharpoons CH_3COO^- + NH_4^+ + H_2S$ $H_2S + 2NH_3 \rightleftharpoons 2NH_4^+ + S^=$ $Al^{3+} + 3OH^- \rightleftharpoons \underline{Al(OH)_3} \downarrow$ colorless — white $Cr^{3+} + 3OH^- \rightleftharpoons \underline{Cr(OH)_3} \downarrow$ bluish green — light green $Zn^{++} + S^= \rightleftharpoons \underline{ZnS} \downarrow$ colorless — white $Fe^{++} + S^= \rightleftharpoons \underline{FeS} \downarrow$ faint green — black $Mn^{++} + S^= \rightleftharpoons \underline{MnS} \downarrow$ light pink — flesh $Co^{++} + S^= \rightleftharpoons \underline{CoS} \downarrow$ pink — black $Ni^{++} + S^= \rightleftharpoons \underline{NiS} \downarrow$ green — black	NH_4OH neutralizes the acids in the solution and provides OH^- for the precipitation of $Al(OH)_3$ and $Cr(OH)_3$ without giving a sufficient concentration of OH^-, due to the presence of NH_4^+, for the ions of Groups IV and V to precipitate. The $S^=$ is increased to a concentration suitable for the precipitation of the insoluble sulfides of Group III. A large excess of NH_4OH should be avoided because it has a small solvent effect on $Al(OH)_3$ and $Cr(OH)_3$. More CH_3CSNH_2 should be added if Group III is not precipitated soon after Group II.
22. Dissolve the precipitate in HNO_3.	$\underline{Al(OH)_3} + 3H_3O^+ \rightleftharpoons Al^{3+} + 6H_2O$ $\underline{Cr(OH)_3} + 3H_3O^+ \rightleftharpoons Cr^{3+} + 6H_2O$ $\underline{3ZnS} + 2NO_3^- + 8H_3O^+ \rightleftharpoons 3Zn^{++} + 2NO \uparrow + \underline{3S^\circ} + 12H_2O$ $\underline{FeS} + NO_3^- + 4H_3O^+ \rightleftharpoons Fe^{3+} + NO \uparrow + \underline{S}^\circ + 6H_2O$ $\underline{3MnS} + 2NO_3^- + 8H_3O^+ \rightleftharpoons 3Mn^{++} + 2NO \uparrow + \underline{3S^\circ} + 12H_2O$ $\underline{3CoS} + 2NO_3^- + 8H_3O^+ \rightleftharpoons 3Co^{++} + 2NO \uparrow + \underline{3S^\circ} + 12H_2O$ $\underline{3NiS} + 2NO_3^- + 8H_3O^+ \rightleftharpoons 3Ni^{++} + 2NO \uparrow + \underline{3S^\circ} + 12H_2O$	The precipitated hydroxides and sulfides dissolve readily in a hot solution of HNO_3. A small amount of sulfur residue may remain on the filter medium and may enclose a small amount of the sulfides.

Procedure	Equations	Purpose—Discussion
Evaporate the HNO_3 solution to incipient dryness. Add 1 drop of thymolphthalein indicator, an excess of NaOH, and a few drops of H_2O_2. Place the tube in the hot water bath.	*Division A:* $Fe^{3+} + 3OH^- \rightleftharpoons \underline{Fe(OH)_3}\downarrow$ red $2Fe^{++} + 4OH^- + H_2O_2 \rightleftharpoons$ $\underline{2Fe(OH)_3}\downarrow$ red $Mn^{++} + 2OH^- + H_2O_2 \rightleftharpoons$ $\underline{MnO_2}\downarrow + 2H_2O$ black $Ni^{++} + 2OH^- \rightleftharpoons \underline{Ni(OH)_2}\downarrow$ light green $2Co^{++} + 4OH^- + H_2O_2 \rightleftharpoons$ $\underline{2Co(OH)_3}\downarrow$ dark brown *Division B:* $\underline{Al(OH)_3} + OH^- \rightleftharpoons Al(OH)_4^-$ colorless $\underline{2Cr(OH)_3} + 4OH^- + 3H_2O_2 \rightleftharpoons$ $2CrO_4^= + 8H_2O$ yellow $\underline{Zn(OH)_2} + 2OH^- \rightleftharpoons Zn(OH)_4^=$ colorless	Al^{3+}, Cr^{3+}, and Zn^{++} first form with OH^-, $Al(OH)_3$, $Cr(OH)_3$, and $Zn(OH)_2$. These hydroxides, however, are amphoteric and dissolve in excess alkali metal hydroxides. The H_2O_2 oxidizes the Cr^{3+} to $Cr^{6+}(CrO_4^=)$. The hydroxides of Fe^{3+}, Mn^{++}, Ni^{++}, and Co^{++} are not amphoteric and do not dissolve in excess alkali metal hydroxides. The H_2O_2 oxidizes Mn^{++} to Mn^{4+}, and the Co^{++} to Co^{3+}. Heating favors the dissolution of the amphoteric hydroxides and increases the rate of the oxidation reactions.
23. Add a small excess of CH_3COOH to the filtrate (Division B).	$CH_3COOH + OH^- \rightleftharpoons$ $CH_3COO^- + H_2O$ $Al(OH)_4^- + 4CH_3COOH \rightleftharpoons$ $Al^{3+} + 4CH_3COO^- + 4H_2O$ $2CrO_4^= + 2CH_3COOH \rightleftharpoons$ $Cr_2O_7^= + 2CH_3COO^- + H_2O$ $Zn(OH)_4^= + 4CH_3COOH \rightleftharpoons$ $Zn^{++} + 4CH_3COO^- + 4H_2O$	The acid neutralizes the hydroxide and changes $Al(OH)_4^-$ and $Zn(OH)_4^=$ to $Al(OH)_3$ and $Zn(OH)_2$. The excess acid then dissolves these hydroxides. The $CrO_4^=$ is changed to $Cr_2O_7^=$ in an acid solution. The extent of the change is small in the buffered acetic acid solution. At a pH of 9.3 and below, thymolphthalein is colorless. If the solution becomes colorless on the addition of CH_3COOH, the absence of $CrO_4^=$ is indicated. If $CrO_4^=$ is present, the solution will be yellow.

CHEMICAL REACTIONS IN THE ANALYSIS OF GROUP III
(Continued)

Procedure	Equations	Purpose—Discussion
23a. Add 1 drop of $Pb(CH_3COO)_2$ solution.	$Pb(CH_3COO)_2 + CrO_4^{=} \rightleftharpoons$ $\underset{\text{yellow}}{\underline{PbCrO_4 \downarrow}} + 2CH_3COO^-$	$PbCrO_4$ is sufficiently insoluble to precipitate from a solution containing CH_3COOH and CH_3COO^-.
23b. Add 2 drops of aluminon reagent. Place the tube in the hot water bath.	$Al^{3+} + 3OH^- \rightleftharpoons \underset{\text{white}}{\underline{Al(OH)_3 \downarrow}}$ $Al^{3+} + 3OH^- + \text{aluminon} \rightleftharpoons$ $\underset{\text{red}}{\underline{Al(OH)_3 \downarrow}}$ $CH_3COO^- + H_2O \rightleftharpoons$ $CH_3COOH + OH^-$	The red adsorption compound is not formed in an alkaline solution. By heating Al^{3+} in an acetic acid-acetate buffered solution in which the Hp is greater than 4, $Al(OH)_3$ is rather completely precipitated (p. 213) and coagulated. The aluminon dye is adsorbed on the $Al(OH)_3$ to form a red lake (p. 216), which is stable in ammoniacal solutions once it is formed in a slightly acid or neutral solution.
23c. Add diethylaniline and potassium hexacyanoferrate (III).	$3Zn^{++} + 2Fe(CN)_6^{3-} \rightleftharpoons$ $\underset{\text{yellowish}}{\underline{Zn_3[Fe(CN)_6]_2 \downarrow}}$ $2Zn^{++} + Fe(CN)_6^{4-} \rightleftharpoons$ $\underset{\text{white}}{\underline{Zn_2Fe(CN)_6 \downarrow}}$ $Zn^{++} + Fe(CN)_6^{3-}$ + diethylaniline $\rightleftharpoons Zn_2Fe(CN)_6 \cdot$ reddish-colored product	A solution containing $Fe(CN)_6^{3-}$ and diethylaniline reacts in the presence of Zn^{++} with the formation of $Zn_2Fe(CN)_6$ and a reddish-colored product which in turn imparts its color to the precipitated $Zn_2Fe(CN)_6$. The reduction of $Fe(CN)_6^{3-}$ to $Fe(CN)_6^{4-}$ by diethylaniline is a slow reaction unless Zn^{++} is present to form the exceedingly insoluble $Zn_2Fe(CN)_6$. Al^{3+} and $CrO_4^{=}$ do not give a red precipitate with $Fe(CN)_6^{3-}$ and diethylaniline.

Procedure	Equations	Purpose—Discussion
24. Dissolve the precipitate (Division A) in HNO_3 to which a drop or two of $NaNO_2$ has been added.	$Fe(OH)_3 + 3H_3O^+ \rightleftharpoons$ $Fe^{3+} + 6H_2O$ $Ni(OH)_2 + 2H_3O^+ \rightleftharpoons$ $Ni^{++} + 4H_2O$ $MnO_2 + 2H_3O^+ + NO_2^- \rightleftharpoons$ $Mn^{++} + NO_3^- + 3H_2O$ $2Co(OH)_3 + 4H_3O^+ + NO_2^- \rightleftharpoons$ $2Co^{++} + NO_3^- + 9H_2O$	Iron and nickel hydroxides are readily soluble in HNO_3, but MnO_2 and $Co(OH)_3$ are not. By the addition of NO_2^-, the Mn^{4+} is reduced to Mn^{++} and the Co^{3+} to Co^{++} and solution is easily effected.
24a. Add NH_2SO_3H (sulfamic acid) and NH_4SCN.	$NO_2^- + NH_2SO_3H \rightleftharpoons$ $HSO_4^- + N_2 \uparrow + H_2O$ $Fe^{3+} + 3SCN^- \rightleftharpoons Fe(SCN)_3$ red	The addition of NH_2SO_3H destroys the NO_2^- so that it will not interfere with the test for Fe^{3+}. The appearance of a blood-red color is a sensitive test for Fe^{3+}.
24b. Add NH_2SO_3H and solid sodium bismuthate.	$2Mn^{++} + 5BiO_3^- + 14H_3O^+ \rightleftharpoons$ $2MnO_4^- + 21H_2O + 5Bi^{3+}$ purple	The sulfamic acid is added to eliminate the NO_2^- so that it will not interfere with the test for Mn^{++}. The appearance of the purple color is a sensitive and specific test for Mn^{++}.
24c. Add 1 drop of bromthymol blue indicator and tartaric acid. Then add NH_4OH until the yellow color changes to blue. To this solution add dimethylglyoxime. Then add 1 or 2 drops of 4-N CH_3COOH.	$Ni^{++} + 2 \begin{bmatrix} CH_3-C=N-OH \\ \mid \\ CH_3-C=N-OH \end{bmatrix}$ dimethylglyoxime $+ 2H_2O \rightleftharpoons \begin{bmatrix} CH_3-C=NOH \\ \mid \\ CH_3-C=NO- \end{bmatrix}_2 Ni$ $+ 2H_3O^+$	The scarlet chelate compound is formed in a dilute ammoniacal solution. A large excess of NH_3 decreases the sensitivity of the reaction because of the formation of $Ni(NH_3)_6^{++}$. Too much acid also decreases the sensitivity of the test because it tends to reverse the reaction for the formation of the precipitates (see p. 207). The tartaric acid forms a complex with Fe^{3+} so that $Fe(OH)_3$ is not precipitated when the solution is made alkaline.

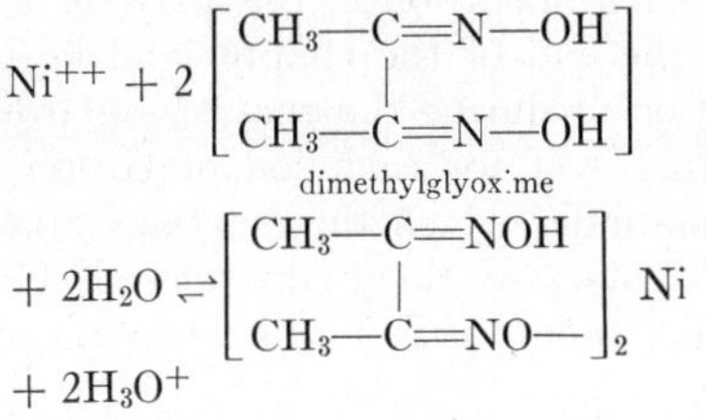

CHEMICAL REACTIONS IN THE ANALYSIS OF GROUP III
(Continued)

Procedure	Equations	Purpose—Discussion
24d. Add 1 drop of bromthymol blue and tartaric acid. Then add NH_4OH until the yellow changes to blue. To this solution add 3 or 4 drops of 2-nitroso-1-naphthol. Then add 1 or 2 drops of 6-*N* HCl.	Co^{++} + 2-nitroso-1-naphthol ⇌ purple-red precipitate	The purple-red precipitate forms in an ammoniacal solution but after it has been formed it does not dissolve in dilute acids. Apparently Co^{++} is first converted to Co^{3+} and this reacts to form a purple-red precipitate that is insoluble in dilute acids (see p. 207). If Ni^{++} is present, a brownish-yellow precipitate will form in an alkaline solution, but this precipitate is readily soluble in dilute acids.

REVIEW QUESTIONS

1. Name the ions of Group III and state the colors of their aqueous solutions. Which form complex ions with NH_3?
2. Draw up a schematic outline for the analysis of Group III cations.
3. Discuss the reasons for each operation in the analysis of Group III.
4. Study the reactions at the end of the chapter and be prepared to write equations for those that occur during the analysis of Group III cations.
5. Describe the confirmatory test for each ion of Group III, and in each case state the conditions under which the reactions take place.
6. Give the formulas and colors of the hydroxides of Group III cations. What is the color of each sulfide that forms when Group III cations are precipitated?
7. Write the formulas of all the complex ions you encountered during the analysis of Group III. Describe the conditions under which they are formed.
8. Discuss the acidity conditions required for the precipitation of Group III cations. If the ions of Group II were not removed, would all of them precipitate with Group III?
9. Explain why Mg^{++} of Group IV is not precipitated with the ions of Group III. Under what conditions would Mg^{++} be precipitated with Group III?
10. Why is the precipitate of hydroxides and sulfides of Group III dissolved in nitric acid rather than hydrochloric acid?
11. Why do NiS and CoS not dissolve readily in 1-*N* HCl when it is known that they will not precipitate in 0.3-*N* HCl?

12. What is the function of H_2O_2 in separating the ions of Group III into two divisions or subgroups?
13. List the amphoteric ions of Group III and write equations that illustrate how this property is utilized in the analysis.
14. What acidity conditions are required for the confirmatory tests for Al^{3+}, Cr^{3+}, and Zn^{++}? How is the proper pH achieved? What does a colorless solution in Procedure 23 indicate about the presence or absence of any of these ions?
15. In making the confirmatory test for Al^{3+}, why is it preferable to have the solution in which $Al(OH)_3$ is formed slightly acidic?
16. What difficulty would arise if the acidity of the solution were too high when the confirmatory test for Cr^{3+} is made? Use equations to illustrate your answer.
17. Give a possible explanation of the confirmatory test for Zn^{++}. What kind of precipitate would have been obtained by adding $K_4Fe(CN)_6$? What other ions of Group III form relatively insoluble cyanoferrates (II) (ferrocyanides)? Give their formula and color.
18. Suppose it is desired to separate Al^{3+}, CrO_4^{--}, and Zn^{++} from one another. Study the reactions of these ions and suggest a possible scheme.
19. Why is a small quantity of $NaNO_2$ added to the mixture when $Fe(OH)_3$, $Ni(OH)_2$, MnO_2, and $Co(OH)_3$ are dissolved by HNO_3? How is the excess NO_2^- removed? Write the equations for these reactions.
20. Under what conditions of acidity does sodium bismuthate form MnO_4^- from Mn^{++}? Under what conditions is CrO_4^{--} formed from Cr^{3+}?
21. Why is tartaric acid added to the solutions that are being tested for Ni^{++} and Co^{++} if Fe^{3+} was present?
22. Under what conditions of acidity, etc., are the confirmatory tests for Ni^{++} and Co^{++} made? What is the effect of changes in acidity after the precipitates are formed?
23. Discuss the interference of phosphates in the analysis for Group III. What other anions might interfere?
24. If phosphates are present in the solution to be analyzed for Group III, what changes must be made in the procedure?
25. Suggest a way of separating Fe^{3+}, Mn^{++}, Ni^{++}, and Co^{++} from one another.
26. Suppose chromium were present in an unknown solution as CrO_4^{--} and manganese as MnO_4^-; would they be precipitated with Group III?
27. What ions of Group III are absent:
    a. If a solution of the nitrates of the ions is colorless?
    b. If excess $NH_3 + NH_4^+$ forms no precipitate in the absence of H_2S or CH_3CSNH_2?
    c. If only a white precipitate and no colored solution is formed with excess $NH_3 + NH_4^+$?
    d. If, in the presence of H_2S or CH_3CSNH_2, excess $NH_3 + NH_4^+$ yields only a white precipitate?
    e. If a pink precipitate is obtained with NH_3 and H_2S?
    f. If a colorless filtrate is obtained in Procedure 22?

28. What ion or ions of Group III are indicated as being present in each of the following cases:
   a. The unknown solution is dark green.
   b. No precipitate is obtained with $NH_3 + NH_4^+$, but a white precipitate is formed when CH_3CSNH_2 (or H_2S) is added.
   c. A black residue remains when the sulfides of Group III are treated with 1-*N* HCl.
   d. A reddish-brown precipitate is obtained in Procedure 22.
   e. No precipitate is obtained at first with $NH_3 + NH_4^+$, but eventually, in contact with air, a brown precipitate forms.
   f. A white precipitate forms with a small quantity of NH_3 but dissolves when an excess is added.
29. Name a reagent that will separate the following by dissolving the first but not the second: (a) $Zn(OH)_2$ from $Al(OH)_3$; (b) $Al(OH)_3$ from $Fe(OH)_3$; (c) $Zn(OH)_2$ from $Co(OH)_2$; (d) FeS from CoS; (e) $Fe(OH)_3$ from MnO_2; (f) $Cr(OH)_3$ from $Ni(OH)_2$; (g) $Co(OH)_2$ from $Fe(OH)_3$.
30. What reagent will form a precipitate with the first ion but not the second: (a) Cr^{3+} but not Ni^{++}; (b) Co^{++} but not Zn^{++}; (c) Cr^{3+} but not Zn^{++}; (d) Fe^{3+} but not Al^{3+}; (e) Cr^{3+} but not CrO_4^{--}; (f) Fe^{3+} but not Co^{++}; (g) Fe^{3+} but not Fe^{++}?
31. It is desired to distinguish between two solutions, one containing $Al^{3+} + Co^{++}$ and the other $Al^{3+} + Zn^{++}$. What single reagent could be used?
32. Suggest a reagent that would distinguish between the following two solutions: (a) $Cr^{3+} + Co^{++}$ and (b) $Ni^{++} + Co^{++}$.
33. What two reagents could be used to separate the following mixture: $Al(OH)_3$, ZnS, CoS?
34. How could you distinguish between the two substances listed in each of the following: (a) $Al(OH)_3$ and $Co(OH)_2$; (b) Fe^{3+} and Mn^{++}; (c) Fe^{++} and Fe^{3+}; (d) Cr^{3+} and CrO_4^{--}; (e) ZnS and NiS; (f) CoS and FeS; (g) MnO_2 and $Fe(OH)_3$? If each of these pairs of substances were mixed, how would you identify the cations in each?
35. Draw up a schematic outline for the separation and identification of the following groups of ions: (a) Al^{3+}, Cr^{3+}, Zn^{++}; (b) Cr^{3+}, Zn^{++}, Fe^{++}, Ni^{++}; (c) Mn^{++}, Co^{++}, Ni^{++}; (d) Zn^{++}, Fe^{3+}, Mn^{++}, Ni^{++}.
36. Write equations for the reactions by which the ions in the following solutions could be separated and identified. Do not write equations for reactions that do not involve the ions. (a) Al^{3+}, Zn^{++}, Fe^{3+}; (b) Cr^{3+}, Fe^{3+}, Mn^{++}; (c) Al^{3+}, Cr^{3+}, Co^{++}; (d) Zn^{++}, Mn^{++}, Co^{++}, Ni^{++}; (e) Ag^+, Cu^{++}, Cr^{3+}, Mn^{++}; (f) Hg_2^{++}, As^{3+}, Bi^{++}, Al^{3+}, Ni^{++}.
37. An unknown solution, when made 0.3-*N* to HCl and then treated with CH_3CSNH_2, yielded no precipitate. When the solution containing CH_3CSNH_2 was made alkaline with NH_3 a black precipitate formed that did not dissolve readily in dilute HCl but did dissolve in hot 4-*N* HNO_3, giving a green solution. What cation is apparently present? How could it be confirmed?
38. A solution known to contain only ions of Group III is treated with excess $NH_3 + NH_4^+$. What ions will form a precipitate? If CH_3CSNH_2 is then

added to the filtrate, what sulfides will be formed? Make a schematic outline for identifying the ions of Group III based on this method.

39. When excess NH_3 was added to the filtrate from Group II (0.3-*N* to HCl and containing CH_3CSNH_2), a black precipitate formed that dissolved readily in dilute HNO_3. When the solution was treated with NaOH and H_2O_2 the solution became yellow and a reddish-brown precipitate formed. What ions are indicated by this behavior? How could they be confirmed?

40. A solution of the ions of Group III was light green and gave a black precipitate with $NH_3 + NH_4^+ + CH_3CSNH_2$. The precipitate dissolved in HNO_3 and produced a green solution. When this solution was treated with NaOH and H_2O_2 and then filtered, a colorless filtrate and a light-green precipitate remained. The addition of CH_3CSNH_2 and then CH_3COOH to the filtrate gave a white precipitate. The light-green precipitate dissolved readily in dilute HNO_3. Adding NH_3 to this solution gave a green precipitate that dissolved in excess NH_3. What conclusions can be drawn? How could the ions be confirmed?

41. Write a description of what you would observe during the analysis of solutions containing the following ions: (a) Al^{3+} and Mn^{++}; (b) Fe^{3+} and Co^{++}; (c) Cr^{3+}, Zn^{++}, and Ni^{++}.

42. Titanium, if present in an unknown solution, will precipitate as $Ti(OH)_4$ along with the ions of Group III (see p. 108). This hydroxide does not dissolve in excess NH_3 or NaOH, or in alkaline solutions of NaOH and H_2O_2. It does dissolve in H_2SO_4 and in HNO_3 solutions along with $Fe(OH)_3$, $Co(OH)_3$, and $Ni(OH)_2$. Nitric acid does not dissolve MnO_2. Fe^{3+} can be separated from Ti^{4+} by precipitating $Fe(OH)_3$ with $NaHCO_3$. Ti^{4+} apparently forms a complex carbonate ion. When H_2O_2 is added to a sulfuric acid solution containing Ti^{4+}, a yellow to red color is produced.

From this information, devise a procedure that could be used for unknown solutions containing Ti^{4+} with the other Group III cations.

REVIEW QUESTIONS ON THE THEORY OF GROUP III ANALYSIS *

1. What factors affect the extent of hydration of an ion? Illustrate the effect of hydration on the properties of ions such as Na^+, K^+, Al^{3+}.
2. Show that the hydrolysis of the hydrated aluminum ion is the same as its reaction with water as a cation acid. Compare this with the reaction of an anion base with water.
3. Compare and explain the extent of hydrolysis when aluminum chloride and aluminum sulfide are added to water.
4. Why are the hydroxides rather than the sulfides of aluminum and chromium obtained when Group III is precipitated?
5. Compare the value of K_a for the hydrated aluminum and the hydrated zinc ion with K_a for acetic acid.
6. Explain why NH_4^+ dissolves or will prevent the precipitation of $Zn(OH)_2$, $Mn(OH)_2$, $Co(OH)_2$, and $Ni(OH)_2$. What hydroxides of Group III would be precipitated by NH_3 in the presence of NH_4^+?

* See footnote, p. 133.

7. Give the formulas of the precipitates formed by the ions of Groups III–IV with dilute NH_3. What other ions also form a precipitate with dilute NH_3?
8. List the complex ions that result from treating the hydroxides of Groups III–IV and the other cations with excess NH_3.
9. Explain why NH_4^+ prevents the precipitation of $Mg(OH)_2$ by NH_3. What difficulties would arise in analyzing Group III if NH_4^+ were not present when the group precipitated?
10. Summarize the results obtained when the ions of Group III are treated with NH_4^+ and NH_3. If H_2S is added to this mixture, what changes result?
11. Show how Zn^{++} could be separated from Co^{++}, Ni^{++}, Fe^{++}, and Mn^{++} by precipitation of sulfides. Why would a buffered solution be better than a solution of HCl of the same pH?
12. Zinc was actually added to an unknown solution, but none was found. Suggest a possible reason.
13. Name some difficulties in cation analysis that result from co-precipitation and post-precipitation.
14. Write equations for the reaction of each amphoteric hydroxide of Group III with H_3O^+ and with OH^-. Name some other hydroxides or oxides that dissolve in excess strong acid and in excess alkali hydroxide.
15. How does the acidic character of the hydroxides or oxides of the elements in a family of the periodic table vary with the atomic weight? How does it change with a change in oxidation state? Illustrate.
16. Under what conditions can $Fe(OH)_3$ be made to react with NaOH?
17. If the concentration of NaOH in a solution containing the ions of Groups III and IV is low, which ions will form hydroxides? Which ones dissolve when the concentration of NaOH is increased?
18. Make a summary table that lists the ions in each of the following groups:
    a. Those that form slightly soluble hydroxides with dilute NaOH.
    b. Those that are dissolved by excess NaOH.
    c. Those that are precipitated by excess NH_4OH.
    d. Those that are precipitated by NH_4OH in the presence of NH_4Cl.
19. Formulate the behavior of Al^{3+}, Cr^{3+}, and Fe^{3+} in an acetic acid-acetate buffered solution at elevated temperatures. Illustrate the general nature of the micelles that are formed. What determines whether aluminum hydroxide micelles are positively or negatively charged?
20. When aluminum hydroxide is formed in a solution that is slightly more acidic than the isoelectric point, what ions are most readily adsorbed?
21. What ions tend to contaminate aluminum hydroxide when it is precipitated from a solution more basic than the isoelectric point?
22. What happens to the structure and properties of an aluminum hydroxide precipitate after extended heating at an elevated temperature?
23. Why should the solution from which aluminum hydroxide is to be precipitated be slightly acidic before aluminon is added to form a lake?

24. What substances might interfere in the aluminon test for aluminum? How can this possibility be avoided? Why does colloidal silicic acid not interfere in this test?
25. What conditions favor the coagulation and precipitation of the colloidal hydrous oxides?

PROBLEMS

1. The solution from Group II is 0.3-*N* to HCl and has a volume of 1 ml. Calculate the number of drops of 15-*N* NH_4OH required to react with the HCl (assume 1 drop = 0.05 ml.).
2. What will be the concentration of NH_4^+ and NH_3 in Problem 1 if 1 drop of 15-*N* NH_4OH is added in excess of that required to react with the HCl? What is the pH of this solution?
3. a. How many millimoles of H_2S will be required to react with the cations of Group III if 2 drops of 0.1-*M* solutions of each cation are present?
   b. Assuming 50% hydrolysis of the CH_3CSNH_2, how many millimoles of this reagent would be required?
   c. To how many drops of a 5% solution of CH_3CSNH_2 does this correspond?
4. In Procedure 22, 7 drops of 4-*N* NaOH was added in excess of that required to react with the HNO_3. In Procedure 23 this NaOH was neutralized with 4-*N* CH_3COOH and 2 drops were added in excess. Calculate the concentration of CH_3COO^- and CH_3COOH in this solution. What is its pH?
5. How many drops of 4-*N* NaOH and how many milligrams of H_2O_2 are theoretically required to react with the cations of Group III in Procedure 22 if 2 drops of 0.1-*M* solutions of each cation are present? How many times these theoretical amounts were added in Procedure 22?
6. What weight of sulfur will be precipitated when H_2S reacts with 2 mg. of $Cr_2O_7^{--}$ and 1 mg. of Fe^{3+} in acid solution?
7. Using the apparent value of 1×10^{-23} for the $K_{s.p.}$ of ZnS, show that 0.3-*M* HCl should dissolve or prevent the precipitation of ZnS.
8. Calculate the quantity of $Mg(OH)_2$ and $Zn(OH)_2$ that dissolves in a solution in which the concentration of NH_4^+ is maintained at (a) 0.001-*M* and (b) 0.1-*M*.
9. What concentration of NH_4^+ must be present in 0.1-*M* NH_3 to prevent the precipitation of $Mg(OH)_2$ from 0.05-*M* Mg^{++}?
10. Will 0.1-*M* NH_3 cause the precipitation of $Zn(OH)_2$? Prove your answer by means of calculations.
11. What weight of zinc must there be in 1 liter of solution before a precipitate of $Zn(OH)_2$ will form in a solution 0.1-*M* with respect to both NH_4^+ and NH_3? Take into consideration both the reduction in concentration of OH^- by the common-ion effect and the formation of the complex tetrammine zinc ion.
12. Calculate the concentration of Pb^{++} in a saturated solution of $PbSO_4$ and of $PbCrO_4$. Explain why ammonium acetate dissolves $PbSO_4$ but not $PbCrO_4$.

13. Calculate the solubility of ZnS in 1-*M* CH_3COOH (0.4% ionized).
14. What must be the concentration of H_3O^+ to allow the precipitation of MnS from 0.05-*M* Mn^{++}? What is the pH of this solution? What indicator would be chosen to determine when enough alkali or acid has been added to the solution?
15. It is desired to precipitate ZnS as completely as possible from a solution which is 0.1-*M* with respect to both Zn^{++} and Fe^{++}, without precipitating FeS. What concentration of H_3O^+ or OH^- should be used?
16. A solution containing Mn^{++} and Zn^{++} is made slightly alkaline (1×10^{-5}-*M* OH^-) with a buffer and then saturated with H_2S. Calculate the concentration of each of the cations left in solution.
17. Will a saturated solution of CO_2 appreciably increase the solubility of MnS over its solubility in water? Show the magnitude of the effect by the appropriate calculations.
18. If no precipitate of ZnS is obtained when H_2S is passed through a 0.1-*M* CH_3COOH (1.34% ionized), calculate the maximum concentration of Zn^{++} that could be present.

CHAPTER 13

PRELIMINARY EXPERIMENTS AND REACTIONS FOR CATIONS OF GROUPS IV AND V *

IONS OF GROUP IV

Test Solution †	Ion	Concentration (mg./ml.)
0.1-*M* Barium nitrate	Ba^{++}	13.7
0.1-*M* Strontium nitrate	Sr^{++}	8.8
0.1-*M* Calcium nitrate	Ca^{++}	4.0

† If desired, test solutions may be prepared to contain 10 mg. of cation per ml. (Appendix C).

The Barium Ion, Ba^{++}

Ba-1. Test for Precipitation of $Ba(OH)_2$ and BaS. To 1 ml. of water add 1 drop of the barium nitrate test solution. Then add 1 drop of 4-*N* NH_4OH and note whether a precipitate forms. Now add 1 drop of a 5% solution of thioacetamide. Place the tube in the hot water bath. Does a precipitate form? (Save this solution for Ba-2.) Repeat the first test, using 1 drop of 4-*N* NaOH in place of NH_4OH. Record and explain the results. Compare them with the results obtained for the ions of Group III and for Mg^{++}. Test the reaction of Ba^{++} with NaOH again by adding 1 drop of NaOH to 10 drops of the test solution. Explain the results of these tests.

Solubility: $Ba(OH)_2 = 1.9 \times 10^{-2}$ g./ml. at 20° (15.2 mg. Ba^{++}/ml.).

Ba-2. Precipitation of $BaCO_3$. To the solution from Ba-1 add 1 drop of 2-*N* $(NH_4)_2CO_3$. Note the color of the precipitate and write the equation for the reaction. Filter off the precipitate and wash it with a little water. (Save the precipitate for Ba-3.)

Solubility: $BaCO_3 = 1.4 \times 10^{-5}$ g./ml. (9.7 μg. Ba^{++}/ml.).

* Study the discussion of the Procedures for Group IV (pp. 244 ff.) and the chemical reactions in the analysis of Group IV (pp. 260 ff.) before doing these Preliminary Experiments.

Ba-3. Dissolution of $BaCO_3$. To the filter tube containing the $BaCO_3$, add 2 or 3 drops of 4-*N* CH_3COOH and 1 ml. of water. Force the solution into a test tube. Write the equation for the reaction. (Save the solution for Ba-4.)

Ba-4. Precipitation of $BaCrO_4$. To the solution from Ba-3 add 1 drop of phenolphthalein indicator, and then add 4-*N* NH_4OH drop by drop, until the solution has a faint red color. (NOTE: Do not add an excess of NH_4OH.) To this solution add 2 or 3 drops of 0.1-*M* K_2CrO_4. Place the tube in the hot water bath for 1 minute or longer. Filter off the precipitate and wash it with water. (Save it for Ba-5.)

Ba-5. Tests for Ba^{++} by the Formation of $BaSO_4$. To the precipitate on the filter medium add 4 or 5 drops of 1-*N* HCl and 1 ml. of water. Force the solution through the filter medium into a test tube and add 1 drop of 3% H_2O_2. (NOTE: The H_2O_2 reacts with the $Cr_2O_7^{--}$ with the formation of a "blue" color, presumably due to H_3CrO_8, which fades in a short time in a warm acid solution.) Place the tube in the hot water bath and add 2 or 3 drops of 0.5-*M* NH_2SO_3H (sulfamic acid). Note the color of the precipitate and write the equation for the reaction.

Solubilities: $BaCrO_4 = 3.6 \times 10^{-6}$ g./ml. (2.0 μg. Ba^{++}/ml.).
$BaSO_4 = 2.3 \times 10^{-6}$ g./ml. (1.4 μg. Ba^{++}/ml.).

$BaSO_4$ is the least soluble of all the barium salts.

The Strontium Ion, Sr^{++}

Sr-1. Test for Precipitation of $Sr(OH)_2$ and SrS. To 1 ml. of water add 1 drop of the strontium nitrate test solution. Then add 1 drop of 4-*N* NH_4OH and note whether a precipitate forms. Now add 1 drop of a 5% solution of thioacetamide. Place the tube in the hot water bath. Does a precipitate form? (Save the solution for Sr-2.) Repeat the first test, but use 1 drop of 4-*N* NaOH instead of NH_4OH. Record and explain the results. Compare them with those in Ba-1 and those obtained with Group III ions and for Mg^{++}. To 10 drops of the Sr^{++} test solution add 2 drops of 4-*N* NaOH. Explain the results of these tests.

Solubility: $Sr(OH)_2 = 5.2 \times 10^{-3}$ g./ml. at 20° (3.7 mg. Sr^{++}/ml.).

Sr-2. Precipitation of $SrCO_3$. To the solution from Sr-1 add 1 drop of 2-*N* $(NH_4)_2CO_3$. Note the color of the precipitate and write the equation for the reaction. Filter off the precipitate and wash it with a little water. (Save it for Sr-3.)

Solubility: $SrCO_3 = 4.5 \times 10^{-6}$ g./ml. (2.6 μg. Sr^{++}/ml.).

$SrCO_3$ is the least soluble of all the strontium salts.

Sr-3. Dissolution of $SrCO_3$. To the filter tube containing the $SrCO_3$ add 2 or 3 drops of 4-*N* CH_3COOH and 1 ml. of water. Force the solution into a test tube. Write the equation for the reaction. (Save the solution for Sr-4.)

Sr-4. Test for Precipitation of $SrCrO_4$ and the Formation of $SrSO_4$. To the solution from Sr-3 add 1 drop of phenolphthalein indicator; then add 4-*N* NH_4OH drop by drop, until the solution has a faint pink color. (NOTE: Do not add an excess of NH_4OH.) Now add 1 drop of 0.1-*M* K_2CrO_4. Place the tube in the hot water bath. Does a precipitate form? (See Ba-4.) Now add 2 drops of 4-*N* CH_3COOH to the solution, and then 3 drops of a 0.25-*M* solution of hydrazine sulfate ($N_2H_4 \cdot H_2SO_4$). Allow the tube to remain in the hot water bath for 2 or 3 minutes. Note the color of the precipitate and write the equation for the reaction. (NOTE: Only the SO_4^{--} needs to be considered in this reaction.)

Solubilities: $SrCrO_4 = 1.2 \times 10^{-3}$ g./ml. (0.52 mg. Sr^{++}/ml.).
$SrSO_4 = 9.7 \times 10^{-5}$ g./ml. (0.046 mg. Sr^{++}/ml.).

The Calcium Ion, Ca^{++}

Ca-1. Test for Precipitation of $Ca(OH)_2$ and CaS. To 1 ml. of water add 1 drop of the calcium nitrate test solution. Then add 1 drop of 4-*N* NH_4OH and note whether a precipitate forms. Now add 1 drop of a 5% solution of thioacetamide. Place the tube in the hot water bath. Does a precipitate form? (Save the solution for Ca-2.) Repeat the first test, but use 1 drop of 4-*N* NaOH instead of NH_4OH. Record and explain the results. Compare them with those in Ba-1 and Sr-1, and with those obtained with Group III and for Mg^{++}. To 10 drops of the Ca^{++} test solution add 2 drops of 4-*N* NaOH. Explain the results of these tests.

Solubility: $Ca(OH)_2 = 9.4 \times 10^{-4}$ g./ml. (0.5 mg. Ca^{++}/ml.).

Ca-2. Precipitation of $CaCO_3$. To the solution from Ca-1 add 1 drop of 2-*N* $(NH_4)_2CO_3$. Note the color of the precipitate and write the equation for the reaction. Filter off the precipitate and wash it with a little water. (Save it for Ca-3.)

Solubility: $CaCO_3 = 6.9 \times 10^{-6}$ g./ml. (2.8 μg. Ca^{++}/ml.).

Ca-3. Dissolution of $CaCO_3$. To the filter tube containing the $CaCO_3$ add 2 or 3 drops of 4-*N* CH_3COOH and 1 ml. of water. Force the solution into a test tube. Write the equation for the reaction. (Save the solution for Ca-4.)

Ca-4. Test for Precipitation of $CaCrO_4$. To the solution from Ca-3 add 1 drop of phenolphthalein indicator, then add 4-*N* NH_4OH drop by drop, until the solution has a faint pink color. (NOTE: Do not add an excess of NH_4OH.) To this solution add 1 drop of 0.1-*M* K_2CrO_4. Place the tube in the hot water bath. Does a precipitate form? Compare the results with those from Ba-4 and Sr-4. (Save the solution for Ca-5.)

Solubility: $CaCrO_4 = 2.3 \times 10^{-2}$ g./ml. (5.9 mg. Ca^{++}/ml.).

Ca-5. Test for Precipitation of $CaSO_4$ and CaC_2O_4. To the solution from Ca-4 add 2 drops of 4-*N* CH_3COOH and 3 drops of a 0.25-*M* solution of hydrazine sulfate. Allow the tube to remain in the hot water bath for 2 or 3 minutes. Does a precipitate form? Now add 2 drops of 0.1-*N* $(NH_4)_2C_2O_4$ to the solution. Note the color of the precipitate and write the equation for the reaction.

Solubilities: $CaSO_4 = 6.7 \times 10^{-4}$ g./ml. (0.2 mg. Ca^{++}/ml.).
$CaC_2O_4 = 6.1 \times 10^{-6}$ g./ml. (1.9 μg. Ca^{++}/ml.).

CaC_2O_4 is the least soluble of all the calcium salts.

Summary of the Properties of the Ions of Group IV and Mg^{++}

From the Preliminary Experiments and other available information, indicate the precipitates that would form with the reagents listed in Column 1 of the chart below. If the information as to whether a reaction occurs is not readily available, make the necessary tests by adding 2 drops of the appropriate test solution to 1 ml. of water, and then adding 1 or 2 drops of the reagent.

Reagent	Ba^{++}	Sr^{++}	Ca^{++}	Mg^{++}
4-*N* NH_4OH				
4-*N* $NH_4OH + CH_3CSNH_2$				
4-*N* NaOH				
4-*N* NH_4OH + 6-*N* NH_4Cl				
2-*N* $(NH_4)_2CO_3$				

Reagent	Ba^{++}	Sr^{++}	Ca^{++}	Mg^{++}
0.1-*M* K_2CrO_4 + 4-*N* CH_3COOH				
4-*N* H_2SO_4				
0.5-*M* NH_2SO_3H				
0.25-*M* $N_2H_4 \cdot H_2SO_4$				
0.1-*N* $(NH_4)_2C_2O_4$				

IONS OF GROUP V

Test Solution	Ion	Concentration (mg./ml.)
0.1-*M* Magnesium nitrate	Mg^{++}	2.4
0.1-*M* Potassium nitrate	K^+	3.9
0.1-*M* Sodium nitrate	Na^+	2.3
0.1-*M* Ammonium nitrate	NH_4^+	1.8

The Magnesium Ion, Mg^{++}

Mg-1. Precipitation of $Mg(OH)_2$. To each of two test tubes add 1 ml. of water and 2 drops of the magnesium nitrate test solution. Add 1 drop of 6-*N* NH_4Cl to one of the tubes. Now add 2 drops of 4-*N* NH_4OH to each tube. Place the tubes in the hot water bath. Explain why a precipitate forms in the tube to which only NH_4OH was added, but not in the tube to which both NH_4OH and NH_4Cl were added. To a third test tube add 1 ml. of water, 1 drop of the magnesium test solution, and 1 drop of 4-*N* NaOH. Compare the results of this test with those obtained in Ba-1, Sr-1, and Ca-1.

Solubility: $Mg(OH)_2 = 6.5 \times 10^{-6}$ g./ml. (2.7 μg. Mg^{++}/ml.).

Mg-2. Confirmatory Test for Mg^{++}. *Lake Formation by* $Mg(OH)_2$ *and Titan-Yellow.* To each of two test tubes add 1 ml. of water and 2 drops of the magnesium nitrate test solution; then add 1 drop of 6-*N* NH_4Cl. Now add 1 drop of titan-yellow reagent to one of the tubes, and then add 2 drops of 4-*N* NaOH to both tubes. Place them in the hot water bath and note the difference in the color of the precipitates. Why does NaOH precipitate $Mg(OH)_2$ from a solution which contains an ammonium salt whereas NH_4OH does not?

Mg-3. Sensitivity of the $Mg(OH)_2$*-Titan-Yellow Test for* Mg^{++}. To one clean test tube add 2 ml. of *distilled water* and to another clean tube add 2 ml. of *tap water*. Now add 1 drop of titan-yellow reagent and 1 drop of 4-*N* NaOH to each of these tubes. Is the presence of Mg^{++} indicated in the tap water? (NOTE: One part of Mg^{++} in 3,000,000 parts of water (0.3 μg. Mg^{++}/ml.) may be detected by this test.)

The Potassium Ion, K^+

K-1. Confirmatory Test for K^+ by the Formation of $K_2AgCo(NO_2)_6$. To 2 ml. of water add a small quantity (about 50 mg.) of *solid* sodium hexanitrocobaltate (III), $Na_3Co(NO_2)_6$, from the tip of a micro spatula. After the salt has dissolved, divide the solution into two parts and add 1 drop of the silver nitrate test solution to one part. Now add 1 drop of the potassium nitrate test solution to each part. Note the color of the precipitates and write the equation for the reactions. (The formula of the precipitate in the tube to which the $AgNO_3$ was added is $K_2AgCo(NO_2)_6$, and the formula of the precipitate in the other tube is $K_3Co(NO_2)_6$.)

K-2. Comparison of $K_2AgCo(NO_2)_6$ and $K_3Co(NO_2)_6$ as Confirmatory Precipitates for K^+. Which is less soluble, $K_2AgCo(NO_2)_6$ or $K_3Co(NO_2)_6$? This question may be answered as follows: To 10 ml. of water add 1 drop of the potassium nitrate test solution. Calculate the grams of K^+/ml. in this diluted solution. To 2 ml. of water add a small quantity (about 50 mg.) of *solid* sodium hexanitrocobaltate (III) from the tip of a micro spatula. After the salt has dissolved, divide the solution into two equal parts and add 1 drop of the $AgNO_3$ test solution to one part. Now add the diluted potassium nitrate solution to each part, drop by drop, and shake the tube after each drop. Observe the contents of the tubes by transmitted light and record the number of drops of KNO_3 that were required before a precipitate was visible in each tube.

The Sodium Ion, Na^+

Na-1. Confirmatory Test for Na^+ by the Formation of a Precipitate with a Uranyl Zinc Acetate Reagent. To a test tube add 10 drops of the uranyl zinc acetate reagent,* and then add 1 drop of the sodium nitrate test solution. Note the yellow color and crystalline nature of the precipitate. Write the equation for the reaction. What is the molecular weight of the salt? What percentage of sodium is contained in this compound?

* Barber and Kolthoff, *J. Am. Chem. Soc.* **50**, 1625 (1928).

(NOTE: Do not heat the precipitate in the hot water bath. The solubility of the precipitate increases markedly at high temperatures.)

The Ammonium Ion, NH_4^+

NH_4^+-1. Nessler's Test for NH_4^+. To each of two test tubes add 1 ml. of water. Then add 1 drop of the ammonium nitrate test solution to one of these tubes. Now add 1 drop of Nessler's reagent to each tube. Record the results and write the equation for the reaction. (NOTE: The test for NH_3 with Nessler's reagent is very sensitive.)

NH_4^+-2. Sensitivity of Nessler's Test for NH_3. To 10 ml. of distilled water add 1 drop of the ammonium nitrate test solution. Calculate the weight of NH_3, in grams, in 1 ml. of this diluted ammonium nitrate solution. Add 1 ml. of distilled water to one test tube and 1 ml. of the diluted NH_4NO_3 solution to another tube. Now add 1 drop of Nessler's reagent to each tube. Note the color of the solution in each tube. (NOTE: Nessler's reagent imparts a yellowish-brown color to 100 ml. of water containing 1 drop of a 0.1-*M* solution of NH_4NO_3.)

NH_4^+-3. Ammonia Test for NH_4^+. To a test tube add 1 drop of the ammonium nitrate test solution and 1 drop of 4-*N* NaOH. Place a small plug of cotton or glass wool in a filter tube and push the medium into place in the lower end of the tube. (Do not pack the cotton too tightly.) To the filter tube add 1 ml. of water and 1 drop of bromthymol blue indicator. Depress the rubber bulb and insert the end of it into the filter tube; while air is being drawn through the solution in the filter tube, put the filter tube in the test tube containing the NH_3 solution. Now place the assembly in the hot water bath. The evolved NH_3 (gas) will be drawn through the solution in the filter tube and the indicator will turn blue. Write the equation for the reaction by which NH_3 was obtained.

NH_4^+-4. Formation of $(NH_4)_3Co(NO_2)_6$. Interference with the Test for K^+. To 2 ml. of water add a small amount (about 50 mg.) of *solid* sodium hexanitrocobaltate (III). After the salt has dissolved, divide the solution into two parts and add 1 drop of the ammonium nitrate test solution to one part. To the other part add 1 drop of the potassium nitrate test solution. Does there appear to be a difference in the solubility of $(NH_4)_3Co(NO_2)_6$ and $K_3Co(NO_2)_6$? (NOTE: The concentration of the $Na_3Co(NO_2)_6$ in the solution determines whether a precipitate will form in both tubes.) This experiment definitely shows that no ammonium salts should be present when testing for K^+ with sodium hexanitrocobaltate (III).

SUMMARY OF REACTIONS OF CATIONS OF GROUPS IV–V

Reagents	Barium—$Ba(NO_3)_2$	Strontium—$Sr(NO_3)_2$	Calcium—$Ca(NO_3)_2$	Magnesium—$Mg(NO_3)_2$
Acids and water	Metal $Ba + 2H_3O^+ \rightarrow Ba^{++} + H_2\uparrow + 2H_2O$ $Ba + 2H_2O \rightarrow Ba^{++} + 2OH^- + H_2\uparrow$	Metal $Sr + 2H_3O^+ \rightarrow Sr^{++} + H_2\uparrow + 2H_2O$ $Sr + 2H_2O \rightarrow Sr^{++} + 2OH^- + H_2\uparrow$	Metal $Ca + 2H_3O^+ \rightleftharpoons Ca^{++} + H_2\uparrow + 2H_2O$ $Ca + 2H_2O \rightleftharpoons Ca^{++} + 2OH^- + H_2\uparrow$	Metal $Mg + 2H_3O^+ \rightleftharpoons Mg^{++} + H_2\uparrow + 2H_2O$ $Mg + 2H_2O$ (steam) $\rightleftharpoons MgO + 2H_2\uparrow$
Precipitants	Insoluble salts: $Ba_3(PO_4)_2$, $BaSO_4$, $BaCrO_4$, $BaCO_3$, $Ba(IO_3)_2$, BaC_2O_4, $BaSO_3$, BaS_2O_3, BaF_2, $Ba(OH)_2$.	Insoluble salts: $Sr_3(PO_4)_2$, $SrCO_3$, SrC_2O_4, $SrSO_4$, SrF_2, $SrCrO_4$, $Sr(OH)_2$.	Insoluble salts: CaC_2O_4, $CaCO_3$, $CaSO_3$, CaF_2, $Ca_3(PO_4)_2$, $CaSO_4$.	Insoluble salts: $MgNH_4PO_4$, $Mg(OH)_2$, $Mg_3(PO_4)_2$, MgF_2, $MgCO_3$, MgC_2O_4.
$(NH_4)_2CO_3$	$Ba^{++} + CO_3^= \rightleftharpoons \underset{\text{white}}{\underline{BaCO_3}}\downarrow$ $BaCO_3$ dissolves readily in dilute acids. NH_4^+ does not prevent the precipitation of $BaCO_3$.	$Sr^{++} + CO_3^= \rightleftharpoons \underset{\text{white}}{\underline{SrCO_3}}\downarrow$ $SrCO_3$ dissolves readily in dilute acids. NH_4^+ does not prevent the precipitation of $SrCO_3$.	$Ca^{++} + CO_3^= \rightleftharpoons \underset{\text{white}}{\underline{CaCO_3}}\downarrow$ $CaCO_3$ dissolves readily in dilute acids. NH_4^+ does not prevent the precipitation of $CaCO_3$.	No precipitate is formed because of the high concentration of NH_4^+ in the reagent.
NaOH	$Ba^{++} + 2OH^- \rightleftharpoons \underset{\text{white}}{\underline{Ba(OH)_2}}\downarrow$	$Sr^{++} + 2OH^- \rightleftharpoons \underset{\text{white}}{\underline{Sr(OH)_2}}\downarrow$	$Ca^{++} + 2OH^- \rightleftharpoons \underset{\text{white}}{\underline{Ca(OH)_2}}\downarrow$	$Mg^{++} + 2OH^- \rightleftharpoons \underset{\text{white}}{\underline{Mg(OH)_2}}\downarrow$
$(NH_4)_2C_2O_4$	$Ba^{++} + C_2O_4^= \rightleftharpoons \underset{\text{white}}{\underline{BaC_2O_4}}\downarrow$ The precipitate is soluble in hot CH_3COOH and dissolves readily in HCl.	$Sr^{++} + C_2O_4^= \rightleftharpoons \underset{\text{white}}{\underline{SrC_2O_4}}\downarrow$ The precipitate is soluble in hot CH_3COOH and dissolves readily in HCl.	$Ca^{++} + C_2O_4^= \rightleftharpoons \underset{\text{white}}{\underline{CaC_2O_4}}\downarrow$ CaC_2O_4 is practically insoluble in CH_3COOH, but dissolves in HCl.	$Mg^{++} + C_2O_4^= \rightleftharpoons \underset{\text{white}}{\underline{MgC_2O_4}}\downarrow$ The precipitate forms only in reasonably concentrated solutions. It is readily soluble in acetic acid.

Dilute H_2SO_4	$Ba^{++} + SO_4^{=} \rightleftharpoons \underset{\text{white}}{\underline{BaSO_4}} \downarrow$ $BaSO_4$ is insoluble in acids.	$Sr^{++} + SO_4^{=} \rightleftharpoons \underset{\text{white}}{\underline{SrSO_4}} \downarrow$ $SrSO_4$ is reasonably soluble in strong acids. It is transposed by $CO_3^{=}$ to $SrCO_3$.	$Ca^{++} + SO_4^{=} \rightleftharpoons \underset{\text{white}}{\underline{CaSO_4}} \downarrow$ The precipitate forms only when reasonably concentrated solutions are used. It is soluble in strong acids.	—
K_2CrO_4	$Ba^{++} + CrO_4^{=} \rightleftharpoons \underset{\text{yellow}}{\underline{BaCrO_4}} \downarrow$ $BaCrO_4$ is insoluble in dilute acetic acid but soluble in strong acids.	$Sr^{++} + CrO_4^{=} \rightleftharpoons \underset{\text{yellow}}{\underline{SrCrO_4}} \downarrow$ $SrCrO_4$ is soluble in acetic acid and in strong acids.	$Ca^{++} + CrO_4^{=} \rightleftharpoons \underline{CaCrO_4} \downarrow$ A precipitate is formed only in *concentrated* solutions. It is readily dissolved by dilute acetic acid.	—
Na_2HPO_4	$Ba^{++} + HPO_4^{=} \rightleftharpoons \underset{\text{white}}{\underline{BaHPO_4}} \downarrow$ The precipitate is soluble in acetic acid. In ammoniacal solutions $Ba_3(PO_4)_2$ is obtained.	$Sr^{++} + HPO_4^{=} \rightleftharpoons \underset{\text{white}}{\underline{SrHPO_4}} \downarrow$ The precipitate is soluble in acetic acid. In ammoniacal solutions $Sr_3(PO_4)_2$ is obtained.	$Ca^{++} + HPO_4^{=} \rightleftharpoons \underset{\text{white}}{\underline{CaHPO_4}} \downarrow$ The precipitate is soluble in acetic acid. In ammoniacal solutions $Ca_3(PO_4)_2$ is obtained.	$Mg^{++} + HPO_4^{=} \rightleftharpoons \underset{\text{white}}{\underline{MgHPO_4}} \downarrow$ The precipitate is soluble in acetic acid. If NH_4OH and NH_4^+ are in the solution, a precipitate of $MgNH_4PO_4$ is obtained. $Mg^{++} + NH_4^+ + PO_4^{3-} \rightleftharpoons \underset{\text{white}}{\underline{MgNH_4PO_4}} \downarrow$
Flame	Yellowish-green	Crimson	Brick-red	—

SUMMARY OF REACTIONS OF CATIONS OF GROUPS IV–V (*Continued*)

Reagents	Sodium—$NaNO_3$	Potassium—KNO_3	Ammonium—NH_4NO_3
Acids and water	Metal $2\underline{Na} + 2H_3O^+ \rightleftharpoons 2Na^+ + H_2\uparrow + 2H_2O$ $2\underline{Na} + 2H_2O \rightleftharpoons + 2Na^+ + 2OH^- + H_2\uparrow$	Metal $2\underline{K} + 2H_3O^+ \rightleftharpoons 2K^+ + H_2\uparrow + 2H_2O$ $2\underline{K} + 2H_2O \rightleftharpoons 2K^+ + 2OH^- + H_2\uparrow$	—
Precipitants	Slightly soluble salts: $(UO_2)_3ZnNa(CH_3COO)_9 \cdot 6H_2O$, $NaSb(OH)_6$ or $Na_2H_2Sb_2O_7$, Na_2SiF_6.	Slightly soluble salts: $K_2NaCo(NO_2)_6$, K_2PtCl_6, $KHC_4H_4O_6$, K_2SiF_6, $KClO_4$, $K_2AgCo(NO_2)_6$.	Slightly soluble salts: $(NH_4)_2NaCo(NO_2)_6$, $(NH_4)_2PtCl_6$, $NH_4HC_4H_4O_6$, HOHgNHHgI.
$Na_3Co(NO_2)_6$ + $AgNO_3$	—	$2K^+ + Ag^+ + Co(NO_2)_6^{3-} \rightleftharpoons \underset{\text{yellow}}{\underline{K_2AgCo(NO_2)_6}}\downarrow$ The reaction is carried out in a dilute acetic acid solution. $Co(OH)_2$ precipitates in an alkaline solution. Reducing agents interfere with the reaction by reducing NO_2^-.	$2NH_4^+ + Ag^+ + Co(NO_2)_6^{3-} \rightleftharpoons \underset{\text{yellow}}{\underline{(NH_4)_2AgCo(NO_2)_6}}\downarrow$ Since NH_4^+ forms a precipitate similar to the one formed by K^+, ammonium salts must be volatilized before $Na_3Co(NO_2)_6$ is used to test for K^+ (see potassium).
H_2PtCl_6	—	$2K^+ + PtCl_6^= \rightleftharpoons \underset{\text{yellow}}{\underline{K_2PtCl_6}}\downarrow$ The precipitate is much less soluble in alcohol than in water. I^- and CN^- interfere with the reaction by forming stable complex ions with platinum.	$2NH_4^+ + PtCl_6^= \rightleftharpoons \underset{\text{yellow}}{\underline{(NH_4)_2PtCl_6}}\downarrow$ Ammonium salts must be removed before a test for K^+ is made (see potassium).
$NaHC_4H_4O_6$	—	$K^+ + HC_4H_4O_6^- \rightleftharpoons \underset{\text{white}}{\underline{KHC_4H_4O_6}}\downarrow$ The precipitate forms in concentrated solutions only. It is soluble in NaOH or HCl.	$NH_4^+ + HC_4H_4O_6^- \rightleftharpoons \underset{\text{white}}{\underline{NH_4HC_4H_4O_6}}\downarrow$ Ammonium salts must be removed before a test for K^+ is made (see potassium).

$KSb(OH)_6$ or $K_2H_2Sb_2O_7$	$Na^+ + Sb(OH)_6^- \rightleftharpoons \underset{\text{white}}{\underline{NaSb(OH)_6}}\downarrow$ The precipitate forms best in a slightly alkaline solution.	—	—
Uranyl-acetate-zinc-acetate mixture	$Na^+ + Zn^{++} + 3UO_2^{++} + 9CH_3COO^- + 6H_2O \rightarrow \underset{\text{yellow}}{\underline{(UO_2)_3ZnNa(CH_3COO)_9 \cdot 6H_2O}}\downarrow$ The precipitate forms in concentrated solutions of the reagent. It is less soluble in alcohol than in water.	—	—
$HClO_4$	—	$K^+ + ClO_4^- \rightleftharpoons \underset{\text{white}}{\underline{KClO_4}}\downarrow$ $KClO_4$ is reasonably soluble in water but is very slightly soluble in alcohol.	—
NaOH or $Ca(OH)_2$	—	—	$NH_4^+ + OH^- \rightleftharpoons NH_3\uparrow + H_2O$ When the solution is warmed, NH_3 is evolved and may be detected by its effect on indicators.
Nessler's reagent	—	—	$2HgI_4^= + OH^- + NH_3 \rightleftharpoons \underset{\text{light brown}}{\underline{HOHgNHHgI}}\downarrow + H_2O + 7I^-$ This is a very sensitive test for NH_3. Hg^+, Sb^{+++}, and Sn^{++} should be absent.
Flame	Yellow. The flame is colorless when viewed through a cobalt glass.	Violet. The flame is reddish-violet when viewed through a cobalt glass.	—

Flame Tests for the Ions of Groups IV and V

Place 2 or 3 drops of the test solutions of Ba^{++}, Sr^{++}, Ca^{++}, K^{+}, and Na^{+} in separate depressions of a spot plate or in separate test tubes. Dip a platinum wire with a small loop at the end into the Ba^{++} solution. Hold the loop in a gas flame at a point about midway between the tip of the inside blue cone and the outer edge of the flame. Note the color imparted to the flame by the barium salt.

Clean the platinum wire by dipping it into concentrated or 6-*N* HCl in a depression of a spot plate and then burning off the HCl and barium salt in the gas flame. Repeat this process until no greenish color is imparted to the flame.

Repeat the test for each of the other ions, and tabulate the results. Clean the wire after each test.

Prepare a mixture of Ba^{++}, Sr^{++}, and Ca^{++} and observe the order in which the colors appear and disappear when the wire is dipped in the mixture and held in the flame.

Prepare a mixture of K^{+} and Na^{+} and observe the color of the flame both with and without a cobalt glass or chrome alum solution filter. Record the results.

The above tests may be used in the Procedures as further evidence of the presence or absence of the ions of Group IV and K^{+} and Na^{+}. The final precipitate or solution obtained in the Procedures for the confirmatory test for each ion is acidified with HCl and tested with a platinum wire and gas flame.

If a small spectograph is available, observe the number, color, and relative position of the prominent lines in the spectrum. If a calibration chart or wave-length scale is available with the instrument, record the wave length of the most prominent lines for each of the five ions. Repeat the spectrographic test, using a mixture of the five ions, and note if the lines for each element are visible.

CHAPTER 14

ANALYSIS OF CATIONS OF GROUPS IV AND V. GENERAL UNKNOWN SOLUTION FOR CATIONS

SCHEMATIC OUTLINE OF THE PROCEDURE

Group IV

25. **Filtrate from Group III:** Ba^{++}, Sr^{++}, Ca^{++}, Mg^{++}, K^+, Na^+, (NH_4^+)
Contains NH_4OH and NH_4^+. Add $(NH_4)_2CO_3$.

31. **Filtrate:** Group V	26. **Precipitate:** $BaCO_3$, $SrCO_3$, and $CaCO_3$ Add CH_3COOH, CH_3COONH_4, and K_2CrO_4.		
	27. **Precipitate:** $BaCrO_4$	28. **Filtrate:** Sr^{++} and Ca^{++} Add CH_3COOH and $N_2H_4 \cdot H_2SO_4$.	
	Add HCl (flame test). Add H_2O_2 and sulfamic acid. *White ppt.:* $BaSO_4$	29. **Precipitate:** $SrSO_4$ Add $(NH_4)_2CO_3$, then CH_3COOH (flame test). Add satd. $CaSO_4$. *White ppt.:* $SrSO_4$	30. **Filtrate:** Ca^{++} Add $(NH_4)_2C_2O_4$. *White ppt.:* CaC_2O_4 Dissolve in $(NH_4)_2SO_4$. Add alcohol. *White ppt.:* CaC_2O_4. Add HCl (flame test).
	Barium	*Strontium*	*Calcium*

Group V

31. **Filtrate from Group IV:** Mg^{++}, K^+, Na^+, (NH_4^+)
Add HNO_3. Evaporate and ignite.
Add water and HNO_3. Test separate parts as follows:

32. Mg^{++}: Add one part to titan-yellow and NaOH. *Reddish ppt.:* $Mg(OH)_2$	33. K^+: Add second part to $AgNO_3$ and $Na_3Co(NO_2)_6$ solution. *Yellowish-orange ppt.:* $K_2AgCo(NO_2)_6$	34. Na^+: Add third part to uranyl zinc acetate reagent. *Yellow crystalline ppt.:* $Na(UO_2)_3Zn(CH_3COO)_9 \cdot 6H_2O$
Magnesium	*Potassium*	*Sodium*

35. Test the original solution for NH_4^+ by a or b:
a. Add NaOH. Filter. Add Nessler's reagent. *Brown ppt.:* NH_4^+ present.
b. Add NaOH. Gas evolved for NH_3. (See Exp. NH_4^+-3, p. 237.)

DISCUSSION OF THE PROCEDURES FOR GROUP IV

The ions of Group IV (Ba^{++}, Sr^{++}, and Ca^{++}) precipitate when ammonium carbonate is added to the filtrate from Group III. This filtrate contains NH_3 and NH_4^+ as well as some unhydrolyzed CH_3CSNH_2 which does not interfere with the precipitation of the carbonates. Both NH_3 and NH_4^+ must be present because they maintain the OH^- concentration at a value that permits a concentration of CO_3^{--} high enough to precipitate $BaCO_3$, $SrCO_3$, and $CaCO_3$ but not $MgCO_3$. At the same time the OH^- concentration in this buffered solution is not high enough to allow $Mg(OH)_2$ to precipitate. When the precipitation of this group is carried out at elevated temperatures, easily filtered crystalline precipitates are obtained. After the carbonates are dissolved by acetic acid, the ions must be separated from one another and confirmatory tests must be made.

Separation and Tests for the Ions of Group IV

The alkaline earth ions of Group IV are all found in the second group of the periodic table and do not show marked differences in properties. They have no amphiprotic properties, form few complex ions, and have an oxidation state of 2+ in solution. Because the solubilities of their salts do not differ widely, the separation and identification of these elements present some difficulty. However, by properly controlling precipitation conditions, satisfactory separations can be made. Table 14.1 shows the relative solubilities of some of the compounds of Ba^{++}, Sr^{++}, Ca^{++}, and Mg^{++} that are useful in the separation and identification of these ions.

TABLE 14.1. Solubilities of Some Alkaline Earth Salts in g./ml. (Order of Increasing Solubility)

Carbonates	$SrCO_3$ 4.5×10^{-6}	$CaCO_3$ 6.9×10^{-6}	$BaCO_3$ 1.4×10^{-5}	$MgCO_3$ 2.7×10^{-4}
Chromates	$BaCrO_4$ 3.6×10^{-6}	$SrCrO_4$ 1.2×10^{-3}	$CaCrO_4$ 2.3×10^{-2}	$MgCrO_4$ soluble
Sulfates	$BaSO_4$ 2.3×10^{-6}	$SrSO_4$ 9.7×10^{-5}	$CaSO_4$ 6.7×10^{-4}	$MgSO_4$ soluble
Oxalates	CaC_2O_4 6.1×10^{-6}	SrC_2O_4 4.2×10^{-5}	BaC_2O_4 7.5×10^{-5}	MgC_2O_4 1.0×10^{-3}
Hydroxides	$Mg(OH)_2$ 6.5×10^{-6}	$Ca(OH)_2$ 9.4×10^{-4}	$Sr(OH)_2$ 5.2×10^{-3}	$Ba(OH)_2$ 1.9×10^{-2}

Since $BaCrO_4$ is much less soluble than the chromates of the other ions in the group, its precipitation is a means of separating Ba^{++} from Sr^{++} and Ca^{++}. If the concentration of Sr^{++} is relatively high, some $SrCrO_4$ may be precipitated with the $BaCrO_4$ in neutral or alkaline solution. However, if the precipitation is carried out in a buffered solution of acetic acid and ammonium acetate, no strontium chromate will form and the precipitation of barium chromate will be sufficiently complete. A more detailed discussion of this separation will be given in a later section.

The presence of barium is confirmed by dissolving the $BaCrO_4$ in dilute hydrochloric acid and then precipitating $BaSO_4$ from this acid solution by adding sulfamic acid (NH_2SO_3H). On hydrolysis, this reagent produces a concentration of SO_4^{--} that is sufficiently high to precipitate $BaSO_4$, even when the concentration of Ba^{++} is low, but not high enough to precipitate $SrSO_4$ or $CaSO_4$ from solutions with a rather high concentration of Sr^{++} or Ca^{++}. Consequently, even if some $SrCrO_4$ does precipitate when chromate is added to the solution to separate Ba^{++}, $SrSO_4$ will not precipitate with the sulfamic acid. It is reasonably certain, then, that Ba^{++} is present if a white precipitate forms with the sulfamic acid. Additional confirmation may be obtained by using a flame test (p. 242) on the hydrochloric acid solution of the $BaCrO_4$. A green color is imparted to the flame if barium is present.

After the Ba^{++} is removed from the solution containing the ions of Group IV, Sr^{++} is separated by precipitation as $SrSO_4$. This is done by adding hydrazine sulfate [$N_2H_4 \cdot H_2SO_4$ or $(N_2H_5)HSO_4$] to a solution acidified with CH_3COOH. The hydrazine sulfate in water gives rise to SO_4^{--}:

$$N_2H_4 \cdot H_2SO_4 \rightleftharpoons N_2H_5^+ + HSO_4^-$$

$$HSO_4^- \xrightarrow{+H_2O} \rightleftharpoons H_3O^+ + SO_4^{--}$$

An increase in the acidity of the solution due to the added acetic acid decreases the concentration of SO_4^{--}. Usually $Cr_2O_7^{--}$ is present because an excess of CrO_4^{--} was used to precipitate $BaCrO_4$. Some of the $N_2H_5^+$ is oxidized by the $Cr_2O_7^{--}$:

$$3N_2H_5^+ + 2Cr_2O_7^{--} + 13H_3O^+ \rightleftharpoons 3N_2\uparrow + 4Cr^{3+} + 27H_2O$$

It has been found that hydrazine sulfate precipitates $SrSO_4$ but not $CaSO_4$ in the concentrations normally used in the solutions analyzed, i.e., about 0.5 to 2 mg./ml. Some of the factors contributing to this separation (p. 252) appear to be the limited concentration of SO_4^{--}, the slower rate of precipitation of $CaSO_4$ as compared to $SrSO_4$, the greater tendency of Ca^{++} to form complex ions, and the greater effect of acidity on the solubility of $CaSO_4$ arising from the acetic acid and the hydrolysis of $N_2H_5^+$ and the ionization of HSO_4^-.

The presence of strontium is reaffirmed by transposing the $SrSO_4$ to $SrCO_3$, the least soluble of the strontium salts listed in Table 14.1. The $SrCO_3$ is then dissolved by acetic acid and $SrSO_4$ is reprecipitated by a saturated solution of $CaSO_4$. If the sulfate precipitate obtained with the hydrazine sulfate had been $CaSO_4$ instead of $SrSO_4$, very little if any precipitate would be obtained when the saturated solution of calcium sulfate is added at this point in the analysis. Only $SrSO_4$ would be precipitated. The presence of Sr^{++} may be further confirmed by a flame test on the acetic acid solution obtained when the carbonate is dissolved. A crimson red flame confirms the presence of strontium. However, the color of the flame produced by a large amount of calcium may be confused with the color produced by a small amount of strontium. Comparative flame tests will aid in distinguishing between strontium and calcium.

The filtrate obtained from the separation of Sr^{++} is tested for Ca^{++} by precipitating it as CaC_2O_4. The presence of calcium is confirmed by dissolving the CaC_2O_4 in $(NH_4)_2SO_4$ and then reprecipitating the CaC_2O_4 by adding alcohol to the solution. If the oxalate precipitate had been SrC_2O_4 instead of CaC_2O_4, it would be converted to $SrSO_4$ but would not dissolve in the $(NH_4)_2SO_4$ because Sr^{++} does not form complex sulfate ions. In this case no precipitate will form when the alcohol is added. A flame test can be used to confirm further the presence of Ca^{++}. This is done by filtering off the CaC_2O_4, adding 1 drop of HCl, and testing the moist precipitate for flame coloration. Calcium imparts a brick-red color to the flame.

DISCUSSION OF THE PROCEDURES FOR GROUP V

The ions of Group V (Mg^{++}, K^+, Na^+, NH_4^+) do not form insoluble compounds with any of the group reagents. No single precipitant has been found for this group of ions. Consequently, individual tests are made for each ion. Because ammonium salts are added several times during the analysis, the original unknown solution must be tested for NH_4^+.

Since the solution remaining after Groups I–IV have been separated contains an appreciable concentration of NH_4^+, the ammonium salts must be removed before the test for K^+ is made. This is so because NH_4^+ forms a precipitate with $Na_3Co(NO_2)_6$ just as K^+ does. The NH_4^+ is removed by adding excess nitric acid, evaporating the solution to dryness, and then heating the evaporation tube strongly until the NH_4NO_3 is decomposed and the ammonium salts are completely expelled. The nitric acid also aids in the decomposition of the unhydrolyzed thioacetamide. The residue from this treatment contains magnesium, potassium, and sodium as nitrites and nitrates. It is dissolved in water and separate portions of the solution are tested for Mg^{++}, K^+, and Na^+.

EQUILIBRIA INVOLVED IN THE ANALYSIS OF GROUP IV

Precipitation of the Carbonates

In an aqueous solution of ammonium carbonate, the ions are rather extensively hydrolyzed.

$$H_2O + CO_3^{--} \rightleftharpoons HCO_3^- + OH^-$$
$$NH_4^+ + H_2O \rightleftharpoons NH_3 + H_3O^+$$
$$\overline{NH_4^+ + CO_3^{--} \rightleftharpoons NH_3 + HCO_3^-}$$

This hydrolysis results in a rather low concentration of CO_3^{--}. If ammonium salts are also present, as is the case in the general procedure for the analysis of all the groups, the above equilibria are shifted toward the right and the CO_3^{--} ion concentration is further reduced. It will be so low in a solution of ammonium carbonate that the precipitation of $BaCO_3$, $SrCO_3$, and $CaCO_3$ will not be sufficiently complete. The extent of the hydrolysis is decreased and consequently the concentration of CO_3^{--} is increased by the addition of ammonium hydroxide, because both NH_3 and OH^- tend to shift the above equilibria to the left, thereby increasing the concentration of CO_3^{--}. But the concentration of CO_3^{--} must not be too high, for $MgCO_3$ will precipitate with Group IV. To make this separation, the concentration of CO_3^{--} must be such that

$$[Ba^{++}][CO_3^{--}] > 4.9 \times 10^{-9}, \qquad \text{and} \qquad [Mg^{++}][CO_3^{--}] < 1 \times 10^{-5}$$

Moreover, the OH^- ion concentration must not be too high, or $Mg(OH)_2$ will precipitate. This concentration can be kept at the desired value by adjusting the concentration of NH_4^+:

$$NH_3 + H_2O \rightleftharpoons NH_4^+ + OH^-; \quad [OH^-] = \frac{[NH_3]}{[NH_4^+]} K_{NH_3}$$

Consequently, the separation can be made by having the proper concentrations of NH_3 and NH_4^+ in solution. The ratio of $[NH_3]$ to $[NH_4^+]$ must be such that the OH^- ion concentration will be low enough to prevent the precipitation of $Mg(OH)_2$ and $MgCO_3$. But this concentration must not be too low, because the presence of OH^- is required to repress the hydrolysis of CO_3^{--}

and thereby permit the analytically complete precipitation of $BaCO_3$, $SrCO_3$, and $CaCO_3$. If the concentration of NH_3 is not higher than 0.1-*M*, the presence of 0.1-*M* NH_4^+ will usually adjust the OH^- to the appropriate value (see Problem 16, p. 267).

Dissolution of the Carbonates

The carbonates of barium, strontium, and calcium are readily dissolved by strong acids such as hydrochloric acid and by weak acids such as acetic acid. The reactions may be formulated as shown in the following equations for $BaCO_3$.

$$\underline{BaCO_3} \rightleftharpoons Ba^{++} + \boxed{CO_3^{--} + H_3O^+}$$

$$\rightleftharpoons \boxed{HCO_3^- + H_3O^+} + H_2O$$

$$\rightleftharpoons H_2CO_3 + H_2O \rightleftharpoons 2H_2O + CO_2 \uparrow$$

In a saturated solution of barium carbonate, the ion concentration product $[Ba^{++}][CO_3^{--}]$ is equal to the solubility product constant K_{BaCO_3}. The H_3O^+ reacts with CO_3^{--} to produce the very weak acid HCO_3^- ($K_a = 4.7 \times 10^{-11}$). This causes the ion concentration product to be less than K_{BaCO_3}; hence the solid dissolves until $[Ba^{++}][CO_3^{--}]$ is again equal to K_{BaCO_3}. If the concentration of H_3O^+ is sufficiently high, the quantity of H_2CO_3 formed will exceed that in a saturated solution of CO_2 at atmospheric pressure and CO_2 will escape. As the CO_2 escapes, more H_2CO_3 forms and this demands more HCO_3^- which can be made available only through the production of more CO_3^{--} by dissolution of the carbonate. The loss of CO_2 from the system in this way causes all the above equilibria to be shifted toward the right until the precipitate dissolves.

The carbonates are somewhat soluble in ammonium salts because the NH_4^+ hydrolyzes, with the formation of some H_3O^+:

$$\begin{array}{rcl} BaCO_3 \rightleftharpoons Ba^{++} + & \boxed{CO_3^{--}} & \\ NH_4^+ + H_2O \rightleftharpoons NH_3 + & \boxed{H_3O^+} & \\ & \rightleftharpoons & HCO_3^- + H_2O \end{array}$$

The formation of the weak acid HCO_3^- causes the above equilibria to be shifted toward the right; this means that more $BaCO_3$ must dissolve. As was said in the preceding section, the addition of NH_3 tends to counteract this effect and thereby reduces the quantity of $BaCO_3$ that will dissolve. $BaCO_3$, $SrCO_3$, and $CaCO_3$ are somewhat soluble in solutions of NH_4Cl, but the amounts of $MgCO_3$ normally encountered in qualitative analysis are completely dissolved, even in the presence of some ammonia. This is true because the concentration of CO_3^{--} is relatively high in a saturated solution of $MgCO_3$. The H_3O^+ from the NH_4^+ reduces the concentration of CO_3^{--} so much that even when all the $MgCO_3$ is dissolved the ion concentration product $[Mg^{++}][CO_3^{--}]$ does not equal K_{MgCO_3}.

Similarly, even though $Mg(OH)_2$ is relatively insoluble (see Table 14.1), it dissolves in solutions of NH_4Cl.

$$\begin{array}{rcl} Mg(OH)_2 & \rightleftharpoons & Mg^{++} + \boxed{2OH^-} \\ 2NH_4^+ + 2H_2O & \rightleftharpoons & 2NH_3 + \boxed{2H_3O^+} \\ & & \quad \rightleftharpoons 4H_2O \end{array}$$

The formation of the slightly ionized water molecule reduces the concentration of OH^- and shifts the equilibria to the right until the $Mg(OH)_2$ has dissolved. This is in agreement with what was said in the preceding section—that $Mg(OH)_2$ is not precipitated by NH_3 from a solution that contains a sufficient concentration of NH_4^+.

Separation of Ba^{++} from Sr^{++} and Ca^{++} by Precipitation of $BaCrO_4$

In this separation it is desired to control the concentration of CrO_4^{--} so that the concentration of Ba^{++} will be reduced to at least 0.0001-*M* and $SrCrO_4$ will not be precipitated from a 0.1-*M* Sr^{++} solution. The conditions desired are as follows:

$$[Ba^{++}][CrO_4^{--}] > 2.0 \times 10^{-10}; \quad (0.0001)[CrO_4^{--}] > 2.0 \times 10^{-10}, \text{ or } [CrO_4^{--}] > 2.0 \times 10^{-6}$$

$$[Sr^{++}][CrO_4^{--}] < 3.6 \times 10^{-5}; \quad (0.1)[CrO_4^{--}] < 3.6 \times 10^{-5}, \text{ or } [CrO_4^{--}] < 3.6 \times 10^{-4}$$

That is, the concentration of CrO_4^{--} must be maintained between 3.6×10^{-4} and 2.0×10^{-6} mole/liter. When the concentration of Sr^{++} is not greater than 0.1-*M*, a concentration of 3.6×10^{-4} for CrO_4^{--} permits a more complete precipitation of $BaCrO_4$ but not the precipitation of $SrCrO_4$.

The concentration of CrO_4^{--} in a solution of a chromate is controlled by the concentration of H_3O^+. This is shown by the following equilibria:

$$Cr_2O_7^{--} + 3H_2O \rightleftharpoons 2HCrO_4^- + 2H_2O \rightleftharpoons 2CrO_4^{--} + 2H_3O^+$$

Too high a concentration of H_3O^+ shifts the equilibria too far toward the left, thereby converting too much of the CrO_4^{--} to $Cr_2O_7^{--}$, and $BaCrO_4$ will not precipitate. The equilibrium constant for the above reaction is

$$\frac{[CrO_4^{--}]^2[H_3O^+]^2}{[Cr_2O_7^{--}]} = 2.4 \times 10^{-15}$$

A concentration of H_3O^+ of about 1×10^{-5} mole/liter (pH = 5) adjusts the concentration of CrO_4^{--} to about 5×10^{-4} mole per liter, as can be seen if we substitute this value for $[H_3O^+]$ and 0.01 for $[Cr_2O_7^{--}]$ in the expression for the equilibrium constant. As shown above, this concentration of CrO_4^{--}

is approximately the value desired for the separation of Ba^{++} and Sr^{++}. (5.5×10^{-5} mg. of Ba^{++}/ml. and 6.6 mg. of Sr^{++}/ml. will remain in solution.) A buffered solution of acetic acid and ammonium acetate is used to obtain the required concentration of H_3O^+. Such a solution is also required because when chromate ions are removed from the solution during the formation of $BaCrO_4$, the above equilibria are shifted toward the right. This tends to increase the concentration of H_3O^+; but the acetate ion in the buffered solution unites with the H_3O^+ to form the slightly ionized acetic acid molecules and consequently the concentration of H_3O^+ does not build up.

The above system is buffered with respect not only to H_3O^+ but also to CrO_4^{--}. At a pH of 5, most of the chromate in the solution is in the form of $Cr_2O_7^{--}$ and only a small amount is present as CrO_4^{--} ($[CrO_4^{--}] = 5 \times 10^{-4}$). Although this excess $Cr_2O_7^{--}$ is not effective in causing the precipitation of $BaCrO_4$, it does serve as a reservoir for CrO_4^{--}. Hence, as CrO_4^{--} is used up in precipitating $BaCrO_4$, the above equilibria are shifted to the right and more CrO_4^{--} is regenerated from the relatively large supply of $Cr_2O_7^{--}$. The H_3O^+ ions that are formed react with the acetate ions of the buffered solution.

As a result of these two processes, the concentration of both CrO_4^{--} and H_3O^+ does not change much during the precipitation, and the solution is said to be "buffered" with respect to these two ions. If a dilute solution of K_2CrO_4 (5×10^{-4} mole/liter) were used instead of the buffered solution, the precipitation of $BaCrO_4$ would rapidly deplete the solution of CrO_4^{--} before much of the Ba^{++} was removed from the system.

Dissolution of Chromates

When an acid is added to a slightly soluble chromate such as $BaCrO_4$, the following reactions occur:

$$2BaCrO_4 \rightleftharpoons 2Ba^{++} + \boxed{\begin{array}{c} 2CrO_4^{--} \\ + \\ 2H_3O^+ \end{array}}$$

$$\updownarrow$$

$$2HCrO_4^- + 2H_2O$$

$$\rightleftharpoons Cr_2O_7^{--} + H_2O$$

$BaCrO_4$ is so slightly soluble that the concentration of H_3O^+ in acetic acid does not reduce the concentration of CrO_4^{--} sufficiently to dissolve much of the precipitate. However, $BaCrO_4$ is soluble in solutions of strong acids. In water $SrCrO_4$ is about 430 times and $CaCrO_4$ about 10,000 times more soluble (in moles per liter) than is $BaCrO_4$. The concentration of CrO_4^{--} in a saturated solution of either $SrCrO_4$ or $CaCrO_4$ is high enough to form an appreciable amount of $HCrO_4^-$ which, with its subsequent change to $Cr_2O_7^{--}$ in acetic acid solution, reduces the concentration of CrO_4^{--}; and $SrCrO_4$ and $CaCrO_4$ dissolve in acetic acid solution or in dilute solutions of stronger acids.

Separation of Sr^{++} from Ca^{++} by Precipitation of $SrSO_4$

Table 14.1 shows that $CaSO_4$ is considerably more soluble than $SrSO_4$ (6.7×10^{-4} g./ml. for $CaSO_4$ compared to 9.7×10^{-5} g./ml. for $SrSO_4$, or 0.2 mg. of Ca^{++}/ml. compared to 0.046 mg. of Sr^{++}/ml.). If a solution is saturated with respect to *both sulfates*, the following expressions must hold:

$$[Ca^{++}][SO_4^{--}] = 2.4 \times 10^{-5}$$

$$[Sr^{++}][SO_4^{--}] = 2.8 \times 10^{-7}$$

The concentration of SO_4^{--} is the same in both expressions; hence, dividing the first expression by the second, we obtain

$$\frac{[Ca^{++}]}{[Sr^{++}]} = \frac{2.4 \times 10^{-5}}{2.8 \times 10^{-7}} = 86$$

That is, in a solution in equilibrium with both these precipitates, the calcium ion concentration will be 86 times that of the strontium ion. Since $SrSO_4$ is considerably less soluble than $CaSO_4$, the concentration of SO_4^{--} resulting from the $SrSO_4$ will not significantly affect the solubility of $CaSO_4$. Consequently the concentration of Ca^{++} and of SO_4^{--} is essentially that in a saturated solution of $CaSO_4$, or 4.9×10^{-3} moles/liter (0.2 mg. of Ca^{++}/ml.). The concentration of Sr^{++} is 1/86 of this, or 5.7×10^{-5} moles/liter (0.005 mg. of Sr^{++}/ml.). Higher concentrations of SO_4^{--} than that of a saturated solution of $CaSO_4$ will reduce the concentration of both Sr^{++} and Ca^{++}, but the ratio of their concentrations will remain 1 to 86. However, at high concentrations of SO_4^{--}, Ca^{++} apparently forms complex sulfate ions $Ca(SO_4)_2^{--}$ and the ratio will be greater. Other substances such as triethanolamine also form complexes with Ca^{++} and facilitate the separation of Sr^{++} from Ca^{++}.

The sulfates of this group are somewhat soluble in acid solution because of the tendency of SO_4^{--} to form HSO_4^{-}, a moderately weak acid with an ionization constant of 1.2×10^{-2}. The formation of this ion reduces the concentration of SO_4^{--} in a saturated solution of the sulfate so that more of the solid must dissolve to make the ion concentration product equal to the solubility product constant. The solubility of $BaSO_4$ is not greatly affected by acid and that of $SrSO_4$ increases somewhat. However, the effect of acids on the solubility of $CaSO_4$ is appreciable. In a solution that is 1-M to H_3O^+ the concentration of Ca^{++} is about 0.044 mole/liter, whereas in water it is only 0.0049 mole/liter, or about 2 mg. of Ca^{++}/ml. in the acid solution compared to about 0.2 mg. in water.

If sulfuric acid is used to precipitate Sr^{++} and Ca^{++} as sulfates, two effects are apparent. One is an increase in solubility because of the H_3O^+, and the other is a decrease in solubility because of the common-ion effect of SO_4^{--}. The completeness of the separation that would be obtained by precipitation with 1-M H_2SO_4 may be estimated in the following way. Sulfuric acid, H_2SO_4, is a dibasic acid that ionizes rather completely to give H_3O^+ and HSO_4^-.

The HSO_4^- then ionizes further in accordance with the expression

$$\frac{[H_3O^+][SO_4^{--}]}{[HSO_4^-]} = 1.2 \times 10^{-2}$$

Substituting in this expression for a 1-*M* solution of H_2SO_4 gives a concentration of about 0.012-*M* for SO_4^{--}. Using this value in the expressions for the solubility product constants for $SrSO_4$ and $CaSO_4$, we have

$$[Sr^{++}](0.012) = 2.8 \times 10^{-7}, \quad \text{or} \quad [Sr^{++}] = 2.3 \times 10^{-5} \text{ mole/liter}$$
$$[Ca^{++}](0.012) = 2.4 \times 10^{-5}, \quad \text{or} \quad [Ca^{++}] = 2.0 \times 10^{-3} \text{ mole/liter}$$

This means that after $SrSO_4$ has been precipitated, the concentration of Sr^{++} will be about 0.002 mg./ml. The concentration of Ca^{++} at which a precipitate of $CaSO_4$ would be obtained is 2×10^{-3} mole/liter, or about 0.08 mg. of Ca^{++}/ml. The concentration of SO_4^{--} remains essentially constant even though some of it would be removed by the precipitation of $SrSO_4$. As SO_4^{--} is used, more is regenerated from the relatively large supply of HSO_4^-, thus making the system more or less "buffered" with respect to SO_4^{--} at about 0.012-*M*. The concentration of SO_4^{--} is probably too low to cause the formation of significant concentrations of the complex calcium sulfate ion, $Ca(SO_4)_2^{--}$.

Since more than 0.1 mg. of Ca^{++}/ml. is usually present in an unknown solution, the above separation does not seem to be adequate. Addition of another acid with H_2SO_4 would permit a greater concentration of Ca^{++} but it would also increase somewhat the solubility of $SrSO_4$. Sometimes, instead of trying to make a more or less complete separation, we add $(NH_4)_2SO_4$. This precipitates practically all the Sr^{++} and only part of the Ca^{++}. The concentration of Ca^{++} in the saturated solution of $CaSO_4$ is high enough for a confirmatory test by precipitation of CaC_2O_4; so, for identification purposes, complete separation is not necessary. Of course, a method which does produce analytically complete separation is more desirable. Other difficulties also arise in the precipitation of the sulfates because of their tendency to form rather stable supersaturated solutions, particularly when cold. For this reason the sulfates should be precipitated at elevated temperatures and the solutions should be shaken frequently.

It has been found that a satisfactory separation of Sr^{++} from Ca^{++} can be obtained with a slightly acid solution of hydrazine sulfate (p. 245) at a concentration of from 0.1- to 0.03-*M*. In an aqueous solution of hydrazine sulfate, $N_2H_4 \cdot H_2SO_4$ or $(N_2H_5)HSO_4$, the following equilibria exist:

$$\begin{array}{ccccc} (N_2H_5)HSO_4 \rightleftharpoons & N_2H_5^+ & + & HSO_4^- \\ & \uparrow\downarrow + H_2O & & \uparrow\downarrow + H_2O \\ & N_2H_4 + H_3O^+ & & H_3O^+ + SO_4^{--} \end{array}$$

The ionization of HSO_4^- and the hydrolysis of $N_2H_5^+$ ($K_{N_2H_4} = 8.5 \times 10^{-7}$) results in a higher concentration of H_3O^+ and a lower concentration of SO_4^{--} than would be found in an equal molar concentration of $(NH_4)_2SO_4$. On the other hand, the concentration of H_3O^+ is lower and that of SO_4^{--} is higher in a solution of $N_2H_4 \cdot H_2SO_4$ than in an equal molar solution of H_2SO_4. Thus it appears that $N_2H_4 \cdot H_2SO_4$ yields a concentration of SO_4^{--} somewhere between that with $(NH_4)_2SO_4$ and H_2SO_4. From the above equilibria it is seen that the concentration of SO_4^{--} can be controlled to some extent by adjusting the concentration of H_3O^+ to the appropriate value. This is done in the Procedures by the addition of CH_3COOH. The control of the concentration of SO_4^{--}, the tendency for Ca^{++} to form complex ions with SO_4^{--}, and the formation of supersaturated solutions of $CaSO_4$ make the use of hydrazine sulfate satisfactory in separating Sr^{++} from Ca^{++}.

Metathesis or Transposition of $SrSO_4$ to $SrCO_3$

If a precipitate of $SrSO_4$ is treated with sodium or ammonium carbonate, most of the $SrSO_4$ will be converted to the less soluble $SrCO_3$:

$$SrSO_4 \rightleftharpoons \boxed{\begin{array}{c} Sr^{++} \\ + \\ CO_3^{--} \end{array}} + SO_4^{--}$$

$$\rightleftharpoons SrCO_3 \downarrow$$

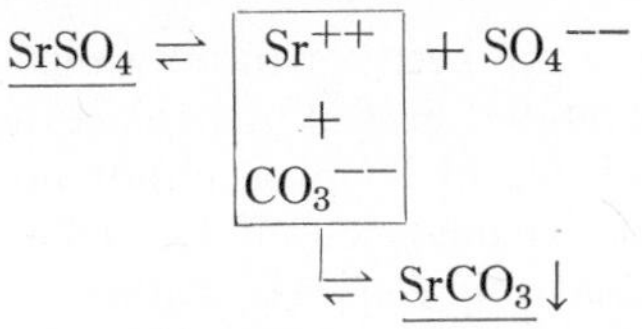

The extent to which this transposition takes place can be calculated from the solubility product constants of $SrSO_4$ and $SrCO_3$ in the following way.

If $SrSO_4$ is treated with a solution of a carbonate until equilibrium is reached and the solution is saturated with respect to both $SrSO_4$ and $SrCO_3$,

$$[Sr^{++}][SO_4^{--}] = 2.8 \times 10^{-7}$$
$$[Sr^{++}][CO_3^{--}] = 9.4 \times 10^{-10}$$

The concentration of Sr^{++} has the same value in both equations. Hence, dividing one equation by the other, we have

$$\frac{[SO_4^{--}]}{[CO_3^{--}]} = \frac{2.8 \times 10^{-7}}{9.4 \times 10^{-10}} = 300$$

That is, the concentration of SO_4^{--} in the solution is 300 times greater than that of CO_3^{--}. Thus, most of the $SrSO_4$ will dissolve and be converted into $SrCO_3$. If, for example, the concentration of CO_3^{--} is about 0.001-M at equilibrium, that of SO_4^{--} will be 0.30-M. In other words, when a solution of sodium or ammonium carbonate is added to a precipitate of $SrSO_4$, the CO_3^{--} is used up in converting $SrSO_4$ to $SrCO_3$. If the solid carbonate, Na_2CO_3 or $(NH_4)_2CO_3$, is added to the system until the concentration of CO_3^{--} has reached 0.001-M, enough $SrSO_4$ will be transposed to make the solution 0.30-M to SO_4^{--}. For a 1-ml. volume, this means that about 55 mg. of $SrSO_4$ (corresponding to 26 mg. of Sr^{++}) would dissolve and reprecipitate as $SrCO_3$ in the above experiment. Actually the concentration of carbonate used for transpositions is much larger (1 to 1.5-M) than that used in the above calculation. Consequently, $SrSO_4$ is practically completely converted to $SrCO_3$, whereas $BaSO_4$ would be only partially converted under the same conditions.

The advantage of transposing $SrSO_4$ to $SrCO_3$ is that the carbonate dissolves easily in acetic acid, whereas the sulfate is not appreciably soluble in even strong acids. Therefore, transposition or metathesis of one solid into another can be used in many cases to produce a compound that is soluble in a given reagent.

Transposition with sodium carbonate is also frequently used to bring the anions of relatively insoluble salts into solution prior to a qualitative analysis for the anions. In the case of $SrSO_4$, most of the anion is given up and will be found in the carbonate solution. In other cases, the ratio of the solubility product constants is not as favorable. However, if a relatively high concentration of sodium carbonate (1.5-*M*) is used, sufficient quantities of the anions can be obtained for tests (see p. 363).

Precipitation and Dissolution of Oxalates

After Ba^{++} and Sr^{++} have been separated from the solution of Group IV cations, calcium is precipitated as CaC_2O_4. Since both BaC_2O_4 and SrC_2O_4 are relatively insoluble (Table 14.1), a precipitate obtained by the addition of $(NH_4)_2C_2O_4$ may be due to these ions if for some reason the separation of Ba^{++} or Sr^{++} was not relatively complete. Either the precipitation of CaC_2O_4 must be carried out under conditions that are not likely to permit BaC_2O_4 and SrC_2O_4 to precipitate, or the oxalate precipitate obtained must be tested for Ca^{++} by a suitable characteristic reaction.

Both BaC_2O_4 and SrC_2O_4 are readily dissolved by strong acids and by hot acetic acid. CaC_2O_4, being somewhat more insoluble, is only slightly dissolved by acetic acid, but it is soluble in solutions of strong acids containing a fairly high concentration of H_3O^+. The reason for its solubility in acid solutions is evident from the following considerations.

In a saturated solution of CaC_2O_4 in water,

$$\underline{CaC_2O_4} \rightleftharpoons Ca^{++} + C_2O_4^{--}$$

and

$$[Ca^{++}][C_2O_4^{--}] = 2.3 \times 10^{-9}$$

but if an acid is added, the H_3O^+ unites with some of the $C_2O_4^{--}$ and shifts the following equilibria toward the right:

$$\begin{array}{l} CaC_2O_4 \rightleftharpoons Ca^{++} + \boxed{\begin{array}{c} C_2O_4^{--} \\ + \\ H_3O^+ \end{array}} \\ \qquad\qquad\qquad\qquad \rightleftharpoons HC_2O_4^- + H_2O \end{array}$$

The concentration of H_3O^+ in a solution of acetic acid is not high enough to dissolve appreciable quantities of CaC_2O_4 because CH_3COOH is a weaker acid ($K_a = 1.8 \times 10^{-5}$) than $HC_2O_4^-$ (6.4×10^{-5}). However, in a solution that is 1-*M* to H_3O^+ and at equilibrium with CaC_2O_4, the following expressions hold:

$$[Ca^{++}][C_2O_4^{--}] = 2.3 \times 10^{-9}$$

$$\frac{[H_3O^+][C_2O_4^{--}]}{[HC_2O_4^-]} = 6.4 \times 10^{-5}$$

Dividing the first expression by the second and remembering that $[C_2O_4^{--}]$ must be the same in both, we obtain

$$\frac{[Ca^{++}][HC_2O_4^-]}{[H_3O^+]} = 3.6 \times 10^{-5}$$

Since most of the oxalate from the CaC_2O_4 that dissolves will be in the form of $HC_2O_4^-$ when the H_3O^+ concentration is this high, the concentration of Ca^{++} will be very nearly equal to that of $HC_2O_4^-$; hence

$$[Ca^{++}] = \sqrt{(1)(3.6 \times 10^{-5})} = 6.0 \times 10^{-3}\text{-}M$$

This corresponds to about 0.24 mg. of Ca^{++}/ml. Thus it is clear that a reasonably high acid concentration is required to dissolve appreciable amounts of CaC_2O_4 or to prevent it from precipitating. A similar calculation for SrC_2O_4 indicates that the concentration of Sr^{++} is about 0.03-*M*, or 2.7 mg. of Sr^{++}/ml. in a 1-*M* solution of H_3O^+; and for BaC_2O_4 it is 0.04-*M*, or 5.7 mg. of Ba^{++}/ml.

From the above it can be seen that adjusting the acidity of the solution allows the precipitation of CaC_2O_4 but prevents the precipitation of the small concentrations of Ba^{++} and Sr^{++} that may be present. However, acid solutions decrease the completeness of the precipitation of CaC_2O_4 and make the test less sensitive. Precipitation in neutral or slightly ammoniacal solutions increases the completeness of the precipitation of CaC_2O_4 but it also increases the possibility of mistaking a small quantity of BaC_2O_4 or SrC_2O_4 for a small quantity of CaC_2O_4.

In the procedure for the identification of Ca^{++}, the oxalate is precipitated in ammoniacal solution and then dissolved in fairly concentrated $(NH_4)_2SO_4$. This converts any BaC_2O_4 or SrC_2O_4 to $BaSO_4$ and $SrSO_4$. Even though the CaC_2O_4 is quite insoluble, it is dissolved because Ca^{++} forms a complex sulfate ion when the concentration of SO_4^{--} is high. CaC_2O_4 can then be reprecipitated from this solution by the addition of alcohol. It is reasonably certain that any precipitate that appears at this point is CaC_2O_4, not $BaSO_4$ or $SrSO_4$. Flame tests may be used, if desired, for further confirmation.

The Phosphates of Group IV and Mg^{++}

Although the slightly soluble phosphates are not used in the Procedures for the analysis of this group of ions, they are analytically important compounds. In some schemes of analysis, Mg^{++} is precipitated as NH_4MgPO_4; and if phosphates are present in the unknown solutions, the ions of this group may be precipitated with Group III (p. 207).

In neutral solutions Ba^{++}, Sr^{++}, and Ca^{++} are precipitated by $(NH_4)_2HPO_4$ or Na_2HPO_4 as $BaHPO_4$, $SrHPO_4$, and $CaHPO_4$ respectively. In such solutions the concentration of PO_4^{3-} is not high enough to form the normal phosphates, $M_3(PO_4)_2$, where M represents any of the above cations. However, in ammoniacal solutions the normal phosphates are formed:

$$2HPO_4^{--} + 2OH^- \rightleftharpoons 2H_2O + 2PO_4^{3-}$$

$$3M^{++} + 2PO_4^{3-} \rightleftharpoons \underline{M_3(PO_4)_2} \downarrow$$

Both the normal phosphates and the monohydrogen phosphates are readily soluble in acetic acid or in stronger acids:

$$\underline{M_3(PO_4)_2} \rightleftharpoons 3M^{++} + \boxed{\begin{matrix} 2PO_4^{3-} \\ + \\ 2H_3O^+ \end{matrix}}$$

$$\rightleftharpoons \boxed{\begin{matrix} 2HPO_4^{--} \\ + \\ 2H_3O^+ \end{matrix}} + 2H_2O$$

$$\rightleftharpoons 2H_2PO_4^- + 2H_2O$$

The formation of the very weak acid HPO_4^{--} ($K_a = 1 \times 10^{-12}$) and then $H_2PO_4^-$ ($K_a = 6.2 \times 10^{-8}$) reduces the concentration of PO_4^{3-} and of HPO_4^- to such an extent that the precipitate dissolves. Acetic acid ($K_a = 1.8 \times 10^{-5}$) is sufficiently strong to dissolve these precipitates or to prevent them from forming.

The phosphates of many of the doubly and triply charged cations are relatively insoluble in neutral or alkaline solution but practically all of them are soluble in strong acid solutions. If the concentration of H_3O^+ is maintained at 10^{-5} by means of an acetic acid-sodium acetate buffered solution, Al^{3+}, Cr^{3+}, and Fe^{3+} can be precipitated as phosphates (p. 208).

If NH_4^+ and NH_3 are present with Mg^{++} when ammonium phosphate is added to the solution, a white crystalline precipitate of NH_4MgPO_4 is obtained. Its appearance can be used as a test for both Mg^{++} and the phosphates. The precipitate is readily soluble in acetic acid:

$$NH_4MgPO_4 \rightleftharpoons Mg^{++} + NH_4^+ + \boxed{\begin{matrix} PO_4^{3-} \\ + \\ H_3O^+ \end{matrix}}$$

$$\rightleftharpoons HPO_4^{--} + H_2O$$

The formation of the very weak acid HPO_4^{--} causes the equilibria to shift toward the right; and if a sufficient concentration of H_3O^+ is present, all the precipitate will dissolve. Excess NH_3 may result in the formation of a gelatinous precipitate of $Mg_3(PO_4)_2$ and perhaps some $Mg(OH)_2$. However, with a sufficient concentration of NH_4^+, the solution is buffered and its pH is not high enough to create these complications. Arsenates form the same type of precipitate (NH_4MgAsO_4) with Mg^{++} in the presence of NH_4^+ and NH_3. Both Zn^{++} and Mn^{++} form slightly soluble ammonium phosphates similar to the one formed by Mg^{++}.

LABORATORY WORK—ANALYSIS OF KNOWN AND UNKNOWN SOLUTIONS

1. Obtain from the storeroom a solution that contains all the ions of Groups IV and V. Add 10 drops of the solution to 1 ml. of water and analyze it according to the Procedures for the analysis of Groups IV and V.

2. (Optional.) Request a student to prepare an unknown from the test solutions. Analyze it according to the Procedures for Groups IV and V. (Preparation of the unknown: To 1 ml. of water add 2 drops of the test solutions for any 4 or 5 ions of these two groups.)

3. Obtain Unknown No. 5 from the storeroom and analyze it according to the Procedures for Groups IV and V. Use 10 drops of the unknown solution in 1 ml. of water for the analysis. Report the results on an Unknown Report Blank, indicating, if requested by the instructor, the approximate concentration of each ion in the unknown solution (0.1, 1, or 5 mg./ml.).

4. Obtain Unknown No. 6 from the storeroom and analyze it for the ions of Groups III, IV, and V. Use 10 drops of the unknown solution in 1 ml. of water for the analysis. Report the results of the analysis on an Unknown Report Blank, indicating, if requested by the instructor, the approximate concentration of each ion (0.1, 1, or 5 mg./ml.).

5. Obtain Unknown No. 7 from the storeroom and analyze it for the ions of Groups I–V. This is a general unknown solution and may contain ions of all the groups. Use 5 drops of the unknown solution in 1 ml. of water for the analysis. Report the results on an Unknown Report Blank, indicating, if requested by the instructor, the approximate concentration of each ion (0.1, 1, or 5 mg./ml.).

6. Additional unknown solutions for cation analysis may be assigned by the instructor. These may include general unknown solutions, metal samples (p. 269), alloys, solid salts (p. 359), ores, etc.

Analysis of Groups IV–V, Known or Unknown. To 1 ml. of water add 1 drop of 6-*N* NH_4Cl, 1 drop of 15-*N* NH_4OH, and 10 drops of the Groups IV–V known or unknown solution. Proceed with the analysis with Procedures 25 through 35.

Analysis of General Unknown Solutions for Cations of Group IV. The solution at this point is the filtrate from Group III, Procedure 21. It contains the ions of both Groups IV and V. The solution is ammoniacal and contains ammonium salts and some unhydrolyzed thioacetamide. Proceed with the analysis with Procedure 25.

25. To the solution, which should have a volume of from 1 to 2 ml., add 5 drops of 2-*N* $(NH_4)_2CO_3$. Place the tube in the hot water bath for about 1 minute. To the clear solution above the precipitate add 1 drop of $(NH_4)_2CO_3$. If more precipitate forms in the clear solution, add $(NH_4)_2CO_3$ until precipitation is complete. Filter off the precipitate and wash it with water to which 1 drop of $(NH_4)_2CO_3$ has been added. Discard the *wash* solution.

31. **Filtrate:** Group V.

26. **Precipitate:** $BaCO_3$, $SrCO_3$, and $CaCO_3$. Add to the precipitate on the filter medium 1 ml. of water and 3 drops of 4-*N* CH_3COOH. Stir the precipitate with a micro stirring rod. A clear solution will be obtained if sufficient CH_3COOH was added to dissolve the carbonates. Force the solution into the test tube and wash the filter medium with a little water. To the solution add 1 drop of phenolphthalein indicator, and then add 4-*N* NH_4OH drop by drop, until a pink color appears in the solution. Now add 1 drop of 4-*N* CH_3COOH and 1 drop of 6-*N* CH_3COONH_4. To this solution add 1 drop of 0.1-*M* K_2CrO_4. (If there is no precipitate, Ba^{++} is absent.) If a precipitate forms, add K_2CrO_4 until the precipitation of the $BaCrO_4$ is complete; 3 to 5 drops should be sufficient. Filter off the precipitate and wash it with a little water (10 drops). (NOTE: If the filtrate has a yellow color, sufficient K_2CrO_4 was added to precipitate all the Ba^{++}.)

27. **Precipitate:** $BaCrO_4$. Dissolve in 1 ml. of 0.1-*N* HCl. (A flame test may be made at this point if desired.) Add 1 drop of 3% H_2O_2, place the tube in the hot water bath, and add 5 drops of 0.5-*M* sulfamic acid. A white precipitate confirms the presence of barium. (NOTE: The H_2O_2 reduces the $Cr_2O_7^{--}$ (orange) to Cr^{3+} (green) and facilitates the detection of a white ($BaSO_4$) precipitate.)

28. **Filtrate:** Sr^{++} and Ca^{++}. Place the tube in the hot water bath, add 2 drops of 4-*N* CH_3COOH, and then 3 drops of 0.25-*M* $N_2H_4 \cdot H_2SO_4$ (hydrazine sulfate). Allow the tube to remain in the hot water bath for 2 minutes or longer. Filter off the precipitate. To the filtrate add 1 drop of hydrazine sulfate to check for complete precipitation of Sr^{++}. Refilter if a precipitate forms. Wash the precipitate with a little water.

29. **Precipitate:** $SrSO_4$. To reaffirm the presence of Sr^{++}, add 10 drops of 2-*N* $(NH_4)_2CO_3$. Place the filter tube in a test tube and set the assembly in the hot water bath, stir the precipitate with a micro stirring rod, and allow the solution to run through the precipitate. Discard the filtrate. Wash the precipitate remaining on the filter medium with water. To the precipitate add 2 drops of 4-*N* CH_3COOH and 10 drops of water. Force the solution into a clean test tube. (A flame test may be made at this point if desired.) Place the test tube in the hot water bath and add 1 ml. of a saturated solution of $CaSO_4$. Allow the tube to remain in the hot water bath for 1 minute or longer. A white precipitate confirms the presence of strontium.

30. **Filtrate:** Ca^{++}. Add 2 drops of 0.1-*N* $(NH_4)_2C_2O_4$. A white precipitate shows the presence of calcium. To reaffirm the presence of Ca^{++}, filter off the CaC_2O_4 and wash the precipitate with a little water. To the precipitate on the filter medium add 5 drops of 4-*N* $(NH_4)_2SO_4$. Stir the precipitate with a micro stirring rod and allow the solution in the filter tube to become heated. Force the solution slowly into the test tube and wash the filter medium with 1 ml. of water. Refilter if necessary to obtain a clear filtrate. To the filtrate add 1 ml. of methyl, or denatured, alcohol. If Ca^{++} is present, a white precipitate of CaC_2O_4 will form. (A flame test may be made at this point by filtering off the CaC_2O_4, and adding 1 drop of HCl to the precipitate.)

PROCEDURES FOR THE ANALYSIS OF GROUP V

Analysis of Groups IV–V Known or Unknown. Use the filtrate from the analysis of Group IV. Besides the ions of Group V this filtrate contains ammonia and ammonium salts. Proceed with the analysis according to Procedures 31–35.

Analysis of General Unknown Solutions for the Cations of Group V. The solution at this point is the filtrate from Group IV; it contains ammonia, ammonium salts, and some unhydrolyzed thioacetamide. Continue with the analysis according to Procedures 31–35.

---

31. **Filtrate from Group IV.** Transfer the filtrate from Group IV to an evaporation test tube, add 1 ml. of 4-*N* HNO_3, and boil the solution carefully until a dry residue is obtained. Continue to heat the tube strongly until the ammonium salts are expelled from every part of the tube. Allow the tube to cool. Add 1 drop of 4-*N* HNO_3 and 1 ml. of water. (NOTE: If the solution is not clear, it should be filtered.) Test separate parts of the solution with Procedures 32–34.

---

32. Mg^{++}: To 1 ml. of water add 1 drop of titan-yellow reagent and 2 drops of 4-*N* NaOH. Place the tube in the hot water bath and add 5 drops of the solution from the evaporation test tube. If magnesium is present, a reddish precipitate will be obtained.

---

33. K^+: To a test tube add 1 ml. of water, and a small quantity of solid $Na_3Co(NO_2)_6$ from the point of a micro spatula. Shake the tube and make certain that the solution is clear. None of the $Na_3Co(NO_2)_6$ should remain undissolved. To this solution add 1 drop of the silver nitrate test solution. Now add 5 drops of the solution from the evaporation test tube. If potassium is present, a yellowish-orange precipitate will form. Do not heat the solution in the hot water bath. (A flame test for K^+ may also be made on the solution from 31 by observing the flame through a cobalt glass filter. This absorbs the yellow color due to Na^+ and allows the purple color of K^+ to be seen.)

---

34. Na^+: To a test tube add 1 ml. (20 drops) of the uranyl zinc acetate reagent. Then add 5 drops of the solution from the evaporation test tube. Shake the tube and allow it to stand for 1 or 2 minutes. If sodium is present, a yellow crystalline precipitate will be obtained. (NOTE: Do not heat the tube in the hot water bath.) A flame test for Na^+ may also be made on the solution from 31. An intense yellow flame lasting for several seconds indicates Na^+.

---

35. *Test for* NH_4^+: Test the original known or unknown solution by one or both of the following methods.

a. To 1 ml. of distilled water add 1 drop of the known or unknown solution and 2 drops of 4-*N* NaOH. Filter off any precipitate that forms. To the filtrate add 1 drop of Nessler's reagent. A brown precipitate shows the presence of NH_4^+. (NOTE: If, on the addition of the Nessler's reagent, only a yellow color appears in the solution, a trace of NH_4^+ should be reported. This reaction is exceedingly sensitive.)

b. To a test tube add 5 drops of the known or unknown solution and 5 drops of 4-*N* NaOH. Place a small plug of cotton in a filter tube and push it in place in the lower part of the tube. (Do not pack it too tightly.) To the filter tube add 1 ml. of water and 1 drop of bromthymol blue indicator. Depress the rubber bulb and insert the end of the bulb in the filter tube. (NOTE: As the pressure on the rubber bulb is released, air should be drawn slowly through the solution in the filter tube.) Place the filter tube in the test tube and set the assembly in the hot water bath. Any NH_3 evolved will be drawn through the indicator solution and it will become *blue*. (NOTE: This test is not as sensitive as the one with Nessler's reagent. NH_4^+ should not be reported as present in the known or unknown solution unless the blue color is obtained.)

Procedure	Equations	Purpose—Discussion
25. Add $(NH_4)_2CO_3$.	$CO_3^{=} + H_2O \rightleftharpoons HCO_3^- + OH^-$ $Ba^{++} + CO_3^{=} \rightleftharpoons \underset{\text{white}}{\underline{BaCO_3}} \downarrow$ $Sr^{++} + CO_3^{=} \rightleftharpoons \underset{\text{white}}{\underline{SrCO_3}} \downarrow$ $Ca^{++} + CO_3^{=} \rightleftharpoons \underset{\text{white}}{\underline{CaCO_3}} \downarrow$	The extent of the hydrolysis of $CO_3^{=}$ is reduced by OH^- from the NH_4OH. However, the presence of NH_4^+ maintains the concentration of OH^- at a value which permits a concentration of $CO_3^{=}$ high enough to precipitate Ba^{++}, Ca^{++}, Sr^{++}, as carbonates, but low enough to prevent the precipitation of $MgCO_3$. The concentration of OH^- must also be low enough to prevent the precipitation of $Mg(OH)_2$.
Add CH_3COOH to the carbonates.	$\underline{BaCO_3} + 2CH_3COOH \rightleftharpoons Ba^{++}$ $+ 2CH_3COO^- + H_2O + CO_2 \uparrow$ $\underline{CaCO_3} + 2CH_3COOH \rightleftharpoons Ca^{++}$ $+ 2CH_3COO^- + H_2O + CO_2 \uparrow$ $\underline{SrCO_3} + 2CH_3COOH \rightleftharpoons Sr^{++} +$ $2CH_3COO^- + H_2O + CO_2 \uparrow$	Acetic acid should be added until effervescence ceases.
26. Adjust the acidity of the solution and add K_2CrO_4.	$CH_3COOH + NH_3 \rightleftharpoons$ $CH_3COO^- + NH_4^+$ $Ba^+ + CrO_4^{=} \rightleftharpoons \underset{\text{yellow}}{\underline{BaCrO_4}} \downarrow$	The solution is buffered and slightly acidic (pH about 5). Ba^{++} is rather completely precipitated, but Sr^{++} and Ca^{++} are not. The solution must not be too acidic, for Ba^{++} will not be completely precipitated. If the solution is too alkaline, some $SrCrO_4$ may form if Sr^{++} is present in high concentration.
27. Add HCl, H_2O_2, and sulfamic acid. Heat in the water bath.	$2BaCrO_4 + 2H_3O^+ \rightleftharpoons$ $2Ba^{++} + Cr_2O_7^{=} + 3H_2O$ $Cr_2O_7^{=} + 7H_2O_2 + 2H_3O^+ \rightleftharpoons$ $7H_2O + 2H_3CrO_8$-blue $2H_3CrO_8 + 6H_3O^+ \rightleftharpoons$ $2Cr^{3+} + 5O_2 \uparrow + 12H_2O$ $NH_2SO_3H + 2H_2O \rightleftharpoons$ $H_3O^+ + NH_4^+ + SO_4^{=}$ $Ba^{++} + SO_4^{=} \rightleftharpoons \underset{\text{white}}{\underline{BaSO_4}} \downarrow$	The $BaCrO_4$ is easily dissolved in dilute HCl. The orange-yellow color of $Cr_2O_7^{=}$ sometimes obscures the fine white precipitate of $BaSO_4$. The H_2O_2 reduces the $Cr_2O_7^{=}$ to Cr^{3+} and aids in the detection of the precipitate. Sulfamic acid hydrolyzes in a hot solution and gives a concentration of $SO_4^{=}$ sufficient to precipitate $BaSO_4$, but not $SrSO_4$ or $CaSO_4$ if present.

CHEMICAL REACTIONS IN THE ANALYSIS OF GROUP IV
(Continued)

Procedure	Equations	Purpose—Discussion
28. Add CH_3COOH, then $N_2H_4 \cdot H_2SO_4$.	$Sr^{++} + N_2H_4 \cdot H_2SO_4 + H_2O \rightleftharpoons$ $SrSO_4 \downarrow + N_2H_5^+ + H_3O^+$ white	Hydrazine sulfate gives a concentration of $SO_4^=$ sufficient to precipitate $SrSO_4$ rather rapidly in a hot solution. $CaSO_4$ does not precipitate as readily with this reagent.
29. Convert $SrSO_4$ to $SrCO_3$. Dissolve $SrCO_3$ in acetic acid. Reprecipitate.	$SrSO_4 + CO_3^= \rightleftharpoons$ $SrCO_3 \downarrow + SO_4^=$ white $SrCO_3 + 2CH_3COOH \rightleftharpoons Sr^{++} +$ $2CH_3COO^- + CO_2 + H_2O$ $Sr^{++} + SO_4^= \rightleftharpoons SrSO_4$ white	The reaffirming test is based on the lesser solubility of $SrCO_3$ than of $SrSO_4$, the solubility of $SrCO_3$ by CH_3COOH, and the greater solubility of $CaSO_4$ than of $SrSO_4$.
30. Add $(NH_4)_2C_2O_4$.	$Ca^{++} + C_2O_4^= \rightleftharpoons CaC_2O_4 \downarrow$ white	The $C_2O_4^=$ will precipitate CaC_2O_4 from a solution containing Ca^{++} if the concentration of $(NH_4)_2SO_4$ is not large. CaC_2O_4, the least soluble of the calcium salts, is soluble in $(NH_4)_2SO_4$.
30. Add 4-*N* $(NH_4)_2SO_4$ to CaC_2O_4.	$SrC_2O_4 + SO_4^= \rightleftharpoons$ $SrSO_4 \downarrow + C_2O_4^=$ $BaC_2O_4 + SO_4^= \rightleftharpoons$ $BaSO_4 \downarrow + C_2O_4^=$ $CaC_2O_4 + 2SO_4^= \rightleftharpoons$ $C_2O_4^= + Ca(SO_4)_2^=$	Any BaC_2O_4 or SrC_2O_4 that might be present in the oxalate precipitate will be converted to the sulfates. This will occur even though SrC_2O_4 is less soluble than $SrSO_4$, because of the high concentration of $SO_4^=$.
30. Add alcohol to the solution containing $Ca(SO_4)_2^=$ and $C_2O_4^=$.	$Ca(SO_4)_2^= + C_2O_4^= + \text{alcohol} \rightleftharpoons$ $CaC_2O_4 \downarrow + 2SO_4^= + \text{alcohol}$ white	CaC_2O_4 is less soluble in an alcohol solution.

CHEMICAL REACTIONS IN THE ANALYSIS OF GROUP V

Procedure	Equations	Purpose—Discussion
31. Add HNO_3 and evaporate to dryness. Heat until the ammonium salts are expelled.	$NH_3 + H_3O^+ \rightleftharpoons NH_4^+ + H_2O$ $CO_3^= + 2H_3O^+ \rightleftharpoons CO_2\uparrow + 3H_2O$ $3CH_3CSNH_2 + 2NO_3^- + 2H_3O^+ \rightleftharpoons 3CH_3COO^- + 3NH_4^+ + \underline{3S^\circ} + 2NO\uparrow$ $NH_4^+ + NO_3^- \rightleftharpoons N_2O\uparrow + 2H_2O$ $4H_3O^+ + NO_3^- + 3Cl^- \rightleftharpoons Cl_2\uparrow + NOCl + 6H_2O$ $2KNO_3 \rightleftharpoons 2KNO_2 + O_2\uparrow$ $2NaNO_3 \rightleftharpoons 2NaNO_2 + O_2\uparrow$	The NH_3 is neutralized by the acid. The carbonates are decomposed by the acid. The thioacetamide is decomposed by the acid and gives a white precipitate of sulfur. The NH_4NO_3 decomposes into nitrous oxide and water when heated. A slight explosion is often noted. NH_4^+ and Cl^- must be removed because they form precipitates with the reagents used in testing for K^+. The nitrates of potassium and sodium are converted into nitrites at 400° and 380° respectively. On heating until the NH_4^+ salts are expelled, the only products left are the nitrites and nitrates of sodium, potassium, and magnesium. These salts are readily soluble in water.
32. Add Mg^{++} to a solution of NaOH and titan-yellow.	$Mg^{++} + 2OH^- \rightleftharpoons \underset{\text{white}}{\underline{Mg(OH)_2}}\downarrow$ $\underline{Mg(OH)_2} + \text{titan-yellow} \rightleftharpoons \underset{\text{red lake}}{\underline{Mg(OH)_2}}\downarrow$	The titan-yellow is adsorbed on the surface of the $Mg(OH)_2$, producing a "red" color. Heating the solution in the water bath coagulates the precipitate.
33. Add K^+ to a solution of $Na_3Co(NO_2)_6$ and $AgNO_3$.	$2K^+ + Ag^+ + Co(NO_2)_6^{3-} \rightleftharpoons \underset{\text{yellow}}{\underline{K_2AgCo(NO_2)_6}}$	NH_4^+ gives a similar precipitate with $Co(NO_2)_6^{3-}$ and therefore must be removed by ignition before the test for K^+ can be made. The precipitate is readily soluble in a hot solution.

CHEMICAL REACTIONS IN THE ANALYSIS OF GROUP V

(Continued)

Procedure	Equations	Purpose—Discussion
34. Add Na^+ to uranyl zinc acetate reagent.	$Na^+ + Zn^{++} + 3UO_2^{++} + 6H_2O + 9CH_3COO^- \rightleftharpoons \underset{\text{yellow}}{\underline{Na(UO_2)_3Zn(CH_3COO)_9 \cdot 6H_2O}} \downarrow$	This reagent is a sensitive test for Na^+ only when it is highly concentrated; therefore the volume of the reagent must greatly exceed the volume of the solution tested for Na^+. The precipitate is readily soluble in a hot solution.
35a. Add NaOH and Nessler's reagent to the original known or unknown solution.	*Formation of Nessler's reagent:* $Hg^{++} + 2I^- \rightleftharpoons \underline{HgI_2}$ $\underline{HgI_2} + 2I^- \rightleftharpoons HgI_4^=$ Add NaOH. *Use of Nessler's reagent:* $NH_4^+ + OH^- \rightleftharpoons NH_3 + H_2O$ $NH_3 + 2HgI_4^= + 3OH^- \rightleftharpoons \underset{\text{light brown}}{\underline{HOHgNHHgI}} + 2H_2O + 7I^-$	This is a very sensitive test for NH_3.
35b. Add NaOH, heat, and draw the evolved NH_3 through H_2O containing bromthymol blue indicator.	$NH_4^+ + OH^- \rightleftharpoons NH_3 + H_2O$ $NH_3 + H_2O \rightleftharpoons NH_4^+ + OH^-$	The gaseous NH_3 is drawn through the water by means of suction from the depressed bulb. The reaction of NH_3 with water increases the concentration of OH^- and turns the bromthymol blue indicator "blue." The bromthymol blue indicator is yellow at a pH of 6.0 but has a blue color at a pH of 7.6.

REVIEW QUESTIONS ON ANALYTICAL PROCEDURES

1. List the cations of Groups IV and V. What is the group reagent for the precipitation of Group IV? Name any special conditions required for the complete precipitation of this group.
2. Why is there no group reagent for the cations of Group V?
3. Draw up a schematic outline for the analysis of Group IV and of Group V.
4. Discuss the reasons for each operation in the analysis of Groups IV and V.
5. Study the reactions at the end of the chapter and be prepared to write equations for all of them that occur during the analysis of Groups IV and V.
6. Give the formulas and colors of each precipitate that is formed during the analysis of Groups IV and V.
7. Describe the confirmatory test for each cation of Groups IV and V, stating in each case the conditions under which the reactions take place.
8. Which ions of Groups IV and V might be precipitated with preceding groups: (a) if NaOH instead of NH_4OH were used to make the filtrate from Group II alkaline; (b) if NH_4OH were used but no NH_4^+ were present; (c) if phosphates were present; (d) if oxalates or fluorides were present?
9. Explain why both NH_3 and NH_4^+ must be present when the carbonates of Group IV are precipitated.
10. What difficulties would arise in precipitating the carbonates of Group IV (a) if no NH_4OH were present; (b) if NH_4Cl were not added; (c) if Na_2CO_3 were used rather than $(NH_4)_2CO_3$?
11. List the general properties common to the ions of Group IV.
12. List the carbonates, chromates, sulfates, oxalates, and hydroxides of Ba^{++}, Sr^{++}, Ca^{++}, and Mg^{++} in the order of increasing solubility.
13. Of the precipitates listed in Question 12, name the least soluble Ba^{++}, Sr^{++}, Ca^{++}, and Mg^{++} compound.
14. Which of the four ions in Question 12 form the least soluble carbonate? Chromate? Sulfate? Oxalate? Hydroxide?
15. Why is the precipitation of $BaCrO_4$ carried out in an acetic acid-ammonium acetate buffered solution?
16. Discuss the confirmatory test for Ba^{++} and state what the most likely interference, if any, would be.
17. How is $SrSO_4$ precipitated from a solution containing Ca^{++} without obtaining $CaSO_4$? How can we affirm the fact that the precipitate obtained by this procedure is due to Sr^{++}?
18. $SrSO_4$ is not readily soluble in acids. How can it be converted to a compound that will dissolve readily in dilute acids? Explain.
19. Explain the confirmatory test for Ca^{++}, and describe how additional evidence for its presence is secured.
20. How can Ba^{++}, Sr^{++}, and Ca^{++} be confirmed by means of flame tests? At what points in the procedure should these tests be made? List the colors imparted to a flame by salts of these ions.
21. Why must individual tests be made for the ions of Group V? Describe these tests. What color do the ions of Group V impart to a flame?
22. Why is it necessary to eliminate ammonium salts before the test for K^+ is made?

23. Write equations and describe in detail what happens during the test for NH_4^+ that is based on the evolution of NH_3.
24. What reagents might be used for the following separations: (a) Mg^{++} from Sr^{++}; (b) Ca^{++} from Ba^{++}; (c) Mg^{++} from Ca^{++}; (d) Sr^{++} from Ba^{++}; (e) Na^+ from K^+; (f) NH_4^+ from K^+?
25. What cations of Group IV are identified by each of the following: (a) gives a green flame test; (b) forms a precipitate with saturated $CaSO_4$ solution but not with CrO_4^{--} in acetic acid-ammonium acetate solutions; (c) forms a slightly soluble chromate in either dilute acid or alkaline solution?
26. A solution is known to contain Mg^{++} or Ca^{++}, or both. How would you determine the composition in the fewest number of steps?
27. What single test would you use to distinguish between the following: (a) Mg^{++} and K^+; (b) $CaCO_3$ and CaC_2O_4; (c) $SrCrO_4$ and $BaCrO_4$; (d) NH_4Cl and KCl?
28. If Pb^{++} were present with Group IV cations, with which ion would it be precipitated?

REVIEW QUESTIONS ON THE THEORY OF GROUP IV ANALYSIS *

1. Formulate the equilibria existing in a solution of ammonium carbonate. Explain why ammonium carbonate does not provide sufficiently complete precipitation of the carbonates of Group IV.
2. Why does ammonium carbonate not precipitate $BaCO_3$ rather completely, whereas sodium carbonate does?
3. On the basis of the solubility product principle, the common-ion effect, and the hydrolysis of ions, explain why both NH_4^+ and NH_3 must be present when the carbonates of Group IV are precipitated. Approximately what concentration of NH_4^+ and NH_3 is needed? What is the concentration of OH^- in this solution?
4. If the concentration of NH_3 is too high, what difficulty will be encountered in the precipitation of Group IV? If the concentration of NH_3 is too high compared to that of NH_4^+, what difficulties will there be?
5. Formulate the dissolution of carbonates by acids. What requirement must the concentration of H_3O^+ meet for a carbonate precipitate to be completely dissolved?
6. Show by a suitable formulation why carbonates of Ba^{++}, Sr^{++}, and Ca^{++} are somewhat soluble in solutions of ammonium salts. Why is $MgCO_3$ rather highly soluble in such solutions? Show by suitable ionic equilibria why NH_3 reduces the solubility of carbonates in solutions of ammonium salts.
7. Formulate the reaction of $Mg(OH)_2$ with a solution of NH_4Cl.
8. On the basis of the solubility product principle and buffered solutions, explain the use of acetic acid and ammonium acetate in separating Ba^{++} from Sr^{++} and Ca^{++} by precipitation of $BaCrO_4$.
9. Show why the solution in Question 8 is buffered with respect not only to H_3O^+ but also to CrO_4^{--}.
10. Formulate the dissolution of $BaCrO_4$ in solutions of strong acids. Why does acetic acid have so little effect on $BaCrO_4$, yet readily dissolve $SrCrO_4$?

* See footnote, p. 133.

11. If a solution is saturated with respect to both $CaSO_4$ and $SrSO_4$, what is the ratio of the concentration of Ca^{++} to that of Sr^{++} in the solution? What is the concentration of both Ca^{++} and Sr^{++} in such a solution?
12. What is the effect of acids, of excess SO_4^{--}, of triethanolamine, of hydroxylamine, and of hydrazine on the solubility of $CaSO_4$? An increase in the concentration of H_3O^+ has a greater effect on the solubility of $CaSO_4$ than on that of $SrSO_4$. Explain.
13. Discuss the precipitation of $SrSO_4$ and $CaSO_4$ with 1-*M* H_2SO_4. How complete a separation is obtained? Show why the H_2SO_4 solution is "buffered" with respect to SO_4^{--}.
14. Summarize the schemes for precipitating $SrSO_4$ in the presence of Ca^{++}.
15. Formulate the transposition of $SrSO_4$ to $SrCO_3$. In a solution saturated with respect to both these salts, what is the ratio of $[SO_4^{--}]$ to $[CO_3^{--}]$?
16. Compare the solubilities of the oxalates of Ba^{++}, Sr^{++}, and Ca^{++} in water and in dilute acid solutions. Derive an expression for the concentration of Ca^{++} in an acid solution that is in equilibrium with excess CaC_2O_4.
17. Discuss the basis of the confirmatory test for Ca^{++} used in the Procedures and explain why incomplete precipitation of Ba^{++} and Sr^{++} does not interfere.
18. Under what conditions are the different phosphates of Ba^{++}, Sr^{++}, and Ca^{++} formed? Write equations for the reactions of the phosphate precipitates with acids and explain why they are so readily soluble in dilute acid solutions.
19. When NH_4MgPO_4 is precipitated, why is it necessary to use a buffered solution containing NH_3^+ and NH_3? What is the effect of excess acid and of excess NH_3 on NH_4MgPO_4? Use equations to illustrate your explanation. Write the formulas for other similar precipitates.

PROBLEMS

1. If a solution contains 2 mg. each of Ba^{++}, Sr^{++}, and Ca^{++}, what total weight of carbonates will be obtained from the solution?
2. How many drops of 4-*N* CH_3COOH would be required to dissolve the carbonate precipitate in Problem 1? (Assume 1 drop = 0.05 ml.)
3. How many drops of 0.1-*M* K_2CrO_4 are required to react with 5 mg. of Ba^{++}?
4. When the $SrSO_4$ obtained from 10 drops of 0.1-*M* Sr^{++} is treated with excess ammonium carbonate, how many mg. of $SrCO_3$ are obtained? How many drops of 1-*N* CH_3COOH will be required to dissolve this carbonate?
5. How many milligrams of $Na(UO_2)_3Zn(CH_3COO)_9 \cdot 6H_2O$ are obtained for each milligram of Na^+ precipitated?
6. When a solution containing 5 mg. of NH_4^+ is treated with NaOH and heated, ammonia is evolved. How many cubic centimeters of NH_3 measured at 25° C. and 740 mm. mercury pressure will be obtained?
7. If the NH_3 obtained in Problem 6 is dissolved in 1 ml. of water, what will be the molarity of the solution? What will its pH be?
8. What weight of $K_2AgCo(NO_2)_6$ in milligrams is obtained from 1 mg. of K^+?

PROBLEMS ON THE THEORY OF GROUP IV ANALYSIS *

9. Calculate the molar solubility of $BaCO_3$ and of $MgCO_3$ from their respective solubility product constants. How many milligrams of Ba^{++} and of Ca^{++} are there in 1 ml. of the saturated solutions of their carbonates?

10. What concentration of CO_3^{--} is required for the precipitation of (a) $BaCO_3$ from 0.01-*M* Ba^{++}; (b) $MgCO_3$ from 0.01-*M* Mg^{++}?

11. What concentration of OH^- is required to start the precipitation of $Mg(OH)_2$ from 0.1-*M* $MgSO_4$? What is the pH of this solution?

12. Calculate the concentration of OH^- in a solution that is 0.1-*M* to NH_3 and to NH_4^+ and compare it with the value for OH^- obtained in Problem 11. Will $Mg(OH)_2$ precipitate from this solution if it is also 0.01-*M* to Mg^{++}?

13. Calculate the concentration of H_3O^+ and of OH^- in 0.0001-*M* CH_3COOH. What concentration of Mg^{++} can exist in equilibrium with this concentration of OH^-? Can $Mg(OH)_2$ be precipitated from a solution that is 0.0001-*M* to CH_3COOH?

14. Will $Zn(OH)_2$ precipitate from 0.0001-*M* CH_3COOH? Prove your answer by making the necessary calculations.

15. Is the concentration of OH^- in a solution that is 1.0-*M* to CH_3COONa large enough to produce a precipitate with (a) 0.1-*M* Mg^{++}; (b) 0.1-*M* Ca^{++}; (c) 0.1-*M* Zn^{++}?

16. a. Calculate the concentration of OH^- in a solution that is 0.1-*M* to NH_3 and 0.2-*M* to NH_4^+.
b. From the hydrolysis constant for CO_3^{--}, calculate the concentration of CO_3^{--} that there is in equilibrium with 0.1-*M* HCO_3^- and the OH^- concentration found in (a).
c. Is the concentration of CO_3^{--} in (b) large enough to cause the precipitation of $BaCO_3$ from 0.05-*M* Ba^{++}; of $MgCO_3$ from 0.05-*M* Mg^{++}?
d. Will the concentration of OH^- in (a) cause the precipitation of $Mg(OH)_2$?

17. If the concentration of CO_3^{--} is 0.01-*M* in a solution after the precipitation of Ba^{++} and Sr^{++}, calculate the milligrams of each cation left in 5 ml. of solution. How many milligrams of $BaSO_4$ will be precipitated if Na_2SO_4 is added to the solution until the concentration of SO_4^{--} is 0.01-*M*?

18. A carbonate will be dissolved completely by an acid if the concentration of H_3O^+ derived from the acid is greater than the concentration of H_3O^+ which can exist in equilibrium with a saturated solution of CO_2.

a. Calculate the concentration of H_3O^+ in 0.01-*M* CH_3COOH, and in 0.034-*M* H_2CO_3. (0.034-*M* H_2CO_3 corresponds to a saturated solution of CO_2.) Will carbonates dissolve completely in 0.01-*M* CH_3COOH?
b. Repeat the calculations for 0.1-*M* HCN.

19. Calculate the concentration of CrO_4^{--} in a saturated solution (a) of $BaCrO_4$ and (b) of $SrCrO_4$.

20. If the concentration of Ba^{++} is 0.01-*M*, what concentration of CrO_4^{--} will be required to start the precipitation of $BaCrO_4$? What concentration

* See footnote, p. 133.

of CrO_4^{--} will be required to start the precipitation of $SrCrO_4$ from a solution that is 0.1-*M* to Sr^{++}?

21. A concentration of H_3O^+ of about 1×10^{-5} mole/liter is favorable for the separation of Ba^{++} and Sr^{++} by the precipitation of $BaCrO_4$. What should the concentration of CH_3COO^- be in a 1-*M* solution of CH_3COOH to give the desired concentration of H_3O^+?

22. Substitute the following values in the expression for the dichromate-chromate equilibrium and calculate the concentration of CrO_4^{--}: $[H_3O^+] = 2 \times 10^{-5}$ mole/liter; $[Cr_2O_7^{--}] = 0.01$ mole/liter. How much lower is the concentration of CrO_4^{--} in this solution than in one that is 1×10^{-5} mole/liter to H_3O^+?

23. In a properly buffered solution there is a large reserve of $Cr_2O_7^{--}$ that reacts with water to form more CrO_4^{--} as $BaCrO_4$ precipitates. This buffered solution maintains the concentration of CrO_4^{--} at about 5×10^{-4} mole/liter. If, instead of the buffered solution, 2 ml. of 5×10^{-4}-*M* K_2CrO_4 is added to 2 ml. of 0.01-*M* Ba^{++}, what percentage of the Ba^{++} will be precipitated? What will be the concentration of the CrO_4^{--} and Ba^{++} left in solution?

24. Calculate the concentration of SO_4^{--} in saturated solutions of (a) $SrSO_4$; (b) $CaSO_4$.

25. If excess solid $SrSO_4$ and $CaSO_4$ are in the same vessel and in equilibrium with the solution in contact with them, what is the approximate concentration of SO_4^{--}? What is the ratio of the concentration of Ca^{++} to Sr^{++}? How many milligrams of the two sulfates together will be obtained by evaporating 10 ml. of the saturated solution?

26. Show that the concentration of SO_4^{--} in 0.5-*M* H_2SO_4 is approximately 0.012 mole/liter. What is the concentration of SO_4^{--} in 1-*M* H_2SO_4?

27. Calculate the molar solubility of the following in a solution that is 0.012-*M* to SO_4^{--}: (a) $BaSO_4$; (b) $SrSO_4$; (c) $CaSO_4$. How many milligrams of each cation will there be in 1 ml. of these saturated solutions?

28. Using the results in Problem 27, determine whether an oxalate precipitate would be obtained in the saturated sulfate solutions if they were made 0.1-*M* to $C_2O_4^{--}$.

29. How many mg./ml. of Ca^{++} remain unprecipitated in (a) a saturated solution of CaC_2O_4 in water; (b) a saturated solution of CaC_2O_4 in the presence of 0.01-*M* $C_2O_4^{--}$? If the solution is 0.5-*M* to H_3O^+, calculate the mg./ml. of Ca^{++} left in solution.

30. a. If a solution containing Sr^{++}, SO_4^{--}, and CO_3^{--} is allowed to come to equilibrium with the solids formed, what is the ratio of the concentration of SO_4^{--} to CO_3^{--}?

b. Repeat the calculations for a solution containing Ba^{++}, SO_4^{--}, and CO_3^{--}.

c. If the final concentration of CO_3^{--} in (b) is 0.05-*M*, what will be the concentration of SO_4^{--} in solution?

d. How many milligrams of $BaSO_4$ will be transposed to $BaCO_3$ if the volume of the solution is maintained at 2 ml. and sufficient carbonate is added to maintain CO_3^{--} at 0.05-*M*?

CHAPTER 15

ANALYSIS OF METALS AND ALLOYS. IDENTIFICATION OF THE CATION AND ANION IN SINGLE SOLID SALTS

ANALYSIS OF METALS AND ALLOYS

Sampling

It is necessary to obtain a representative sample of the metal or alloy, preferably in a form that offers a large surface. Metallic samples frequently consist of a single metal, a single alloy, or at least a uniform mixture or conglomerate of metals. In this case, any part of such a sample is suitable for the analysis. The sample should be converted to turnings, filings, sawings, shavings, a powder, or flattened pieces. This may be done with a lathe, a steel file, a hacksaw, cutting pliers, a mortar and pestle for brittle metals, a hammer for malleable metals, or a hardened steel knife for soft metals. Traces of the tool metal may be found during the analysis.

The size of the sample used for the analysis should be such that metals present in the alloy to an extent of only 0.2 to 0.5% can be detected easily, but the sample must not be too large because difficulties will arise in the analysis. The sensitivity of most of the semimicro tests is about 0.01 to 0.001 mg. of any one ion. Hence, about 10 mg. of the sample should be used for a single analysis. A 20-mg. sample may be dissolved if it is desired to make check analyses and special tests. Special procedures are required for the detection of traces of certain metals in alloys.

Industrial alloys or special alloys prepared for courses in qualitative analysis may contain almost any of the common metals and they may show unexpected resistance to dissolution in acids. Hence, the same acid may not be suitable for the dissolution of all metallic samples. The metals of Groups IV and V, with the exception of magnesium, are seldom present in alloys, but in special cases they too may be present.

Dissolution of a Metal or an Alloy

Place 10 mg. of the sample (metallic) in each of two test tubes. (In estimating 10 mg. of a sample, keep in mind that 1 drop of water weighs 50 mg. and that the specific gravity of alloys is between 2.5 and 11. Thus, in general, the volume of the sample should be about 0.1 the volume of an average drop of water.) To one tube (A) add 15 to 20 drops of 6-*N* HCl, and to the other tube (B) add 15 to 20 drops of 4-*N* HNO_3. Place both tubes in the hot water bath. If neither sample has dissolved completely in 5 minutes, add 15 to 20 drops of 4-*N* HNO_3 to Tube A, and 15 to 20 drops of 6-*N* HCl to Tube B. A clear *solution* of the alloy should be obtained in one or both of the tubes in 4 or 5 minutes unless a high concentration of lead and some silver was present in the sample. The chlorides of these metals result in the formation of a white precipitate. Alloys that contain antimony and/or tin ordinarily yield a white precipitate on treatment with dilute HNO_3 only, but the precipitate dissolves readily when HCl is added. Metallic samples containing chromium do not dissolve readily in dilute HNO_3, nor after the addition of dilute HCl. However, treating the sample first with HCl and then with HNO_3 usually dissolves it. (NOTE: Examine the bottom of the test tube carefully to make sure that the alloy has dissolved completely.)

Alloy Dissolves in 6-N HCl. If the alloy dissolved in HCl, transfer the solution to an evaporation test tube and evaporate to incipient (moist) dryness. To the cooled residue add 1 drop of 6-*N* HCl and 1 ml. of water. Transfer the solution to a small test tube and start to analyze the alloy, using the Procedures for the Analysis of Group II; begin with Procedure 7 at the line, "To this solution add 5 drops of a 5% solution of thioacetamide" (p. 173).

Alloy Dissolves in 4-N HNO_3. If the alloy dissolved in HNO_3, transfer the solution to an evaporation test tube and evaporate to incipient dryness. Refer to the Preliminary Examination and Preparation of the Sample for Analysis on page 126 and continue as indicated there.

Alloy Dissolves in 6-N HCl and 4-N HNO_3. If the alloy dissolved in a combination of HCl and HNO_3 (aqua regia), transfer the solution to an evaporation test tube and evaporate to incipient dryness. Refer to the Preliminary Examination and Preparation of the Sample for Analysis on page 126 and continue as indicated there.

Discussion

For samples that contain active metals such as Al and Mg, it is preferable to use HNO_3, or HCl in combination with HNO_3, rather than HCl alone. This is true because As, Sb, and nonmetallic components such as P, Si, and S, if present, may be converted to their hydrogen compounds (AsH_3, SbH_3, etc.) and be lost as gases. Also small amounts of inactive metals may not be dissolved and hence may escape notice.

Some alloys may resist dissolution by the treatments just outlined. In this case try increasing the concentration of the acids. Occasionally it may be necessary to use concentrated HCl and a little liquid Br_2. In other cases, particularly with alloys high in silicon, it may be necessary to fuse the sample with NaOH in a silver or nickel crucible. Nitric acid usually dissolves the metallic components that remain after this treatment.

Besides the elements included in the Procedures, some of the ferroalloys will contain Si, W, Mo, V, and Ti. The groups in which these elements will be precipitated in the general Procedures are indicated in the discussion on page 107. Other alloys containing elements not in the regular Procedures may be encountered outside of courses in elementary qualitative analysis. The groups in which many of these elements precipitate are named in the discussion on page 108, but more advanced texts * must be consulted for the details of the analyses.

IDENTIFICATION OF A SINGLE SOLID SUBSTANCE

The purpose of this section is to describe a method of identifying some of the simpler solid substances so that those who do not go on with the more intensive study of the anions will have an introduction to the method of analyzing them.

It is assumed that the substance is a simple acid, metallic oxide, metallic hydroxide, or a salt of one of the 24 cations with one of the following anions: S^{--}, Cl^-, $C_2O_4^{--}$, PO_4^{3-}, CO_3^{--}, CrO_4^{--}, NO_3^-, or CH_3COO^-. It is also assumed that the sample is soluble in water or in dilute acids, and that Ba^{++}, Sr^{++}, Ca^{++}, and Mg^{++} are absent when $C_2O_4^{--}$, PO_4^{3-}, and SO_4^{--} are present.

Identification of the Cation

Observe the color of the substance, because this gives some indication of its composition. A white substance shows the absence of colored cat-

* See footnote, p. 104.

ions or chromates. (NOTE: A solution of a single substance may be given as an unknown. In this case omit the following directions for dissolving the sample.)

Dissolve about 5 mg. of the solid (a quantity about equal in size to a match head) in 1 ml. of water. Observe the color of the solution. To 1 ml. of water in a test tube add 1 drop of bromthymol blue indicator and 1 drop of methyl red indicator. Then add 1 or 2 drops of the solution which contains the sample. If the indicator solution turns green, the added solution is basic; if the indicator solution turns red or pink, the added solution is acidic. A basic solution may be due to a hydroxide or a metallic oxide, or to the hydrolysis of a salt derived from a strong base and a weak acid. An acid solution may be due to a free acid or an acid salt, or to the hydrolysis of a salt derived from a weak base and a strong acid. If the color of the indicator solution does not definitely change when the solution of the sample is added, most likely the sample is a salt derived from strong base and a strong acid, or one derived from a weak base and a weak acid.

If the sample is not soluble in water, pour off part of the water and add 10 drops of 4-*N* HNO_3. Evaporate the solution to incipient dryness and analyze it according to the Procedures for Cation Analysis, Groups I through V. When the cation has been identified, do not analyze the solution further because only one cation will be present. Sometimes traces of certain cations are found, but comparative tests will show that these are not the cation of the sample. If no cation is found, the sample is probably an acid.

Identification of the Anion

SAMPLE SOLUBLE IN WATER. If the cation is Na^+, K^+, or NH_4^+, omit the following treatment with Na_2CO_3. Otherwise, dissolve 10 mg. of the sample in 2 ml. of water. To this solution add 2-*N* Na_2CO_3 until no further precipitation occurs (between 5 and 10 drops). Set the test tube in the hot water bath for 1 or 2 minutes. Filter the solution, divide it into three parts, and test them for the anions as outlined in the Procedures below.

SAMPLE INSOLUBLE IN WATER. Put 10 mg. of the sample in a 25-ml. Erlenmeyer flask and add 1 ml. of 2-*N* Na_2CO_3. Boil the solution gently for several minutes. Replace the water drop by drop as the solution evaporates. Filter the mixture and wash the filter with 1 ml. of water. Add the wash water to the filtrate. Divide the solution into three parts and analyze them by the Procedures which follow.

PROCEDURES FOR IDENTIFYING THE ANION

Part 1. **Test for S^{--} and Cl^-.** To one part of the prepared solution add 1 drop of methyl red indicator and 4-*N* HNO_3 drop by drop, until the solution changes from yellow to red. Now add 3 drops of 1-N $AgNO_3$ and 3 drops of 4-*N* HNO_3. A black precipitate shows the presence of S^{--}. A white precipitate that dissolves when 5 drops of 15-*N* NH_4OH is added to the solution shows the presence of Cl^-.

Part 2. **Tests for $C_2O_4^{--}$ and PO_4^{3-}.** To the second part of the prepared solution add 1 drop of methyl red indicator and then 4-*N* HNO_3 until the solution just changes from yellow to red. Heat the solution to boiling to expel CO_2. Now add 1 drop of 15-*N* NH_4OH, or more if the solution is not yellow, and 3 drops of 1-*N* $Ca(CH_3COO)_2$. Filter. *Reserve the filtrate for the test for CrO_4^{--} and SO_4^{--}.*

Precipitate: CaC_2O_4 or $Ca_3(PO_4)_2$. Add 4 drops of 4-*N* CH_3COOH, stir the precipitate, and then force the solution through the filter medium. Wash the filter with 1 ml. of water to which has been added 1 drop of 4-*N* CH_3COOH. Add the wash water to the filtrate.

Residue: CaC_2O_4. Add 1 drop of 6-*N* HCl and 1 ml. of water to the residue. Force the solution through the filter medium. Add 2 drops of 0.01-*M* $KMnO_4$ to the filtrate and place the tube in a hot water bath. If the purple color of the MnO_4^- is slowly discharged, $C_2O_4^{--}$ is present.

Filtrate: PO_4^{3-}. Add 5 drops of 4-*N* HNO_3 and 5 drops of 1-*N* ammonium molybdate. Heat the solution in the hot water bath for a few minutes. A *yellow* precipitate confirms PO_4^{3-}.

Test for CrO_4^{--} and SO_4^{--}. (Filtrate from CaC_2O_4 or $Ca_3(PO_4)_2$.) Add to the solution 3 drops of 1-*N* $Ba(CH_3COO)_2$. A yellow precipitate indicates CrO_4^{--} and a white precipitate indicates SO_4^{--}. Filter the mixture and wash the precipitate with 0.5 ml. of water. Add to the precipitate 0.5 ml. of water and 1 drop of 6-*N* HCl. Stir the precipitate and force the solution into a test tube. Wash the residue with 0.5 ml. of water to which has been added 1 drop of 1-*N* HCl. Add the wash solution to the filtrate.

Residue: $BaSO_4$. Place the filter tube in an empty test tube, add 10 drops of 2-*N* Na_2CO_3 to the residue, and set the assembly in the hot water bath for 5 to 10 minutes. Allow the Na_2CO_3 solution to pass slowly through the $BaSO_4$. To the filtrate add 1 drop of paranitrophenol indicator, acidify the filtrate with 6-*N* HCl, and then add 1 drop of 1-*N* $Ba(CH_3COO)_2$. A white precipitate confirms SO_4^{--}.

Filtrate: $Cr_2O_7^{--}$. Add 1 drop of 3% H_2O_2. A blue color shows the original presence of CrO_4^{--}.

Part 3. **Test for NO_3^- and CH_3COO^-.** Divide the solution into two parts, a and b.

a. **Test for NO_3^-.** Add 1 drop of p-nitrophenol indicator; then add 4-*N* H_2SO_4 drop by drop, until the yellow solution becomes colorless. Now add 1 or 2 drops of the nitron reagent. A white precipitate shows the presence of NO_3^-.

b. **Test for CH_3COO^-.** If the solution is alkaline with Na_2CO_3, evaporate carefully to moist dryness and determine the presence of CH_3COO^- by Procedure 25 of the anion analysis for detection of the acetate ion (p. 330). If the solution is not alkaline with Na_2CO_3, add a small amount of solid $CaCO_3$ or $Ca(OH)_2$ and then determine the presence of CH_3COO^- by Procedure 25.

Test for CO_3^{--}. This test is made on a small quantity of the original sample. Place about 5 mg. of the sample in the gas-generating tube (Fig. 16.1) and add about 1 ml. of water. Pack a rubber-tipped filter tube with a small plug of cotton and place the rubber-tipped end tightly in the longer arm of the gas-generating tube. To the filter tube add about 10 drops of water and 2 or 3 drops of a saturated solution of $Ba(OH)_2$. Then add 4 or 5 drops of 4-*N* CH_3COOH to the shorter arm of the tube, and then, by means of the rubber bulb, cause bubbles to pass through the $Ba(OH)_2$ for a period of 1 minute or longer. A white precipitate in the $Ba(OH)_2$ proves the presence of CO_3^{--}. (NOTE: See Procedures for the Analysis of Group II, Procedure 8, p. 313.)

If none of the anions are found, the sample is probably a metallic hydroxide or a metallic oxide.

Examine the results of the analysis to see that all your observations can be explained. For example, the color of the original salt and the color of the solution should be accounted for. If the salt is soluble in water, a cation and an anion that form an insoluble salt cannot be the correct explanation. The acidity or basicity of the solution should be explained on the basis of the ions found in it.

GENERAL REVIEW QUESTIONS ON ANALYSIS FOR CATIONS

1. Draw up a schematic outline for the separation and identification of the following groups of ions; use the fewest number of steps:

   a. Hg_2^{++}, Bi^{3+}, Hg^{++}, Zn^{++}, Sr^{++}.
   b. Sn^{++}, Mn^{++}, Ni^{++}, Ca^{++}, K^+.
   c. Cd^{++}, Al^{3+}, Cr^{3+}, Fe^{3+}, NH_4^+.
   d. Pb^{++}, Bi^{3+}, Cr^{3+}, Mg^{++}, Na^+.
   e. Ag^+, Pb^{++}, As^{3+}, Sb^{3+}, Ba^{++}.

2. A solution is known to contain the following ions: Ag^+, Cd^{++}, Zn^{++}, and Ba^{++}. Describe what you would see during the analysis. Write equations for the reactions by which these ions may be separated and identified.
3. Repeat Question 2 for the following groups of ions:

   a. Sb^{3+}, Cr^{3+}, Mn^{++}, Sr^{++}.
   b. Cu^{++}, Sn^{++}, Al^{3+}, Co^{++}, Ni^{++}.
   c. Fe^{3+}, Mn^{++}, Ba^{++}, Mg^{++}.
   d. Ag^+, Hg_2^{++}, Hg^{++}, Zn^{++}.

4. What would be observed if 4-*N* NH_4OH were added dropwise, and then to excess, to each of the following groups of cations:

   a. Ag^+, Zn^{++}, Sr^{++}, Mg^{++}.
   b. Cu^{++}, Bi^{3+}, As^{3+}, Ba^{++}.
   c. Al^{3+}, Cr^{3+}, Ni^{++}, Ca^{++}.
   d. Cd^{++}, Zn^{++}, Sr^{++}, Mg^{++}.
   e. Pb^{++}, Al^{3+}, Zn^{++}.

   Write equations for the reactions.
5. Repeat Question 4, the reagents being as follows: (a) 4-*N* NaOH; (b) H_2S in 0.3-*M* HCl; (c) H_2S in ammoniacal solution.
6. A solution is known to contain one or more of the following cations: Bi^{3+}, Sn^{++}, Al^{3+}, Zn^{++}, Cd^{++}, Ba^{++}, K^+. The following observations were made:

   a. Dropwise addition of NH_4OH produced a precipitate that dissolved in excess reagent.

b. Dropwise addition of NaOH produced a precipitate that dissolved in excess reagent.
c. Addition of ammonium sulfate produced a white precipitate. On the basis of this information, state which of the above ions are shown to be present and which are shown to be absent. Also list those whose presence or absence is in doubt.

7. A solution may contain one or more of the following ions: Cd^{++}, Cu^{++}, Sb^{3+}, Cr^{3+}, Sr^{++}, Na^+. The following observations were made:

a. The solution is colorless.
b. With CH_3CSNH_2 in acid solution, an orange and then a yellow precipitate formed.
c. NH_4OH formed a precipitate that dissolved with excess reagent.

State which ions are shown to be present, absent, or doubtful.

8. The labels were lost from three pieces of aluminum alloys. They were known to be the following:

a. Lynite: 90% Al, 7.8% Cu, 1.5% Zn, 1.3% Fe.
b. Alloy 3S: 98% Al, 1.2% Mn.
c. Magnalium: 90% Al, 10% Mg.

Devise a method for identifying the pieces in the fewest possible steps.

9. It is necessary to determine whether a piece of metal containing lead is ordinary half-and-half solder (50% Pb, 50% Sn) or type metal (58% Pb, 26% Sn, 15% Sb, 1% Cu). Devise a scheme to identify the metal.
10. German silver contains 52% Cu, 26% Zn, and 22% Ni. U.S. coin silver is 90% Ag and 10% Cu, and silver solder is 80% Ag, 13% Cu, and 6.8% Zn. Devise a procedure to determine which of these alloys a piece of metal might be.
11. A paint pigment was supposed to be sublimed white lead obtained during the roasting of galena. Its composition is 75% $PbSO_4$, 20% PbO, and 5% ZnO. The presence of $BaSO_4$ as an adulterant is suspected. How can this be determined?
12. Paris green is $Cu_3(AsO_3)_2 \cdot Cu(CH_3COO)_2$. How can we determine whether a certain green material contains the ions present in this compound?
13. If a solution is neutral and the only anion present is Cl^-, what cations are probably absent?
14. If a solution containing the chlorides of the cations is made slightly alkaline (pH 9 to 10) and no precipitate forms, which ions are probably absent?
15. When the solution for Group II is treated with CH_3CSNH_2 or H_2S and a white precipitate is obtained, what ions may be present? Another white precipitate is obtained when the solution for Group III is treated with NH_4OH and CH_3CSNH_2 or H_2S. What ions may be present? Which are known to be absent?
16. A white residue on some fruit was suspected of being an insecticide, $PbHAsO_4$. How could the presence or absence of lead and arsenic be proved most readily? Look up the properties of arsenates; how could it be determined that the arsenic was in the form of an arsenate?

17. a. If Zn^{++} were extensively co-precipitated with Group II sulfides, where and in what form would it appear during the analysis of Group II?

b. If Ba^{++} were co-precipitated with Group III ions, where and in what form would it appear during the analysis of Group III?

c. A student neglected to remove Group I cations before precipitating Group II cations. What difficulties, if any, would he encounter in the analysis?

PART 2

QUALITATIVE ANALYSIS FOR THE ANIONS

and Analysis of General Unknown Solutions for Cations and Anions

CHAPTER 16

GENERAL SCHEME OF QUALITATIVE ANALYSIS FOR THE ANIONS

Discussion

Many different systems for the analysis of the more common anions have been devised. However, for various reasons, a concise systematic method similar to that employed for the cations is not as satisfactory or as instructive as the more flexible elimination method followed by group analyses.

In the analysis of the cations, small groups of the ions are separated from the solution by successive precipitations with the different group reagents. These groups are then subdivided so that specific tests may be made for each individual ion. A different scheme of analysis for the anions is followed because there are so many analytical interferences between the anions and because, in practical work, relatively few anions are encountered in any one sample. In the scheme of analysis for the anions, elimination tests are first applied by means of a series of elimination reagents. A summary of all the anions shown to be absent usually leaves only a relatively few for which tests must be made in the analytical procedures for the different groups of anions. This process often considerably decreases the time required for analysis. Furthermore, the elimination tests impress upon the student the differences and similarities in the properties of the anions.

Grouping the Ions for Analytical Procedures. After the elimination tests have shown which ions are absent, positive tests must be made for the remaining ions. For this purpose, the anions have been divided into four analytical groups on the basis of their reaction with group reagents (Table 16.1).

If the elimination tests show, for example, that all ions except S^{--}, I^-, NO_2^-, BO_2^-, and CH_3COO^- are absent, separate portions of the solution are analyzed by the Procedures for Group I and Group III. Tests for all the ions proved absent are omitted. The scheme is flexible

TABLE 16.1. Analytical Groups for the Anions

Group	Group Reagent	Ions	Precipitate or Gas	Color of Precipitate or Odor of Gas
I	$AgNO_3$ plus dilute HNO_3	$S^{=}$	Ag_2S	Black
		$(S_2O_3^{=})$	$Ag_2S_2O_3$-Ag_2S	White-black
		I^-	AgI	Yellow
		Br^-	AgBr	Cream
		SCN^-	AgSCN	White
		CN^-	AgCN	White
		Cl^-	AgCl	White
		(ClO^-)	AgCl	White
II	Dilute NH_4OH and $Ca(CH_3CO_2)_2$	F^-	CaF_2	White
		$C_2O_4^{=}$	CaC_2O_4	White
		$SO_3^{=}$	$CaSO_3$	White
		PO_4^{3-}	$Ca_3(PO_4)_2$	White
		AsO_4^{3-}	$Ca_3(AsO_4)_2$	White
		AsO_3^{3-}	$Ca_3(AsO_3)_2$	White
		$CO_3^{=}$	$CaCO_3$	White
	$Ba(CH_3CO_2)_2$	$SO_4^{=}$	$BaSO_4$	White
		$CrO_4^{=}$	$BaCrO_4$	Yellow
III	No group reagent	ClO_3^-		
		$H_2PO_2^-$		
		NO_2^-		
		NO_3^-		
		BO_2^-		
		CH_3COO^-		
IV	Diluted HCl	ClO^-	Cl_2	Chlorine
	Special tests for gases	$CO_3^{=}$	CO_2	Odorless
		$S^{=}$	H_2S	Rotten eggs
		$SO_3^{=}$	SO_2	Burning sulfur
		$S_2O_3^{=}$	$SO_2 + \underline{S}$	Burning sulfur
		CN^-	HCN	Bitter almonds
		NO_2^-	$NO + NO_2$	Concd. HNO_3 fumes

and allows the student to use his own ingenuity and knowledge of the properties of the anions to make short-cuts and confirmatory tests. He must always keep in mind possible interferences and incompatibilities. This requires thorough knowledge of the properties and characteristic reactions of the anions and their acids. Hence, careful study of the Preliminary Experiments is important for successful and rapid anion analysis.

PRELIMINARY EXPERIMENTS. The Preliminary Experiments with the *anion test solutions* (Appendix E) are designed to acquaint the student with a number of the characteristic reactions of anions when other anions are absent. A brief description of the properties of the anion and its acid is given with the Preliminary Experiments.

The laboratory work has been arranged as follows. After the Preliminary Experiments for a group of anions have been completed, a solution which contains all the anions of the group (a known solution) is analyzed. This is followed by the analysis of an unknown solution which may contain any or all of the anions of the group. When the analysis of the known and unknown solutions for all the groups has been completed, a general unknown solution is analyzed. In this analysis the elimination tests are made first in order to determine which groups are present and which Procedures should be followed. Finally, directions are given for the analysis of a solid unknown for both cations and anions.

TESTING FOR EVOLVED GASES. A number of the anions form volatile or unstable acids. These acids or their decomposition products may be detected by their reaction with suitable reagents. Several different schemes may be devised to carry out these tests.

An apparatus which can be used for most of the tests is shown in Fig. 16.1. To make it, a 10-mm. side tube is sealed to the bottom of a 13 x 100-mm. test tube. The top of the test tube and the 10-mm. side tube are fitted with rubber tubes as connectors. Pressure filter tubes are then placed in these rubber connectors, or a rubber-tipped filter tube may be used for the longer tube. To use the apparatus the sample is placed in the gas-generating tube *C*. The reagent that is used to test for the gas is placed in the reagent tube *A* over a plug of cotton. An acid or other reagent is added through the side tube *B*. Air is then forced through the apparatus with the rubber bulb so as to sweep the gases out of the solution and through the reagent.

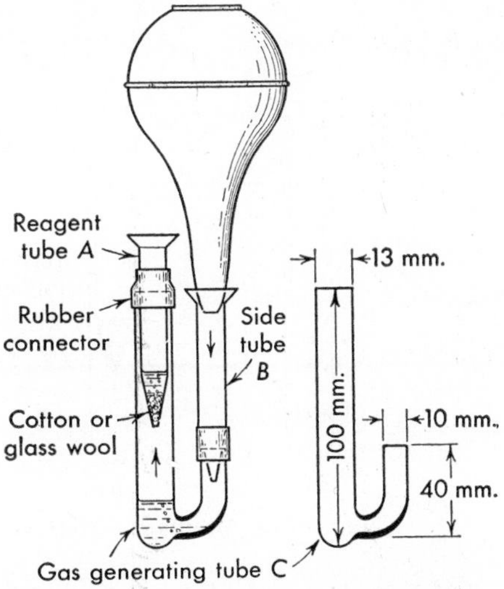

FIG. 16.1. Gas-Testing Apparatus.

Another use of this device is illustrated by the following. If a precipitate that is in a pressure filter tube is to be tested for a carbonate, place the filter tube in the position of the side tube *B*. Put 5 to 10 drops of saturated $Ba(OH)_2$ in the reagent tube *A*. Now add 0.5 ml. of water and 1 drop of 6-*N* HCl to the precipitate in the side tube. Immediately force the solution through the filter medium with the pressure bulb and pass the gases through the $Ba(OH)_2$ solution. It is usually necessary to hold the reagent tube *A* so that it will not be blown out. A white precipitate in the $Ba(OH)_2$ solution shows the presence of a carbonate in the original precipitate.

The special features of this gas-testing apparatus are as follows: It is rapid; the air bubbles stir up the solution and sweep the gases from it;

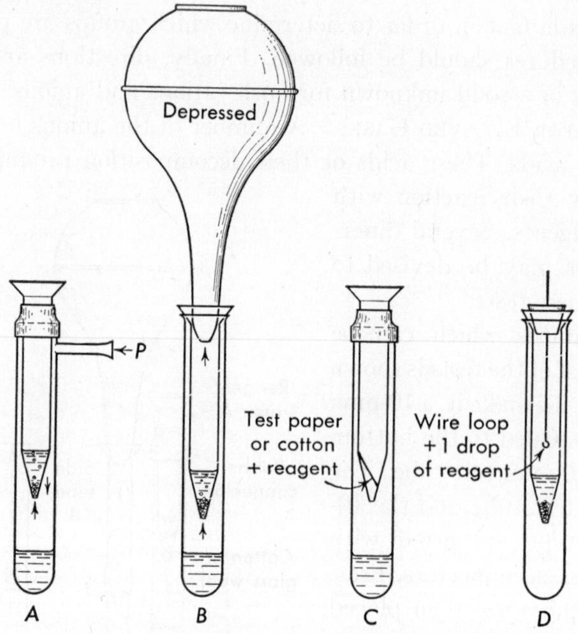

FIG. 16.2. Alternative Methods of Testing for Evolved Gases.

all the gases can be forced through the reagent; the cotton plug breaks the gas up into very small bubbles so that good contact between the reagent and the gas is achieved; the tube may be heated by placing it in a hot water bath; tests may be made on either solids or liquids.

If a gas-generator tube is not available, tests for gases may be made with the apparatus shown in Fig. 16.2. The part in Fig. 16.2*D* is especially useful in testing for fluorides. Directions for making gas tests usually call for the apparatus shown in Fig. 16.1, but that in Fig. 16.2 may be used, the Procedures being modified as necessitated by the difference in construction.

CHAPTER 17

PRELIMINARY EXPERIMENTS AND PROPERTIES OF GROUP I ANIONS

S^{--}, $S_2O_3^{--}$, I^-, Br^-, SCN^-, CN^-, CL^-, CLO^-

THE SULFIDE ION, S^{--}

Gram-ion weight: 32.06.
Test solution: 0.1-*M* sodium sulfide, Na_2S.
Concentration: 3.2 mg. of S^{--}/ml.

Hydrosulfuric Acid, H_2S

A solution of hydrosulfuric acid is obtained when hydrogen sulfide (m.p., −85.5° C.; b.p., −60.7° C.) is passed into water. At 20° C. and a pressure of 760 mm., 1 volume of water dissolves 2.9 volumes of the gas. The solution is about 0.1-*M*. Hydrogen sulfide has the odor of decaying eggs and a nauseating taste. The gas is very poisonous; 1 part of H_2S in 1000 parts of air is highly toxic and may prove fatal if breathed for any length of time. With water H_2S forms a very weak acid. The primary ionization constant is 1.2×10^{-7}; the secondary, 1.0×10^{-15}. H_2S is oxidized to free sulfur and some SO_4^{--} in acid solution by such oxidizing agents as HClO, MnO_4^-, $Cr_2O_7^{--}$, Fe^{3+}, HNO_2, Cl_2, Br_2, I_2, and O_2.

Salts

Most metal sulfides except those of the alkaline earths and the alkali metals have very low solubility in water. The sulfides of the metals of Groups I and II (cations) are not soluble in moderately concentrated acid solutions, but, with the exception of HgS, they are dissolved by concentrated HNO_3. The sulfides of the alkali metals are appreciably hydrolyzed and the sulfides of chromium and aluminum are completely hydrolyzed in aqueous solutions. Alkaline solutions of the sulfides are oxidized by the oxygen of the air, forming free S which interacts with S^{--} to form polysulfides such as S_2^{--}. The polysulfides are partially oxidized by oxygen to SO_3^{--}, $S_2O_3^{--}$, and SO_4^{--}. They also react with CN^- to form SCN^-. Nonoxidizing acids react with S^{--}, forming H_2S which escapes from the solution.

Reactions

1. *Hydrolysis of Na_2S. Precipitation of Ag_2S.* To 1 ml. of water add 1 drop of the sodium sulfide test solution and 1 drop of bromthymol blue indicator (yellow — 6.0 : 7.6 — blue). Is this solution acid or alkaline? Why? To the blue solution add 1 drop of 4-*N* HNO_3. Note the change in color of the indicator. To this solution add 1 drop of 1-*N* $AgNO_3$. Note the color of the precipitate and write the equation for the reaction. (NOTE: Ag_2S is insoluble in dilute acids, ammonia, thiosulfate, and cyanide solutions, but is soluble in hot HNO_3 and in dilute acid solutions of thiourea.)

2. *Evolution of H_2S. $BiCl_3$ Spot Test.* To 1 ml. of water add 1 drop of the sodium sulfide test solution and 1 drop of 4-*N* H_2SO_4. Place the tube in the hot water bath and cover the mouth of the test tube with a piece of filter paper. Spot a drop of 0.1-*N* $BiCl_3$ on the filter paper at the place where it covers the test tube. Note the darkening of the $BiCl_3$ spot. Write equations for all the reactions. Is a white precipitate formed in the solution in the test tube? If so, what is it? Write an equation for the reaction for its formation.

3. *Nitropentacyanoferrate (III) (Nitroferricyanide) Test for S^{--}.* To 10 ml. of water add 1 drop of the sodium sulfide test solution and 2 drops of 15-*N* NH_4OH. Then add 2 or 3 drops of a 1% solution of $Na_2Fe(NO)(CN)_5$. (The violet color obtained with this reagent is a sensitive test for S^{--}.)

THE THIOSULFATE ION, $S_2O_3^{--}$

Gram-ion weight: 112.12.
Test solution: 0.1-*M* sodium thiosulfate, $Na_2S_2O_3$.
Concentration: 11.2 mg. of $S_2O_3^{--}$/ml.

Thiosulfuric Acid, $H_2S_2O_3$

This acid does not exist in the free state. A dilute aqueous solution of it may be obtained when a solution of $Na_2S_2O_3$ is acidified with a weak acid. However, the acid is rather unstable and decomposes into H_2SO_3 and free sulfur, and the H_2SO_3 decomposes into H_2O and SO_2.

Salts

The most important of the thiosulfates is $Na_2S_2O_3 \cdot 5H_2O$. This salt, erroneously called "hypo," is used in photography to "fix" films and prints; that is, it is used to dissolve the unreduced silver halides from the photographic emulsions. The thiosulfates of Ba^{++}, Pb^{++}, and Ag^{+} are only slightly soluble in water; most other thiosulfates are soluble. $Ag_2S_2O_3$ decomposes as follows:

$$\underline{Ag_2S_2O_3} + 2H_2O \rightarrow \underline{Ag_2S} + H_3O^+ + HSO_4^-$$

With excess $S_2O_3^{--}$, $Ag_2S_2O_3$ forms the complex ion $Ag_2(S_2O_3)_3^{4-}$. In dilute acid solution $S_2O_3^{--}$ is oxidized to SO_4^{--} by MnO_4^-, $Cr_2O_7^{--}$, HClO, and H_2O_2, and to $S_4O_6^{--}$ by I_2.

Reactions

1. *Reaction of $S_2O_3^{--}$ with Ag^+.* To 1 ml. of water add 1 drop of the sodium thiosulfate test solution and 1 drop of bromthymol blue indicator. Is the solution acid or alkaline? Why? Now add 1 drop of 4-*N* HNO_3 and 1 drop of 1-*N* $AgNO_3$, and note carefully the color changes in the precipitate. Write the equations for the reactions.

2. *Reaction of $S_2O_3^{--}$ with Bi^{3+}.* To 1 ml. of water add 1 drop of the sodium thiosulfate test solution and 1 drop of 0.1-*N* $BiCl_3$. Place the tube in the hot water bath for 1 or 2 minutes. The dark-brown precipitate is Bi_2S_3. Write the equations for the reactions.

3. *Dissolution of AgBr by $S_2O_3^{--}$.* Add 1 drop of 0.1-*N* $AgNO_3$ and 1 drop of 1-*N* KBr to a test tube. To the precipitate, AgBr, add 10 drops of the sodium thiosulfate test solution. Write the equation for the reaction.

THE IODIDE ION, I^-

Gram-ion weight: 126.92.
Test solution: 0.1-*M* potassium iodide, KI.
Solution: 12.7 mg. of I^-/ml.

Hydriodic Acid, HI

Hydrogen iodide is a gas at ordinary room temperature (m.p., −50.8° C.; b.p., −35.5° C.). At a temperature of 10° C. and under a pressure of 760 mm., 425 ml. of HI will dissolve in 1 ml. of water. The commercial hydriodic acid contains about 45% HI; its specific gravity 20°/4° is 1.5. Under a pressure of 760 mm., an aqueous solution of hydriodic acid forms a constant-boiling mixture with a boiling point of 127° and a specific gravity of 1.7; it contains 57% HI.

The following oxygen acids of iodine are known: HIO (unstable), HIO_3, and HIO_4 or H_5IO_6. The anions of these acids are not included in the scheme of analysis.

Salts

All the commonly occurring iodides are soluble in or are decomposed by water, except AgI, Hg_2I_2, PbI_2, HgI_2, BiI_3, CuI_2, Cu_2I_2, PdI_2, TlI, and AuI. BiOI and SbOI are only slightly soluble in water.

I^- forms complex ions such as the following: HgI_4^{--}, PbI_4^{--}, and BiI_4^-. In dilute acid solution I^- is oxidized to free iodine by Fe^{3+}, MnO_4^-, $Cr_2O_7^{--}$, HNO_2, NO_3^-, Cl_2, Br_2, HClO, H_2O_2, etc. It is oxidized to IO_3^- in concentrated solutions of some of the oxidizing agents.

Reactions

1. *Precipitation of AgI.* To 1 ml. of water add 1 drop of the potassium iodide test solution, 1 drop of 4-*N* HNO_3, and 1 drop of 1-*N* $AgNO_3$. Write the equation for the reaction. Place the tube in the hot water bath for 1 or 2 minutes, filter, and wash the precipitate with water. Proceed to the next experiment.

2. *Test for Solubility of AgI in NH_4OH-$AgNO_3$ Reagent.* To the precipitate on the filter medium add about 10 drops of Miller's reagent (ammoniacal solution of silver nitrate) and stir the precipitate with a micro stirring rod. Note whether the precipitate dissolves in the reagent. (NOTE: AgI is also insoluble in concentrated (15-*N*) NH_4OH. Try it.)

3. *Oxidation of I^- by HNO_2. Color of I_2 in CCl_4.* To 1 ml. of water add 1 drop of the potassium iodide test solution, 1 drop of 4-*N* HNO_3, 2 or 3 drops of CCl_4, and 1 drop of 0.1-*N* $NaNO_2$. Shake the tube and note the color of the CCl_4. Write the equation for the reaction.

4. *Oxidation of I^- by H_2O_2. Color of Starch-I_2 Complex.* To 1 ml. of water add 1 drop of the potassium iodide test solution, 1 drop of 4-*N* HNO_3, and 1 drop of starch emulsion. Place the tube in the hot water bath for a half to 1 minute. Note the color of the solution. Now add 1 drop of 3% H_2O_2 and allow the tube to remain in the hot water for a short time. Note the color of the solution. Write the equation for the reaction.

5. *Reaction with Cu^{++} to Form Cu_2I_2.* To 1 ml. of water add 1 drop of the potassium iodide test solution, 1 drop of $Cu(NO_3)_2$ test solution, and 1 drop of Na_2SO_3 test solution. The white precipitate is Cu_2I_2. Write the equation for the reaction. (NOTE: Bromides and chlorides do not give a precipitate with $Cu(NO_3)_2$ and Na_2SO_3.)

THE BROMIDE ION, Br^-

Gram-ion weight: 79.916.
Test solution: 0.1-*M* potassium bromide, KBr.
Concentration: 8.0 mg. of Br^-/ml.

Hydrobromic Acid, HBr

Hydrogen bromide is a gas at ordinary room temperature (m.p., −86.0° C.; b.p., −67.1° C.). At a temperature of 0° and under a pressure of 760 mm.,

221 g. of the gas dissolves in 100 g. of water. The commercial acid contains about 47% HBr and has a specific gravity 25°/4° of 1.48. Under a pressure of 760 mm. an aqueous solution of hydrobromic acid forms a constant-boiling mixture with a boiling point of 126° C. and contains about 47.5% HBr.

Two oxygen acids of bromine are known: HBrO and $HBrO_3$. Their anions are not included in the scheme of analysis.

Salts

Most of the commonly occurring metal bromides are soluble in water except AgBr, Hg_2Br_2, and $PbBr_2$. BiOBr and SbOBr are only slightly soluble.

Br^- is not as strong a reducing agent as I^-. Acid solutions of the strongest oxidizing agents, such as MnO_4^-, $Cr_2O_7^{--}$, Cl_2, HClO, and concentrated H_2SO_4, oxidize Br^- to Br_2.

Reactions

1. *Precipitation of AgBr.* To 1 ml. of water add 1 drop of the potassium bromide test solution, 1 drop of 4-*N* HNO_3, and 1 drop of 1-*N* $AgNO_3$. Write the equation for the reaction. Place the tube in the hot water bath for 1 or 2 minutes, filter, and wash the precipitate with water. Proceed with the next experiment.

2. *Test for Dissolution of AgBr by NH_4OH Reagent. Dissolution by Concd. NH_4OH.* To the precipitate on the filter medium add about 10 drops of Miller's reagent. Stir the precipitate with a micro stirring rod and note whether it dissolves in the reagent. Now add about 5 drops of concentrated NH_4OH to the filter tube containing the AgBr precipitate and note whether the precipitate dissolves. Write the equation for the reaction.

3. *Oxidation of Br^- by ClO^-. Reaction of Br_2 with Fluorescein to Form Eosin.* To 1 ml. of water add 1 drop of the potassium bromide test solution, 1 drop of fluorescein, 1 drop of 4-*N* NH_4OH, and 1 drop of 5% NaClO. Now add 1 to 3 drops of 4-*N* CH_3COOH. Note the appearance of the red color of eosin in the solution.

THE THIOCYANATE ION, SCN^-

Gram-ion weight: 58.08.
Test solution: 0.1-*M* potassium thiocyanate, KSCN.
Concentration: 5.8 mg. of SCN^-/ml.

Thiocyanic Acid, HSCN

Thiocyanic acid is a solid at 5° C. On melting, the solid forms an oily yellow liquid which boils at 85° C. and has an unpleasant odor and a decided irritating action on the mucous membrane. Like HCN, it is poisonous. On standing, the acid decomposes and polymerizes, with the formation of HCN and a yellow solid, $H_2S_3C_2N_2$, known as perthiocyanic acid. HSCN is a strong acid and dissolves readily in water, alcohol, and ether, but it decomposes slowly.

Salts

Most thiocyanates are soluble in water, except those formed with Ag^+, Pb^{++}, Hg^{++}, Cu^{++}, and Tl^+. The latter are soluble in excess alkali thiocyanates with the formation of complex ions such as $Ag(SCN)_2^-$, $Hg(SCN)_4^{--}$, etc. Soluble thiocyanates decompose with the formation of a variety of products when they are heated in dilute acid solution or when the solids are heated strongly in a flame. Thiocyanates are oxidized to SO_4^{--} and CNO^- and/or CN^- by strong oxidizing agents such as MnO_4^- and HClO.

Reactions

1. *Precipitation of AgSCN.* To 1 ml. of water add 1 drop of the potassium thiocyanate test solution, 1 drop of 4-*N* HNO_3, and 1 drop of 1-*N* $AgNO_3$. Write the equation for the reaction. Place the tube in the hot water bath for 1 or 2 minutes, filter, and wash the precipitate with water. Proceed to the next experiment.

2. *Test for Dissolution of AgSCN by NH_4OH-$AgNO_3$ Reagent and by NH_4OH. Reaction of SCN^- with Fe^{3+}.* To the precipitate on the filter medium add about 10 drops of Miller's reagent. Stir the precipitate with a micro stirring rod and note whether it dissolves in the reagent. Now add about 5 drops of concentrated NH_4OH to the filter tube containing the AgSCN precipitate, and note whether the precipitate dissolves. Write the equation for the reaction. Filter the solution into a test tube and add 1 drop of bromthymol blue indicator and 1 drop of 1-*N* KBr. Write the equation for the reaction. Now add 4-*N* HNO_3 until the blue color of the indicator changes to yellow; then add 1 drop of $Fe(NO_3)_3$. Note the red color and write the equation for the reaction.

3. *Formation of $Cu_2(SCN)_2$.* To 1 ml. of water add 1 drop of the potassium thiocyanate test solution and 1 drop of $Cu(NO_3)_2$ test solution. Now add a small amount of solid Na_2SO_3 and 1 drop of 4-*N* HNO_3. The white precipitate is $Cu_2(SCN)_2$. Write the equations for the reactions.

THE CYANIDE ION, CN^-

Gram-ion weight: 26.02.
Test solution: 0.1-*M* potassium cyanide, KCN.
Concentration: 2.6 mg. of CN^-/ml.

Hydrocyanic Acid, HCN

Anhydrous HCN is a very volatile liquid at ordinary temperature (m.p., $-14°$ C.; b.p., 26.8° C.). An aqueous solution may be prepared by dissolving HCN in water. On standing, such a solution interacts with water and forms $HCOONH_4$. Hydrocyanic acid is an exceedingly weak acid ($K_a = 4 \times 10^{-10}$); it is expelled from solutions of its salts by an acid as weak as carbonic acid. As a gas, HCN is used as a fumigant and a poison for vermin. The salts of the acid are used extensively in electroplating and dye manufacturing, and for extracting gold from gold-bearing ores. HCN and its salts are *extremely poisonous*. Most people are able to recognize its presence in the air by its odor—the odor of bitter almonds.

Salts

The alkali and alkaline earth cyanides, and mercuric cyanide, are soluble in water, but the heavy metal cyanides are insoluble. Since HCN is a very weak acid, the alkali and alkaline earth cyanides hydrolyze in water and produce an alkaline solution. But mercuric cyanide is practically un-ionized in water. An aqueous solution of $Hg(CN)_2$ does not give the usual reactions for Hg^{++} or CN^-. Mercuric cyanide is reported to be nonpoisonous. CN^- is oxidized to CNO^- in alkaline solution by such oxidizing agents as MnO_4^-, ClO^-, and H_2O_2. CN^- forms a number of very stable complex ions, such as $Fe(CN)_6^{4+}$, $Ag(CN)_2^-$, $Co(CN)_6^{3-}$, $Hg(CN)_4^{--}$, etc. Alkali polysulfides convert CN^- to SCN^-.

Reactions

1. *Hydrolysis of KCN. Precipitation of AgCN.* To 1 ml. of water add 1 drop of the potassium cyanide test solution and 1 drop of bromthymol blue indicator. Is this solution acid or alkaline? Why? Add 1 drop of 4-*N* HNO_3 to the blue solution and note the change in the color of the indicator. To the acid solution add 1 drop of 1-*N* $AgNO_3$. Write the equation for the reaction. Filter off the precipitate and wash it with water. Proceed with the next experiment.

2. *Dissolution of AgCN by NH_4OH-$AgNO_3$ Reagent. Formation of Blue Oxidation Product from Benzidine.* Add about 10 drops of Miller's reagent to the precipitate on the filter medium and stir it with a micro stirring rod. Does the precipitate dissolve? (NOTE: Disregard the blue color imparted to the solution by the indicator.) Force the solution through the filter medium into a test tube. Add to the solution 1 drop of 1-*N* KBr, 1 drop of benzidine reagent, 1 drop of 0.1-*N* $CuSO_4$, and 2 drops of 4-*N* CH_3COOH. Note the deep blue color of the solution. What is the color of the indicator on the acid side of its pH range? Does the indicator interfere with the test?

3. *Dissolution of AgCN by Hg^{++}.* Add 1 drop of the potassium cyanide test solution to 10 drops of Miller's reagent. Does a precipitate form? To this solution add 2 drops of 4-*N* CH_3COOH. Note the formation of a precipitate and write the equation for the reaction. Now add from 1 to 5 drops of 0.1-*M* $Hg(NO_3)_2$. Shake the tube vigorously after each drop is added. Note that the precipitate dissolves. Write the equation for the reaction.

THE CHLORIDE ION, Cl^-

Gram-ion weight: 35.457.
Test solution: 0.1-*M* sodium chloride, NaCl.
Concentration: 3.5 mg. of Cl^-/ml.

Hydrochloric Acid, HCl

Hydrogen chloride is a gas at ordinary room temperatures (m.p., −111° C.; b.p., −85° C.). The gas is extremely soluble in water; 442 volumes of it dissolve in 1 volume of water at a temperature of 20° C. and under a pressure of 760 mm. HCl is practically completely ionized in dilute aqueous solution. Hydrochloric acid is therefore one of the strongest acids. The commercial concentrated acid has a specific gravity 25°/4° of 1.19 and contains about 38% HCl. When an aqueous solution of the acid is boiled, a constant-boiling mixture is obtained. Under a pressure of 760 mm., the distillate contains 20.24% of HCl and has a boiling point of 110° C.

Several oxygen acids of chlorine are known: HClO, $HClO_2$, $HClO_3$, and $HClO_4$. Only HClO is included in the analysis of the anions of Group I.

Salts

All the commonly occurring metal chlorides are soluble in water except AgCl, Hg_2Cl_2, $PbCl_2$, and the oxychlorides, BiOCl and SbOCl. The chlorides of Pd^{++}, Cu^+, Tl^+, and Au^+ are somewhat insoluble in water.

Cl^- is more difficult to oxidize to Cl_2 than Br^- to Br_2 and I^- to I_2. Only strong oxidizing agents, such as MnO_4^-, BiO_3^-, and MnO_2, in concentrated acid solution will oxidize Cl^- to Cl_2.

Reactions

1. *Precipitation of AgCl.* To 1 ml. of water add 1 drop of the sodium chloride test solution, 1 drop of 4-*N* HNO_3, and 1 drop of 1-*N* $AgNO_3$. Write the equation for the reaction. Place the tube in the hot water bath for 1 or 2 minutes. Filter off the precipitate and wash it with water. Proceed with the next experiment.

2. *Dissolution of AgCl by NH_4OH-$AgNO_3$ Reagent and by Hg^{++}.* Add about 10 drops of Miller's reagent to the precipitate on the filter

medium. Stir the precipitate with a micro stirring rod and note whether it dissolves. Write the equation for the reaction. Force the solution through the filter medium into a test tube and add 2 drops of 4-N CH_3COOH. Write the equation for the reaction. Add 2 drops of 0.1-M $Hg(NO_3)_2$ to the solution containing the precipitate. Does it dissolve? (NOTE: See Experiment 3 for the cyanide ion.)

3. *Liberation of Cl_2 and Reaction of Cl_2 with Starch-Iodide Paper.* To a test tube add 1 drop of the sodium chloride test solution and 5 drops of 4-N HNO_3, and a small amount of solid sodium bismuthate, $NaBiO_3$. Moisten a piece of starch-iodide paper, fold the paper, and hang one end of it inside the test tube. What color is imparted to the paper? Write the equations for the reactions.

THE HYPOCHLORITE ION, ClO^-

Gram-ion weight: 51.457.
Test solution: 0.1-M sodium hypochlorite, $NaClO$.
Concentration: 5.1 mg. of ClO^-/ml.

Hypochlorous Acid, HClO

The acid, $HClO$, may be obtained by adding Cl_2O to water or by acidifying a solution of $NaClO$. When Cl_2 is passed into water, HCl and $HClO$ are formed. $HClO$ decomposes quite readily into HCl and O_2 when warmed or exposed to light. As an acid, $HClO$ is very weak ($K_a = 3.7 \times 10^{-8}$ at 17° C.); it is even weaker than H_2CO_3. Hypochlorous acid is one of the strongest oxidizing agents in both acid and alkaline solutions.

The behavior of $HClO$ in an acid and in a base medium is as follows:

$$
\begin{array}{ccccc}
& & HClO & & \\
& & \Big|\Big| & +H_2O & \\
\boxed{\begin{array}{l} OH^- \\ H_3O^+ \end{array}} + \boxed{\begin{array}{l} Cl^+ \\ Cl^- \end{array}} & \longleftarrow & & \longrightarrow & \boxed{\begin{array}{l} H_3O^+ \\ OH^- \end{array}} + \boxed{\begin{array}{l} ClO^- \\ Na^+ \end{array}} \\
& \longleftarrow \text{acid} & & \text{alkali} \longrightarrow & \\
\downarrow \qquad \downarrow & & & & \downarrow \\
2H_2O \quad Cl_2 & & & & 2H_2O
\end{array}
$$

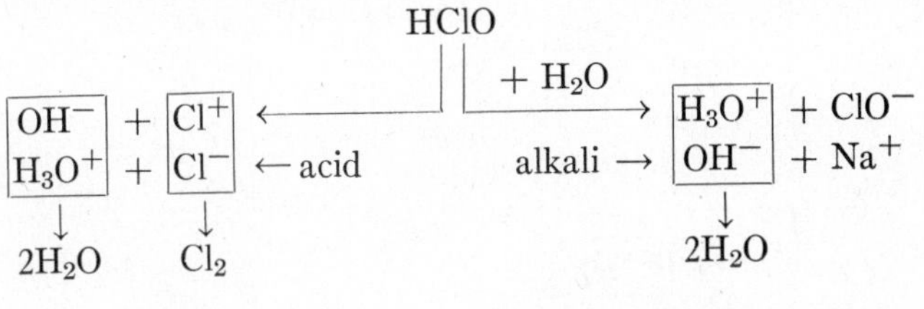

Salts

The two most available salts are $NaClO$ and $Ca(ClO)_2$. Because of the method of preparation, a solution of $NaClO$ always contains $NaCl$. Solutions of sodium hypochlorite are used for bleaching and as antiseptics, being sold under various trade names such as Hilex, Oxol, Clorox, Zonite, etc. Chloride of lime, commonly known as bleaching powder, also contains hypochlorite. Most hypochlorites are soluble in water.

Reactions

1. *Hydrolysis of NaClO. Oxidation of Indicators. Reaction with Ag^+.* To 1 ml. of water add 1 drop of the sodium hypochlorite test solution and 1 drop of bromthymol blue indicator. Why is the solution made blue by the indicator? Place the tube in the hot water bath for about 1 minute. Why is the blue color of the indicator destroyed? Add 1 drop of the $AgNO_3$ test solution to the colorless solution. Write the equation for the reaction. (NOTE: AgClO is very soluble in water. Place the test tube in the hot water for about 1 minute and note the color of the precipitate. If the precipitate is white, add a drop or two of the $AgNO_3$ test solution. Write the equation for the reaction.

2. *Formation of Red Oxidation Product with Benzidine.* Fill a test tube with water and add 1 drop of the sodium hypochlorite test solution and 1 drop of benzidine reagent. (NOTE: A dilute solution of a hypochlorite gives a blue color with benzidine. A 1% solution, or even less, colors benzidine red, and a red precipitate may form.)

3. *Reaction with Mn^{++}.* To 1 ml. of water add 1 drop of the sodium hypochlorite test solution and 1 drop of $Mn(NO_3)_2$ test solution. Shake the tube and note the formation of a brown precipitate, $HMnO_2$ or $Mn(OH)_3$. Write the equation for the reaction.

CHAPTER 18

ANALYSIS OF GROUP I ANIONS

SCHEMATIC OUTLINE OF THE PROCEDURE

1. $S^{=}(S_2O_3^{=})$ *, I^-, Br^-, SCN^-, CN^-, Cl^-, (ClO^-) * + anions of Groups II and III
   Adjust acidity. Add $NaNO_2$, $AgNO_3$, and then HNO_3.

2. **Precipitate:** Ag_2S (from $S^{=}$ or $S_2O_3^{=}$), AgI, AgBr, AgSCN, AgCl (from Cl^- or ClO^-)
   Add $Ag(NH_3)_2NO_3$ + NH_4OH.

3. **Filtrate:** CN^-, Cl^- Divide.		4. **Residue:** Ag_2S, AgI, AgBr, AgSCN Add NH_4OH.		
		5. **Filtrate:** SCN^-, Br^- Divide.		6. **Residue:** Ag_2S, AgI. *Black ppt.:* Ag_2S $S^{=}$ or $S_2O_3^{=}$ present
a. **Test for CN^-:** Add KBr + benzidine + $CuSO_4$ + CH_3COOH. *Blue-colored oxidation product*	b. **Test for Cl^-:** Add CH_3COONH_4 + $Hg(NO_3)_2$ + CH_3COOH. *White ppt.:* AgCl	a. **Test for SCN^-:** Add KBr, HNO_3, and $Fe(NO_3)_3$. *Red color:* $Fe(SCN)_3$	b. **Test for Br^-:** Add NaClO and filter. Add CH_3COOH, HCHO, fluorescein, and HClO. *Pink color:* Eosin	**Test for I^-:** Add NH_4OH, CH_3CSNH_2. To filtrate add H_2O_2, H_2SO_4, and starch. *Blue color*
Cyanide	*Chloride or hypochlorite*	*Thiocyanate*	*Bromide*	*Sulfide or thiosulfate* *Iodide*

* $S_2O_3^{--}$ and ClO^- are enclosed in parentheses because these ions are precipitated not as $Ag_2S_2O_3$ and AgClO but as Ag_2S and AgCl.

DISCUSSION OF THE PROCEDURE

The anions of this group are those whose silver salts are sparingly soluble in dilute nitric acid. Precipitation is carried out in a neutral solution and the nitric acid is added to the precipitated silver salts. If this were not done, the ions which form volatile or slightly soluble gases in acid solution (S^{--}, $S_2O_3^{--}$, CN^-, and ClO^-) would be partially lost. Furthermore, the oxidizing ions, such as ClO^-, CrO_4^{--}, and ClO_3^-, would interact more rapidly with the reducing ions in this group—S^{--}, $S_2O_3^{--}$, I^-, Br^-, SCN^-, and CN^-. In neutral solution ClO^- oxidizes I^-, S^{--}, $S_2O_3^{--}$, Br^-, SCN^-, and CN^- to IO_3^-, SO_4^{--}, SO_4^{--}, Br_2, SO_4^{--}, CO_3^{--}, N_2, and CNO^- respectively. Hence if ClO^- is present, these reducing ions will be absent. Whereas $H_2PO_2^-$ gives a white precipitate with Ag^+, the AgH_2PO_2 changes to Ag° and PO_4^{3-}. Consequently, $H_2PO_2^-$ is oxidized to PO_4^{3-} with NO_2^- before the silver salts are precipitated in Procedure 1. This prevents the formation of Ag°.

ClO^-, $S_2O_3^{--}$, and $H_2PO_2^-$ are usually not included in the Group I known or unknown solution because no provision is made in this group for determining whether a white precipitate of AgCl is due to Cl^- and/or ClO^-, or whether a black precipitate of Ag_2S is due to S^{--} and/or $S_2O_3^{--}$. To make these distinctions, special tests are described in the Procedures for Group I (p. 296). These ions may be in the general unknown solution.

DIRECTIONS FOR LABORATORY WORK

1. Obtain from the storeroom a solution that contains the anions of Group I (ClO^- and $S_2O_3^{--}$ omitted) and analyze it by following the Procedures for Group I.

2. (Optional.) Request a student to prepare an unknown solution from the test solutions. Analyze it in accordance with the Procedures for Group I. (Preparation of the unknown: To 1 ml. of water add 1 drop of the test solution for four different anions of Group I. Omit ClO^- and $S_2O_3^{--}$.)

3. Obtain from the storeroom anion Unknown No. 1 * and analyze it in accordance with the Procedures for Group I. ClO^- and $S_2O_3^{--}$ will not be present. Report the results of the analysis on an Unknown Report Blank.

* Passing an oral or written examination on the Procedures, the chemical reactions, and the reasons for the different operations is generally a prerequisite to obtaining an unknown solution.

PROCEDURES FOR ANALYZING GROUP I ANIONS

S^{--}, ($S_2O_3^{--}$),* I^-, Br^-, SCN^-, CN^-, Cl^-, (ClO^-) **

1. To 1 ml. of water add 5 drops of the general unknown, or 5 drops of Group I known or unknown. To this solution add 1 drop of p-nitro-phenol indicator (colorless—5.0:7.0—yellow). If the solution is yellow, add 0.01-*N* HNO_3 drop by drop, until the yellow color is discharged. To the colorless solution add 1 drop of 1-*N* $NaNO_2$ and 2 drops of 1-*N* $AgNO_3$. Shake the tube and add 2 drops of 4-*N* HNO_3. Place the tube in the hot water bath for about 1 minute and then filter off the precipitate by means of the pressure filter tube assembly. (Use a tightly packed cotton filter medium.) Test for complete precipitation by adding 1 drop of 1-*N* $AgNO_3$ to the filtrate. If a precipitate forms, filter it off through the same filter tube. Wash the precipitate with 2 or 3 ml. of water to which 1 drop of 4-*N* HNO_3 has been added.

2. **Precipitate:** Ag_2S (from S^{--} or $S_2O_3^{--}$), AgI, AgBr, AgSCN, AgCN, AgCl (from Cl^- or ClO^-). Add to the precipitate on the filter medium 1 ml. of ammoniacal silver nitrate (Miller's reagent). Stir the precipitate with a micro stirring rod and then force the solution through the filter medium into a test tube. (If the filtrate is not clear, refilter.) Wash the undissolved residue with 1 ml. of water, adding the wash water to the filtrate.

3. **Filtrate:** CN^- and/or Cl^-. Divide the filtrate into two parts.

a. **Test for CN^-:** Add 1 drop of 1-*N* KBr, 2 drops of the benzidine reagent, 1 drop of 0.1-*N* $CuSO_4$, and 2 drops of 4-*N* CH_3COOH. A deep blue color shows the presence of CN^-.

b. **Test for Cl^-:** Add 2 drops of 6-*N* CH_3COONH_4, 4 drops of 0.1-*M* $Hg(NO_3)_2$, and 1 drop of 4-*N* CH_3COOH. A white precipitate shows the presence of Cl^-.

4. **Residue:** Ag_2S, black; AgI, yellow; AgBr, yellowish white; AgSCN, white. To the residue add 1 ml. of water and 1 ml. of 15-*N* NH_4OH. Stir the residue with a micro stirring rod and then force the solution through the filter medium into a test tube. If the filtrate is not clear, refilter. Wash the residue with about 1 ml. of water to which 1 or 2 drops of 15-*N* NH_4OH has been added.

5. **Filtrate:** SCN^- and/or Br^-. Test this filtrate for SCN^- and Br^- as follows:

a. **Test for SCN^-:** Place 4 or 5 drops of the filtrate in a test tube, add 1 drop of 1-*N* KBr, 1 drop of p-nitrophenol indicator, and then 4-*N* HNO_3 drop by drop, until the solution is colorless. Now add 2 or 3 drops of $Fe(NO_3)_3$ solution. A red color shows SCN^-.

b. **Test for Br^-:** To about 1 ml. of the filtrate add 4 or 5 drops of a 5% solution of NaClO. Place the tube in the hot water bath for 1 minute, or longer. Filter off the precipitate. Add to it 1 drop of p-nitrophenol indicator; then add 4-*N* CH_3COOH until the yellow color of the indicator is discharged. To the colorless solution add 1 drop of formalin, 1 drop of fluorescein, and from 2 to 5 drops of 5% NaClO. Shake tube; note color of solution by transmitted light. A pink color (eosin) shows bromine.

6. **Residue:** Ag_2S and/or AgI. If the residue is black, S^{--} from S^{--} and/or $S_2O_3^{--}$ is present.

Test for I^-: To the residue add 1 ml. of water, 2 drops of 4-*N* NH_4OH, and 2 drops of a 5% solution of thioacetamide. Stir the residue with a micro stirring rod. Place the tube in the hot water bath and allow the solution to run through the filter medium into a clean test tube. To the filtrate add 5 drops of a 3% solution of H_2O_2. Allow the tube to remain in the hot water bath for 1 minute or longer. Add 1 drop of bromthymol blue indicator. Cool the solution. Now add 4-*N* H_2SO_4 until the blue color is discharged. To this solution add 1 or 2 drops of a starch emulsion. If iodine is present, a blue color will be obtained.

* **Test for $S_2O_3^{--}$:** Use the following test for $S_2O_3^{--}$ in the presence of S^{--} and the other ions of Group I.

To 1 ml. of water add 2 or 3 drops of the unknown solution, and then add 1 drop of p-nitro-phenol indicator. If the solution is yellow, add 1-*N* HCl until it is colorless (acid). Now add 2 or 3 drops of 0.1-*M* $SbCl_3$. An orange-colored precipitate shows the presence of S^{--}. Filter off the precipitate and add 1 drop of $SbCl_3$ to the filtrate, to insure complete precipitation of S^{--}. If an orange-colored precipitate is obtained, filter it off and again test for complete precipitation of S^{--}. After precipitation of S^{--} is complete, place the filtrate in the hot water bath for 2 or 3 minutes, or longer. If $S_2O_3^{--}$ is present, a reddish-orange precipitate will be formed.

** **Test for ClO^-:** If ClO^- is present, S^{--}, $S_2O_3^{--}$, I^-, Br^-, SCN^-, and CN^- will not be found in the solution because they are oxidized. Only the ClO^- and Cl^- will be found together in Group I.

To test for ClO^-, add 1 drop of the unknown solution to 1 ml. of water. Now add 1 drop of the benzidine reagent. If ClO^- is present in small concentration, the solution will become blue. If ClO^- is present in about 1% concentration, the solution will be red and a red precipitate may form.

Procedure	Equations	Purpose—Discussion
1. Adjust the solution to pH 5. Add $NaNO_2$, $AgNO_3$, and HNO_3.	$S^{=} + 2Ag^+ \rightleftharpoons \underset{\text{black}}{\underline{Ag_2S}}$ $S_2O_3^{=} + 2Ag^+ \rightleftharpoons \underset{\text{white}}{\underline{Ag_2S_2O_3}}$ $Ag_2S_2O_3 + 2H_2O \rightleftharpoons \underset{\text{black}}{\underline{Ag_2S}} + H_3O^+ + HSO_4^-$ $I^- + Ag^+ \rightleftharpoons \underset{\text{yellow}}{\underline{AgI}}$ $Br^- + Ag^+ \rightleftharpoons \underset{\text{cream}}{\underline{AgBr}}$ $SCN^- + Ag^+ \rightleftharpoons \underset{\text{white}}{\underline{AgSCN}}$ $CN^- + Ag^+ \rightleftharpoons \underset{\text{white}}{\underline{AgCN}}$ $Cl^- + Ag^+ \rightleftharpoons \underset{\text{white}}{\underline{AgCl}}$ $ClO^- + Ag^+ \rightleftharpoons AgClO$ $3AgClO \rightarrow \underset{\text{white}}{\underline{2AgCl}} + Ag^+ + ClO_3^-$ $H_2PO_2^- + 4NO_2^- + 3H_3O^+ \rightarrow 4NO + HPO_4^{=} + 5H_2O$ Ag_3PO_4, yellow; Ag_2CrO_4, red; Ag_2CO_3, yellow; $Ag_2C_2O_4$, white; and Ag_2SO_3, white, are formed in neutral solutions but dissolve in dilute HNO_3. $H_2PO_2^-$ precipitates Ag°; therefore it is oxidized to PO_4^{3-} by NO_2^-.	The pH of pure water at 20° is 7.0. p-nitro-phenol indicator is yellow if the pH of a solution is 7.0 or more alkaline, and colorless if the pH is 5.0 or more acid. The precipitation is carried out in a low acid concentration (pH 5.0), and the acid concentration is then raised so as to dissolve Ag_3PO_4, etc. If the solution is acid at the beginning, $S^{=}$, $S_2O_3^{=}$, CN^-, and ClO^- are not likely to be present. The acids of these ions are volatile or unstable in acid solution. After the ions are precipitated as silver salts, the concentration of the anions is so low that the interaction with a low concentration of H_3O^+ is slight. The solution should be filtered immediately after the acid is added and the solution is warmed. A yellow precipitate which rapidly turns orange, then brown, and finally black, indicates $S_2O_3^{=}$.
2. Add ammoniacal silver nitrate solution (Miller's reagent).	$AgCN + 2NH_3 \rightleftharpoons Ag(NH_3)_2^+ + CN^-$ $AgCl + 2NH_3 \rightleftharpoons Ag(NH_3)_2^+ + Cl^-$	The NH_3 concentration in Miller's reagent is sufficient to reduce the Ag^+ concentration by the formation of the complex $Ag(NH_3)_2^+$ to a value low enough to bring about the solution of AgCN and AgCl, but not the other silver salts of this group.

CHEMICAL REACTIONS IN THE ANALYSIS OF GROUP I
(Continued)

Procedure	Equations	Purpose—Discussion
3a. Add KBr, benzidine, $CuSO_4$, and CH_3COOH.	$Ag(NH_3)_2^+ + Br^- \rightleftharpoons AgBr + 2NH_3$ $2HCN + 2Cu^{++} + 2H_2O + 2e \rightleftharpoons Cu_2(CN)_2 + 2H_3O^+$ Benzidine + 2e → blue solution $NH_3 + CH_3COOH \rightleftharpoons CH_3COONH_4$	The Ag^+ is precipitated as AgBr so that the CN^- will remain in solution when the solution is acidified. Oxidation of the benzidine to a blue compound takes place in the presence of Cu^{++} and free HCN.
3b. Add CH_3COONH_4, $Hg(NO_3)_2$, and CH_3COOH.	$2CN^- + Hg^{++} \rightleftharpoons Hg(CN)_2$ $NH_3 + CH_3COOH \rightleftharpoons CH_3COONH_4$ $Cl^- + Ag^+ \rightleftharpoons \underline{AgCl}$	$Hg(CN)_2$ is a very slightly ionized compound. The CN^- is tied up with Hg^{++} so that AgCN is not precipitated when the solution is made acid, but AgCl is.
4. Residue: Add 7.5-*N* NH_4OH.	$\underline{AgBr} + 2NH_3 \rightleftharpoons Ag(NH_3)_2^+ + Br^-$ $\underline{AgSCN} + 2NH_3 \rightleftharpoons Ag(NH_3)_2^+ + SCN^-$	Ammonia dissolves these precipitates because the concentration of NH_3 is high enough to form with Ag^+ the complex $Ag(NH_3)_2^+$ and release the Br^- and SCN^- to a large extent; but Ag_2S and AgI are not dissolved by 7.5-*N* ammonia solution to any appreciable extent.
5a. Add KBr, indicator, HNO_3, and $Fe(NO_3)_3$.	$Ag(NH_3)_2^+ + 2HNO_3 \rightleftharpoons Ag^+ + 2NH_4^+ + 2NO_3^-$ $Ag^+ + SCN^- \rightleftharpoons \underline{AgSCN}$ $\underline{AgSCN} + Br^- \rightleftharpoons \underline{AgBr} + SCN^-$ $3SCN^- + Fe^{3+} \rightleftharpoons Fe(SCN)_3$	AgBr is less soluble than AgSCN; therefore Br^- is added to precipitate the Ag^+ as AgBr instead of AgSCN when the solution is acidified. In acid solution with the ferric ion, SCN^- forms a blood-red compound, $Fe(SCN)_3$.

Procedure	Equations	Purpose—Discussion
5b. Add $NaClO$. Heat. Make acid. Add formalin, fluorescein, and $NaClO$.	$ClO^- + 4Ag^+ + 4OH^- \rightleftharpoons \underset{\text{white}}{4Ag^\circ} + ClO_3^- + 2H_2O$ $3ClO^- + 2SCN^- + 6OH^- \rightleftharpoons 2S^= + 2CO_3^= + N_2\uparrow + 3H_2O + 3Cl^-$ $2Ag^+ + S^= \rightleftharpoons \underset{\text{black}}{Ag_2S\downarrow}$ $3ClO^- + 2NH_3 \rightarrow N_2\uparrow + 3Cl^- + 3H_2O$ $HClO + H_3O^+ + 2Br^- \rightleftharpoons Br_2 + Cl^- + 2H_2O$ Br_2 + fluorescein (yellow) $\rightleftharpoons$ eosin (red) $HCHO + 2HClO + H_2O \rightarrow CO_2\uparrow + 2Cl^- + 2H_3O^+$	The Ag^+ precipitates as Ag° in the presence of Br^-, and as Ag_2S in the presence of SCN^-. The formaldehyde reduces the excess ClO^- and makes the test more reliable and sensitive. The eosin color can be seen to advantage by transmitted light, that is, by holding the tube toward the light and looking through the sides of the tube. If Br_2 is not present, the solution will be a fluorescent green, not pink.
6. Add NH_4OH and thioacetamide. Heat. Add H_2O_2 to filtrate. Heat. Add indicator, then H_2SO_4 until acid. Cool. Add starch.	$CH_3CSNH_2 + 3OH^- \rightleftharpoons CH_3COO^- + NH_3 + H_2O + S^=$ $\underline{2AgI} + S^= \rightleftharpoons \underline{Ag_2S}\downarrow + 2I^-$ $CH_3CSNH_2 + 4H_2O_2 + 2OH^- \rightarrow CH_3COO^- + SO_4^= + NH_4^+ + 4H_2O$ $2I^- + H_2O_2 + 2H_3O^+ \rightleftharpoons I_2 + 4H_2O$	Ag_2S is less soluble than AgI; therefore the AgI is converted into Ag_2S and NH_4I. The NH_4I is very soluble and goes into the filtrate. The H_2O_2 converts the $S^=$ into $SO_4^=$ and liberates I_2 in an acid solution. The I_2 gives a blue color with starch.
* **Test for $S_2O_3^=$:** Acidify. Add $SbCl_3$. Heat the filtrate in a water bath.	$3S^= + 2Sb^{3+} \rightarrow \underset{\text{orange}}{Sb_2S_3\downarrow}$ $3S_2O_3^= + 2Sb^{3+} + 9H_2O \rightarrow \underline{Sb_2S_3}\downarrow + 3SO_4^= + 6H_3O^+$	The $S^=$ is precipitated at once as Sb_2S_3 in a cold acid solution. The precipitation of Sb_2S_3 from $S_2O_3^=$ is slow, but it is increased markedly by an increase in temperature. The $S^=$ must be removed completely before heating the filtrate. (NOTE: If only a small amount of a yellow precipitate is obtained on heating, the presence of a little $S_2O_3^=$ is indicated; it should be reported only as a trace.)
** **Test for ClO^-:** Add benzidine reagent.		ClO^- is a powerful oxidizing ion and converts benzidine into "benzidine blue" or into red oxidation products when the concentration of ClO^- is high.

CHAPTER 19

PRELIMINARY EXPERIMENTS AND PROPERTIES OF GROUP II ANIONS

F^-, $C_2O_4^{--}$, SO_3^{--}, PO_4^{3-}, AsO_4^{3-}, AsO_3^{3-}, CO_3^{--}, SO_4^{--}, CrO_4^{--}, ($S_2O_3^{--}$), (BO_2^-)

THE FLUORIDE ION, F^-

Gram-ion weight: 19.00.
Test solution: 0.1-*M* sodium fluoride, NaF.
Concentration: 1.9 mg. of F^-/ml.

Hydrofluoric Acid, HF

Hydrogen fluoride is a gas at ordinary room temperatures (m.p., −83° C.; b.p., 19.4° C.). At low temperatures the gas tends to form polymers, such as H_3F_3 to H_6F_6, and at higher temperatures it exists largely as HF. HF is a colorless corrosive gas with a penetrating odor. Both the gas and the aqueous solution are poisonous; they attack the tissues and produce painful and slow-healing burns. The concentrated commercial acid contains about 47% HF. Under a pressure of 760 mm., an aqueous solution of hydrogen fluoride forms a constant-boiling mixture containing 35.4% HF and boils at 120° C. The specific gravity of the constant-boiling acid is 1.15. The solvent action of HF on silica and glass requires that the acid be kept in wax, hard-rubber, or polyethylene bottles.

In aqueous solution F^- has a strong tendency to unite with the HF molecule to form the complex ion HF_2^-. Because of this tendency, hydrofluoric acid acts like a dibasic acid, forming a series of hydrogen salts such as $NaHF_2$, etc. For this reason the formula of hydrofluoric acid is sometimes written H_2F_2. In dilute solution it acts like a monoprotic acid with an ionization constant of 7.2×10^{-4}; it is therefore a weak acid. The acid is employed extensively in analytical chemistry because of its characteristic action on silicates to form the gas SiF_4.

Salts

The least soluble salt of the fluorides is CaF_2 (1.7×10^{-5} g./ml.). Freshly precipitated CaF_2 is quite soluble in dilute HCl, but when dried it can be dissolved only with difficulty. The fluorides of Sr^{++} and Mg^{++} are rather insoluble in water, and those of Cu^{++}, Fe^{3+}, Ba^{++}, Zn^{++}, and Li^+ are sparingly soluble. F^- forms a number of reasonably stable complex ions, such as $FeF_6{}^{3-}$, $AlF_6{}^{3-}$, $SiF_6{}^{--}$, and $ZrF_6{}^{--}$.

Reactions

1. *Precipitation and Dissolution of CaF_2. Formation of $LaF_3 \cdot 3H_2O$ Lake with Eosin.* To 1 ml. of water add 3 drops of the sodium fluoride test solution and 1 drop of 1-*N* $Ca(CH_3COO)_2$. Write the equation for the reaction. Filter off the precipitate and wash it with water. Add about 1 ml. of water and 2 drops of 4-*N* CH_3COOH to the precipitate on the filter medium. Force the acid solution through the precipitate into a test tube and reserve the filtrate. Now add 1 ml. of water and 1 drop of 6-*N* HCl to the filter tube. Force the acid solution through the precipitate into a test tube. Test both acid solutions as follows: To each solution add 1 drop of eosin, 1 drop of 5% lanthanum nitrate, and 3 drops of 6-*N* CH_3COONH_4. Describe the results, and give the relative solubility of CaF_2 in CH_3COOH and HCl solutions.

2. *Decolorization of a Zirconium-Alizarinsulfonate Lake.* To 1 ml. of water add 1 drop of sodium alizarinsulfonate indicator and 1 drop of 0.1% zirconium nitrate. The reddish-violet color of the solution is due to a lake formed by adsorption of the dye on zirconium hydroxide resulting from the hydrolysis of the zirconium nitrate. Add 1 drop of the sodium fluoride test solution to the reddish solution. Note the color of the solution. (With sodium alizarinsulfonate, Zr^{4+} forms a reddish-violet solution, and with the fluoride ion a colorless complex anion, $ZrF_6{}^{--}$. The yellow color of the solution is due to the liberated alizarin. $C_2O_4{}^{--}$ also changes the reddish-violet color to yellow.)

THE OXALATE ION, $C_2O_4{}^{--}$

Gram-ion weight: 88.02.
Test solution: 0.1-*M* potassium oxalate, $K_2C_2O_4$.
Concentration: 8.8 mg. of $C_2O_4{}^{--}$/ml.

Oxalic Acid, $H_2C_2O_4$

The anhydrous acid is a white powder, but when crystallized from water it is a crystalline solid with the formula $H_2C_2O_4 \cdot 2H_2O$. The hydrated acid melts in its water of crystallization at 98° C., and if maintained at this temperature the anhydrous acid is produced. The acid sublimes at 150° C., and if heated above this point it decomposes into CO, CO_2, and H_2O. The hydrated acid is readily soluble in water and in alcohol, and somewhat soluble in ether. $H_2C_2O_4$ is a diprotic acid of intermediate strength. The primary ionization constant is 5.9×10^{-2}; the secondary, 6.4×10^{-5}.

Salts

The oxalates of Cr^{3+}, Be^{++}, Fe^{3+}, Mg^{++}, and the alkalies are soluble in water. Most of the other oxalates are rather insoluble in water but are soluble in nitric or hydrochloric acid. Normal and hydrogen salts are formed by oxalic acid, such as $K_2C_2O_4$, KHC_2O_4, and $KH_3(C_2O_4)_2 \cdot 2H_2O$. $C_2O_4^{--}$ has a marked tendency to form complex ions, particularly with trivalent cations such as Fe^{3+}, Al^{3+}, and Cr^{3+}. The formation of the complex ion $Fe(C_2O_4)_3^{3-}$ accounts for the effectiveness of oxalic acid in removing rust and ink stains that contain iron, and rust from the radiator systems of cars. $C_2O_4^{--}$ is oxidized by MnO_4^- to CO_2 slowly in the cold but rapidly at elevated temperatures.

Reactions

1. *Precipitation and Dissolution of CaC_2O_4. Reaction with MnO_4^-.* To 1 ml. of water add 1 drop of the potassium oxalate test solution and 1 drop of 1-*N* $Ca(CH_3COO)_2$. Write the equation for the reaction. (NOTE: CaC_2O_4 is the least soluble of all the oxalates.) Filter off the precipitate and wash it with a little water. Add about 1 ml. of water and 2 drops of 4-*N* CH_3COOH to the precipitate on the filter medium. Force the acid solution through the precipitate, and set the test tube containing the filtrate in the hot water bath. Now add 1 ml. of water to the filter tube containing the CaC_2O_4 precipitate and then 1 drop of 6-*N* HCl. Force this solution through the precipitates and set the test tube containing the filtrate in the hot water bath. Add 1 drop of 0.01-*M* $KMnO_4$ to each acid solution. Note and record the reaction in each tube. Write the equation for the reaction in the tube that contains the HCl solution. Proceed to the next experiment.

2. *Quantity of $C_2O_4^{--}$ from Reaction with MnO_4^-.* To the tube containing the HCl solution add 0.01-*M* $KMnO_4$ until a purple color is maintained in it. From the number of drops required, calculate the number of milligrams of CaC_2O_4 that were dissolved by the HCl. Now add 1 or 2 drops of 3% H_2O_2. Explain the results and write the equation for the reaction.

THE SULFITE ION, SO_3^{--}

Gram-ion weight: 80.06.
Test solution: 0.1-*M* sodium sulfite, Na_2SO_3.
Concentration: 8 mg. of SO_3^{--}/ml.

Sulfurous Acid, H_2SO_3

Sulfurous acid exists only in solution. Small amounts of the acid are formed when sulfur dioxide, SO_2, is dissolved in water. Fifty volumes of SO_2 dissolves in 1 volume of water at 20° C. under a pressure of 760 mm., but the SO_2 does not combine with the water to any great extent to form H_2SO_3. The commercial sulfurous acid contains from 5 to 6% of SO_2. The acid is diprotic. The primary ionization constant is 1.2×10^{-2}; the secondary, 1×10^{-7}. SO_2 is readily expelled from its water solution by boiling. On standing open to the air, some of it escapes and some is oxidized to SO_3 which combines with the water to form H_2SO_4. SO_2 has a strong pungent odor and is poisonous when breathed; it is absorbed into the blood stream where it is oxidized to H_2SO_4.

Salts

$CaSO_3$ is the least soluble of the sulfite salts (4.3×10^{-5} g./ml. at 18° C.). Sulfites of the other metals, except the alkalies, are quite insoluble in water. The acid sulfites are all fairly soluble. All the sulfites are oxidized to sulfates when exposed to the air or when dissolved in water that contains oxygen. Consequently, unless freshly prepared from pure salts, sulfite solutions usually contain sulfates. SO_3^{--} is a strong reducing agent and is oxidized to SO_4^{--} in acid solution by most oxidizing agents such as H_2O_2, the halogens, etc.

Reactions

1. *Oxidation to SO_4^{--} by H_2O_2.* To 1 ml. of water add 1 drop of 1-*N* $Ba(CH_3COO)_2$ solution and 1 drop of 6-*N* HCl. Add 1 drop of the sodium sulfite test solution. (NOTE: If a precipitate forms, it is $BaSO_4$ and shows the presence of SO_4^{--}, as $BaSO_3$ is soluble in acid solution.) Filter off the precipitate if much forms, and add 1 drop of 3% H_2O_2 to the filtrate. (If only a small amount forms, add 1 drop of 3% H_2O_2 without filtering off the precipitate.) Write the equation for the reaction.

2. *Decolorization of Malachite Green.* To 1 ml. of water add 1 drop of the sodium sulfite test solution. Then add 1 drop of malachite green and note the decolorization of the dye.

3. *Precipitation and Dissolution of $CaSO_3$. Reaction with MnO_4^-.* To 1 ml. of water add 3 or 4 drops of the sodium sulfite test solution and 1 drop of 1-*N* $Ca(CH_3COO)_2$. Shake the tube and note whether a precipitate has formed. Now place the tube in the hot water bath for 2 minutes. Why does the hot solution favor precipitation? Filter off the precipitate. Add 1 ml. of water and 1 drop of 4-*N* CH_3COOH to the filter tube that contains the precipitate of $CaSO_3$. Force the solution through the precipitate into a test tube. Now add 1 ml. of water and 1 drop of 6-*N* HCl to the filter tube and force this solution through the precipitate into a test tube. Add 1 drop of 6-*N* HCl to the test tube containing the acetic acid solution. Now add 0.01-*M* $KMnO_4$ alternately to each test tube, drop by drop, and count the number of drops added to each one; con-

tinue until there is a violet color in each tube. What is the approximate ratio of the solubility of $CaSO_3$ in dilute acetic acid and in hydrochloric acid? (NOTE: You should find that $CaSO_3$ is relatively insoluble in very dilute acetic acid and soluble in HCl.)

THE PHOSPHATE ION, PO_4^{3-}

Gram-ion weight: 95.02.
Test solution: 0.1-*M* disodium hydrogen phosphate, Na_2HPO_4.
Concentration: 9.5 mg. of PO_4^{3-}/ml.

Phosphoric Acid, H_3PO_4

What is commonly called phosphoric acid and has the formula H_3PO_4 is known specifically as orthophosphoric acid. Two other phosphoric acids are known: metaphosphoric acid, HPO_3, and pyrophosphoric acid, $H_4P_2O_7$. The formation of these acids is shown by the following equations:

$$P_2O_5 + H_2O \rightleftharpoons 2HPO_3$$

$$HPO_3 + H_2O \rightleftharpoons H_3PO_4$$

$$2H_3PO_4 \underset{\text{heat}}{\rightleftharpoons} H_4P_2O_7 + H_2O$$

HPO_3 and $H_4P_2O_7$ change slowly in aqueous solution to H_3PO_4. Commercial orthophosphoric acid, U.S.P. grade, has a specific gravity of approximately 1.71 and contains from 85 to 88% H_3PO_4. If the commercial phosphoric acid is heated in a vacuum, crystals form; they melt at 42.3° C. At a temperature of 180° C., H_3PO_4 begins to lose water, and at 250° C. $H_4P_2O_7$ is obtained. If the $H_4P_2O_7$ is heated strongly, HPO_3, a transparent solid, is produced. Orthophosphoric acid is a triprotic acid with the following ionization constants: $K_1 = 7.5 \times 10^{-3}$; $K_2 = 6.2 \times 10^{-8}$; $K_3 = 1 \times 10^{-12}$.

Salts

The alkali phosphates and the dihydrogen phosphates of the alkaline earths are soluble in water. All the other metal phosphates are only slightly soluble in water but are dissolved by acids. A solution of Na_3PO_4 is strongly alkaline; a solution of Na_2HPO_4 is weakly alkaline; and a solution of NaH_2PO_4 is weakly acidic. Phosphoric acid is used as an acidulant in beverages, and the soluble phosphates are important commercially as fertilizers and water-softening agents.

Reactions

1. *Precipitation and Dissolution of $Ca_3(PO_4)_2$. Formation of NH_4MgPO_4.* To 1 ml. of water add 1 drop of the disodium hydrogen phosphate test solution and 1 drop of the bromthymol blue indicator.

Account for the blue color of the solution. Now add 1 drop of 1-*N* $Ca(CH_3COO)_2$. Write the equation for the reaction, and account for the discharge of the blue color of the indicator. Filter off and wash the precipitate. Add 1 ml. of water and 1 drop of 4-*N* CH_3COOH to the filter tube. Force the acid solution through the filter medium and collect the filtrate in a clean test tube. Add 2 drops of magnesium mixture and 1 drop of 15-*N* NH_4OH to the filtrate. Place the tube in the hot water bath. What is the formula of the precipitate? Filter off the precipitate for use in the next experiment.

2. *Formation of Phosphomolybdic Acid. Oxidation of Benzidine to Benzidine Blue.* To the precipitate from Experiment 1 add 1 ml. of water to which 1 drop of 6-*N* HCl has been added. Force the solution through the precipitate into a test tube. Add 1 drop of 1-*N* $(NH_4)_2MoO_4$ to the solution containing the magnesium phosphate. Place the tube in the hot water bath for half a minute and then add 1 drop of benzidine reagent and 1 drop of 15-*N* NH_4OH. The blue color of the solution and/or precipitate is due to the oxidation of the benzidine by a complex phosphomolybdic acid radical.

3. *Formation of Ammonium Phosphomolybdate.* To a test tube add 5 drops of 1-*N* $(NH_4)_2MoO_4$ and 10 drops of 4-*N* HNO_3. Now add 1 drop of the phosphate test solution. Place the tube in the hot water bath for 1 or 2 minutes. The yellow compound has the formula $(NH_4)_3PO_4 \cdot 12MoO_3$. (NOTE: The AsO_4^{3-} forms an analogous precipitate.)

THE ARSENATE ION, AsO_4^{3-}

Gram-ion weight: 138.91.
Test solution: 0.1-*M* disodium hydrogen arsenate, Na_2HAsO_4.
Concentration: 13.9 mg. of AsO_4^{3-}/ml.

Arsenic Acid, H_3AsO_4

What is commonly called arsenic acid and has the formula H_3AsO_4 is known specifically as orthoarsenic acid. Two other arsenic acids are known: meta-arsenic acid, $HAsO_3$, and pyroarsenic acid, $H_4As_2O_7$. Both the latter acids form the orthoacid with water. Commercial orthoarsenic acid contains from 75 to 80% H_3AsO_4. If the commercial arsenic acid is heated in a vacuum, crystals form; they melt at 35.5° C., and their formula is $2H_3AsO_4 \cdot H_2O$. At 100° C. the $2H_3AsO_4 \cdot H_2O$ loses its molecule of water and becomes H_3AsO_4, a crystalline powder. If the temperature is raised to 160° C., $H_4As_2O_7$ is obtained, and at about 206° C., $HAsO_3$. On further ignition $HAsO_3$ is changed to As_2O_5, and on strong ignition the As_2O_5 is changed to As_2O_3. Orthoarsenic acid is a triprotic acid with the following ionization constants: $K_1 = 4.8 \times 10^{-3}$; $K_2 = 1 \times 10^{-7}$; $K_3 = 1 \times 10^{-13}$.

Salts

All the alkali arsenates are soluble in water, but all the other metal arsenates are only slightly soluble in water but are easily dissolved by acids. All the soluble compounds of arsenic are poisonous and therefore are largely used as insecticides.

Reactions

1. *Precipitation and Dissolution of* $Ca_3(AsO_4)_2$. *Formation of* NH_4MgAsO_4. To 1 ml. of water add 1 drop of 4-*N* NH_4OH, 3 drops of the arsenate test solution, and 1 drop of 1-*N* $Ca(CH_3COO)_2$. Write the equation for the reaction. Place the tube in the hot water bath for 1 or 2 minutes. Filter off the precipitate and wash it with a little water. Add 1 ml. of water and 1 drop of 4-*N* CH_3COOH to the precipitate in the filter tube. Force the acid solution through the filter medium. To the filtrate add 1 drop of the magnesium mixture reagent and 4 drops of 15-*N* NH_4OH. Place the test tube in the hot water bath and shake the tube vigorously three or four times a minute for 2 to 3 minutes to induce the formation and crystallization of the precipitate, NH_4MgAsO_4. Filter off the precipitate and wash it with a little water; then dissolve it in about 10 drops of 6-*N* HCl. To this acid solution add 1 drop of 1-*N* KI and 10 drops of CCl_4. Shake the tube and note the pink color that is imparted to the CCl_4. What is this color due to? Write the equation for the reaction.

2. *Oxidation of* I^- *by* AsO_4^{3-}. To 10 drops of 6-*N* HCl add 1 drop of 1-*N* KI and 1 drop of starch emulsion. Shake the tube and note the color of the solution. Now add 1 drop of the arsenate test solution and shake the tube occasionally. Note the formation of a blue color in the solution. Write the equation for the formation of the free iodine.

3. *Precipitation of* Ag_3AsO_4. To 1 ml. of water add 1 drop of the arsenate test solution and 1 drop of 1-*N* $AgNO_3$. Write the equation for the reaction. (NOTE: AsO_4^{3-} gives a reddish precipitate, Ag_3AsO_4, with Ag^+, and AsO_3^{3-} gives a yellow precipitate, Ag_3AsO_3.)

THE ARSENITE ION, AsO_3^{3-}

Gram-ion weight: 122.91.
Test solution: 0.1-*M* sodium arsenite, $NaAsO_2$ or Na_2HAsO_3.
Concentration: 12.3 mg. of AsO_3^{3-}/ml.

Arsenous Acid, H_3AsO_3

Arsenous oxide, As_2O_3, commonly known as "white arsenic" or "arsenic," is only slightly soluble in water. About 1.5 g. dissolves in 100 g. of water at

15° C. The solution has a weakly acid reaction, and probably contains H_3AsO_3 or $HAsO_2$. The primary ionization constant is 6×10^{-10}. Hence it is a weaker acid than hydrosulfuric. When the solution is concentrated by evaporation and allowed to cool, only the oxide, As_2O_3, crystallizes.

Salts

All the alkali arsenites are soluble in water, but most other metal arsenites are only slightly soluble in water; they are soluble in acids. The alkali arsenites are derived from the metaarsenous acid, $HAsO_2$. In alkaline solution, AsO_3^{3-} may be assumed to be present.

Reactions

1. *Precipitation and Dissolution of $Ca_3(AsO_3)_2$. Oxidation to AsO_4^{3-} by H_2O_2.* To 1 ml. of water add 1 drop of 15-*N* NH_4OH, 3 drops of the arsenite test solution, and 1 drop of 1-*N* $Ca(CH_3COO)_2$. Place the tube in the hot water bath for a few minutes. Write the equation for the reaction. Filter off the precipitate and wash it with a little water. Add 1 ml. of water and 1 drop of 4-*N* CH_3COOH to the filter tube. Force the acid solution through the filter medium. To the filtrate add 4 drops of 15-*N* NH_4OH and 1 drop of the magnesium mixture reagent. Shake the tube and note whether a precipitate has formed. (Do not place the tube in the hot water bath.) If a precipitate has formed, filter it off. Add 1 drop of 3% H_2O_2 to the clear filtrate. Shake the tube and note whether a precipitate has formed. Account for the formation of the precipitate after the addition of the H_2O_2, and write the equation for the reaction. (NOTE: NH_4MgAsO_3 is more soluble than NH_4MgAsO_4.)

2. *Reaction with Ag^+.* To 1 ml. of water add 1 drop of the arsenite test solution and 1 drop of 1-*N* $AgNO_3$. Note the color of the precipitate and write the equation for the reaction.

THE CARBONATE ION, CO_3^{--}

Gram-ion weight, 60.01.
Test solution: 0.1-*M* sodium carbonate, Na_2CO_3.
Concentration: 6 mg. of CO_3^{--}/ml.

Carbonic Acid, H_2CO_3

Carbonic acid exists only in aqueous solutions. When the gas, CO_2, is passed into water, a small amount of the acid is formed. About 1.45 g. of CO_2 dissolves in 1 liter of water at 25° C. Carbonic acid is a very weak diprotic acid. The primary ionization constant is 4.3×10^{-7}; the secondary, 4.7×10^{-11}. Its weakness as an acid is attested by its presence in carbonated beverages. The CO_2 is expelled from aqueous solutions by boiling.

Salts

The carbonates of the alkali metals and ammonium are the only carbonates that are readily soluble in water. The carbonates of the other metals are soluble to only a small extent in water, but are readily dissolved by acids stronger than carbonic acid. The normal alkali carbonates are strongly alkaline, and even the bicarbonates are weakly alkaline. Anhydrous Na_2CO_3 is known commercially as soda ash; the hydrated salt, $Na_2CO_3 \cdot 10H_2O$, is known as washing soda; and $NaHCO_3$ is known as baking soda.

Reactions

Precipitation and Dissolution of $CaCO_3$. Test for Evolved CO_2. To 1 ml. of water add 2 drops of the sodium carbonate test solution and 1 drop of 1-*N* $Ca(CH_3COO)_2$. Place the tube in the hot water bath for 1 or 2 minutes. Filter off the precipitate and wash it with a little water. To test for CO_2, use a gas-generating tube (Fig. 16.1). To this tube add about 0.5 ml. of water. Insert the filter tube containing the $CaCO_3$ precipitate in the rubber tubing on the short arm of the gas-generating tube. Pack another filter tube with a plug of cotton and insert this tube in the rubber tubing on the other arm of the generating tube. To this filter tube add about 0.5 ml. of water and 1 drop of clear $Ba(OH)_2$ solution. Now add about 0.5 ml. of water and 1 drop of 4-*N* CH_3COOH to the filter tube containing the $CaCO_3$ precipitate; and then, by means of the rubber bulb, force the acid solution through this tube. Continue to depress the rubber bulb so that bubbles rise through the $Ba(OH)_2$ solution for about 1 minute. The precipitate that forms in the $Ba(OH)_2$ solution is $BaCO_3$. Write equations for all the reactions involved in the precipitation, dissolution, and reprecipitation of the carbonate ion, CO_3^{--}.

THE SULFATE ION, SO_4^{--}

Gram-ion weight: 96.06.
Test solution: 0.1-*M* sodium sulfate, Na_2SO_4.
Concentration: 9.6 mg. of SO_4^{--}/ml.

Sulfuric Acid, H_2SO_4

The commercial concentrated sulfuric acid has a specific gravity of 1.84 at 15.5°/15.5° C. and contains about 96% H_2SO_4. This acid boils at 270° C. and partially decomposes into SO_3 and H_2O. The boiling point continues to rise, and at 317° C. a constant-boiling mixture is produced which contains 98.3% H_2SO_4. Sulfuric acid is a diprotic acid with the following ionization constants: K_1 (large), and $K_2 = 1.2 \times 10^{-2}$. Acids with boiling points lower than 317° C. can be displaced by H_2SO_4, but those with higher boiling points will displace H_2SO_4 when heated with it. HCl, HBr, and HNO_3 have boiling points under 317° C., and the boiling points of HBO_2 and HPO_3 are above 317° C. Concentrated sulfuric acid has a great affinity for water and is used as a drying agent. The hot concentrated acid is a powerful oxidizing agent and, as such, dissolves copper, mercury, tin, silver, etc., with the formation of sulfates and the liberation of SO_2.

Salts

Sulfuric acid forms two series of salts, the normal and the acid salts, such as Na_2SO_4 and $NaHSO_4$. The barium salt is the least soluble of the sulfates (2.3×10^{-6} g./ml.). The sulfates of lead, mercury (I), calcium, and strontium are not very soluble in water, but most of the other normal sulfates are.

Reactions

1. *Test for Precipitation of $CaSO_4$. Precipitation of $BaSO_4$.* To 1 ml. of water add 1 drop of the sodium sulfate test solution and 1 drop of 1-*N* $Ca(CH_3COO)_2$. Is a precipitate formed? (The solubility of $CaSO_4 \cdot 2H_2O$ is 6.7×10^{-3} g./ml.) To the solution add 1 drop of 1-*N* $Ba(CH_3COO)_2$. Write the equation for the reaction. Now add 1 or 2 drops of 6-*N* HCl to the solution containing the $BaSO_4$ precipitate. Does the precipitate dissolve?

2. *Transposition of $BaSO_4$ to $BaCO_3$.* To 1 ml. of water add 1 drop of the sodium sulfate test solution and 1 drop of $Ba(CH_3COO)_2$. Set the test tube in the hot water bath for 1 minute or longer. Filter off the precipitate and wash it with 1 or 2 ml. of water. Place the filter tube in a test tube and set the assembly in the hot water bath. Add 10 drops of 2-*N* Na_2CO_3 to the filter tube and allow several drops of the Na_2CO_3 solution to pass through the $BaSO_4$ precipitate, but do not force it through. Add 1 drop of p-nitro-phenol indicator to the filtrate, and then add 6-*N* HCl until the yellow color of the indicator disappears. To this colorless solution add 1 drop of $Ba(CH_3COO)_2$. The precipitate is $BaSO_4$. How do you account for the solubility of $BaSO_4$ in a rather concentrated solution of Na_2CO_3?

THE CHROMATE ION, CrO_4^{--}

Gram-ion weight: 116.01.
Test solution: 0.1-*M* potassium chromate, K_2CrO_4.
Concentration: 11.6 mg. of CrO_4^{--}/ml.

Chromic Acid, H_2CrO_4

Free chromic acid has not been isolated, or does it exist to any great extent in solution. Small amounts of it probably exist, along with other chromic acids, in water to which CrO_3 has been added. The reactions of chromium trioxide (CrO_3) and water may be formulated by the following equations:

$$CrO_3 + 2H_2O \rightleftharpoons H_3O^+ + HCrO_4^-$$
$$HCrO_4^- + H_2O \rightleftharpoons H_3O^+ + CrO_4^{--}$$

Salts

The chromates of the alkali metals, ammonium, strontium, calcium, and magnesium are soluble in water. Most other chromates are insoluble in water, but are dissolved in strong acids. Most dichromates are soluble in water. Chromates and dichromates are colored compounds, usually yellow, red, or orange. The important commercial salts are the chromates and dichromates of sodium or potassium. Solutions of the chromates act as buffers, as shown by the following equations:

$$2CrO_4^{--} + 2H_3O^+ \rightleftharpoons Cr_2O_7^{--} + 3H_2O$$
$$Cr_2O_7^{--} + 2OH^- \rightleftharpoons 2CrO_4^{--} + H_2O$$

The chromate ion in alkaline solution is not a strong oxidizing agent, but the dichromate ion in acid solution is a very strong oxidizing agent.

Reactions

1. *Precipitation and Dissolution of $BaCrO_4$. Reaction with H_2O_2.* To 1 ml. of water add 1 drop of the potassium chromate test solution, 1 drop of 15-*N* NH_4OH, and 1 drop of 1-*N* $Ca(CH_3COO)_2$. No precipitate of $CaCrO_4 \cdot 2H_2O$ is formed because its solubility is too high (0.222 g./ml. at 0° C.). To the chromate solution add 1 drop of 1-*N* $Ba(CH_3COO)_2$. Write the equation for the reaction. (The solubility of $BaCrO_4$ is 3.6×10^{-6} g./ml. at 20° C.) Filter off the precipitate and wash it with water. To the filter tube add 1 ml. of water and 1 drop of 6-*N* HCl. Force the acid solution through the filter medium. Add 1 drop of 3% H_2O_2 to the filtrate. The blue color is due to the presence of peroxychromic acid. This acid is unstable, and its exact formula is not known, but it is usually assumed to be H_3CrO_8.

2. *Oxidation of I^- by $Cr_2O_7^{--}$.* To each of two test tubes add 1 ml. of water, 1 drop of the potassium chromate test solution, 1 drop of 4-*N* H_2SO_4, and 1 drop of starch emulsion. Shake the tubes and note the color of the solutions. Now add 1 drop of 1-*N* KI to one of the tubes. Shake the tubes again and note the blue color in the one with the KI solution. To what substance is the blue color on the starch due? Write the equation for the reaction between $Cr_2O_7^{--}$ and I^-.

CHAPTER 20

ANALYSIS OF GROUP II ANIONS

SCHEMATIC OUTLINE OF THE PROCEDURE

7. F^-, $C_2O_4^{=}$, $SO_3^{=}$, PO_4^{3-}, AsO_4^{3-}, AsO_3^{3-}, $CO_3^{=}$, $SO_4^{=}$, $CrO_4^{=}$, ($S_2O_3^{=}$), (BO_2^-) + anions of Groups I and III
   Add NH_4OH + $Ca(CH_3COO)_2$.

8. **Precipitate:** CaF_2, CaC_2O_4, $CaSO_3$, $CaCO_3$, $Ca_3(PO_4)_2$, $Ca_3(AsO_4)_2$, $Ca_3(AsO_3)_2$.
   Add CH_3COOH.

Filtrate: $SO_4^{=}$, $CrO_4^{=}$, ($Cr_2O_7^{=}$), ($S_2O_3^{=}$), (BO_2^-)
See Procedure 14.

Gas: CO_2
Pass through $Ba(OH)_2$.
White ppt.: $BaCO_3$
Carbonate

9. **Residue:** CaF_2, CaC_2O_4, $CaSO_3$
   Add HCl. Divide solution.

10. **Test for $SO_3^{=}$:** Add KI + I_2. Decolorizes. Shows $SO_3^{=}$.
Sulfite

11. **Test for $C_2O_4^{=}$:** Boil to remove SO_2. Add $KMnO_4$. Decolorizes. Shows $C_2O_4^{=}$.
Oxalate

12. **Test for F^-:** Add $KMnO_4$, then H_2O_2. Add eosin, $La(NO_3)_2$, and CH_3COONH_4.
Pink lake: $LaF_3 \cdot 3H_2O$ + eosin
Fluoride

13. **Solution:** PO_4^{3-}, AsO_4^{3-}, AsO_3^{3-}
    Add CH_3COONH_4, magnesium mixture reagent, and NH_4OH.

13a. **Precipitate:** NH_4MgPO_4, NH_4MgAsO_4
     Add HCl. Divide solution.

13b. **Test for PO_4^{3-}:** Add $(NH_4)_2MoO_4$, then benzidine and NH_4OH.
Blue ppt. or solution
Phosphate

13c. **Test for AsO_4^{3-}:** Add thioacetamide. Heat.
Yellow ppt.: As_2S_3
Arsenate

13d. **Filtrate:** AsO_3^-
     Add H_2O_2.
White ppt.: NH_4MgAsO_4
Arsenite

14. **Filtrate from 7:** $SO_4^{=}$, $CrO_4^{=}$, ($Cr_2O_7^{=}$), $(S_2O_3)^{=}$, (BO_2^-)
    Add $Ba(CH_3COO)_2$. Wash precipitate with CH_3COOH.

15. **Precipitate:** $BaSO_4$, $BaCrO_4$
    Add HCl.

SCHEMATIC OUTLINE OF THE PROCEDURE (*Continued*)

16. **Residue:** $BaSO_4$ Add Na_2CO_3. Add HCl and $Ba(CH_3COO)_2$. *White ppt.:* $BaSO_4$ *Sulfate*	17. **Filtrate:** $Cr_2O_7^{=}$ Add H_2O_2. *Blue color* *Chromate*

DISCUSSION OF THE PROCEDURE

The anions of this group are those whose silver salts are soluble in dilute nitric acid solution, but whose calcium and barium salts are sparingly soluble in dilute ammoniacal solution. A portion of the unknown solution (*not* the filtrate from Group I) is first treated with $Ca(CH_3COO)_2$ to precipitate the slightly soluble calcium salts: CaF_2, CaC_2O_4, $CaSO_3$, $Ca_3(PO_4)_2$, $Ca_3(AsO_4)_2$, $Ca_3(AsO_3)_2$, and $CaCO_3$. The filtrate is then treated with $Ba(CH_3COO)_2$ to precipitate $BaSO_4$ and $BaCrO_4$. By this procedure the reducing ions, $C_2O_4^{--}$, SO_3^{--}, and AsO_3^{3-}, are separated from the oxidizing ion, CrO_4^{--}, before acids are added to the system. $Cr_2O_7^{--}$ readily oxidizes $C_2O_4^{--}$, SO_3^{--}, and AsO_3^{3-} in acid solution.

If more than 1 mg./ml. of $S_2O_3^{--}$ is present in a solution to which $Ba(CH_3COO)_2$ is added, a precipitate of BaS_2O_3 will form. However, by filtering the solution while it is hot and washing the precipitate with water acidified with acetic acid, BaS_2O_3 and $Ba(BO_2)_2$, if present, will be dissolved. A test for $S_2O_3^{--}$ is made in the analysis of Groups I and IV, and a test for BO_2^- is made in the analysis of Group III.

DIRECTIONS FOR LABORATORY WORK

1. Obtain from the storeroom a solution that contains all the anions of Group II and analyze it in accordance with the Procedures for Group II.

2. (Optional.) Request a student to prepare an unknown solution from the test solutions. Analyze it in accordance with the Procedures for Group II. (Preparation of the unknown: To 1 ml. of water add 1 drop of the test solution for four different anions of Group II.)

3. From the storeroom obtain anion Unknown No. 2 and analyze it in accordance with the Procedures for Group II. Report the results of your analysis on an Unknown Report Blank.

PROCEDURES FOR THE ANALYSIS OF THE ANIONS OF GROUP II

F^-, $C_2O_4^{--}$, SO_3^{--}, PO_4^{3-}, AsO_4^{3-}, AsO_3^{3-}, CO_3^{--}, SO_4^{--}, CrO_4^{--}, ($S_2O_3^{--}$), (BO_2^-)

---

7. To 1 ml. of water add 5 drops of the general unknown solution, or 5 drops of Group II, known or unknown. Add 1 drop of 15-*N* NH_4OH and 3 drops of 1-*N* $Ca(CH_3COO)_2$. Place the tube in the hot water bath for 2 or 3 minutes. Shake the tube occasionally. Filter off the precipitate through a double-packed cotton filter medium. (NOTE: To prepare a double-packed filter medium, put a small plug of cotton in a filter tube and pack the cotton tightly. On top of this first plug, place some lightly packed cotton.) Wash the precipitate with a small amount of water (0.5 to 1 ml.). Reserve the filtrate for Procedure 14.

---

8. **Precipitate:** CaF_2, CaC_2O_4, $CaSO_3$, $CaCO_3$, $Ca_3(PO_4)_2$, $Ca_3(AsO_4)_2$, $Ca_3(AsO_3)_2$. Place 1 ml. of water in a gas-generating tube. Insert the filter tube containing the precipitate in the rubber tubing on the short arm of the generating tube. Pack a filter tube with a small plug of cotton and insert this tube into the rubber on the other arm of the generating tube and add 1 ml. of water and 1 or 2 drops of satd. $Ba(OH)_2$ to this filter tube. Now add 1 ml. of water and 2 drops of 4-*N* CH_3COOH to the tube containing the precipitate. Stir the precipitate with a micro stirring rod and force the acid solution slowly through the precipitate with a rubber bulb. Continue depressing the bulb until bubbles rise through the $Ba(OH)_2$ solution for 1 or 2 minutes. A white precipitate in the $Ba(OH)_2$ solution proves the presence of CO_3^{--}. Wash the undissolved precipitate with about 0.5 ml. of water to which has been added 1 drop of 4-*N* CH_3COOH. Reserve the solution in the gas-generating tube for Procedure 13.

---

9. **Undissolved precipitate:** CaF_2, CaC_2O_4, $CaSO_3$. To this undissolved precipitate add 1 ml. of water and 1 drop of 6-*N* HCl. Stir the precipitate with a micro stirring rod and force the solution into a test tube. Wash the filter medium with 1 ml. of water acidified with 1 drop of 1-*N* HCl. Add the wash water to the filtrate and divide it into two parts for Tests 10 and 11.

---

10. **Test for SO_3^{--}:** Add 1 drop of the potassium iodide-iodine reagent. If SO_3^{--} is present, the reagent will lose its color.

---

11. **Test for $C_2O_4^{--}$ and/or F^-:** Transfer the solution to an evaporation test tube and boil until all the SO_2 is expelled—about half a minute. Pour the solution into a small test tube, dilute to 1 ml., add 2 drops of 0.01-*M* $KMnO_4$, and place the tube in the hot water bath. The purple color of the MnO_4^- will be discharged if $C_2O_4^{--}$ is present. Keep this solution for the test for F^-, which follows.

---

12. **Test for F^-:** If $C_2O_4^{--}$ is present, continue to add 0.01-*M* $KMnO_4$ until the solution remains brown or purple. Make the brown or purple color disappear by adding 1 drop of 3% H_2O_2. To this colorless solution add 1 drop of eosin, 1 drop of 5% lanthanum nitrate, and 3 drops of 6-*N* CH_3COONH_4. Place the tube in the hot water bath. If F^- is present, the pink precipitate will coagulate and settle to the bottom of the tube.

---

13. **Solution from 8:** PO_4^{3-}, AsO_4^{3-}, AsO_3^{3-}. To the solution add 2 drops of 6-*N* CH_3COONH_4, 3 drops of the magnesium mixture reagent, and 4 drops of 15-*N* NH_4OH. Place the tube in the hot water bath for 1 or 2 minutes. Then filter off the precipitate and use it for 13a. Test filtrate by 13d.

13a. **Precipitate from 13:** NH_4MgPO_4 and/or NH_4MgAsO_4. Add 1 ml. of water and 2 drops of 6-*N* HCl to the precipitate. Stir it with a micro stirring rod and force the solution through the filter medium into a test tube. Wash the filter medium with 1 ml. of water and add this wash water to the filtrate. Divide into two parts for 13b and 13c.

13b. **Test for PO_4^{3-}:** Add 1 drop of 1-*N* $(NH_4)_2MoO_4$ and place the tube in the hot water bath for about half a minute. Remove the tube and add 4 or 5 drops of the benzidine reagent and 1 drop of 15-*N* NH_4OH. If PO_4^{3-} is present, a blue color will appear. (NOTE: A blue precipitate usually forms.)

13c. **Test for AsO_4^{3-}:** Place the tube in the hot water bath and add 1 drop of a 5% solution of thioacetamide. Allow the tube to remain in the hot water for several minutes. If AsO_4^{3-} is present, a yellow precipitate, As_2S_3, will form.

13d. **Filtrate from 13:** AsO_3^{3-}. Place the tube in the hot water bath and add 2 drops of 3% H_2O_2. If AsO_3^{3-} is present, a white precipitate of NH_4MgAsO_4 will form.

14. **Filtrate from 7:** SO_4^{--}, CrO_4^{--}, ($Cr_2O_7^{--}$), ($S_2O_3^{--}$), (BO_2^{-}). Add 2 drops of 1-*N* $Ba(CH_3COO)_2$. Set the tube in the hot water bath for about 1 minute. Filter off the precipitate and wash it with 2 ml. of water to which 1 drop of 4-*N* CH_3COOH has been added. (The CH_3COOH dissolves BaS_2O_3 and $BaBO_2$ if they are in the precipitate.) Discard the filtrate and the wash water.

15. **Precipitate:** $BaSO_4$ and/or $BaCrO_4$. To the precipitate add 0.5 ml. of water and 1 drop of 6-*N* HCl. Stir it with a micro stirring rod and force the solution into a test tube. Wash the filter medium with 0.5 ml. of water to which has been added 1 drop of 1-*N* HCl. Add the wash water to the filtrate.

16. **Undissolved precipitate:** $BaSO_4$. Add 10 drops of 2-*N* Na_2CO_3 to the tube that contains the undissolved precipitate. Place the filter tube in a test tube and set the assembly in the hot water bath. Allow the Na_2CO_3 solution to become hot and to pass through the $BaSO_4$ precipitate, but do not force it with the bulb. Add 1 drop of p-nitrophenol indicator to the filtrate, then add 6-*N* HCl until the solution is colorless. Then add 1 drop of 1-*N* $Ba(CH_3COO)_2$. A white precipitate will form if SO_4^{--} is present.

17. **Filtrate from 15:** $Cr_2O_7^{--}$. Add 1 drop of 3% H_2O_2. A blue color shows the original presence of CrO_4^{--}. (The blue color disappears in a short time.)

Procedure	Equations	Purpose—Discussion
7. Add NH_4OH and $Ca(CH_3COO)_2$.	$Ca^{++} + 2F^- \rightleftharpoons \underline{CaF_2}$ (white) $Ca^{++} + C_2O_4^= \rightleftharpoons \underline{CaC_2O_4}$ (white) $Ca^{++} + SO_3^= \rightleftharpoons \underline{CaSO_3}$ (white) $3Ca^{++} + 2PO_4^{3-} \rightleftharpoons \underline{Ca_3(PO_4)_2}$ (white) $3Ca^{++} + 2AsO_4^{3-} \rightleftharpoons \underline{Ca_3(AsO_4)_2}$ (white) $3Ca^{++} + 2AsO_3^{3-} \rightleftharpoons \underline{Ca_3(AsO_3)_2}$ (white) $Ca^{++} + CO_3^= \rightleftharpoons \underline{CaCO_3}$ (white)	The calcium salts of the ions of Group I are rather soluble. Hence, part of the original solution may be used for analyzing Group II without any preliminary treatment. CaF_2 is often difficult to filter because of its slimy and colloidal nature. Heating and shaking facilitate filtration and decrease the solubility of CaF_2 in acetic acid. An asbestos filter medium may be used if necessary.
8. Add CH_3COOH to the precipitate	$CaCO_3 + 2CH_3COOH \rightarrow Ca^{++} + CO_2\uparrow + H_2O + 2CH_3COO^-$ $Ba(OH)_2 + CO_2 \rightleftharpoons \underline{BaCO_3} + H_2O$ $Ca_3(PO_4)_2 + 4CH_3COOH \rightleftharpoons 3Ca^{++} + 4CH_3COO^- + 2H_2PO_4^-$ $Ca_3(AsO_4)_2 + 4CH_3COOH \rightleftharpoons 3Ca^{++} + 4CH_3COO^- + 2H_2AsO_4^-$. $Ca_3(AsO_3)_2 + 4CH_3COOH \rightleftharpoons 3Ca^{++} + 4CH_3COO^- + 2H_2AsO_3^-$	Cold dilute acetic acid reacts rapidly with carbonates, and readily dissolves $Ca_3(PO_4)_2$, $Ca_3(AsO_4)_2$, and $Ca_3(AsO_3)_2$, but reacts slowly with $CaSO_3$. The small amount of $CaSO_3$ which may dissolve does not interfere with the tests for PO_4^{3-}, AsO_4^{3-}, or AsO_3^{3-}. CaF_2 and CaC_2O_4 are not appreciably soluble in dilute acetic acid.
9. Add dilute HCl.	$CaC_2O_4 + H_3O^+ \rightleftharpoons Ca^{++} + HC_2O_4^- + H_2O$ $CaF_2 + H_3O^+ \rightleftharpoons Ca^{++} + HF_2^- + H_2O$ $CaSO_3 + H_3O^+ \rightleftharpoons Ca^{++} + HSO_3^- + H_2O$ $HSO_3^- + H_3O^+ \rightleftharpoons H_2SO_3 + H_2O$ $H_2SO_3 \rightleftharpoons H_2O + SO_2\uparrow$	CaC_2O_4 and $CaSO_3$ dissolve readily in dilute hydrochloric acid, and freshly precipitated CaF_2 is rather soluble in dilute mineral acids. However, if CaF_2 is dried, it is dissolved with difficulty in HCl or HNO_3. The test for $SO_3^=$ should be made immediately, for otherwise it may be lost as SO_2, or be oxidized to $SO_4^=$.

CHEMICAL REACTIONS IN THE ANALYSIS OF GROUP II
(Continued)

Procedure	Equations	Purpose—Discussion
10. Add potassium iodide-iodine reagent.	$SO_3^{=} + I_2 + 3H_2O \rightleftharpoons SO_4^{=} + 2I^- + 2H_3O^+$	$SO_3^{=}$ is readily oxidized to $SO_4^{=}$ by I_2. The decolorizing of the iodine (or starch-iodine) solution by SO_2 is a sensitive reaction.
11. Boil to expel SO_2. Add $KMnO_4$, and heat.	$H_2SO_3 \rightleftharpoons H_2O + SO_2\uparrow$ $5C_2O_4^{=} + 2MnO_4^- + 16H_3O^+ \rightarrow 2Mn^{++} + 10CO_2\uparrow + 24H_2O$	The SO_2 must be removed because it readily reduces MnO_4^- to Mn^{++} in cold solution, whereas the reaction of MnO_4^- on $C_2O_4^{=}$ is slow in cold solution but rapid in hot solution.
12. Add $KMnO_4$ and H_2O_2.	See preceding equation. $2MnO_4^- + 5H_2O_2 + 6H_3O^+ \rightarrow 2Mn^{++} + 5O_2\uparrow + 14H_2O$ $MnO_2 + H_2O_2 + 2H_3O^+ \rightarrow Mn^{++} + O_2\uparrow + 4H_2O$ $3F^- + La^{3+} + 3H_2O \rightleftharpoons \underline{LaF_3 \cdot 3H_2O}$	$C_2O_4^{=}$ must be destroyed completely by an excess of MnO_4^- or it will interfere with the test for F^-. Likewise, the MnO_4^- or MnO_2 must be destroyed or the color of MnO_4^- will interfere with the F^- test. The eosin forms a pink "lake" with $LaF_3 \cdot 3H_2O$.
13. Add CH_3COONH_4, magnesium mixture, and NH_4OH. 13a. Dissolve the precipitate in acid.	$Mg^{++} + NH_4^+ + PO_4^{3-} \rightleftharpoons \underline{NH_4MgPO_4}$ $Mg^{++} + NH_4^+ + AsO_4^{3-} \rightleftharpoons \underline{NH_4MgAsO_4}$ $\underline{NH_4MgPO_4} + H_3O^+ \rightleftharpoons Mg^{++} + NH_4^+ + HPO_4^{=} + H_2O$ $\underline{NH_4MgAsO_4} + H_3O^+ \rightleftharpoons Mg^{++} + NH_4^+ + HAsO_4^{=} + H_2O$	PO_4^{3-} and/or AsO_4^{3-} are precipitated in an ammoniacal solution as magnesium-ammonium salts of these ions. NH_4MgAsO_3 has a greater solubility than NH_4MgAsO_4, and is not precipitated by the magnesium mixture reagent.

Procedure	Equations	Purpose—Discussion
13b. Add $(NH_4)_2MoO_4$, and warm. Add benzidine and NH_4OH.	$PO_4^{3-} + 12MoO_4^{=} + 27H_3O^+ \rightleftharpoons H_7P(Mo_2O_7)_6 + 37H_2O$ $H_7P(Mo_2O_7)_6$ + benzidine → blue solution or precipitate	$H_7P(Mo_2O_7)_6$ oxidizes benzidine rapidly to benzidine blue and is itself reduced to molybdenum blue. The $H_7P(Mo_2O_7)_6$, phosphomolybdic acid, forms a rather insoluble ammonium salt. AsO_4^{3-} does not interfere with the test for the PO_4^{3-} under the conditions outlined. The test is very sensitive.
13c. Add thioacetamide.	$5CH_3CSNH_2 + 2AsO_4^{3-} + 6H_3O^+ \rightleftharpoons 5CH_3COO^- + 5NH_4^+ + \underset{\text{yellow}}{\underline{As_2S_3}}\downarrow + 4H_2O + \underline{2S^\circ}\downarrow$	CH_3CSNH_2 is hydrolyzed in acidic or basic solutions into acetic acid, ammonia, and hydrogen sulfide. The hydrogen sulfide reduces pentavalent arsenic to the trivalent state, and precipitates the arsenic as As_2S_3. Thioacetamide avoids the generation and use of gaseous hydrogen sulfide.
14. Add $Ba(CH_3COO)_2$.	$Ba^{++} + SO_4^{=} \rightleftharpoons \underset{\text{white}}{\underline{BaSO_4}}$ $Ba^{++} + CrO_4^{=} \rightleftharpoons \underset{\text{light yellow}}{\underline{BaCrO_4}}$	$CaSO_4$ and $CaCrO_4$ are reasonably soluble, and usually are not precipitated in Procedure 7. This affords a means of separating $SO_4^{=}$ and $CrO_4^{=}$ from the other ions of Group II. Large amounts of $S_2O_3^{=}$ and/or BO_2^- must be present to give a precipitate with Ba^{++}, but the barium salts of these ions are readily soluble in dilute acetic acid solution.
15. Add dilute HCl.	$\underline{2BaCrO_4} + 2H_3O^+ \rightleftharpoons 2Ba^{++} + Cr_2O_7^{=} + 3H_2O$	$BaCrO_4$ is readily dissolved by dilute HCl, but $BaSO_4$ is practically insoluble in dilute acids. Reducing ions such as $S_2O_3^{=}$ must be absent or Cr^{6+} will be reduced to Cr^{3+}.

Procedure	Equations	Purpose—Discussion
16. Add Na_2CO_3, acidify the filtrate, and add $Ba(CH_3COO)_2$.	$\underline{BaSO_4} + CO_3^{=} \rightleftharpoons \underset{\text{white}}{\underline{BaCO_3}} + SO_4^{=}$ $CO_3^{=} + 2H_3O^{+} \rightarrow 3H_2O + CO_2\uparrow$ $SO_4^{=} + Ba^{++} \rightleftharpoons \underset{\text{white}}{\underline{BaSO_4}}\downarrow$	By reason of its effective concentration in 2-*N* Na_2CO_3 solution, and the low concentration of $SO_4^{=}$ in $BaSO_4$, $CO_3^{=}$ is able to bring about a small metathesis (exchange) of $SO_4^{=}$ in $BaSO_4$ for $CO_3^{=}$. $SO_4^{=}$ is carried into the filtrate and reprecipitated as $BaSO_4$ in acid solution. Although $BaSO_4$ is at least a hundred times less soluble than $BaCO_3$, a small exchange of $SO_4^{=}$ in $BaSO_4$ for $CO_3^{=}$ is effected by reason of the relatively high ratio of the concentration of $CO_3^{=}$ to $SO_4^{=}$.
17. Add H_2O_2.	$Cr_2O_7^{=} + 7H_2O_2 + 2H_3O^{+} \rightleftharpoons 7H_2O + 2H_3CrO_8$-blue $2H_3CrO_8 + 6H_3O^{+} \rightarrow 2Cr^{3+} + 5O_2 + 12H_2O$	The "blue" color is due to the presence of peroxychromic acid which is often represented by the formula, H_3CrO_8, though the exact formula is not definitely known. The blue color fades in a short time in warm acid solution, but may be retained for a longer period of time if the H_3CrO_8 is dissolved in ether.

CHAPTER 21

PRELIMINARY EXPERIMENTS AND PROPERTIES OF GROUP III ANIONS

ClO_3^-, $H_2PO_2^-$, NO_2^-, NO_3^-, BO_2^-, CH_3COO^-

THE CHLORATE ION, ClO_3^-

Gram-ion weight: 83.457.
Test solution: 0.1-*M* potassium chlorate, $KClO_3$.
Concentration: 8.3 mg. of ClO_3^-/ml.

Chloric Acid, $HClO_3$

Free chloric acid may be prepared by treating a solution of $Ba(ClO_3)_2$ with an equivalent amount of H_2SO_4, filtering off the very insoluble $BaSO_4$, and concentrating the filtrate under 40° C. The solution may be concentrated to about 40% of $HClO_3$. When the temperature is raised above 40° C., the solution decomposes into perchloric acid, $HClO_4$, chlorine dioxide, ClO_2, and water. The chlorine dioxide is unstable and decomposes into Cl_2 and O_2. The 40% acid has the formula $HClO_3 \cdot 7H_2O$, and a specific gravity 14.2°/4° C. of 1.282. $HClO_3$ is a strong acid and a powerful oxidizing agent. The concentrated acid may explode violently if heated with organic matter.

Salts

Potassium chlorate is the least soluble of the stable salts (3.3×10^{-2} g./ml. at 0° C.). This salt is a strong oxidizing agent and is used in the manufacture of matches, explosives, and fireworks. It melts at a temperature of 368° C., and decomposes into KCl and O_2 at 400° C.

Reactions

1. *Reduction of ClO_3^- by HNO_2.* To each of two test tubes add 1 ml. of water, 1 drop of 4-*N* HNO_3, 1 drop of the potassium chlorate test solution, and 1 drop of Ag_2SO_4 solution. Shake the tubes and note whether turbidity appears. (NOTE: Turbidity would be due to the presence of Cl^-.) Place the tubes in the hot water bath, and to one of them add 1 drop of 0.1-*N* sodium nitr*ite*, $NaNO_2$. The white precipitate is AgCl. Write the equations for the reactions.

2. *Oxidation of I^- to I_2.* To 10 drops of 4-*N* H_2SO_4 add 1 drop of 0.1-*N* KI and 1 drop of starch emulsion. Add 1 drop of the potassium chlorate test solution to the cold solution. Shake the tube and note the slow formation of the starch-iodine blue. Write the equation for the reaction.

3. *Oxidation of Fe^{++} to Fe^{3+}.* To each of two test tubes add a small amount of solid iron (II) ammonium sulfate, 1 ml. of water, 3 or 4 drops of ammonium thiocyanate, and 1 drop of 4-*N* H_2SO_4. Place the tubes in the hot water bath, and to one of them add 1 drop of the potassium chlorate test solution. A red color will appear in this tube. Write the equations for the reactions. (NOTE: The solution in the other tube should remain colorless unless Fe^{3+} is present.) The slow oxidation of Fe^{++} by the oxygen of the air will cause the solution in this tube to turn red slowly.

THE HYPOPHOSPHITE ION, $H_2PO_2^-$

Gram-ion weight: 65.036.
Test solution: 0.1-*M* sodium hypophosphite, NaH_2PO_2.
Concentration: 6.5 mg. of $H_2PO_2^-$/ml.

Hypophosphorous Acid, $H \cdot H_2PO_2$

Hypophosphorous acid may be prepared by boiling yellow phosphorus with water that contains barium hydroxide, and then precipitating the barium as barium sulfate.

$$8P + 3Ba(OH)_2 + 6H_2O \rightarrow 2PH_3 + 3Ba(H_2PO_2)_2$$

$$Ba^{++} + 2H_2PO_2^- + 2H_3O^+ + SO_4^{--} \rightleftharpoons \underline{BaSO_4} + 2H_3PO_2 + 2H_2O$$

Acid prepared in this way has a syrupy consistency, but crystals may be obtained by evaporating under reduced pressure and freezing. The crystals melt at 26.5° C. When the acid is heated, it decomposes into phosphine and phosphoric acid.

$$2H_3PO_2 \rightarrow PH_3 + H_3PO_4$$

The acid and its salts are powerful reducing agents. The acid is monoprotic and fairly strong.

Salts

Most hypophosphites are soluble in water.

Reactions

1. *Reduction of Hg^{++} to Hg_2^{++}.* To 1 ml. of water add 1 drop of mercuric nitrate test solution, 1 drop of 1-*N* HCl, and 1 or 2 drops of

the sodium hypophosphite test solution. Shake the tube and note the slow formation of a white precipitate, Hg_2Cl_2. Write the equation for the reaction.

2. *Reduction of IO_3^- to I_2.* To 1 ml. of water add 1 drop of 0.1-*M* potassium iodate solution, KIO_3, 1 drop of starch emulsion, 1 drop of 4-*N* H_2SO_4, and 5 drops of the sodium hypophosphite test solution. Place the tube in the hot water bath and for 1 or 2 minutes note the color changes in the solution. The reactions may be formulated by the following equations:

$$1\begin{cases} 2IO_3^- + 5H_2PO_2^- + 2H_3O^+ \rightarrow 5H_2PO_3^- + I_2 + 3H_2O \\ I_2 + \text{starch} \rightarrow \text{blue solution} \end{cases}$$

$$2 \qquad H_2PO_3^- + I_2 + 3H_2O \rightarrow \underset{\text{colorless solution}}{H_2PO_4^- + 2I^- + 2H_3O^+}$$

(NOTE: The blue color may be restored to the solution by adding IO_3^-.)

3. *Reaction with $(NH_4)_2MoO_4$ in the Presence of H_2SO_3.* To 1 ml. of a saturated solution of SO_2 (sulfurous acid) add 1 drop of 1-*N* $(NH_4)_2$-MoO_4. Place the tube in the hot water bath and to it add 1 drop of the sodium hypophosphite test solution. Note the appearance of a deep blue color in the solution.

THE NITRITE ION, NO_2^-

Gram-ion weight: 46.01.
Test solution: 0.1-*M* sodium nitrite, $NaNO_2$.
Concentration: 4.6 mg. of NO_2^-/ml.

Nitrous Acid, HNO_2

A dilute solution of nitrous acid may be prepared as follows:

$$Ba(NO_2)_2 + 2H_3O^+ + SO_4^{--} \rightleftharpoons \underline{BaSO_4} + 2HNO_2 + 2H_2O$$

However, the solution must be kept at 0° C. because nitrous acid is very unstable and decomposes at room temperature into HNO_3, NO, and water. Nitrous acid is a weak acid with an ionization constant of 4.5×10^{-4}.

Salts

Silver nitrite is the least soluble of the salts of nitrous acid (2.4×10^{-3} g./ml.). Most of the other nitrites are readily soluble in water. Sodium nitrite is the most important commercial salt. In acid solution, the nitrite ion has fairly strong oxidizing properties. It oxidizes I^-, H_2S, HSO_3^-, $S_2O_3^{--}$, Fe^{++}, and NH_4^+, but acts as a reducing agent with MnO_4^-, HClO, and ClO_3^-. A number of complex ions, such as $Co(NO_2)_6^{3-}$, are formed with NO_2^- and certain cations.

Reactions

1. *Oxidation of Fe^{++} to Fe^{3+}.* To 1 ml. of water add a very small amount of solid iron (II) ammonium sulfate, a few drops of 0.1-*N* ammonium thiocyanate, and 1 drop of 1-*N* HCl. Note the color of the solution. Now add 1 drop of the sodium nitrite test solution. The red color is due to $Fe(SCN)_3$. Write the equation for the reaction.

2. *Oxidation of I^- to I_2.* To 1 ml. of water add 1 drop of 0.1-*N* KI, 1 drop of 4-*N* CH_3COOH, and 1 drop of starch emulsion. Then add 1 drop of the $NaNO_2$ test solution. Write the equation for the reaction.

3. *Reduction of $KMnO_4$.* To 1 ml. of water add 1 drop of 0.01-*M* $KMnO_4$ solution and 1 drop of 1-*N* HCl. Then add 1 or 2 drops of the sodium nitrite test solution. Write the equation for the reaction.

4. *Formation of a Diazo Dye.* To 1 ml. of water add 1 drop of α-naphthylamine reagent and 1 drop of sulfanilic acid reagent. Then add 1 drop of the sodium nitrite test solution. (NOTE: The red color is a specific test for the nitrite ion.)

5. *Reaction with NH_2SO_3H to Form Nitrogen.* To 1 ml. of water add 1 drop of 4-*N* H_2SO_4 and 2 drops of the sodium nitrite test solution. Then add a 10% solution of sulfamic acid, NH_2SO_3H, drop by drop. The evolved gas is N_2. Write the equation for the reaction. (NOTE: NO_2^- is easily destroyed by sulfamic acid.)

THE NITRATE ION, NO_3^-

Gram-ion weight: 62.01.
Test solution: 0.1-*M* sodium nitrate, $NaNO_3$.
Concentration: 6.2 mg. of NO_3^-/ml.

Nitric Acid, HNO_3

Commercial concentrated nitric acid has a specific gravity 20°/4° of 1.42 and contains 68% HNO_3 and 32% water. The pure acid is a colorless liquid with a specific gravity of 1.54. It boils at 86° C. and freezes to a white solid at −42° C. An aqueous solution containing 68% HNO_3 has a constant-boiling point of 122.5° C. Nitric acid decomposes slowly into NO_2, water, and O_2, the rate of decomposition depending on the temperature. Below 68° C., decomposition occurs to a small extent; at higher temperatures it is more rapid. Nitric acid is a strong acid and a powerful oxidizing agent. The NO_3^- may be reduced to NO_2^-, NO, or NH_3, as well as to the intermediate stages.

Salts

Most metal nitrates are soluble in water and form stable solutions.

Reactions

1. *Reduction of NO_3^- to NO_2^-.* To each of two test tubes add 1 ml. of water, 1 drop of 4-N CH_3COOH, 1 drop of α-naphthylamine, 1 drop of sulfanilic acid, and a small piece of magnesium metal. Then add 1 drop of the sodium nitrate test solution to one of the tubes. Allow the reactions to proceed for 1 or 2 minutes and note the color of the solution in the tubes. See page 331 for the reaction of α-naphthylamine and sulfanilic acid with NO_2^-. Write the equations for the reactions between NO_3^-, CH_3COOH, and Mg°. (NOTE: The solution in the tube without $NaNO_3$ will be colorless if NO_2^- is absent.)

2. *Oxidation of Fe^{++} to Fe^{3+}.* To 1 ml. of water add a small amount of iron (II) ammonium sulfate and 1 drop of 4-N HNO_3. Place the tube in the hot water bath for 1 or 2 minutes and then add 3 or 4 drops of 0.1-N ammonium thiocyanate. The red color is due to $Fe(SCN)_3$. Write the equation for the reaction.

3. *Reaction with Nitron Reagent.* To 1 ml. of water add 1 drop of the sodium nitrate test solution and 1 drop of a 10% solution of the nitron reagent. Shake the tube vigorously and note the formation of a voluminous white precipitate.

THE BORATE ION, BO_2^-

Gram-ion weight: 42.82.
Test solution: 0.1-M sodium tetraborate, $Na_2B_4O_7$.
Concentration: 4.3 mg. of BO_2^-/ml.

Boric Acid, H_3BO_3

The boric acid commonly bought and sold commercially is known specifically as orthoboric acid. It is obtained in a flaky crystalline form or as a powder. It is odorless, has a faint bitter taste, and feels slippery. It dissolves in water to the extent of 0.0266 g./ml. at 0° C. and 0.402 g./ml. at 100° C. On being heated to 100° C., it loses 1 molecule of water and forms metaboric acid, HBO_2; when heated to 160° C., the HBO_2 is converted to pyro- or tetraboric acid, $H_2B_4O_7$. When heated to 185° C., $H_2B_4O_7$ loses 1 molecule of water, forming the anhydride, B_2O_3. Boric acid is monobasic, with an ionization constant of 5.8×10^{-10}. The pH of a 0.1-M solution is 5.12; that of 0.1-M acetic acid is 2.87.

Salts

The most important salt of boron is "borax," $Na_2B_4O_7 \cdot 10H_2O$. This salt is only slightly soluble in cold water, 0.03 g./ml. at 10° C. At 100° C. the solubility is 1.0 g./ml. The alkali borates are readily soluble in water; the other metal borates are sparingly so, but are soluble in acids and in ammonium salts. An aqueous solution of borates hydrolyzes in the following way:

$$B_4O_7^{--} + 3H_2O \rightleftharpoons 2H_3BO_3 + 2BO_2^- \rightleftharpoons 2H_2O + 2HBO_2 + 2BO_2^-$$
$$H_2O + BO_2^- \rightleftharpoons HBO_2 + OH^-$$

Hence in solutions of tetraborates there exist $B_4O_7^{--}$, H_3BO_3, $H_2BO_3^-$, HBO_2, BO_2^-, and OH^-.

Reactions

1. *Reaction with $AgNO_3$.* To 1 ml. of water add 3 drops of the sodium tetraborate test solution and 1 drop of 1-*N* $AgNO_3$ solution. The brown precipitate is Ag_2O. Write the equation for the reaction. (NOTE: $AgBO_2$ is white.)

2. *Formation of Methyl Borate. Flame Test for Borates.* To each of two test tubes add 1 ml. of methanol (methyl alcohol) and 5 drops of concd. H_2SO_4. Add 4 or 5 drops of the sodium tetraborate test solution to one of the tubes. In each tube insert the rubber end of a medicine dropper from which the closed end has been clipped. Place the tubes in the hot water bath and ignite the vapors which issue from them. Note the difference in the color of the flames. With methanol, H_3BO_3 forms $B(OCH_3)_3$.

3. *Tumeric Test for Borates.* To an evaporation test tube add 2 drops of the sodium tetraborate test solution and 2 drops of 1-*N* oxalic acid. Evaporate the solution to just moist (incipient) dryness. (Do not overheat; be careful.) Add several drops of tincture of turmeric to the moist residue, and again evaporate carefully to low-temperature dryness. The residue will be brownish-red in color.

THE ACETATE ION, CH_3COO^-

Gram-ion weight: 59.05.
Test solution: 0.1-*M* sodium acetate, CH_3COONa.
Concentration: 5.9 mg. of CH_3COO^-/ml.

Acetic Acid, CH_3COOH

Pure acetic acid has a specific gravity 20°/4° of 1.049, boils at 118.1° C., and forms colorless crystals at 16.7° C. Because it crystallizes and forms a solid that resembles ice, it is sometimes called "glacial acetic acid." It has a strong odor, similar to that of sulfur dioxide, and a very acrid taste. Vinegar contains from 4 to 5% acetic acid. The ionization constant is 1.8×10^{-5} at 25° C. It is a weak acid; a 0.1-*M* solution is 1.34% ionized. It reacts with alcohols to form esters with characteristic odors.

Salts

The most important commercial salts are sodium acetate and lead acetate. Most metal acetates are reasonably soluble in water. The least soluble salt is silver acetate (7.2×10^{-3} g./ml. at 0° C.). The acetate ion forms basic salts with some metals, such as $Pb(OH)CH_3COO$.

Reactions

1. *Formation of Basic Iron Acetate.* To 1 ml. of water add 1 drop of the sodium acetate test solution and 1 drop of 0.1-*M* $Fe(NO_3)_3$. Place the tube in the hot water bath for 1 minute or longer. The reddish color is due to the formation of a colloidal solution of "basic iron acetate" (p. 214).

2. *Decomposition of Acetates to Acetone. Iodoform Test.* One of the best ways of detecting the presence of acetates is by decomposing the acetate ion into acetone by means of heat, and then detecting the acetone through the formation of iodoform.

$$2CH_3COO^- \rightarrow CO_3^{--} + \underset{\text{acetone (b.p. 56.5° C.)}}{(CH_3)_2CO}$$

$$(CH_3)_2CO + 3I_2 + 4OH^- \rightarrow \underset{\text{iodoform}}{CHI_3} + CH_3COO^- + 3H_2O + 3I^-$$

Add a small amount of calcium carbonate (solid) to a rimless Pyrex test tube 18 mm. x 145 mm. Then add 5 or 6 drops of the sodium acetate test solution. To a condenser-collector tube (Fig. 21.1) add about 1 ml. of water and invert the tube over the test tube. Heat the test tube to dull redness and collect the vapors in the condenser tube. Remove the condenser-collector tube and invert it so that the liquid is in the closed end of the tube. To the liquid add 1 drop of 4-*N* NaOH and 1 drop of $KI\text{-}I_2$ solution. Shake the tube gently and note the odor and the formation of a white precipitate. (The precipitate is CHI_3 with the characteristic odor of iodoform.)

If a condenser-collector tube is not available, a substitute assembly (Fig. 21.2) may be devised. Clip the closed

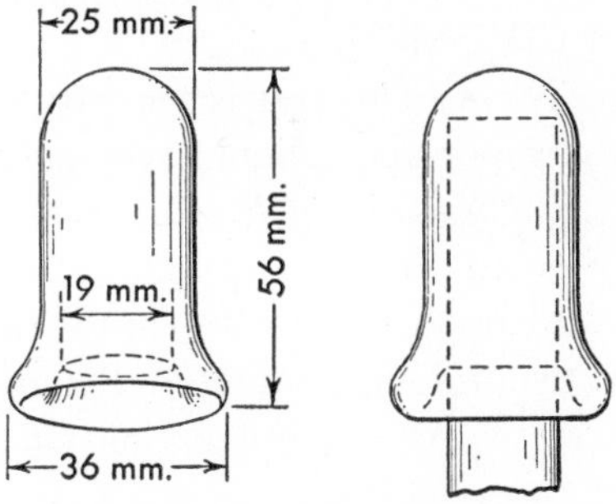

FIG. 21.1. The Condenser-Collector Tube. This tube is made from an evaporation test tube (Fig. 4.14) by flaring and turning the open end inward so as to form a cup with a hole about 19 mm. in diameter. If water is added to this tube and it is inverted over a test tube 18 x 145 mm., it will serve as a condenser and collector for the acetone vapors.

end off the rubber bulb of a medicine dropper. Wrap a small strip of wet cotton around the glass part of the dropper close to the rubber bulb. Press a small plug of wet cotton into a filter tube and invert the tube over the tapered end of the medicine dropper. (This is a small condenser assembly.) Add a small amount of solid $CaCO_3$ and a few drops of a solution containing the acetate ion to a 13 mm. x 100 mm. Pyrex test tube. Insert the condenser assembly into this tube and heat carefully

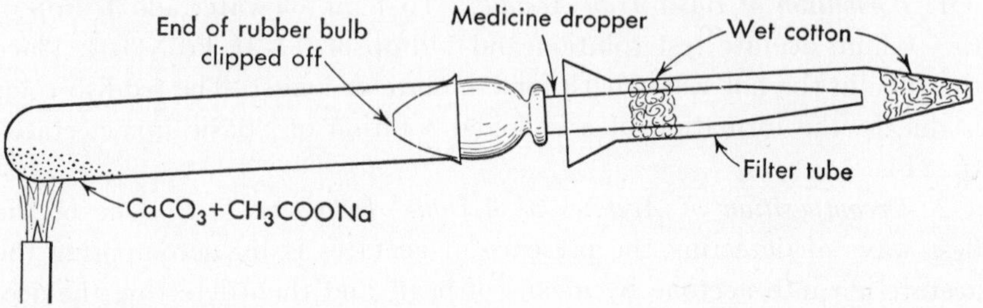

FIG. 21.2. Alternate Assembly for Testing for Acetates by the Formation of Acetone and then Iodoform.

to dull redness the bottom of the test tube containing the $CaCO_3$-CH_3COONa; collect the vapors in the condenser. Remove the condenser assembly and place the filter tube in a small test tube. Add about 1 ml. of water to the condenser through the clipped-off end of the rubber bulb, and then force the solution into the test tube. Add 1 drop of 4-N NaOH and 1 drop of KI-I_2 solution to the test tube. A white precipitate of CHI_3 will form.

(NOTE: This test is sensitive enough to detect the acetone in 1 ml. of the vapor above liquid acetone at room temperature.)

3. *Formation of Ethyl Acetate.* To 1 ml. of ethyl alcohol add 10 drops of concd. H_2SO_4 and 5 drops of sodium acetate test solution. Put some cotton loosely in the top of the test tube and set the tube in the hot water bath for 1 or 2 minutes. Remove the plug and note the odor of ethyl acetate. Write the equation for the reaction.

CHAPTER 22

ANALYSIS OF GROUP III ANIONS

SCHEMATIC OUTLINE OF THE PROCEDURE

18. ClO_3^-, $H_2PO_2^-$, NO_2^-, NO_3^-, BO_2^-, CH_3COO^-, (SO_4^{--}), (F^-) + ions of Groups I and II
Adjust pH. Add Ag_2SO_4. Discard precipitate.

19. **Filtrate:** ClO_3^-, $H_2PO_2^-$, NO_2^-, NO_3^-, BO_2^-, CH_3COO^-, (SO_4^{--}), (F^-)
Test separate portions by Procedures 20–25.

20. **Test for ClO_3^-:**	21. **Test for $H_2PO_2^-$:**	22. **Test for NO_2^-:**	23. **Test for NO_3^-:**	24. **Test for BO_2^-:**	25. **Test for CH_3COO^-:**
Add Ag_2SO_4 + H_2SO_4 + HCHO. *White ppt.:* AgCl	Add H_2SO_4 + $KMnO_4$ + $(NH_4)_2MoO_4$. Heat. Then add H_2SO_4. *Blue color*	Add sulfanilic acid + α-naphthylamine + CH_3COOH. *Red color*	Add H_2SO_4 + nitron reagent. *White ppt.* **Test for NO_3^- in presence of NO_2^- and/or ClO_3^-:** Add sulfamic acid; heat. a. **ClO_3^- absent:** Add nitron reagent. *White ppt.* b. **ClO_3^- present:** Add H_2SO_4 + HCHO. Filter. Add nitron reagent. *White ppt.*	Add HCl. Evaporate and add turmeric. Evaporate. *Reddish color*	Add $CaCO_3$ or $Ca(OH)_2$. Heat. Collect CH_3COCH_3. Add KI-I_2 + NaOH. *White ppt.* Characteristic odor CHI_3
Chlorate	*Hypophosphite*	*Nitrite*	*Nitrate*	*Borate*	*Acetate*

DISCUSSION OF THE PROCEDURES

The anions in this group are those whose silver salts are appreciably soluble in neutral solution: $AgNO_2$, Ag_2SO_4, CH_3COOAg, $AgBO_2$, $AgClO_3$, AgF, $AgNO_3$, and AgH_2PO_2. Since SO_4^{--} and F^- are included in Group II, there are no tests for them in the analysis of Group III; and since they do not interfere with the tests for the other ions of this group, it is not necessary to remove them from the solution. AgH_2PO_2 decomposes into Ag° and PO_4^{3-} rather rapidly in an acid medium, but only slowly in a neutral or alkaline (ammoniacal) medium.

The following ions precipitate as silver salts in neutral solution with Ag_2SO_4 solution: S^{--}, $S_2O_3^{--}$ as S^{--}, I^-, Br^-, SCN^-, CN^-, Cl^-, ClO^- as Cl^-, $C_2O_4^{--}$, SO_3^{--}, PO_4^{3-}, AsO_4^{3-}, CO_3^{--}, CrO_4^{--}, and AsO_3^{3-}.

No single reagent forms a precipitate with the ions of this group. Hence a special test for each ion is made on separate portions of the filtrate from the silver salts which have been precipitated in neutral solution. One ml. of a saturated solution of the silver salts of the anions of this group contains about 0.7 mg. of NO_2^-, 2.5 mg. of CH_3COO^-, 25 mg. of BO_2^-, and 30 mg. of ClO_3^-. $AgNO_3$ is very soluble. Hence the filtrate from the silver salts contains a sufficient quantity of each of these ions for the tests outlined in the Procedures, because the tests are sensitive to much smaller quantities of the anions than those just listed.

DIRECTIONS FOR LABORATORY WORK

1. Obtain from the storeroom a known solution that contains the anions of Group III and analyze it by following the Procedures for Group III.

2. (Optional.) Request a student to prepare an unknown solution from the test solutions. Analyze it in accordance with the Procedures for Group III. (Preparation of the unknown: To 1 ml. of water add 5 drops of the test solutions for three anions of Group III.)

3. From the storeroom secure anion Unknown No. 3 and analyze it in accordance with the Procedures for Group III. Report the results of your analysis on an Unknown Report Blank.

PROCEDURES FOR THE ANALYSIS OF THE ANIONS OF GROUP III

ClO_3^-, $H_2PO_2^-$, NO_2^-, NO_3^-, BO_2^-, CH_3COO^-, (SO_4^{--}), (F^-)

18. If Groups I and II are absent, begin with 19. If Groups I and/or II are present, proceed as follows. To 1 ml. of water add 10 drops of the unknown and 1 drop of phenolphthalein indicator (colorless—8.3:10.0—red). Note the color of the solution. If the solution is red, add 0.01-*N* H_2SO_4 drop by drop, until the red color is just discharged. If the solution is colorless after the indicator is added, add 0.01-*N* NH_4OH drop by drop, until a faint pink can just be observed. To either one of these practically neutral solutions add 10 drops of a saturated solution of Ag_2SO_4. Shake the tube vigorously and filter off a few drops of the solution from the precipitate. Add 1 drop of Ag_2SO_4 solution to the filtrate. If a precipitate forms, add 5 drops of Ag_2SO_4 to the solution in the filter tube, return the filtrate containing the drop of Ag_2SO_4 to the filter tube, and stir the contents of this tube with a micro stirring rod. Filter again and test for complete precipitation. Continue this procedure until a precipitate no longer forms when Ag_2SO_4 is added to the clear filtrate. Discard the precipitate.

19. **Filtrate of Group III unknown:** ClO_3^-, $H_2PO_2^-$, NO_2^-, NO_3^-, BO_2^-, CH_3COO^-, (SO_4^{--}), and (F^-). No tests for SO_4^{--} (added) and F^- are made in the Procedure for Group III. Test separate portions of the solution by Procedures 20 through 25.

20. **Test for ClO_3^-:** To 1 ml. of water add 1 drop of Ag_2SO_4 solution, 1 drop of 4-*N* H_2SO_4, and 2 drops of formaldehyde. Then add 4 or 5 drops of the filtrate of Group III unknown (from 19). Place the tube in the hot water bath for 2 or 3 minutes. If ClO_3^- is present, a white precipitate of AgCl will form.

21. **Test for $H_2PO_2^-$:** To 1 ml. of water add 2 drops of 4-*N* H_2SO_4, 5 drops of 0.01-*M* $KMnO_4$, and 1 drop of 1-*N* $(NH_4)_2MoO_4$. Place the tube in the hot water bath and add to it 4 or 5 drops of the filtrate of Group III unknown (from 19). Now add 1 to 2 ml. of sulfurous acid (SO_2 in water). Leave the tube in the hot water bath for 2 or 3 minutes. If $H_2PO_2^-$ is present, the solution will become deep blue. (NOTE: Some ions will impart a greenish color to the solution; this color does not show the presence of $H_2PO_2^-$.)

22. **Test for NO_2^-:** To 1 ml. of water add 1 drop of 0.5% sulfanilic acid, 1 drop of 0.5% α-naphthylamine, and 1 drop of 4-*N* CH_3COOH. Now add a few drops of the filtrate of Group III unknown (from 19). If NO_2^- is present, the solution will become red.

23. **Test for NO_3^-:** To 1 ml. of water add 1 drop of 4-*N* H_2SO_4 and 1 drop of 10% nitron reagent. Then add 5 drops of the filtrate of Group III unknown (from 19). Put your finger over the end of the tube and shake it vigorously. If NO_3^- is present, a voluminous white precipitate will form. (NOTE: On standing, NO_2^- will produce a white precipitate; hence it must be removed if it is shown to be present in Procedure 22.)

Test for NO_3^- in the presence of NO_2^-: To 1 ml. of water add 4 or 5 drops of the filtrate of Group III unknown (from 19). Then add sulfamic acid drop by drop, shaking the tube after each drop; continue to add the acid until the vigorous evolution of a gas (N_2) stops. If no ClO_3^- was found in Procedure 20, add 2 or 3 drops of the nitron reagent to the tube which is now free of NO_2^-, and shake the tube vigorously. A white precipitate confirms the presence of NO_3^-.

If ClO_3^- was found in 20, add 1 drop of 4-*N* H_2SO_4 and 2 drops of formalin to the tube that is now free of NO_2^-. Place the tube in the hot water bath for 2 or 3 minutes. Filter off any precipitate that may have formed. To the cooled filtrate add 2 or 3 drops of the nitron reagent and shake the tube vigorously. A white precipitate confirms the presence of NO_3^-.

24. **Test for BO_2^-:** To an evaporation test tube add 5 drops of the filtrate of Group III unknown (from 19) and 1 drop of 6-*N* HCl. Evaporate the solution to incipient dryness but be careful not to overheat. Cool the tube and add about 10 drops of turmeric. Again evaporate the solution to incipient dryness. Look at the contents of the tube from the bottom of it. If BO_2^- is present, the residue will be reddish; if no BO_2^- is present, the residue will be yellow.

25. **Test for CH_3COO^-:** To a 13 x 100 mm. test tube add 5 to 10 mg. of dry $CaCO_3$ or $Ca(OH)_2$ from the point of a micro spatula and from 5 to 10 drops of the filtrate of Group III unknown (from 19). Press a small wad of glass wool into the test tube and push it down to within about half an inch of the bottom of the tube. Heat the bottom of the tube carefully until the residue is *just dry;* do not overheat the residue.

Using the assembly shown in Fig. 21.2 (p. 326), insert the clipped end of the rubber bulb in the test tube containing the dried residue. Hold the assembly horizontally and heat the residue strongly. Place the filter tube in a test tube and remove the tube that contains the heated residue from the medicine dropper bulb. Also remove the cotton that was wrapped around the dropper and push it down in the filter tube. Wash the medicine dropper with a small amount of water, allowing the water to run into the filter tube and then into the test tube. Add 2 drops of $KI\text{-}I_2$ solution and 1 drop of 4-*N* NaOH to the test tube. If CH_3COO^- is present, a white precipitate (CHI_3) will form in the solution in the test tube. This precipitate is iodoform and it has the characteristic odor of this compound.

(NOTE: The special condenser-collector apparatus shown in Fig. 21.1, p. 325, may be used instead of the assembly just described.)

CHEMICAL REACTIONS IN THE ANALYSIS OF GROUP III

Procedure	Equations	Purpose—Discussion
18. Remove anions of Groups I and II, if present, from the neutral solution as silver salts.		All anions of Groups I and II are colorless except $CrO_4^{=}$. This anion has a yellow color. Ag_2SO_4 will effectively precipitate the anions of these two groups in a neutral solution, but either an acid or an ammoniacal solution will dissolve appreciable quantities of a number of the silver salts of these two groups. Since $SO_4^{=}$ does not interfere with the tests for the anions of Group III, Ag_2SO_4 is used as the precipitating reagent.
19.	$2ClO_3^- + 3H_2PO_2^- \rightleftharpoons 2Cl^- + 3H_2PO_4^-$. $ClO_3^- + 3NO_2^- \rightleftharpoons Cl^- + 3NO_3^-$ $4ClO_3^- + 3CH_3COO^- + 3H_3O^+ \rightarrow 4Cl^- + 6CO_2\uparrow + 9H_2O$	ClO_3^- is a powerful oxidizing agent in acid solution, and no $H_2PO_2^-$ or NO_2^- will be found in its presence. ClO_3^- in acid solution oxidizes CH_3COO^- to CO_2.
20. Add Ag_2SO_4, H_2SO_4, and formaldehyde.	$2ClO_3^- + 3HCHO \rightarrow 2Cl^- + 3CO_2\uparrow + 3H_2O$ $Cl^- + Ag^+ \rightleftharpoons \underset{\text{white}}{\underline{AgCl}}\downarrow$	Formaldehyde readily reduces ClO_3^- to Cl^- which, with Ag^+, gives a white precipitate, AgCl.
21. Add H_2SO_4, $KMnO_4$, and $(NH_4)_2MoO_4$.	$5H_2PO_2^- + 4MnO_4^- + 12H_3O^+ \rightleftharpoons 5H_2PO_4^- + 4Mn^{++} + 18H_2O$ $H_2PO_4^- + 12MoO_4^{=} + 25H_3O^+ \rightleftharpoons H_7P(Mo_2O_7)_6 + 35H_2O$ $5SO_3^{=} + 2MnO_4^- + 6H_3O^+ \rightleftharpoons 5SO_4^{=} + 2Mn^{++} + 9H_2O$	MnO_4^- in acid solution oxidizes $H_2PO_2^-$ to $H_2PO_4^-$. The latter forms phosphomolybdic acid, $H_7P(Mo_2O_7)_6$, with MoO_3. SO_2 reduces this acid, resulting in the formation of blue compounds. SO_2 also reduces the MnO_4^- to Mn^{++}, whose faint pink color is not seen in the dilute solution. If present, AsO_4^{3-} imparts a light-green color to the solution.
22. Add sulfanilic acid and α-naphthylamine.	NO_2^- + sulfanilic acid + α-naphthylamine → red diazo dye $-NH_2 + HNO_2 + H_3O^+ \rightarrow 3H_2O + \underset{\text{diazo group}}{(-N{=}N-)}$	This is a specific test for NO_2^-, because none of the other anions produce the diazo group with sulfanilic acid and α-naphthylamine. NO_2^- is a strong reducing ion and does not exist in the presence of oxidizing ions.

Procedure	Equations	Purpose—Discussion
23. Add nitron.	$NO_3^- + \text{nitron} \rightleftharpoons$ *white ppt.*	Nitron is an organic compound with a rather complex formula and it forms rather insoluble compounds with a number of other anions. Except for NO_2^-, however, these anions were removed in Procedure 18.
23a. Add sulfamic acid.	$NO_2^- + NH_2SO_3H \rightarrow HSO_4^- + N_2\uparrow + H_2O$	The action of NH_2SO_3H on NO_2^- at a pH of 8.0 or less is vigorous; even traces of NO_2^- are destroyed without the formation of NO_3^-.
23b. Add H_2SO_4 and formaldehyde.	$2ClO_3^- + 3HCHO \rightarrow 2Cl^- + 3CO_2\uparrow + 3H_2O$	ClO_3^- may be present with NO_2^- in a neutral or alkaline medium. ClO_3^- produces a precipitate with the nitron reagent and, in an acid medium, oxidizes NO_2^- to NO_3^-. Therefore the NO_2^- must be removed with sulfamic acid and the ClO_3^- be reduced to Cl^- before a test for NO_3^- can be made with the nitron reagent.
24. Acidify with HCl. Evaporate just to incipient dryness.	$BO_2^- + H_3O^+ \rightleftharpoons H_3BO_3$ $H_3BO_3 + \text{turmeric} \rightarrow$ reddish-brown residue	After the turmeric is added to the incipiently dry residue, the solution should be brought carefully to dryness to obtain the reddish-brown color. Overheating will destroy the turmeric (curcuma) and the reddish-brown color. Turmeric is also destroyed by oxidizing agents such as ClO_3^- and NO_2^-. These anions and NO_3^- are destroyed or expelled by evaporation with HCl. If 1 drop of 4-*N* NaOH is added to the reddish-brown solution, a dark-green color will appear if H_3BO_3 is present.

Procedure	Equations	Purpose—Discussion
25. Convert CH_3COO^- to $(CH_3)_2CO$, and the acetone to CHI_3.	$2CH_3COO^- \rightarrow CO_3^= + (CH_3)_2CO$ $(CH_3)_2CO + 3I_2 + 4OH^- \rightarrow CHI_3 + CH_3COO^- + 3H_2O + 3I^-$	The conversion of CH_3COO^- to $(CH_3)_2CO$ to CHI_3 is a very reliable test for the acetate ion. The condenser-collector tube or the medicine dropper-filter tube assembly provides a simple means of condensing and collecting the acetone. These condensers must be kept cool because the boiling point of acetone is 56.5° C. The $CaCO_3$ or $Ca(OH)_2$ neutralizes the acids that may be present and prevents volatilization of acetic acid when the tube is heated to convert the acetate ion to acetone. The boiling point of acetic acid is 118.1° C.

CHAPTER 23

TESTS FOR GROUP IV ANIONS

DISCUSSION OF THE PROCEDURES

This group of anions is not considered an analytical group similar to Groups I, II, and III. The properties and Preliminary Experiment for all the ions of this group have been given in the study of the other three Groups—ClO^-, S^{--}, CN^-, and $S_2O_3^{--}$ in Group I; CO_3^{--} and SO_3^{--} in Group II; and NO_2^- in Group III.

The ions of this group have one property in common; i.e., they form unstable compounds or volatile acids which escape from acid solutions of the ions, as formulated by the following equations:

$$ClO^- + Cl^- + 2H_3O^+ \rightleftharpoons HClO + H_3O^+ + H_2O + Cl^- \rightleftharpoons Cl_2\uparrow + 3H_2O$$

$$CO_3^{--} + 2H_3O^+ \rightleftharpoons H_2CO_3 + 2H_2O \rightleftharpoons CO_2\uparrow + 3H_2O$$

$$S^{--} + 2H_3O^+ \rightleftharpoons H_2S\uparrow + 2H_2O$$

$$SO_3^{--} + 2H_3O^+ \rightleftharpoons H_2SO_3 + 2H_2O \rightleftharpoons SO_2\uparrow + 3H_2O$$

$$S_2O_3^{--} + 2H_3O^+ \rightleftharpoons H_2SO_3 + S\downarrow + 2H_2O \rightleftharpoons SO_2\uparrow + S\downarrow + 3H_2O$$

$$CN^- + H_3O^+ \rightleftharpoons HCN\uparrow + H_2O$$

$$3NO_2^- + 3H_3O^+ \rightleftharpoons 3HNO_2 + 3H_2O \rightleftharpoons 2NO\uparrow + NO_3^- + H_3O^+ + 3H_2O$$

By virtue of their property of forming gases, special tests may be made for the anions of this group. A considerable amount of time can often be saved in the analysis of a general unknown if the anion elimination tests show the possibility of the presence of one or more members of this group. Furthermore, the special tests for ClO^- and $S_2O_3^{--}$ are necessary in order to distinguish these two ions from Cl^- and S^{--}, respectively, in the analysis of Group I.

Besides a test that takes advantage of the formation of a volatile product, a few other specific tests are given to aid in distinguishing the ion from other ions that might interfere.

SCHEMATIC OUTLINE OF THE PROCEDURE

Test separate portions of the unknown solution as indicated in the following Procedures for ClO^-, $CO_3^=$, NO_2^-, $S^=$, $SO_3^=$, $S_2O_3^=$, CN^-.

26. **Test for ClO^-:** Add $Pb(CH_3COO)_2$. *White ppt.:* $Pb(ClO)_2$ Turns brown. PbO_2	27a. **Test for $CO_3^=$:** Add HCl. Collect gas in $Ba(OH)_2$. *White ppt.:* $BaCO_3$ ($SO_3^=$ interferes.) b. **Test for ClO^-:** Add benzidine or KI and starch to $Ba(OH)_2$. Blue color confirms ClO^-.	28. **Test for $CO_3^=$ in presence of $SO_3^=$ and $S_2O_3^=$:** Add H_2O_2, then HCl. Collect gas in $Ba(OH)_2$. *White ppt.:* $BaCO_3$	29. **Test for NO_2^-:** Add HCl. Collect gas in sulfanilic acid + α-naphthylamine. Red color confirms NO_2^-.	30. **Tests for $S^=$, $SO_3^=$, $S_2O_3^=$:** Add $Pb(CH_3COO)_2$. *Black ppt.:* PbS Filter.		34. **Test for CN^-:** Add $NaHCO_3$. Pass gas through $Cu(CH_3COO)_2$–benzidine reagent. Green to blue color confirms CN^-.
				31. **Filtrate:** $S_2O_3^=$ a. **NO_2^- absent:** Add HCl and pass gas through $KMnO_4$ + H_2SO_4. Purple color disappears. b. **NO_2^- present:** Add $AgNO_3$. *White ppt. changing to black:* $Ag_2S_2O_3$ to Ag_2S	32. **Precipitate:** PbS, $PbSO_3$ Add dilute HCl. Pass gas through $KMnO_4$ + H_2SO_4. Purple color disappears. Confirms SO_3^{--}. 33. **Residue:** PbS Add 6-*N* HCl and pass gas through $Pb(CH_3COO)_2$. *Black ppt.:* PbS	
Hypochlorite	*Carbonate hypochlorite*	*Carbonate*	*Nitrite*	*Thiosulfate*	*Sulfite, sulfide*	*Cyanide*

Interferences between oxidizing and reducing anions must always be kept in mind. For example, if a strong oxidizing agent like ClO^- is present, the following ions—S^{--}, SO_3^{--}, $S_2O_3^{--}$, CN^-, NO_2^-; and $H_2PO_2^-$—will not be present because they are oxidized by ClO^- even in basic solution. (See Table 24.2.) Likewise, if oxidizing anions like CrO_4^{--} and ClO_3^- are present, one or more of the above ions will be oxidized when the solution is made acidic for the gas tests. If a large enough quantity of the oxidizing ions is present, all these reducing ions will be oxidized and no gas will be evolved for the test. Hence, if strong oxidizing agents are present in the original general unknown, the reducing ions of Group IV must be detected by following the Procedures for the analysis of Groups I–III. The elimination tests are valuable in determining which tests to make and in interpreting the results of the special tests given in the Procedures for Group IV.

If Procedure 26 shows that ClO^- is present, the only other ion in this group for which a test should be made is CO_3^{--}. This ion is not affected by oxidizing agents.

If ClO^- is absent, tests for S^{--}, SO_3^{--}, $S_2O_3^{--}$, CN^-, and NO_2^- may all be made, provided anions that are strong oxidizing agents in acid solution are absent. In any case, if a black precipitate was obtained in Group I, the tests for S^{--} and $S_2O_3^{--}$ should be made to determine whether the precipitate was due to S^{--} or to $S_2O_3^{--}$. Since NO_2^- oxidizes S^{--}, SO_3^{--}, and $S_2O_3^{--}$ when the solution is made acidic, both precipitation and gas evolution tests are made for these three ions.

Before making any of the tests, determine whether the solution being tested is acidic or basic. If it is acidic, only small quantities of the ions of this group can be present, and then only in freshly prepared solutions that have been tightly stoppered. To test the solution, add 1 drop of bromthymol blue and 1 drop of methyl red indicator to 1 ml. of water, and add 1 drop of the unknown solution. If the indicators become pink or red, the solution is acidic and the ions of Group IV are probably absent. If the indicators become green or blue, the solution is basic and the ions of this group may be present.

LABORATORY WORK—ANALYSIS OF KNOWN AND UNKNOWN SOLUTIONS

1. Obtain from the storeroom a known solution that contains the anions of Group IV (except ClO^- and NO_2^-) and analyze it in accordance with the Procedures for Group IV. (Do the tests for ClO^- and NO_2^-, using the test solutions.)

2. (Optional.) Request a student to prepare an unknown solution from the test solutions. Analyze it in accordance with the Procedures for Group IV. (Preparation of the unknown: To 1 ml. of water add 1 drop of the test solutions for two or three anions of Group IV. If ClO^- is used, CO_3^{--} is the only other anion of the group that may be present.)

3. From the storeroom obtain anion Unknown No. 4 and analyze it in accordance with the Procedures for Group IV. Report the results of your analysis on an Unknown Report Blank. (NOTE TO INSTRUCTOR: If ClO^- is put in the unknown, CO_3^{--} is the only other ion of this group that should be included.)

PROCEDURES AND SPECIAL TESTS FOR THE ANALYSIS OF THE ANIONS OF GROUP IV

ClO^-, CO_3^{--}, NO_2^-, S^{--}, $S_2O_3^{--}$, SO_3^{--}, CN^-

---

26. **Test for ClO^-:** To 1 ml. of water add 2 drops of the general unknown solution (or 2 drops of Group IV known or unknown). To this solution add 5 drops of 0.1-*N* $Pb(CH_3COO)_2$. (NOTE: The immediate formation of a black precipitate shows the presence of S^{--}, in which case ClO^- cannot be present.) Place the tube in the hot water bath for 3 or 4 minutes. If ClO^- is present, the white precipitate first obtained slowly turns *brown*. The color may be light brown because of the presence of other precipitates.

---

27. **Test for CO_3^{--}. Additional test for ClO^-:**

a. To 1 ml. of water in the gas-generating tube *C* (Fig. 16.1) add 2 drops of the solution to be tested. Place 0.5 ml. of water and 5 drops of saturated $Ba(OH)_2$ in the reagent tube *A* over a plug of glass fiber. Add 3 drops of 6-*N* HCl to the solution through the side tube *B* and then slowly force air through the apparatus with the pressure bulb for 1 or 2 minutes. A white precipitate of $BaCO_3$ in the $Ba(OH)_2$ solution shows the original presence of CO_3^{--}. (NOTE: SO_3^{--} gives the same reaction, but it is absent if ClO^- is present. If ClO^- or other strong oxidizing agents are absent, Procedure 28 should be used to test for CO_3^{--}.)

b. To the reagent tube *A* which contains the $Ba(OH)_2$ solution, add 1 drop of benzidine reagent. If ClO^- was present, a blue color which may change to yellow or red is obtained. (NOTE: One drop of KI and 1 drop of starch solution may be used in place of the benzidine reagent.)

---

28. **Test for CO_3^{--} in the presence of SO_3^{--} and $S_2O_3^{--}$:** To 1 ml. of water in the gas-generating tube *C* add 2 drops of the solution to be tested. To this solution add 2 drops of 3% H_2O_2. (The H_2O_2 oxidizes SO_3^{--} and $S_2O_3^{--}$ to SO_4^{--}.) Place 0.5 ml. of water and 5 drops of saturated $Ba(OH)_2$ in the reagent tube *A* over a plug of glass fiber. Add 3 drops of 6-*N* HCl to the solution through the side tube *B* and then slowly force air through the apparatus with the pressure bulb for 1 or 2 minutes. A white precipitate of $BaCO_3$ in the $Ba(OH)_2$ solution confirms the original presence of CO_3^{--}.

---

29. **Test for NO_2^-:** To 0.5 ml. of water in the gas-generating tube *C* add 2 drops of the solution to be tested. Add 5 drops of water, 3 drops of sulfanilic acid reagent, and 3 drops of α-naphthylamine reagent to the reagent tube *A* over a plug of glass fiber. Now add 2 drops of 6-*N* HCl to the apparatus through the side tube *B*. Force air through the apparatus for 1 or 2 minutes. If NO_2^- is present, the sulfanilic acid-α-naphthylamine solution will turn red.

PROCEDURES AND SPECIAL TESTS FOR THE ANALYSIS OF THE ANIONS OF GROUP IV (*Continued*)

30. **Tests for S^{--}, SO_3^{--}, $S_2O_3^{--}$:** To 0.5 ml. of water add 2 drops of the solution to be tested. To this solution add 5 drops of 0.1-*N* $Pb(CH_3COO)_2$ and 1 drop of 4-*N* CH_3COOH. A black precipitate shows the presence of S^{--}. Filter the solution through a cotton medium in a filter tube to be used as the side tube *B* of the gas-testing apparatus. Allow the filtrate to run into the gas-generating tube *C*. Remove the filter tube with the precipitate and reserve it for use in 32.

31. **Filtrate:** $S_2O_3^{--}$. (Absence of NO_2^-)

a. Place 5 drops of water, 3 drops of 0.01-*M* $KMnO_4$, and 1 drop of 4-*N* H_2SO_4 in the reagent tube *A*. Now place an empty filter tube in position *B*. Set the assembly in a hot water bath for about 1 minute and then add 5 drops of 6-*N* HCl through the side tube. Now slowly force air through the apparatus with a rubber bulb for 1 or 2 minutes. If $S_2O_3^{--}$ is present, the purple color of the $KMnO_4$ will disappear and the solution in the gas-generating tube will become cloudy.

b. **Filtrate:** $S_2O_3^{--}$. (Presence of NO_2^-) NO_2^- interferes with the test in (a) because it oxidizes $S_2O_3^{--}$ in acid solution and the gases decolorize the $KMnO_4$ solution. If NO_2^- is present, add 2 drops of 1-*N* $AgNO_3$ to the filtrate from 30. If a white precipitate forms and slowly changes color from yellow to black, $S_2O_3^{--}$ is present.

32. **Precipitate:** PbS and $PbSO_3$. Wash the precipitate with 1 ml. of water to which has been added 1 drop of 4-*N* CH_3COOH. Clean the gas-generating tube *C* and the reagent tube *A*. Put 5 drops of water, 3 drops of 0.01-*M* $KMnO_4$, and 1 drop 4-*N* H_2SO_4 in the reagent tube *A* over a plug of glass fiber. Now place the filter tube with the precipitate in position *B*, add to it *1 ml. of water* and *1 drop* of 6-*N* HCl. Slowly force the acid solution through the precipitate into the gas-generating tube with the rubber bulb. Warm the solution and continue forcing air through the apparatus for 1 or 2 minutes. If the purple color of the $KMnO_4$ disappears, the original presence of SO_3^{--} is confirmed.

33. (PbS precipitate from 32 or from the original unknown solution.) Wash the black PbS precipitate with 1 ml. of water to which has been added 1 drop of 6-*N* HCl. Clean the gas-generating tube *C* and place 5 drops of water and 1 drop of 0.1-*N* $Pb(CH_3COO)_2$ in the reagent tube *A*. Add to the side tube *B* which contains the black precipitate 5 drops of 6-*N* HCl. Force the solution through the filter medium into the gas-generating tube. Now force air through the apparatus for about 1 minute. A black or brown precipitate in the $Pb(CH_3COO)_2$ solution confirms the presence of S^{--}.

34. **Test for CN^-:** To 0.5 ml. of water in the gas-generating tube *C* add 2 drops of the solution to be tested. Add 5 drops of water and 3 drops of cupric acetate-benzidine reagent to the reagent tube *A*. Now add 5 drops of saturated $NaHCO_3$ to the apparatus through the empty side tube *B*. Force air through the apparatus for 2 or 3 minutes with the rubber bulb. If the cupric acetate-benzidine solution turns green or blue, the presence of CN^- is confirmed.

CHEMICAL REACTIONS IN THE ANALYSIS OF GROUP IV

Procedure	Equations	Purpose—Discussion
26. Add $Pb(CH_3COO)_2$ and heat.	$Pb(CH_3COO)_2 + 2ClO^- \rightleftharpoons$ $\underset{\text{white}}{\underline{Pb(ClO)_2 \downarrow}} + 2CH_3COO^-$ $\underline{Pb(ClO)_2} \rightleftharpoons \underset{\text{brown}}{\underline{PbO_2 \downarrow}} + Cl_2$	If a black precipitate is formed immediately after the addition of $Pb(CH_3COO)_2$, $S^=$ is present and the test is discontinued. ClO^- cannot be present if $S^=$ is present because $S^=$ is oxidized by ClO^- in both basic and acidic solutions. As long as a sufficient quantity of $Pb(CH_3COO)_2$ is added, other anions do not interfere with the test.
27a. Add HCl and pass the gases through $Ba(OH)_2$.	$CO_3^= + 2H_3O^+ \rightleftharpoons$ $H_2CO_3 + 2H_2O$ $H_2CO_3 \rightleftharpoons CO_2 \uparrow + H_2O$ $CO_2 + Ba^{++} + 2OH^- \rightleftharpoons$ $\underset{\text{white}}{\underline{BaCO_3 \downarrow}} + H_2O$	$CO_3^=$ is the only ion of Group IV that is not oxidized by ClO^-. Therefore, if ClO^- is present, $CO_3^=$ is the only ion for which a test is made. If ClO^- is not present, $SO_3^=$ may be present, and the test for $CO_3^=$ in Procedure 28 should be made.
27b. Add benzidine or KI and starch to the $Ba(OH)_2$ solution.	$ClO^- + 2H_3O^+ + Cl^- \rightleftharpoons$ $Cl_2 \uparrow + 3H_2O$ $Cl_2 + 2OH^- \rightleftharpoons ClO^- +$ $Cl^- + H_2O$ ClO^- + benzidine $\rightarrow$ blue oxidation product $ClO^- + 2I^- + H_2O \rightleftharpoons$ $I_2 + Cl^- + 2OH^-$ I_2 + starch $\rightarrow$ blue adsorption compound	The Cl_2 liberated in the gas-generating tube reacts with the $Ba(OH)_2$ to form ClO^-. This ion is then detected by its oxidizing properties.
28. Add H_2O_2, then HCl, and pass the gases through $Ba(OH)_2$.	$SO_3^= + H_2O_2 \rightleftharpoons$ $SO_4^= + H_2O$ $S_2O_3^= + 4H_2O_2 + 2OH^- \rightleftharpoons$ $2SO_4^= + 5H_2O$ $CO_3^= + 2H_3O^+ \rightleftharpoons$ $H_2CO_3 + 2H_2O$ $H_2CO_3 \rightleftharpoons CO_2 \uparrow + H_2O$ $CO_2 + Ba^{++} + 2OH^- \rightleftharpoons$ $\underset{\text{white}}{\underline{BaCO_3 \downarrow}} + H_2O$	The H_2O_2 oxidizes $SO_3^=$ and $S_2O_3^=$ to $SO_4^=$ so that SO_2 will not be evolved from the solution and cause a white precipitate of $BaSO_3$.

Procedure	Equations	Purpose—Discussion
29. Add HCl and pass the gases through sulfanilic acid and α-naphthylamine.	$NO_2^- + H_3O^+ \rightleftharpoons HNO_2 + H_2O$ $3HNO_2 \rightleftharpoons 2NO\uparrow + NO_3^- + H_3O^+$ $2NO + O_2$ (air) $\rightleftharpoons 2NO_2$ $2NO_2 + 2H_2O \rightleftharpoons HNO_2 + NO_3^- + H_3O^+$ HNO_2 + sulfanilic acid + α-naphthylamine → red diazo dye	HNO_2 is a weak, unstable acid. The NO which results from the decomposition of HNO_2 reacts readily with oxygen in the air to form brown NO_2. The NO_2 is carried into the solution that contains sulfanilic acid and α-naphthylamine. The HNO_2 formed by the reaction of NO_2 with water causes the formation of the red diazo dye (see the discussion for Procedure 23a).
30. Add CH_3COOH and $Pb(CH_3COO)_2$	$Pb(CH_3COO)_2 + S^= \rightleftharpoons \underset{\text{black}}{\underline{PbS\downarrow}} + 2CH_3COO^-$ $Pb(CH_3COO)_2 + SO_3^= \rightleftharpoons \underset{\text{white}}{\underline{PbSO_3\downarrow}} + 2CH_3COO^-$	The solution is made slightly acidic with CH_3COOH to prevent the precipitation of PbS_2O_3. The solubility of $PbSO_3$ and PbS is negligible in dilute CH_3COOH.
31a. Add HCl and pass the gases through $KMnO_4$ or malachite green.	$S_2O_3^= + 2H_3O^+ \rightleftharpoons H_2SO_3 + \underline{S}\downarrow + 2H_2O$ $H_2SO_3 \rightleftharpoons SO_2\uparrow + H_2O$ $SO_2 + 2H_2O \rightleftharpoons H_3O^+ + HSO_3^-$ $2MnO_4^- + 5HSO_3^- + H_3O^+ \rightleftharpoons 2Mn^{++} + 5SO_4^= + 4H_2O$	The solution must be heated, for otherwise the reaction between $S_2O_3^=$ and H_3O^+ will be slow. Except with very small amounts of $S_2O_3^=$ a cloudy solution will be produced if the solution in the gas-generating tube is heated for 2 or 3 minutes. This gives two tests for $S_2O_3^=$. A dilute acetic acid solution of malachite green may be used in place of the $KMnO_4$ but the reaction is slower and less sensitive.
31b. Add $AgNO_3$ to the solution containing $S_2O_3^=$ and NO_2^-.	$2Ag^+ + S_2O_3^= \rightleftharpoons \underset{\text{white to yellow}}{\underline{Ag_2S_2O_3\downarrow}}$ $\underline{Ag_2S_2O_3} + 3H_2O \rightleftharpoons \underset{\text{black}}{\underline{Ag_2S\downarrow}} + 2H_3O^+ + SO_4^=$	Since NO_2^- interferes with the gas test for $S_2O_3^=$, the presence of $S_2O_3^=$ is confirmed by precipitation with Ag^+. The sulfide ion, if present, was removed by Procedure 30 as PbS. Hence, a black precipitate in the filtrate from

Procedure	Equations	Purpose—Discussion
		PbS confirms the presence of $S_2O_3^{=}$. The reaction between NO_2^- and $S_2O_3^{=}$ in dilute acetic acid solution is slow, but the test should be made as soon as possible.
32. Add H_2O and HCl; then pass the gases through $KMnO_4$.	$PbSO_3 + 2H_3O^+ \rightleftharpoons H_2SO_3 + Pb^{++} + 2H_2O$ $H_2SO_3 \rightleftharpoons SO_2\uparrow + H_2O$ $SO_2 + 2H_2O \rightleftharpoons H_3O^+ + HSO_3^-$ $2MnO_4^- + 5HSO_3^- + H_3O^+ \rightleftharpoons 2Mn^{++} + 5SO_4^{=} + 4H_2O$	$PbSO_3$ is soluble in dilute HCl, but PbS is not. Do not make the solution more acid than 1 drop of 6-*N* HCl in 1 ml. of water (0.3-*N* HCl), for otherwise some of the PbS may dissolve and give a false indication of the presence of $SO_3^{=}$.
33. Add HCl to PbS and pass the gases through $Pb(CH_3COO)_2$.	$PbS + 2H_3O^+ \rightleftharpoons Pb^{++} + H_2S\uparrow + 2H_2O$ $H_2S + Pb(CH_3COO)_2 \rightleftharpoons \underset{\text{black}}{\underline{PbS}}\downarrow + 2CH_3COOH$	This test may be carried out on the original unknown solution only in the absence of oxidizing agents. A black precipitate of PbS formed when $Pb(CH_3COO)_2$ is added to the original unknown solution is ordinarily sufficient proof of the presence of $S^{=}$ because none of the other anions form a black precipitate with Pb^{++}.
34. Add $NaHCO_3$ and pass the gases through cupric acetate-benzidine reagent.	$CN^- + HCO_3^- \rightleftharpoons HCN + CO_3^{=}$ $Cu^{++} + 2HCN + 2H_2O \rightleftharpoons \underline{Cu(CN)_2}\downarrow + 2H_3O^+$ $\underline{2Cu(CN)_2} \rightleftharpoons \underline{2CuCN} + (CN)_2\uparrow$ $(CN)_2$ + benzidine $\rightleftharpoons$ blue oxidation product	Hydrogen cyanide is so weak as an acid that HCO_3^- reacts with CN^- to form HCN. In other words, CN^- is stronger as a base than $CO_3^{=}$ and therefore takes the proton from HCO_3^-. None of the other volatile or unstable acids, except H_2S, are formed by reaction with HCO_3^-. HCN is oxidized to cyanogen by Cu^{++}. Cyanogen then oxidizes benzidine to give a blue oxidation product.

CHAPTER 24

ANALYSIS OF A GENERAL UNKNOWN SOLUTION—ALL ANION GROUPS

Obtain a general unknown solution * from the storeroom and analyze it for the ions of all groups.

It is assumed that the unknown solution has been prepared from the alkali salts of the anions and that it contains the anions in quantities from 2 to 10 mg./ml. No interfering cations are present.

Before starting the analysis, do the elimination tests described in the next section. Make a list of the ions that are shown to be absent and a list of those that may be present—i.e., all the ions not shown to be absent—as illustrated in Table 24.3. From this list determine whether the unknown must be analyzed by the Procedures for only one or for all of Groups I, II, and III. Omit tests for all ions *proved* to be absent by the elimination tests. If all the ions of Group I, except S^{--} for example, are absent, and if no strong oxidizing agents are present, time may be saved by using the special tests in the Procedures for Group IV. If there is a possibility of Cl^- and ClO^- or of S^{--} and $S_2O_3^{--}$ being present, the special tests in Group IV must be made to distinguish one from the other.

ELIMINATION TESTS

Discussion

The elimination tests are made by adding to the unknown solution a reagent that reacts with several of the anions. If no reaction occurs, this indicates that the ions which normally react with this reagent are absent and it is not necessary to test for them in the analysis. This procedure considerably shortens the time required to make an analysis,

* NOTE TO INSTRUCTOR: When preparing general unknown solutions, care must be used not to mix anions that interact appreciably in alkaline solution (see Table 24.2). Some ions such as S^{--} and CN^- react slowly, especially in the presence of certain oxidizing agents, to give SCN^-. Credit should be allowed if the three ions (S^{--}, CN^-, and SCN^-) are reported. Similarly a solution of S^{--} may contain small amounts of $S_2O_3^{--}$ and SO_4^{--} because of oxidation. SO_3^{--} is often completely oxidized to SO_4^{--} before the analysis is made. The unknown solutions may be prepared from the test solutions, or from other stock solutions. The unknown solutions should contain from 2 to 10 mg./ml. of each anion.

especially an analysis of a commercial product in which more than three or four anions are seldom present.

Most of the elimination tests are based upon the solubility of certain salts of the anions in water and in acidic or ammoniacal solutions. The solubilities of the salts concerned are listed in Table 24.1.

TABLE 24.1. Solubility of Silver, Calcium, and Barium Salts

Salt	Solubility in H_2O in g./ml.	Solubility in Dilute HNO_3	Solubility in NH_4OH	Salt	Solubility in H_2O in g./ml.	Solubility in Dilute CH_3COOH	Solubility in Dilute HCl
Ag_2S	1.5×10^{-18}	i	i	CaF_2	4.8×10^{-7}	i	sl. s.
$Ag_2S_2O_3 \rightarrow Ag_2S$	1.5×10^{-18}	i	i	CaC_2O_4	6.1×10^{-6}	i	s
AgI	2.2×10^{-9}	i	i	$CaCO_3$	6.9×10^{-6}	s	s
$AgCN$	1.1×10^{-8}	i	s	$Ca_3(PO_4)_2$	1.6×10^{-6}	s	s
$AgBr$	1.1×10^{-7}	i	s	$CaSO_3$	4.3×10^{-5}	i	s
$AgSCN$	1.7×10^{-7}	i	s	$Ca_3(AsO_4)_2$	4.8×10^{-5}	s	s
$AgCl$	1.9×10^{-6}	i	s	$Ca_3(AsO_3)_2$	sl. s.	s	s
$AgClO \rightarrow AgCl$	1.9×10^{-6}	i	s	$CaSO_4$	1.07×10^{-3}	s	s
Ag_3PO_4	6.5×10^{-6}	s	s	$Ca(BO_2)_2\cdot 2H_2O$	3.1×10^{-3}	s	s
Ag_3AsO_4	8.5×10^{-6}	s	s	$Ca(H_2PO_2)_2$	1.5×10^{-1}	s	s
Ag_3AsO_3	1.1×10^{-5}	s	s				
Ag_2CrO_4	2.2×10^{-5}	s	s	$Ba_3(PO_4)_2$	4.9×10^{-7}	s	s
Ag_2CO_3	3.6×10^{-5}	s	s	$BaSO_4$	2.3×10^{-6}	i	i
$Ag_2C_2O_4$	6.7×10^{-5}	s	s	$BaCrO_4$	3.6×10^{-6}	i	s
Ag_2SO_3	5.0×10^{-5}	s	s	$BaCO_3$	1.4×10^{-5}	s	s
$AgNO_2$	2.4×10^{-3}	s	s	BaC_2O_4	7.5×10^{-5}	i	s
Ag_2SO_4	7.1×10^{-3} 0°	s	s	$BaSO_3$	1.0×10^{-4}	s	s
$AgCH_3COO$	7.2×10^{-3}	s	s	$Ba_3(AsO_4)_2$	5.5×10^{-4}	s	s
$AgBO_2$	9.0×10^{-2}	s	s	BaF_2	1.3×10^{-3}	s	s
$AgClO_3$	1.0×10^{-1}	s	s	$Ba(H_2PO_2)_2$	3.0×10^{-1}	s	s
AgF	1.95	s	s				
$AgNO_3$	2.13	s	s				
$AgH_2PO_2 \rightarrow Ag^\circ$	Decomposes						

i = insoluble.
s = soluble.
sl. s. = slightly soluble.

Whether a salt is soluble in dilute acid solution depends upon two factors: (1) its solubility in neutral solution, and (2) the weakness of the acid of the anion. Even though the solubility of $Ca_3(PO_4)_2$ in neutral solution is very low, it readily dissolves in dilute acid solutions because HPO_4^{--} is a very weak acid. The formation of HPO_4^{--} and $H_2PO_4^-$ reduces the concentration of PO_4^{---} to such a low value that the ion product constant becomes less than the solubility product constant for

$Ca_3(PO_4)_2$, and the precipitate dissolves. The reaction may be formulated as follows:

$$Ca_3(PO_4)_2 \rightleftharpoons 3Ca^{++} + 2PO_4^{3-}$$
$$PO_4^{3-} + H_3O^+ \rightleftharpoons HPO_4^{--} + H_2O$$
$$HPO_4^{--} + H_3O^+ \rightleftharpoons H_2PO_4^- + H_2O$$

Conversely, PO_4^{3-} is precipitated more completely in alkaline solution than in neutral or very weakly acid solutions because its concentration

TABLE 24.2. Incompatibilities in Alkaline and in Acid Solution

Anion	Anions That Interact with the Anions in Column 1	
	In Dilute Alkaline Solutions	In Dilute Acid Solutions
$S^=$	ClO^-	$S_2O_3^=$, ClO^-, AsO_4^{3-}, AsO_3^{3-}, $Cr_2O_7^=$, $C_2O_4^=$, $SO_3^=$, NO_2^-, ClO_3^-, NO_3^-
$S_2O_3^=$	ClO^-	$S^=$, ClO^-, AsO_4^{3-}, AsO_3^{3-}, $Cr_2O_7^=$, NO_2^-, ClO_3^-, NO_3^-, $H_2PO_2^-$
I^-	ClO^-	ClO^-, AsO_3^{3-}, $Cr_2O_7^=$, NO_2^-, NO_3^-, ClO_3^-
Br^-		ClO^-, ClO_3^-
SCN^-	ClO^-	ClO^-, $Cr_2O_7^=$, ClO_3^-
CN^-	ClO^-	ClO^-, ClO_3^-
Cl^-		ClO^-
ClO^-	$S^=$, $S_2O_3^=$, I^-, SCN^-, CN^-, AsO_3^{3-}, $SO_3^=$, NO_2^-, $H_2PO_2^-$	$S^=$, $S_2O_3^=$, I^-, Br^-, SCN^-, CN^-, Cl^-, AsO_3^{3-}, AsO_4^{3-}, $SO_3^=$, $C_2O_4^=$, NO_2^-, $H_2PO_2^-$
PO_4^{3-}		
AsO_4^{3-}		$S^=$, $S_2O_3^=$, ClO^-, $H_2PO_2^-$
AsO_3^{3-}	ClO^-	$S^=$, $S_2O_3^=$, ClO^-, ClO_3^-, $H_2PO_2^-$
$CrO_4^=$		$S^=$, $S_2O_3^=$, I^-, SCN^-, AsO_3^{3-}, $C_2O_4^=$, $SO_3^=$, NO_2^-, $H_2PO_2^-$
$CO_3^=$		
$C_2O_4^=$		$S^=$, ClO^-, $Cr_2O_7^=$, ClO_3^-
$SO_3^=$	ClO^-	$S^=$, ClO^-, $Cr_2O_7^=$, NO_2^-, ClO_3^-, NO_3^-, $H_2PO_2^-$
NO_2^-	ClO^-	$S^=$, $S_2O_3^=$, I^-, ClO^-, $Cr_2O_7^=$, $SO_3^=$, ClO_3^-, $H_2PO_2^-$
$SO_4^=$		$H_2PO_2^-$
CH_3COO^-		
BO_2^-		
ClO_3^-	$H_2PO_2^-$	$S^=$, $S_2O_3^=$, I^-, Br^-, SCN^-, CN^-, AsO_3^{3-}, $C_2O_4^=$, $SO_3^=$, NO_2^-, $H_2PO_2^-$
F^-		
NO_3^-		$S^=$, $S_2O_3^=$, I^-, AsO_3^{3-}, $SO_3^=$, $H_2PO_2^-$
$H_2PO_2^-$	ClO^-, ClO_3^-	$S_2O_3^=$, ClO^-, AsO_4^{3-}, AsO_3^{3-}, $Cr_2O_7^=$, $SO_3^=$, NO_2^-, $SO_4^=$, ClO_3^-, NO_3^-

is higher in alkaline solution. Of salts that have about the same solubility in neutral solution, those whose anion forms the weakest or most unstable acid dissolve most readily. However, salts like Ag_2S do not dissolve in acid solutions even though H_2S is a weak acid. This is due to the very low solubility of Ag_2S in neutral solution.

The elimination tests are not used to prove the presence of an anion; they determine the absence of a group of ions. After this is determined, positive tests are made to determine which of the ions not proved absent are actually present. That is, the elimination tests are an indirect method of determining which ions should be tested for in the analysis. If the evidence indicating the absence of an ion is questionable, this ion should be included among those for which positive tests are to be made. Characteristic reactions often indicate that a certain ion is present, and in such cases positive tests for the ion should be made. All observations should be explainable when it is known which ions are present. After the analysis is complete, look over the notes you recorded in the elimination tests and see that all your observations can be accounted for. Do not report ions that are incompatible in alkaline solutions before carefully checking the results of the analysis. Table 24.2 lists some of the incompatibilities that exist between the anions in alkaline solutions and in acidic solutions. Some of the ions interact slowly; mixtures of these ions may therefore be found in a freshly prepared solution.

1. Elimination Tests by Preliminary Examination

Although the preliminary examination of the unknown solutions does not give conclusive evidence as to the presence or absence of a given ion, the results of such an examination may be used to corroborate other tests. The approximate nature of these tests must be emphasized, especially when only small amounts of the ions are in solution. Hence, most of the ions listed as absent on the basis of these tests should have a question mark after them; and unless more positive evidence for absence is obtained from the other elimination tests, the ion should be tested for in the systematic procedures.

Test 1-*A*. *Color.* Observe the color of the solution. The anions that exhibit color are listed in Table 24.3. The intensity of the color varies with the concentration of the ion. In concentrated solutions the colors are often different than in dilute solutions. Likewise mixtures of colored ions give hues not shown by other ions. The colors in the table are for solutions with concentrations of ions from 1 mg./ml. to 10 mg./ml. If

TABLE 24.3. Preliminary Examination

Ions	Color of the Dilute Solution of the Alkali Metal Salts of the Anions	1-A Colorless Solution Shows the Probable Absence of	Effect of Alkali Salts of Anions on the Color of the Indicators	1-B If Solution Does Not Turn Green, the Following May Be Absent	Gases Evolved in Acid Solutions of the Anions	1-C No Gas Shows the Possible Absence of Large Amounts of	Odors of Gases Evolved from Acid Solutions of the Anions	1-D No Odor Shows the Probable Absence of	Summary of Ions Which *May Be* Absent	Ions Indicated by Characteristic Behavior
$S^=$	—	—	Green	$S^=$	H_2S	$S^=$ (?)	H_2S (rotten eggs)	$S^=$		
$S_2O_3^=$	—	—	—	—	SO_2	$S_2O_3^=$ (?)	SO_2 (burning sulfur)	$S_2O_3^=$ (?)		
I^-	—	—	—	—	—	—	—	—		
Br^-	—	—	—	—	—	—	—	—		
SCN^-	—	—	—	—	—	—	—	—		
CN^-	—	—	Green	CN^-	HCN	CN^- (?)	HCN (bitter almonds)	CN^- (?)		
Cl^-	—	—	—	—	—	—	—	—		
ClO^-	—	—	Green	ClO^-	Cl_2	ClO^- (?)	Cl_2 (chlorine)	ClO^-		
PO_4^{3-}	—	—	Green	PO_4^{3-} (?)	—	—	—	—		
AsO_4^{3-}	—	—	Green	AsO_4^{3-} (?)	—	—	—	—		
AsO_3^{3-}	—	—	Green	AsO_3^{3-} (?)	—	—	—	—		
$CrO_4^=$	Yellow	$CrO_4^=$	Green	$CrO_4^=$ (?)	—	—	—	—		
$CO_3^=$	—	—	Green	$CO_3^=$	CO_2	$CO_3^=$ (?)	—	—		
$C_2O_4^=$	—	—	Green	$C_2O_4^=$ (?)	—	—	—	—		
$SO_3^=$	—	—	Green	$SO_3^=$ (?)	SO_2	$SO_3^=$ (?)	SO_2 (burning sulfur)	$SO_3^=$ (?)		
NO_2^-	—	—	Green	NO_2^- (?)	NO	NO_2^- (?)	NO and NO_2 (concd. HNO_3)	NO_2^- (?)		
$SO_4^=$	—	—	—	—	—	—	—	—		
CH_3COO^-	—	—	Green	CH_3COO^- (?)	—	—	—	—		
BO_2^-	—	—	Green	BO_2^-	—	—	—	—		
ClO_3^-	—	—	—	—	—	—	—	—		
F^-	—	—	Green	F^- (?)	—	—	—	—		
NO_3^-	—	—	—	—	—	—	—	—		
$H_2PO_2^-$	—	—	—	—	—	—	—	—		

the solution is colorless, the ions listed under 1-A *may be* absent. This assumes the absence of colored cations.

Test 1-B. Acidity or Basicity. To 1 ml. of water add 1 drop of bromthymol blue and 1 drop of methyl red. To this orange-yellow solution add 1 drop of the unknown solution. The colors produced by dilute solutions (1 mg. to 10 mg./ml.) of the alkali metal salts of the anions are given in Table 24.3. This test has little significance unless it is known that the solution contains only the normal alkali metal salts of the anions. It does not apply to solid unknowns dissolved by solvents or solutions other than distilled water. If no change in color occurs and if the solution is made from the normal alkali metal salts, the ions listed under 1-B *may be* absent.

If the solution turns red, free acid or an acid salt is indicated, and only small amounts of the following ions can be present: CO_3^{--}, S^{--}, NO_2^{-}, SO_3^{--}, $S_2O_3^{--}$, CN^{-}.

Test 1-C. Evolution of Gases. To 0.5 ml. of water add 3 drops of the unknown and 1 drop of 6-*N* HCl. Observe the solution closely to determine whether any small bubbles of gas are evolved. Place the tube in a hot water bath for 30 seconds and again examine the solution for the evolution of gases. The gases evolved from dilute acid solutions of the anions are listed in Table 24.3. If no gas is evolved, the ions listed under 1-C *may be* absent. Since the gases evolved from small amounts of the anions are sometimes difficult to see, this test is *not conclusive evidence for the absence of the gas-evolving anions.* If other evidence for their absence is not obtained from the other tests, the analysis should include the ions listed in 1-C.

Test 1-D. Odors. When noting the odor of gases or solutions, *do not inhale the gases.* Draw the gases liberated in Test 1-C a short way into the nose and immediately blow them out again. This is important whether or not an odor is detected, because some people cannot recognize the odor of the poisonous gas, HCN. Hydrogen sulfide is as poisonous as HCN, but its odor is more easily detected.

If a white precipitate or a cloudy precipitate remains in the acidified solution, it is probably due to free sulfur from one or more of the following reactions: decomposition of $S_2O_3^{--}$, reaction of SO_3^{--} and S^{--}, reaction of oxidizing agents with S^{--}.

From the results of this preliminary examination, make a list of the ions which may be absent. Place a question mark after the ions because none of these tests are conclusive evidence for the absence of the ions. If any characteristic precipitates, odors, or colors indicate the presence of a certain ion, make a note of this behavior. Do not take this as proof of the presence of the ion, but use it as a guide for further tests in the schematic analysis.

2. Elimination Tests with Silver Nitrate

To 0.5 ml. of distilled water add 1 drop of the solution to be tested. To this solution add 1 drop of methyl red indicator (red — 4.2 : 6.3 — yellow) and 1 drop of bromthymol blue indicator (yellow — 6.0 : 7.6 — blue). Adjust the color of the solution to yellow by adding 0.01-*N* HNO_3 drop by drop if the solution is blue or green, or by adding 0.01-*N* NH_4OH if it is orange or pink. When the color of the indicators is yellow, the pH of the solution is between 6 and 7, i.e., approximately neutral.

Test 2-A. Silver Salts Insoluble in Neutral Solution. Add 2 drops of 1-*N* $AgNO_3$. The precipitates that may form are listed in Table 24.4. If no precipitate is formed, all the ions listed under 2-A in the table are absent; no test for them is required.

Test 2-B. Colored Silver Salts. Observe the color of the precipitate. If only a *white* precipitate is obtained, the ions listed under 2-B in Table 24.4 are probably absent. Those with a question mark are doubtful because the color of the precipitate may be masked by a large amount of white precipitate.

Test 2-C. Silver Salts Insoluble in Dilute Nitric Acid. Add 2 drops of 4-*N* HNO_3 to the mixture from 2-B. The precipitates that do not dissolve are listed in Table 24.4. If no precipitate remains, the ions listed under 2-C are absent.

Test 2-D. Colored Silver Salts Insoluble in Dilute Nitric Acid. Observe the color of the precipitate. If only a *white* precipitate remains undissolved, the ions listed under 2-D are probably absent.

Test 2-E. Silver Salts Insoluble in Ammonium Hydroxide. To the solution from 2-D, add 10 drops of 15-*N* NH_4OH. The precipitates that do not dissolve are listed in Table 24.4. If the precipitate completely dissolves, the ions listed under 2-E are absent.

From these tests make a list of the ions that are shown to be absent. If any characteristic precipitate or reaction seems to indicate the presence of a certain ion, make a note of this behavior. Do not take this as final proof of the presence of an ion, but use it as a guide for further tests.

TABLE 24.4. Anion Elimination Tests with Silver Nitrate

Anion	Precipitates Formed with $AgNO_3$ in Neutral Solution	2-A No Precipitate Shows the Absence of	2-B A White Precipitate Only Shows the Absence of	Precipitates Not Dissolved by Dilute HNO_3	2-C No Precipitate Shows the Absence of	2-D A White Precipitate Only Shows the Absence of	Precipitates Not Dissolved by Concd. NH_4OH	2-E No Precipitate Shows the Absence of	Summary of Ions Shown to Be Absent	Ions Indicated by Characteristic Behavior
$S^{=}$	Ag_2S (black)	$S^{=}$	$S^{=}$	Ag_2S	$S^{=}$	$S^{=}$	Ag_2S	$S^{=}$		
I^-	AgI (yellow)	I^-	I^- (?)	AgI	I^-	I^- (?)	AgI	I^-		
Br^-	$AgBr$ (cream)	Br^-	Br^- (?)	$AgBr$	Br^-	Br^- (?)	—	—		
SCN^-	$AgSCN$ (white)	SCN^-	—	$AgSCN$	SCN^-	—	—	—		
CN^-	$AgCN$ (white)	CN^-	—	$AgCN$	CN^-	—	—	—		
Cl^-	$AgCl$ (white)	Cl^-	—	$AgCl$	Cl^-	—	—	—		
ClO^-	$AgCl$ (white)	ClO^-	—	$AgCl$	ClO^-	—	—	—		
$S_2O_3^{=}$	$Ag_2S_2O_3$ (white) $\rightarrow$ Ag_2S (black)	$S_2O_3^{=}$	$S_2O_3^{=}$	Ag_2S	$S_2O_3^{=}$	$S_2O_3^{=}$	Ag_2S	$S_2O_3^{=}$		
PO_4^{3-}	Ag_3PO_4 (yellow)	PO_4^{3-}	PO_4^{3-} (?)	—	—	—	—	—		
AsO_4^{3-}	Ag_3AsO_4 (reddish)	AsO_4^{3-}	AsO_4^{3-}	—	—	—	—	—		
AsO_3^{3-}	Ag_3AsO_3 (yellow)	AsO_3^{3-}	AsO_3^{3-}	—	—	—	—	—		
$CrO_4^{=}$	Ag_2CrO_4 (red)	$CrO_4^{=}$	$CrO_4^{=}$	—	—	—	—	—		
$CO_3^{=}$	Ag_2CO_3 (yellow)	$CO_3^{=}$	$CO_3^{=}$ (?)	—	—	—	—	—		
$C_2O_4^{=}$	$Ag_2C_2O_4$ (white)	$C_2O_4^{=}$	—	—	—	—	—	—		
$SO_3^{=}$	Ag_2SO_3 (white)	$SO_3^{=}$	—	—	—	—	—	—		
NO_2^-	* $AgNO_2$ (white)	—	—	—	—	—	—	—		
CH_3COO^-	* $Ag(CH_3COO)$ (white)	—	—	—	—	—	—	—		
BO_2^-	* $AgBO_2$ (white)	—	—	—	—	—	—	—		
ClO_3^-	—	—	—	—	—	—	—	—		
SO_4	* Ag_2SO_4 (white)	—	—	—	—	—	—	—		
F^-	—	—	—	—	—	—	—	—		
NO_3^-	—	—	—	—	—	—	—	—		
$H_2PO_2^-$	AgH_2PO_2 (white) $\rightarrow$ Ag° (black)	$H_2PO_2^-$	$H_2PO_2^-$ (?)	Ag°	$H_2PO_2^-$	$H_2PO_2^-$	Ag°	$H_2PO_2^-$		

* These precipitates will not form unless the concentration of the anions is higher than 5 mg./ml. Since only 1 drop of the original solutions is used, these precipitates are not formed in this test.

3. Elimination Tests with Calcium Acetate and Barium Acetate

Test 3-A. Insoluble Calcium Salts. To 1 ml. of water add 1 drop of the solution to be tested and then add 1 drop of 4-*N* NH_4OH and 1 drop of 1-*N* $Ca(CH_3COO)_2$. The precipitates that form are listed in Table 24.5. If no precipitate forms, the ions listed under 3-A are absent and no test for them is required.

Test 3-B. Soluble Calcium Salts—Insoluble Barium Salts. If no precipitate is formed in Test 3-A, add 1 drop of 1-*N* $Ba(CH_3COO)_2$. The precipitates that form are listed in Table 24.5. If no precipitate forms, the ions listed under 3-B are absent. (NOTE: This test is valid only if no precipitate was obtained in Test 3-A. If a precipitate is formed in 3-A, it may be filtered off and $Ba(CH_3COO)_2$ added to the filtrate. In this case, Test 3-C must be made on a new sample of the unknown solution.)

Test 3-C. Ions Converted to Sulfates by HNO_3 and Calcium and Barium Salts Insoluble in HNO_3. Add 4 drops of 4-*N* HNO_3 to the tube from 3-A and 3-B (or to 1 drop of the unknown solution in 1 ml. of water); add 1 drop of 1-*N* $Ca(CH_3COO)_2$ and 1 drop of 1-*N* $Ba(CH_3COO)_2$, and then 4 drops of 4-*N* HNO_3. Place the tube in a hot water bath for 2 or 3 minutes. The precipitates that remain undissolved are listed in Table 24.5. If no precipitates remain, the ions listed under 3-C are absent.

Test 3-D. Ions Not Decomposed by HCl. To 1 ml. of water in an evaporation test tube add 1 drop of the unknown solution and 1 drop of 6-*N* HCl. Boil the solution until its volume is about 0.5 ml. Filter if a white precipitate is formed. (The white precipitate is probably sulfur from the decomposition of $S_2O_3^{--}$ or from the interaction of S^{--} with SO_3^{--} or an oxidizing agent in the acid solution.) Add 1 drop of phenolphthalein and then 4-*N* NH_4OH until the solution is pink. Now add 1 drop of 1-*N* $Ca(CH_3COO)_2$ and 1 drop of 1-*N* $Ba(CH_3COO)_2$. The precipitates that form are listed in Table 24.5. If reducing anions are present, CrO_4^{--} (yellow) may be converted to Cr^{3+} (green). In this case $BaCrO_4$ will not form. If no precipitate is formed, the ions listed under 3-D are absent.

From these tests make a list of the ions that are shown to be absent. If any characteristic precipitates, odors, or reactions indicate the presence of a certain ion, record the fact. Do not take this as final proof of the presence of the ion, but use the result as a guide for further tests in the analysis for the ions of Group II.

TABLE 24.5. Anion Elimination Tests with Calcium Acetate-Barium Acetate Reagent

Ions	Precipitates Formed with $Ca(CH_3COO)_2$	3-A No Precipitate Shows the Absence of	Additional Precipitates Formed with $Ba(CH_3COO)_2$	3-B No Precipitate Shows the Absence of	Precipitates Remaining Undissolved After Heating with HNO_3	3-C Ions Absent if the Precipitate Completely Dissolves	Precipitates Formed with Ca^{++}-Ba^{++} After Heating with HCl	3-D No Precipitate Shows the Absence of	Summary: Ions Shown to Be Absent	Ions Indicated by Characteristic Behavior
$S^{=}$	—	—	—	—	—	—	—	—		
I^{-}	—	—	—	—	—	—	—	—		
Br^{-}	—	—	—	—	—	—	—	—		
SCN^{-}	—	—	—	—	—	—	—	—		
CN^{-}	—	—	—	—	—	—	—	—		
Cl^{-}	—	—	—	—	—	—	—	—		
ClO^{-}	—	—	—	—	—	—	—	—		
$S_2O_3^{=}$	—	—	BaS_2O_3 (?)	$S_2O_3^{=}$ (?)	$BaSO_4$	$S_2O_3^{=}$	—	—		
PO_4^{3-}	$Ca_3(PO_4)_2$ (white)	PO_4^{3-}	—	—	—	—	$Ca_3(PO_4)_2$	PO_4^{3-}		
AsO_4^{3-}	$Ca_3(AsO_4)_2$ (white)	AsO_4^{3-}	—	—	—	—	$Ca_3(AsO_4)_2$	AsO_4^{3-}		
AsO_3^{3-}	$Ca_3(AsO_3)_2$ (white)	AsO_3^{3-}	—	—	—	—	$Ca_3(AsO_3)_2$	AsO_3^{3-}		
$CrO_4^{=}$	—	—	$BaCrO_4$	$CrO_4^{=}$	—	—	$BaCrO_4$	$CrO_4^{=}$ (?)		
$CO_3^{=}$	$CaCO_3$ (white)	$CO_3^{=}$	—	—	—	—	—	—		
$C_2O_4^{=}$	CaC_2O_4 (white)	$C_2O_4^{=}$	—	—	—	—	CaC_2O_4	$C_2O_4^{=}$		
$SO_3^{=}$	$CaSO_3$ (white)	$SO_3^{=}$	—	—	$BaSO_4$	$SO_3^{=}$	—	—		
NO_2^{-}	—	—	$Ba(NO_2)_2$ (?)	NO_2^{-} (?)	—	—	—	—		
CH_3COO^{-}	—	—	—	—	—	—	—	—		
BO_2^{-}	—	—	—	—	—	—	—	—		
ClO_3^{-}	—	—	—	—	—	—	—	—		
$SO_4^{=}$	—	—	$BaSO_4$	$SO_4^{=}$	$BaSO_4$	$SO_4^{=}$	$BaSO_4$	$SO_4^{=}$		
F^{-}	CaF_2 (white)	F^{-}	—	—	CaF_2 (?)	F^{-} (?)	CaF_2	F^{-}		
NO_3^{-}	—	—	—	—	—	—	—	—		
$H_2PO_2^{-}$	—	—	—	—	—	—	—	—		

4. Elimination Tests for Oxidizing Anions

Test 4-A. Ions That Oxidize $MnCl_2$. To a test tube add 10 drops of a reagent made by saturating concd. HCl with $MnCl_2$. To this reagent add 1 drop of the solution to be tested and place the tube in a hot water bath. The results obtained with the different anions are listed in Table 24.6. If no coloration or precipitate is obtained, the ions under 4-A are absent.

TABLE 24.6. Elimination Tests for Oxidizing Anions

Ions	Results with Concd. HCl and $MnCl_2$	4-A No Precipitate Shows the Absence of	Results with Di-phenyl-benzidine in 85% H_2SO_4	4-B No Coloration or Precipitate Shows the Absence of	Summary of Ions Shown to Be Absent	Ions Indicated by Characteristic Behavior
$S^=$	—	—	—	—		
I^-	—	—	Reddish coloration	I^-		
Br^-	—	—	Blue (slow)	Br^-		
SCN^-	—	—	—	—		
CN^-	—	—	—	—		
Cl^-	—	—	—	—		
ClO^-	Black ppt.	ClO^-	Blue solution	ClO^-		
$S_2O_3^=$	Murky (S) white	$S_2O_3^=$	Murky (S) white	$S_2O_3^=$		
PO_4^{3-}	—	—	—	—		
AsO_4^{3-}	—	—	—	—		
AsO_3^{3-}	—	—	—	—		
$CrO_4^=$	Black ppt.	$CrO_4^=$	Blue-red-yellow	$CrO_4^=$		
$CO_3^=$	—	—	—	—		
$C_2O_4^=$	—	—	—	—		
$SO_3^=$	—	—	—	—		
NO_2^-	—	—	Blue solution	NO_2^-		
CH_3COO^-	—	—	—	—		
BO_2^-	—	—	—	—		
ClO_3^-	Black ppt.	ClO_3^-	Blue-purple-yellow	ClO_3^-		
$SO_4^=$	—	—	—	—		
F^-	—	—	—	—		
NO_3^-	Black ppt.	NO_3^-	Blue solution	NO_3^-		
$H_2PO_2^-$	—	—	—	—		

Test 4-B. Ions That Oxidize Di-phenyl-benzidine. To a test tube add 10 drops of di-phenyl-benzidine (0.01%) in 85% sulfuric acid. To this reagent add 1 drop of the solution to be tested and place the tube in the hot water bath. The results obtained with different anions are listed in Table 24.6. If no coloration appears, the ions listed under 4-B are absent.

From the results of these tests make a list of the ions that are shown to be absent. If any characteristic precipitates or colors indicate the presence of a certain ion, record the fact. Do not take this as proof of the presence of the ion, but use the result as a guide for further tests.

5. Elimination Tests for Reducing Anions

Test 5-A. Ions That Reduce $KMnO_4$. To 1 ml. of distilled water add 1 drop of the solution to be tested. To this solution add 1 drop of 4-*N* H_2SO_4 and 1 drop of 0.01-*M* $KMnO_4$. Place the tube in the hot water bath for 1 minute. The results obtained with the different anions are

TABLE 24.7. Elimination Tests for Reducing Anions

Ion	Results with $KMnO_4$ and H_2SO_4	5-A No Precipitate or Discharge of Color Shows the Absence of	Results with $K_3Fe(CN)_6$ + $Fe(NO_3)_3$ + HNO_3	5-B No Coloration Shows the Absence of	Summary of Ions Shown to Be Absent	Ions Indicated by Characteristic Behavior
$S^=$	Colorless	$S^=$	Green to blue	$S^=$		
I^-	Brown color	I^-	Blue color	I^-		
Br^-	Brown ppt.	Br^-	——	——		
SCN^-	——	——	Red color	SCN^-		
CN^-	——	——	——	——		
Cl^-	——	——	——	——		
ClO^-	——	——	——	——		
$S_2O_3^=$	Colorless (white S)	$S_2O_3^=$	Blue color	$S_2O_3^=$		
PO_4^{3-}	——	——	——	——		
AsO_4^{3-}	——	——	——	——		
AsO_3^{3-}	Colorless	AsO_3^{3-}	Green	AsO_3^{3-}		
$CrO_4^=$	——	——	——	——		
$CO_3^=$	——	——	——	——		
$C_2O_4^=$	Colorless	$C_2O_4^=$	Green (slow)	$C_2O_4^=$		
$SO_3^=$	Colorless	$SO_3^=$	Green to blue	$SO_3^=$		
NO_2^-	Colorless	NO_2^-	Blue color	NO_2^-		
CH_3COO^-	——	——	——	——		
BO_2^-	——	——	——	——		
ClO_3^-	——	——	——	——		
$SO_4^=$	——	——	——	——		
F^-	——	——	——	——		
NO_3^-	——	——	——	——		
$H_2PO_2^-$	Colorless	$H_2PO_2^-$	Green	$H_2PO_2^-$		

listed in Table 24.7. If the color of the permanganate is not discharged or if a precipitate is not formed, the ions listed under 5-A are absent.

Test 5-B. Ions That Reduce Ferriferricyanide. Prepare an acid solution of ferriferricyanide by adding 1 drop of 4-*N* HNO_3, 1 drop of K_3Fe-

$(CN)_6$ test solution, and 1 drop of $Fe(NO_3)_3$ test solution to 0.5 ml. of water. To this solution add 1 drop of the solution to be tested. Place the tube in a hot water bath for 1 minute. The results obtained with the different anions are listed in Table 24.7. If no coloration appears, the ions listed under 5-B are absent.

From the results of these tests make a list of the ions that are shown to be absent. If any characteristic colors or precipitates indicate the presence of a given ion, record the fact. Do not take this as proof of the presence of the ion, but use the results as a guide for further tests.

Summary of Anion Elimination Tests

Record the final results of the anion elimination tests in a table similar to Table 24.8. List the ions shown to be absent by each series of elim-

TABLE 24.8. Summary of Anion Elimination Tests

NOTE: Place opposite the anion the number of the elimination test which showed the anion to be absent.

Anion	Anions Shown to Be Absent by						
	1-A, B, C, D	2-A, B, C, D, E	3-A, B, C, D	4-A, B	5-A, B	Summary of Anions Absent	Ions That May Be Present
$S^=$							
I^-							
Br^-							
SCN^-							
CN^-							
Cl^-							
ClO^-							
$S_2O_3^=$							
PO_4^{3-}							
AsO_4^{3-}							
AsO_3^{3-}							
$CrO_4^=$							
$CO_3^=$							
$C_2O_4^=$							
$SO_3^=$							
NO_2^-							
CH_3COO^-							
BO_2^-							
ClO_3^-							
$SO_4^=$							
F^-							
NO_3^-							
$H_2PO_2^-$							

ination tests. If the absence of an ion is questionable, place a question mark after it and include it in the list of ions for which tests must be made. In the last column of the table list all the anions that were not proved absent. Determine the groups in which these ions occur. Proceed with the analysis of these groups, but omit tests for all ions definitely shown to be absent. Select the special tests given for the anions of Group IV when they eliminate the necessity of analyzing for a complete group.

Check the groups in which the ions in the last column occur. Analyze the unknown solution according to the Procedures for these groups.

Group I (S^{--}, I^-, Br^-, SCN^-, CN^-, Cl^-, ClO^-, $S_2O_3^{--}$).
Group II (F^-, $C_2O_4^{--}$, SO_3^{--}, PO_4^{3-}, CO_3^{--}, SO_4^{--}, CrO_4^{--}, AsO_4^{3-}, AsO_3^{3-}).
Group III (NO_2^-, NO_3^-, BO_2^-, CH_3COO^-, ClO_3^-, $H_2PO_2^-$).

Check the ions of Group IV that may be present. If one or two of these ions are the only ones in a group, you may save some time by using the special tests given in the Procedures for Group IV. Consider possible interferences that may result when the solution is acidified.

Group IV (ClO^-, CO_3^{--}, SO_3^{--}, $S_2O_3^{--}$, S^{--}, NO_2^-, CN^-).

GENERAL REVIEW QUESTIONS ON THE ANALYSIS FOR ANIONS

1. Of the 23 anions in the scheme of analysis, give the formula of the one with a color and name its color. Name some other colored anions.
2. If solutions were made from the sodium salts of the 23 anions, which solutions would have (a) a basic reaction, (b) an acidic reaction, (c) a neutral reaction to bromthymol blue indicator? Explain, in general, why these different solutions show basic, acidic, and neutral reactions.
3. If the 23 anion solutions were acidified, which would evolve a gas? Write the formulas of the gas evolved from the different solutions.
4. Of the 23 anion solutions, give the formulas of the anions which may be classified as good oxidizing anions.
5. Of the 23 anion solutions, give the formulas of the anions which may be classified as good reducing anions.
6. Write the formulas of the precipitates obtained when silver nitrate is added to solutions of the anions and the solutions are then acidified.
7. Which anions might escape detection by the formation of a precipitate if the solution was first acidified before the silver nitrate was added? Why?
8. The solubility of $Ca_3(PO_4)_2$ is 1.6×10^{-6} g./ml., and that of AgCl is 1.9×10^{-6} g./ml. in water at 20°. If a water solution containing precipitates of $Ca_3(PO_4)_2$ and AgCl is acidified with a weak acid such as acetic,

the $Ca_3(PO_4)_2$ precipitate dissolves readily, but the AgCl precipitate does not dissolve. How do you account for the difference in the solubility of these two salts in an acid solution?

9. The solubility of $BaCrO_4$ is 3.6×10^{-6} g./ml., and that of $BaSO_4$ is 2.3×10^{-6} g./ml. in water at 20°. If a solution containing these precipitates is acidified with a strong acid, the $BaCrO_4$ dissolves readily, but the $BaSO_4$ does not dissolve. Why is this?
10. The solubility of most of the silver salts of the anions is low. How do you account for the fact that only 7 of the silver salts of the 23 anions are not soluble in a solution acidified with nitric acid?
11. When silver nitrate is added to a solution containing ClO^-, a precipitate of AgCl is obtained, instead of AgClO. Why?
12. When silver nitrate is added to a solution containing $S_2O_3^{--}$, a precipitate of Ag_2S and S° is obtained, instead of $Ag_2S_2O_3$. Why?
13. Of the silver salts of Group I, which are not soluble in an ammoniacal silver nitrate solution (Miller's reagent)? Why are they not soluble in this reagent?
14. Of the silver salts of Group I, which are soluble in a strong ammonia solution? Why is this?
15. Which of the silver salts of Group I are not soluble in a 0.1-*N* solution of sodium cyanide? Why? (NOTE: The instability constant for $Ag(CN)_2^-$ is 3.8×10^{-19}.)
16. In the confirmatory test for CN^- in Group I, a solution of KBr is added. Why is this reagent necessary? If KBr is not added, will a blue color appear in the presence of Cl^- only, when the benzidine reagent is added?
17. In the confirmatory test for Cl^- in Group I, a solution of $Hg(NO_3)_2$ is added. Why is this reagent necessary? Why is CH_3COONH_4 added?
18. In the test for SCN^-, a solution of $Fe(NO_3)_3$ is added. Which is a more sensitive test for SCN^-, a solution of $Fe(NO_3)_3$ or $FeCl_3$?
19. In testing a solution of I_2 with starch, why should the test be made in a cold solution?
20. In precipitating the calcium salts of Group II, why is it advisable to precipitate them in a hot solution?
21. What factors determine to a large extent the solubility of $CaCO_3$, $Ca_3(PO_4)_2$, $Ca_3(AsO_4)_2$, and $Ca_3(AsO_3)_2$ in a dilute acetic acid solution?
22. Why are CaF_2, CaC_2O_4, and $CaSO_3$ less soluble in dilute acetic acid than the other calcium salts of Group II? Why are these salts soluble in strong acids?
23. If the filtrate from the dissolution of the calcium salts soluble in dilute acetic acid was heated, would the salts be reprecipitated? Why or why not?
24. In testing for SO_3^{--}, why is a solution of iodide-iodine reagent used instead of a water solution of iodine?
25. In testing for $C_2O_4^{--}$ with MnO_4^-, why must the SO_2 be expelled from the solution?
26. Why must $C_2O_4^{--}$ and MnO_4^- be eliminated before testing for F^-?
27. In testing for F^- with lanthanum nitrate, why is eosin added to the solution?

28. If $MgNH_4PO_4$ and $MgNH_4AsO_4$ were ignited, what products would be obtained?
29. Though SO_3^{--} is placed in the unknown solution, in many cases it is not found. Why?
30. What are the colors of the salts, Ag_3AsO_4, Ag_3AsO_3, and Ag_3PO_4?
31. If AsO_3^{3-} is treated with the ammonium molybdate-nitric acid reagent and the solution is heated, what will be the formula of the precipitate? Why?
32. The solubility of $BaSO_4$ is 2.3×10^{-6} g./ml., and that of $BaCO_3$ is 1.4×10^{-5} g./ml. How would you convert the $BaSO_4$ to $BaCO_3$?
33. What formula has been assigned to the compound that gives a blue color to an acidified chromate solution when H_2O_2 is added?
34. Why is a solution of Ag_2SO_4 used to precipitate the anions of Groups I and II before tests are made for the anions of Group III? Can you suggest another silver salt that might be used? Why must the solution from which Groups I and II are removed have a pH near 7? Could some other salt than that of silver be used?
35. What reagents other than HCHO could be used to reduce Cl^{5+} to Cl^-?
36. If $H_2PO_2^-$ is treated with the ammonium molybdate-nitric acid reagent and the solution is heated, what formula will the precipitate have? Why?
37. Can H_2O_2 be used in place of MnO_4^- to oxidize $H_2PO_2^-$ to PO_4^{3-}?
38. Instead of SO_2 in water, the solid Na_2SO_3 may be used to produce the blue color in testing for PO_4^{3-}. Why is this possible? Is the salt as satisfactory?
39. Why is it necessary to eliminate NO_2^- and ClO_3^- before testing for NO_3^- with nitron reagent?
40. Why is the iodoform test more sensitive for the acetate ion than the formation of ethyl or methyl acetate?
41. There are at least fifty tests for the nitrite ion. Why is the sulfanilic acid-α-naphthylamine test usually selected?
42. If you add Ba^{++} and sulfamic acid to a solution assumed to contain NO_2^- and obtain a white precipitate, does this prove the presence of NO_2^-? What precaution is necessary in making this test?
43. Why is the analysis of unknowns of the anions more difficult and less accurate than the analysis of the cations?
44. Which of the anions in Groups I–III may be obtained commercially as the corresponding acid?
45. Which of the anions in Groups I–III could be detected by using the Procedures for analyzing cations?
46. Assuming that all the anions of Group I are present in an unknown, write balanced equations for the reactions by which each ion may be separated and identified. Use the proper marking for the equations, such as underlining, arrows, color of precipitates, etc.
47. An unknown was made up to contain $S_2O_3^{--}$, I^-, SO_3^{--}, and ClO_3^-. Which ions might not be present when this unknown was analyzed?
48. An unknown was made up to contain CN^-, CO_3^{--}, NO_3^-, and $Cr_2O_7^{--}$. Which ions might not be present when this unknown was analyzed?

49. An unknown was made up to contain I^-, AsO_3^{3-}, NO_2^-, and ClO_3^-. Which ions might not be present when this unknown was analyzed?
50. An unknown was made up to contain ClO^-, CrO_4^{--}, ClO_3^-, and $C_2O_4^{--}$. Which ions might not be present when this unknown was analyzed?
51. If all the anions were placed in an acidified solution of an unknown, which ions might be present when the unknown was analyzed? (NOTE: Assume equal concentrations of each ion in the original unknown.)

CHAPTER 25

SYSTEMATIC ANALYSIS OF A SOLID UNKNOWN FOR CATIONS AND ANIONS

A complete systematic analysis of a solid unknown material, such as a mixture of salts, involves the following operations:

1. Physical examination.
2. Preliminary tests.
3. Preparation of the solution, and analysis for the anions.
4. Preparation of the solution, and analysis for the cations.
5. Examination of the results, and decision as to probable composition of the original material.

The analysis of metals and alloys has already been described (p. 269). The analysis of a solution that may contain mixtures of both cations and anions is carried out in the same way as is the analysis of a solid, but with modifications necessitated by the fact that the substances are already in solution. The physical examination and the preliminary tests are sometimes more complete if it is desired to determine more definitely which substances or combinations of ions were present originally in the solid material.

1. Physical Examination

HOMOGENEITY. Examine the solid with a hand lens if one is available, and determine whether the substance appears to be homogeneous or heterogeneous. If more than one component is present, separate them and observe whether the different solids are crystalline, and whether they are hard or soft. Touch each component with moist litmus to determine whether it gives an acidic, basic, or neutral reaction. Other physical characteristics such as density, melting point, flame colorations, etc., may be determined in special cases. Cautiously note the odor. Not many dry salts have an odor; but when they are moist, partial decomposition may result in the formation of gases with characteristic odors.

COLOR. The color of the different components often gives some indication of the composition. However, conclusions must be drawn carefully because some salts have different colors depending on their degree of hydration. Combinations of colored cations and colored anions also produce a variety of colors. Furthermore, the color of certain natural minerals is different from the color of the same compounds precipitated from solution. Table 25.1 lists the colors of some of the more common inorganic substances.

TABLE 25.1. Color of Some Common Inorganic Substances

Color	Substances
Black	Ag_2S, Hg_2S, HgS, PbS, Cu_2S, CuS, FeS, CoS, NiS, CuO, NiO, Fe_3O_4, FeO, MnO_2. Finely divided metals and carbon.
Brown	Bi_2S_3, SnS, Bi_2O_3, PbO_2, Ag_2O, CdO, $CuCrO_4$, CuBr.
Red	HgS, Sb_2S_3, As_2S_3, Fe_2O_3, HgO, Pb_3O_4, BiOI, HgI_2, $(NH_4)_2Cr_2O_7$, $FeCl_3$ (anhyd.), $K_3Fe(CN)_6$, $Ag_2Cr_2O_7$. Certain other dichromates, iodides, and cobalt salts.
Pink	Hydrated cobalt salts and manganous salts.
Yellow	As_2S_3, As_2S_5, SnS_2, CdS, HgO, AgI, PbO. Most chromates, ferric salts, ferrocyanides, ferricyanides, and some iodides.
Orange	Sb_2S_5. Many dichromates.
Green	Nickel salts, hydrated ferrous salts, some cupric salts such as $CuCO_3$ and $CuCl_2$, and certain chromic salts.
Blue	Hydrated cupric salts, anhydrous cobaltous salts.
Purple	Permanganates and certain chromic salts.

2. Preliminary Tests

SAMPLING. If the substance is in the form of small crystals or if it is not homogeneous, grind it to the finest possible powder before taking samples for the preliminary tests or for the analysis. If this is not done, the sample will not be representative and may not contain some of the components. Furthermore, small particles are more rapidly dissolved by the solvents.

Test for Organic Matter. Place 5 to 10 mg. (about the size of a match head) in a 6-mm. glass tube that is 4 or 5 inches long and closed at one end. Tamp the sample in the bottom of the tube and then heat it, first gently and then strongly. If the sample turns dark and a brown tarry liquid condenses on the walls of the tube above it, organic matter is present and must be removed before the tests for the cations are made.

Observe the sample while you are heating it. Water condensing in the upper part of the tube indicates hydrates, hydrous oxides, or substances that decompose with the formation of water. A change in color may indicate the presence of certain hydrates, such as those of copper or cobalt salts; some oxides also change color when heated. If no water condenses on the tube, the presence of easily fusible substances is indicated; and if oxygen is evolved, oxycompounds such as the chlorates, nitrates, and peroxides may be present. The evolution of gases with characteristic odors and colors may give some indication of the composition of the sample. Certain substances, such as ammonium salts, As_2O_3, HgS, $HgCl_2$, and some metals, sublime and condense in the upper portion of the tube.

Test for Organic Matter in a Liquid Unknown. If the unknown is a liquid, evaporate it first in a small crucible and then warm it gently with 1 drop of concentrated sulfuric acid. Charring indicates organic matter. A solid material may also be tested for organic matter in this way.

Solubility Tests. *a. Water.* Add 1 ml. of water to 5 mg. of the sample in a test tube, and shake the tube for several minutes. If the sample does not dissolve, place the tube in the hot water bath. The solubility of various substances in water is given in handbooks and in Appendix G. A new solid sometimes forms as the result of the hydrolysis of such substances as $SnCl_4$, $BiCl_3$, and $SbCl_3$.

Note the color of the solution. The colored ions for which tests are made are listed in Table 25.2.

Table 25.2. Color of Dilute Aqueous Solutions of Ions

Color	Ions
Yellow to orange	$CrO_4^{=}$, $Fe(CN)_6^{3-}$, Fe^{3+}, $S_2^{=}$, $Fe(CN)_6^{4-}$, $Cr_2O_7^{=}$
Pink	Co^{++}, Mn^{++} (faint)
Green to blue	Ni^{++}, Fe^{++}, Cr^{3+}, Cu^{++}

To 1 ml. of water add 1 drop of bromthymol blue indicator and 1 drop of methyl red indicator. Add a few drops of the aqueous solution to the indicator solution. If the color of the indicator changes to green, the solution is basic; if the color changes to pink or red, the solution is acidic. A basic solution indicates hydroxides or oxides or salts that hydrolyze to give basic solutions, such as sulfides, carbonates, phosphates, cyanides, borates, etc. (See Table 24.3.) An acidic solution indicates free acid, acid salts, or salts that hydrolyze to give acid solutions, such as $CuCl_2$, $FeCl_3$, $Al_2(SO_4)_3$, etc.

b. Dilute Hydrochloric Acid. If the sample does not dissolve completely in water, pour off most of the liquid and add 10 drops of 6-*N* HCl. Observe carefully whether or not a gas is evolved. (See Table 24.3.) Put your thumb over the mouth of the tube and shake the tube; then raise your thumb and note whether there is pressure in the tube and a gas escapes. Now note the odor cautiously. (See Table 24.3.) Dilute HCl dissolves many salts that are not dissolved by water, particularly the slightly soluble salts of the weak acids.

c. Concentrated Hydrochloric Acid. If the sample does not dissolve in dilute HCl, put 2 mg. of it in a test tube and add 10 to 15 drops of concentrated HCl. Set the tube in the hot water bath and note the extent to which the material dissolves.

d. Dilute Nitric Acid. If the sample does not dissolve completely in the concentrated HCl, add 10 drops of 4-*N* HNO_3 to 2 mg. of it and place the tube in a hot water bath. Observe the solution and see whether a precipitate, a colored solution, or a colored gas forms.

e. Concentrated Nitric Acid. Add 6 to 8 drops of concentrated HNO_3 to 2 mg. of the sample in a test tube. Place the tube in the hot water bath and note any reaction that occurs.

f. Aqua Regia. If the sample is not soluble in the concentrated HNO_3, add about 1 ml. of concentrated HCl to the tube from *e* and set it in the hot water bath.

The behavior of the sample with each of the solvents should give some information about the substances it contains. Dilute nitric acid, for example, dissolves certain sulfides that are not dissolved by dilute hydrochloric acid. Hydrochloric acid causes AgCl, Hg_2Cl_2, and $PbCl_2$ to form, but does not dissolve them. These precipitates do not form with dilute nitric acid. Hot concentrated HCl dissolves MnO_2, PbO_2, Sb_2O_3, H_2SnO_3, $BaCrO_4$, which are not soluble in HNO_3. Concentrated HNO_3 is a very strong oxidizing agent and dissolves sulfides that are unaffected by HCl. However, part of the sulfide is converted to S and part of it to SO_4^{--}. The SO_4^{--} may cause $BaSO_4$, $SrSO_4$, $PbSO_4$, and some $CaSO_4$ to precipitate. Nitric acid oxidizes Hg_2^{++} to Hg^{++}, Fe^{++} to Fe^{3+}, AsO_2^- to

AsO_4^{3-}, Sb^{3+} to Sb_2O_5 or Sb_2O_4, Sn^{++} to H_2SnO_3. Iodides, bromides, sulfides, sulfites, thiosulfites, etc. (Table 24.7) are also oxidized by HNO_3. Hence, if nitric acid is used as a solvent, the solution may not contain the ions originally in the sample; instead, it will contain their oxidation products.

Aqua regia dissolves certain compounds that are not dissolved by either HCl or HNO_3 alone. However, as a result of oxidation, aqua regia may cause the formation of new compounds not originally present. The following substances are not completely dissolved by aqua regia: $PbSO_4$, $BaSO_4$, $SrSO_4$, $CaSO_4$; ignited $Cr_2(SO_4)_3$, $Fe_2(SO_4)_3$, $Al_2(SO_4)_3$; AgI, AgBr, AgSCN, AgCN, $Ag_4Fe(CN)_6$, $Ag_3Fe(CN)_6$, all of which may be partially converted to AgCl by the aqua regia; $PbCl_2$, $PbCrO_4$ (fused); ignited or native oxides, Al_2O_3, Fe_2O_3, Cr_2O_3, SnO_2, Sb_2O_4, SnO_2; CaF_2 (native or ignited); $Fe_4[Fe(CN)_6]_3$; silicates, H_2SiO_3, SiO_2; C and S.

Further preliminary tests may be made on the residue that is not dissolved by the acid treatments. Such tests are essentially the same as those used for the analysis of the insoluble residue (see p. 367).

3. Preparation of the Solution and the Analysis for the Anions

REMOVAL OF INTERFERING CATIONS. *a. Sample Soluble in Water.* If the sample was shown to be soluble in water, dissolve about 20 mg. in 2 ml. of water. Observe the color of the solution. Add 1 drop of bromthymol blue indicator and 1 drop of methyl red indicator. If the solution is pink or red, it is acidic. In this case, add 4-*N* NaOH to the solution until the color is yellow or green. Now add 1 drop of 1.5-*M* Na_2CO_3. *If no precipitate forms* with either NaOH or Na_2CO_3, the solution is ready for analysis of the anions. Carry out as many of the elimination tests as possible. Reserve one-third of the solution for a check analysis, and analyze the remainder for as many of the different groups of anions as the elimination tests make necessary. Tests for the carbonate ion must be made on the original unknown sample.

If a precipitate forms, add 10 drops of 1.5-*M* Na_2CO_3 and set the tube in the hot water bath for at least 10 minutes. Keep the water in the bath near its boiling point. Filter the solution and observe its color (see Elimination Test 1, Table 24.3). Reserve 5 drops of this solution for the test for the acetate ion (Procedure 25). To the remainder add 1 drop of bromthymol blue and 1 drop of methyl red indicator. Now add 4-*N* CH_3COOH drop by drop, shaking the tube after each drop until the solution is yellow. Take care to prevent the solution from becoming acidic (pink). The solution is now ready for the elimination tests and the analysis according to the Procedures for the different groups. A test for the carbonate ion must be made on the original unknown material.

(NOTE: Boiling with Na_2CO_3 removes nearly all the metals except As, Sb, the alkali metals, small quantities of the amphoteric elements, and small amounts of ions that form complex ammines such as $Cu(NH_3)_4^{++}$. The ions that are not precipitated usually do not interfere with the anion analysis.)

b. Sample Not Completely Soluble in Water. If the preliminary tests show that the sample is not completely soluble in water, place about 20 mg. of the finely ground solid in a 25-ml. Erlenmeyer flask and add 2 ml. of 1.5-*M* Na_2CO_3. Boil the solution gently for at least 10 minutes. Occasionally add water to replace the water that evaporates. Filter the solution through a cotton medium in the pressure filter tube and then wash the residue with 10 drops of water which contains 1 drop of 1.5-*M* Na_2CO_3.

Add 1 ml. of 4-*N* CH_3COOH to the precipitate and stir it with a stirring rod. If the precipitate completely dissolves, the sample has been completely converted to carbonates. If a residue remains, force the acetic acid solution through the filter medium and wash the residue thoroughly with 2 ml. of water. Now add 10 drops of 1.5-*M* Na_2CO_3 to the residue, place the filter tube in an empty test tube, and set the assembly in a hot water bath. Allow the solution to flow slowly through the filter medium. After 5 minutes force the remainder of the Na_2CO_3 solution into the test tube and add it to the first sodium carbonate solution. (Reserve the residue for tests described in the following sections.) Note the color of the solution, keep part of it for a test for CH_3COO^-, and then neutralize this "prepared solution" in the manner described in the preceding section. Make the elimination tests and analyze the solution for the anions. Test the original sample for CO_3^{--}.

TEST FOR IONS NOT TRANSPOSED. Sodium carbonate transposes most substances except certain phosphates, fluorides, sulfides, silicates, halides of silver, AgCN, and AgSCN. Hence the residue, or the original solid, must be tested for the anions of these substances by methods outlined in the following Procedures.

Untransposed solid: Phosphates, fluorides (mineral), sulfides, AgCl, AgBr, AgI, AgCN, AgSCN. Add 5 drops of 4-*N* HNO_3, place the filter tube in an empty test tube, and set the assembly in the hot water bath. Stir the precipitate; then, after 1 or 2 minutes, add 0.5 ml. of water and force the solution through the filter medium.

Solution: PO_4^{3-}. Add 3 drops of 1-*N* ammonium molybdate reagent and warm the solution to about 60° C. for several minutes. A yellow precipitate confirms the presence of PO_4^{3-}.	**Residue:** AgCl, AgBr, AgI, AgCN, AgSCN, Ag_2S. Analyze the residue for the anions by Procedures 2 through 6.

Test for sulfide. Some sulfides are converted to a soluble form by the Na_2CO_3 treatment. Hence, the sulfide ion may be found in the analysis of the "prepared solution." If not, a small portion of the original sample or of the untransposed solid may be treated as follows: To about 3 mg. of the sample in a test tube (or in the gas-testing apparatus, Fig. 16.1) add a micro spatula pointful of powdered or granular zinc. Add 10 drops of water and 10 drops of 6-*N* HCl. In the mouth of the tube put a small plug of cotton moistened on its under side with 1 drop of 0.1-*N* $Pb(CH_3COO)_2$. If a sulfide is present, the $Pb(CH_3COO)_2$ will turn dark. Other sulfur-containing compounds, such as SCN^-, $S_2O_3^{--}$, and SO_3^{--}, may also be reduced to H_2S. (NOTE: This test may be used to confirm the presence of Ag_2S in a black residue that is not dissolved by a solution of KCN in Procedure 3.)

Test for fluoride: Test a small portion of the original sample or the untransposed solid for the fluoride by mixing it with a small quantity of powdered SiO_2 and concd. H_2SO_4 on a glass wool plug (Fig. 16.2D). A drop of water in the wire loop will turn cloudy after the tube has been in the hot water bath for a short time if F^- is present.

4. Preparation of the Solution and Analysis for Cations

ORGANIC MATTER AND INTERFERING ANIONS. Organic matter, particularly organic acids and carbohydrates, interferes with the analysis by forming complexes, colored substances, and colloidal solutions. Sometimes organic substances, such as the oxalate ion or tartrate ion, cause the precipitation of part of the ions of Group IV with those of Group III. Because of these and other difficulties, organic matter must be removed before the analysis for the cations is begun.

Certain anions also interfere with the cation analysis. For example, PO_4^{3-}, CrO_4^{--}, SiO_3^{--}, and F^- cause the metals of Group IV to precipitate with those of Group III. High concentrations of CH_3COO^- sometimes interfere with the precipitation of Cr^{3+}, especially in the absence of Fe^{3+} and Al^{3+}. Oxidizing anions, SO_3^{--}, and $S_2O_3^{--}$ cause sulfur to precipitate when H_2S is passed into the acid solution. Br^- and I^- may create difficulties because of the formation of complex ions and because of their oxidation by HNO_3. Certain other anions, such as SCN^- and $Fe(CN)_6^{3-}$, give rise to color interferences.

REMOVAL OF ORGANIC MATTER AND INTERFERING ANIONS. Sometimes it is desirable to make two analyses, one on the water-soluble portion of the sample and the other on the water-insoluble portion, especially when it is desired to determine which salts were present originally in the sample. However, the treatment suggested here is sufficient for most purposes.

If the sample was completely soluble in any of the solvents used in the preliminary tests, dissolve 20 to 30 mg. of it in 1 ml. of the solvent. Evaporate the solution to about 0.5 ml. in an evaporation test tube and add 5 drops of 4-*N* H_2SO_4; if organic matter was present, also add 5 drops of concd. HNO_3. Evaporate to white fumes of SO_3 and continue as directed in the following paragraph. *If the sample was not soluble* in aqua regia or any of the other solvents, place 20 to 30 mg. of it in an evaporation test tube with 0.5 ml. of water, and add 5 drops of 4-*N* H_2SO_4 and 5 drops of concd. HNO_3. Evaporate to white fumes of SO_3 and continue as directed in the following paragraph.

If the residue that remains after evaporation to white fumes of SO_3 is black because of the incomplete decomposition of organic matter, cool the tube and add 5 drops of concd. HNO_3. Again evaporate to white fumes of SO_3. Continue this process until the organic matter is destroyed. Finally, add 5 drops of concd. HCl and evaporate the solution until the HCl and most of the H_2SO_4 have been driven off. This will convert CrO_4^{--} and MnO_4^- to Cr^{3+} and Mn^{++} respectively. If most of the excess acid is not removed by evaporation, too great a dilution may be required to adjust the acidity for the precipitation of Group II.

Cool the tube, add 2 ml. of water, and filter through a *cotton* filter medium. Analyze the filtrate for the cations, beginning with the Procedures for Group II. Ag^+ and Pb^{++} will be in the insoluble residue as AgCl and $PbSO_4$. Hg_2^{++} is oxidized by the concd. HNO_3 to Hg^{++}. Hence it is not necessary to test the solution for the ions of Group I. Analyze the insoluble residue as suggested in the following Procedures.

ANALYSIS OF INSOLUBLE RESIDUE

Insoluble residue: $PbSO_4$, $BaSO_4$, $SrSO_4$, AgCl, etc. Add to the residue on the filter medium 10 drops of 1-*N* CH_3COONH_4 and 1 drop of 4-*N* CH_3COOH. Place the filter tube in an empty test tube and set the assembly in the hot water bath for several minutes. Stir the residue occasionally. Finally, force the solution into the test tube. Wash the residue with 1 ml. of water.

Filtrate: Pb^{++}. Add 1 drop of thioacetamide and 1 drop of 4-*N* NH_4OH. A black precipitate shows the presence of Pb^{++}.

Residue: AgCl, AgBr, etc. Add 5 drops of 1-*N* KCN, stir the precipitate, and then force the solution through the medium. Wash the residue with 0.5 ml. of water. Add the wash water to the KCN solution.

Solution: $Ag(CN)_2^-$. Add 1 drop of thioacetamide and 1 drop of 4-*N* NH_4OH. A black precipitate indicates the presence of Ag^+. Filter the mixture through a glass fiber filter medium, wash it thoroughly, and then dissolve the Ag_2S in concd. HNO_3. Add 0.5 ml. of H_2O and 1 drop of 6-*N* HCl. A white precipitate confirms the presence of Ag^+.

Residue: $BaSO_4$, $SrSO_4$, etc. Remove the cotton filter with the residue, place it in a small nickel crucible, and then heat the crucible until all the cotton has been burned off and a white residue remains. Add to the residue a spatula pointful of anhydrous Na_2CO_3 and about one-half as much K_2CO_3. Add a few mg. (an amount about equal to a match head) of $NaNO_3$. (The $NaNO_3$ oxidizes certain substances which are difficult to dissolve and converts them to more soluble compounds.) Place the crucible in a small clay triangle and then heat it strongly with a Meker burner for several minutes after the carbonates have fused. Cool the crucible, add 1 ml. of water, and warm until the solid has disintegrated. Filter the mixture and retain the filtrate.

Add to the residue 10 drops of 4-*N* HNO_3 and set the tube in a hot water bath for several minutes. Force the solution through the filter medium and wash with 1 ml. of water. Add the nitric acid solution to the aqueous filtrate. Now add to the combined solutions 1 drop of phenolphthalein and then 4-*N* HNO_3 until the color of the indicator is discharged. Evaporate the solution to about 1 ml. and analyze it for the cations, beginning with Procedure 1.

5. Examination of the Results; Probable Composition of the Material

After the analyses for the anions and cations have been completed, examine the results to see that they are consistent with all the physical and chemical properties observed. If the analysis is correct, all the observations should be accounted for. For example, a sample that is completely soluble in water would not contain both Pb^{++} and SO_4^{--}. Besides the solubility, the color and other properties of the solids, the color of the solutions, the acidity or basicity of the aqueous solution of the solid, etc., should all be accounted for.

After careful consideration of all the properties of the sample, it is often possible to state the probable composition of the original sample. Analyzing a solution of it determines only the cations and anions, but gives no information as to how they were originally combined. However, the preliminary tests on the physical properties, the solubility, and any interactions when the sample is dissolved provide some information which aids in determining the initial compounds in it.

Estimate the relative amounts of the cations and anions in the sample. Comparative tests with the test solutions are useful for this. If one or two of the ions appear to be present in much larger quantities than the others, indicate this by "large amount"; if only a very small amount is present, indicate this by "trace." A skilled analyst usually estimates the approximate percentage composition of the sample or gives the approximate concentration of the ions in a solution.

APPENDIXES

APPENDIX A

LIST OF APPARATUS *

RETURNABLE

3 Beakers, Pyrex, 20 ml., 50 ml., 250 ml.
1 Burner, preferably a micro burner
1 Condenser-collector tube * (anion analysis, Fig. 21.1)
4 Filter tubes, pressure * (Fig. 4.7A)
1 Flask, Pyrex, Florence, 500 ml.
1 Flask, Pyrex, Erlenmeyer, 25 ml.
1 Gas-testing tube * (anion analysis, Fig. 16.1)
1 Graduate, 5 ml.
1 Spatula, micro, Monel metal * (Fig. 4.7B)
10 Test tubes, Pyrex, 13 x 100 mm., No. 2370, without rim
1 Test tube, Pyrex, 16 x 150 mm., without rim
2 Test tubes for evaporations, Pyrex, 25 x 70 mm. (Fig. 4.17)
1 Test tube holder, semimicro, wire (Fig. 4.14)
1 Apparatus holder, wooden block, 43 holes (Fig. 4.23)
1 Tripod (legs should be 5 inches high for use with micro burner)
1 Tube, tapered, for wash bottle * (Fig. 4.12)
1 Hot water bath rack, metal, 8-hole * (Fig. 4.13)
1 Wire, Chromel or Nichrome, No. 18 B. & S. gauge, 3 inches long

NONRETURNABLE

1 Bottle, 1 oz., filled with absorbent cotton
1 Bottle, 1 oz., filled with No. 790 Corning fiber glass
1 Bulb, rubber, 2 oz., ear syringe, No. A-591 (Meinecke & Co., New York City) or No. 527 (Davol Rubber Co., Providence, R.I.) (Fig. 4.10)
10 Corks, No. 3
10 Droppers, medicine
1 File, triangular, small
Glass tubing, 6 mm. (about 100 cm.)
Glass rod, 3 mm. (about 50 cm.)
Labels, 1 sheet
Matches, safety, 1 box
1 Policeman, rubber (Fig. 4.18)
1 Sponge

* The special apparatus may be obtained from Geo. T. Walker & Co., Minneapolis, Minn., and from the Wilkens-Anderson Co., Chicago, Ill. The dimensions and sizes given in the text should be specified. Other laboratory supply houses may also be able to supply some of the special equipment.

2 Stoppers, rubber, 2-hole, No. 5
1 Test tube brush, semimicro, tapered * (Fig. 4.19)
1 Test tube brush, semimicro, not tapered * (Fig. 4.19)
1 Towel
Tubing, rubber, 1 ft., ¼ inch
Tubing, rubber, 3 ft., ⅜ inch
1 Wire, platinum, 2 inches, No. 24 B. & S. gauge for flame tests (Chromel is usable for some flame tests)
1 Wire gauze, 4 x 4 inches

APPENDIX B

APPROXIMATE COMPOSITION OF COMMERCIAL CONCENTRATED ACIDS AND BASES

Acid	Specific Gravity 25°/4°	Approximate Percentage	Compound	Approximate Molarity	Approximate Normality
Hydrochloric acid	1.19	38	HCl	12.4	12.4
Nitric acid	1.42	70	HNO_3	15.8	15.8
Sulfuric acid	1.84	95	H_2SO_4	17.8	35.6
Acetic acid	1.05	99	CH_3COOH	17.3	17.3
Ammonia	0.90	28	NH_3	14.8	14.8

APPENDIX C

TEST SOLUTIONS—CATIONS

Salt	Formula	Weight of Salt Required for 1 Liter of Solution		Dissolve Salt in
		0.1 Gram Ion with Respect to the Cation	Containing 10 mg./ml. with Respect to the Cation	
Group I				
Silver nitrate	$AgNO_3$	17.0 g.	15.8 g.	Water
Mercury (I) nitrate	$Hg_2(NO_3)_2 \cdot 2H_2O$	56.1	14.0	1-*N* HNO_3
Lead nitrate	$Pb(NO_3)_2$	33.1	16.0	Water
Group II				
Bismuth nitrate	$Bi(NO_3)_3 \cdot 5H_2O$	48.5	23.2	1-*N* HNO_3
Copper (II) nitrate	$Cu(NO_3)_2 \cdot 3H_2O$	24.2	38.0	0.01-*N* HNO_3
Cadmium nitrate	$Cd(NO_3)_2 \cdot 4H_2O$	30.9	27.5	Water
Mercury (II) nitrate	$Hg(NO_3)_2$	32.5	16.4	0.1-*N* HNO_3
Sodium arsenate	$Na_2HAsO_4 \cdot 7H_2O$	31.2	41.8	Water
Antimony (III) chloride	$SbCl_3$	22.8	18.7	2-*N* HCl
Tin (II) chloride	$SnCl_2 \cdot 2H_2O$	22.6	19.0	2-*N* HCl
Group III				
Iron (III) nitrate	$Fe(NO_3)_3 \cdot 9H_2O$	40.4	72.4	0.01-*N* HNO_3
Aluminum nitrate	$Al(NO_3)_3 \cdot 9H_2O$	37.5	139.0	0.01-*N* HNO_3
Chromium (III) nitrate	$Cr(NO_3)_3 \cdot 9H_2O$	40.0	77.0	0.01-*N* HNO_3
Manganese (II) nitrate, 50%	$Mn(NO_3)_2$	23 ml.	42 ml.	Water
Zinc nitrate	$Zn(NO_3)_2 \cdot 6H_2O$	29.8 g.	45.5 g.	Water
Nickel nitrate	$Ni(NO_3)_2 \cdot 6H_2O$	29.1	49.5	Water
Cobalt nitrate	$Co(NO_3)_2 \cdot 6H_2O$	29.1	49.4	Water
Group IV				
Barium nitrate	$Ba(NO_3)_2$	26.1	19.0	Water
Strontium nitrate	$Sr(NO_3)_2 \cdot 4H_2O$	28.4	32.0	Water
Calcium nitrate	$Ca(NO_3)_2 \cdot 4H_2O$	23.6	59.0	Water
Group V				
Magnesium nitrate	$Mg(NO_3)_2 \cdot 6H_2O$	25.6	106.0	0.01-*N* HNO_3
Sodium nitrate	$NaNO_3$	8.5	37.0	Water
Potassium nitrate	KNO_3	10.1	26.0	Water
Ammonium nitrate	NH_4NO_3	8.0	44.5	Water

APPENDIX D

INORGANIC REAGENTS FOR CATION ANALYSIS

Name of Reagent	Formula of Solute	Mol. Wt.	Approximate *N* or *M*	Ml. or Grams Required to Make 250 ml. of Solution
Acids				
Acetic acid	CH_3COOH	60.03	4-*N*	60 ml. (99.8%)
Hydrochloric acid	HCl	36.46	6-*N*	122 ml. (sp. gr. 1.19:38%)
Hydrochloric acid	HCl	36.46	1-*N*	20 ml. (sp. gr. 1.19:38%)
Nitric acid	HNO_3	63.02	4-*N*	64 ml. (sp. gr. 1.42:69%)
Sulfamic acid	NH_2SO_3H	97.09	0.5-*M*	12.14 g.
Sulfuric acid	H_2SO_4	98.08	4-*N*	28 ml. (sp. gr. 1.84:96%)
Tartaric acid	$H_2C_4H_4O_6$	150.09	1-*N*	19 g.
Bases				
Ammonium hydroxide	NH_3	17.02	Concd. 15-*N*	(sp. gr. 0.90:28%–29%)
Ammonium hydroxide	NH_3	17.02	4-*N*	68 ml. (sp. gr. 0.90:29%)
Ammonium hydroxide	NH_3	17.02	1-*N*	17 ml. (sp. gr. 0.90:29%)
Sodium hydroxide	$NaOH$	40.01	4-*N*	42 g. (95%)
Salts				
Ammonium acetate	CH_3COONH_4	77.06	6-*N*	115 g.
Ammonium acetate	CH_3COONH_4	77.06	1-*N*	19 g.
Ammonium carbonate	$(NH_4)_2CO_3 \cdot H_2O$	114.11	2-*N*	28 g. + 20 ml. concd. NH_4OH + water
Ammonium chloride	NH_4Cl	53.50	6-*N*	80 g.
Ammonium iodide	NH_4I	144.96	1-*N*	36 g.
Ammonium molybdate	$(NH_4)_2MoO_4$	196.08	1-*N*	25 g. + 20 ml. 4-*N* NH_4OH + 50 g. NH_4NO_3 + H_2O
Ammonium nitrate	NH_4NO_3	80.05	1-*N*	20 g.
Ammonium oxalate	$(NH_4)_2C_2O_4 \cdot H_2O$	142.09	0.5-*N*	9.0 g.

Ammonium sulfate	$(NH_4)_2SO_4$	132.14	4-*N*	66 g.
Ammonium thiocyanate	NH_4SCN	76.11	0.1-*N*	2 g.
Calcium sulfate	$CaSO_4 \cdot 2H_2O$	172.17	Satd.	1 g.
Hydrogen peroxide	H_2O_2	34.02	3%	
Hydrazine sulfate	$(N_2H_4) \cdot H_2SO_4$	130.01	0.25-*M*	8.1 g.
Lead acetate	$Pb(CH_3COO)_2 \cdot 3H_2O$	379.30	0.1-*N*	5 g.
Magnesium nitrate mixture				25 g. $Mg(NO_3)_2 \cdot 6H_2O$ 75 g. NH_4NO_3 45 ml. concd. NH_4OH + water
Nessler's reagent	(1) 10 g. KI and 14 g. HgI_2 in 50 ml. of water (2) 30 g. NaOH in 150 ml. of water. (Cool.) Add (2) to (1) slowly and with constant stirring. Allow to stand 2 hours or longer. (Filter, if necessary.) A clear yellowish solution should be obtained.			
Potassium chromate	K_2CrO_4	194.21	0.5-*M*	24 g.
Potassium cyanide	KCN	65.11	1-*N*	16.5 g.
Potassium cyanoferrate (III)	$K_3Fe(CN)_6$	329.25	0.1-*N*	2.8 g.
Sodium bismuthate	$NaBiO_3$	280.0		Solid
Sodium hexanitrocobaltate (III)	$Na_3Co(NO_2)_6$	404.02		Solid
Sodium hypochlorite	NaClO	74.45	5%	
Sodium nitrite	$NaNO_2$	69.01	1-*N*	17.2 g.
Tin (II) chloride	$SnCl_2 \cdot 2H_2O$	225.65	1-*N*	Heat 28 g. in 50 ml. of 12-*N* HCl. Dilute to 250 ml. and add 5 g. of tin metal.
Uranyl zinc acetate	30 g. $UO_2(CH_3COO)_2 \cdot 2H_2O$ + 80 g. $Zn(CH_3COO)_2 \cdot 2H_2O$ + 10 ml. 99% CH_3COOH. Dilute the solution to 250 ml., warm, and allow it to stand 24 hours. Use the clear solution.			

ORGANIC REAGENTS FOR CATION ANALYSIS

Reagent	Concentration	Ml. or Grams Required to Make 250 ml. of Solution
Alcohol, methyl or denatured		
Aluminon	0.2%	0.5 g. in water
Antipyrine-KI	1%	2.5 g. of antipyrine in water. Add 5 g. of KI
Diethylaniline	0.5%	25 drops in 50% H_3PO_4
Dimethylglyoxime	1%	2.5 g. in 95% alcohol
Formalin (40% solution of formaldehyde)	40%	
m-Nitrophenylarsonic acid	0.5%	Dissolve 1.2 g. in warm water
2-Nitroso-1-naphthol	0.05%	Dissolve 0.125 g. in 250 ml. of water. Add 1 ml. of 4-*N* NaOH
Thioacetamide	5%	Dissolve 12.5 g. in 250 ml. of warm water
Titan yellow	0.1%	0.25 g. in water
Indicators:		
Bromcresol green	0.04%	0.1 g. + 14.3 ml. 0.01-*N* NaOH
Bromthymol blue	0.04%	0.1 g. + 16.0 ml. 0.01-*N* NaOH
2,4-Dinitrophenol	0.07%	0.175 g. ground with 4 ml. 0.1 *N*-NaOH + water
Malachite green	0.02%	0.05 g. in water
Phenolphthalein	0.1%	0.25 g. + 125 ml. alcohol + 125 ml. water
Phenol red	0.04%	0.1 g. + 28.2 ml. 0.01-*N* NaOH
Thymol blue	0.05%	0.125 g. + alcohol
Thymolphthalein	0.1%	0.25 g. + 125 ml. alcohol + 125 ml. water

APPENDIX E

TEST SOLUTIONS—ANIONS

These solutions should be made up preferably at about the time they are required.

Salt	Formula	Formula Weight	Weight of Salt Required for 1 Liter of 0.1-*M* Solution with Respect to the Anion Concerned
Sodium acetate	$CH_3COONa \cdot 3H_2O$	136.09	13.61
Disodium hydrogen arsenate	$Na_2HAsO_4 \cdot 7H_2O$	312.02	31.2
Sodium arsenite, meta	$NaAsO_2$	129.91	13.0
Sodium borate, tetra	$Na_2B_4O_7 \cdot 10H_2O$	381.43	38.1
Potassium bromide	KBr	119.01	11.9
Sodium carbonate, anhyd.	Na_2CO_3	106.0	10.6
Potassium chlorate	$KClO_3$	122.56	12.3
Sodium chloride	NaCl	58.45	5.8
Potassium chromate	K_2CrO_4	194.20	19.4
Potassium cyanide	KCN	65.11	6.5
Sodium fluoride	NaF	42.00	4.2
Sodium hypochlorite *	NaClO *	74.45	7.4 *
Sodium hypophosphite	$NaH_2PO_2 \cdot H_2O$	106.04	10.6
Potassium iodide	KI	166.02	16.6
Sodium nitrate	$NaNO_3$	85.01	8.5
Sodium nitrite	$NaNO_2$	69.01	6.9
Sodium oxalate	$Na_2C_2O_4$	134.01	13.4
Disodium hydrogen phosphate	$Na_2HPO_4 \cdot 12H_2O$	358.17	35.8
Sodium sulfate, anhyd.	Na_2SO_4	142.05	14.2
Sodium sulfide	$Na_2S \cdot 9H_2O$	240.19	24.0
Sodium sulfite, anhyd.	Na_2SO_3	126.05	12.6
Sodium thiocyanate	NaSCN	81.08	8.1
Sodium thiosulfate	$Na_2S_2O_3 \cdot 5H_2O$	248.19	24.8

* Dilute 150 ml. of a 5% NaClO solution to 1 liter.

APPENDIX F

REAGENTS FOR ANION ANALYSIS *

Name of Reagent	Formula of Solute	Formula Weight of Solute	Approximate Concentration	Grams or ml. of Solute Required for 250 ml. of Solution
Acids				
* Acetic acid	CH_3COOH	60.03	4-*N*	60 ml. (99.8%)
* Hydrochloric acid	HCl	36.46	6-*N*	122 ml. (sp. gr. 1.19:38%)
* Hydrochloric acid	HCl	36.46	1-*N*	20 ml. (sp. gr. 1.19:38%)
* Nitric acid	HNO_3	63.02	4-*N*	64 ml. (sp. gr. 1.42:69%)
Nitric acid	HNO_3	63.02	0.01-*N*	Dilute 0.6 ml. 4-*N* to 250 ml.
Oxalic acid	$H_2C_2O_4 \cdot 2H_2O$	126.05	1-*N*	16 g.
* Sulfamic acid	$NH_2 \cdot SO_2OH$	97.09	0.5-*M*	12.14 g.
* Sulfuric acid	H_2SO_4	98.08	4-*N*	28 ml. (sp. gr. 1.84:96%)
Sulfuric acid	H_2SO_4	98.08	0.01-*N*	Dilute 0.6 ml. 4-*N* to 250 ml.
Sulfuric acid	H_2SO_4	98.08	Concd. (36-*N*)	sp. gr. 1.84:96%
Sulfurous acid	H_2SO_3	82.08	5% SO_2	Saturate water with SO_2 gas
Bases				
* Ammonium hydroxide	NH_3	17.02	Concd. (15-*N*)	sp. gr. 0.90:28%(NH_3)
* Ammonium hydroxide	NH_3	17.02	4-*N*	68 ml. (sp. gr. 0.90:28%)
Ammonium hydroxide	NH_3	17.02	0.01-*N*	Dilute 0.6 ml. 4-*N* to 250 ml.
Barium hydroxide	$Ba(OH)_2 \cdot 8H_2O$	315.50	Satd.	9 g.
* Sodium hydroxide	$NaOH$	40.01	4-*N*	40 g.
Salts and metals				
* Ammonium acetate	CH_3COONH_4	77.06	6-*N*	115.6 g.
* Ammonium molybdate	$(NH_4)_2MoO_4$	196.08	1-*N*	25 g. in 20 ml. 4-*N* NH_3
* Ammonium thiocyanate	NH_4SCN	76.11	0.1-*N*	2 g.
** Antimony (III) chloride	$SbCl_3$	228.13	0.1-*M*	5.7 g. (dissolve in 2-*N* HCl)

Barium acetate	$Ba(CH_3COO)_2 \cdot H_2O$	273.46	1-*N*	34 g.
Bismuth chloride	$BiCl_3$	315.37	0.1-*N*	26.3 g. (dissolve in 2-*N* HCl)
Calcium acetate	$Ca(CH_3COO)_2 \cdot H_2O$	176.20	1-*N*	22 g.
Calcium carbonate	$CaCO_3$	100.0	Solid	
** Copper (II) nitrate	$Cu(NO_3)_2 \cdot 3H_2O$	241.63	0.1-*M*	6 g.
Copper (II) sulfate	$CuSO_4 \cdot 5H_2O$	249.71	0.1-*N*	3.1 g.
** Iron (III) nitrate	$Fe(NO_3)_3 \cdot 9H_2O$	400.4	0.1-*M*	10 g.
Iron (II) ammonium sulfate	$Fe(NH_4)_2(SO_4)_2 \cdot 6H_2O$	392.15	Solid	
* Hydrogen peroxide	H_2O_2	34.02	3%	
Lanthanum nitrate	$La(NO_3)_3 \cdot 6H_2O$	433.04	5%	12.5 g.
Magnesium metal	Mg			
* Magnesium mixture reagent				25 g. $Mg(NO_3)_2 \cdot 6H_2O$ 75 g. NH_4NO_3 45 ml. concd. NH_3
** Manganese nitrate	$Mn(NO_3)_2 \cdot 6H_2O$	287.04	0.1-*M*	9 ml. 50% $Mn(NO_3)_2$
** Mercury (II) nitrate	$Hg(NO_3)_2 \cdot H_2O$	342.64	0.1-*M*	8.6 g. (dissolve in 0.1-*N* HNO_3)
Miller's reagent				4.2 ml. concd. NH_3 6.3 g. KNO_3 0.42 g. $AgNO_3$
Potassium bromide	KBr	119.01	1-*N*	29.8 g.
Potassium iodate	KIO_3	214.02	0.1-*N*	5.4 g.
Potassium iodide	KI	166.02	1-*N*	41.5 g.
Potassium iodide	KI	166.02	0.1-*N*	4.2 g.
Potassium iodide-iodine	KI_3	419.8	1-*M*	41.5 g. KI + 63.5 g. I_2
Potassium permanganate	$KMnO_4$	158.03	0.01-*M*	0.4 g.
Silver nitrate	$AgNO_3$	169.89	1-*N*	42 g.
Silver nitrate	$AgNO_3$	169.89	0.1-*N*	4.2 g.
Silver sulfate	Ag_2SO_4	311.82	Satd.	2 g.
* Sodium bismuthate	$NaBiO_3$	280.0	Solid	
Sodium carbonate	Na_2CO_3	106.0	2-*N*	27 g.
* Sodium hypochlorite	NaClO	74.75	5%	

REAGENTS FOR ANION ANALYSIS (Continued)

Name of Reagent	Formula of Solute	Formula Weight of Solute	Approximate Concentration	Grams or ml. of Solute Required for 250 ml. of Solution
Sodium nitropentacyanoferrate (III)	$Na_2Fe(NO)(CN)_5 \cdot 2H_2O$	297.96	1%	2.5 g.
* Sodium nitrite	$NaNO_2$	69.01	1-*N*	17 g.
Sodium sulfite	Na_2SO_3	126.05	Solid	
Sodium sulfite	Na_2SO_3	126.05	0.1-*M*	3.1 g.
Zirconium nitrate	$Zr(NO_3)_4 \cdot 5H_2O$	429.56	0.1%	0.25 g. in 25 ml. concd. HCl. Dilute to 250 ml.
Organic Reagents				
Benzidine			0.05%	0.125 g. in 2-*N* CH_3COOH
Carbon tetrachloride				
Eosin			0.01%	0.025 g. in water
Fluorescein			0.1%	0.25 g. in 50% alcohol
* Formalin			40%	
* Malachite green			0.02%	0.05 g. in water
Methanol				
α-Naphthylamine			0.5%	1.25 g. in water (filter)
Nitron			10%	25 g.
Sodium alizainsulfonate			0.1%	0.25 g. in water
Starch emulsion			1%	2.5 g. soluble starch. Boil
Sulfanilic acid			0.5%	1.25 g. in water
Turmeric (tincture)				Saturate 95% alcohol (filter)
* Thioacetamide			5%	12.5 g. in water
Indicators	Color Change			
* Bromthymol blue	Yellow—6.0:7.6—Blue		0.04%	0.1 g. + 15 ml. 0.01-*N* NaOH
p-Nitrophenol	Colorless—5.0:7.0—Yellow		0.1%	0.25 g. in water
* Phenolphthalein	Colorless—8.3:10.0—Red		0.1%	0.25 g. in 95% alcohol

* Reagents with a single asterisk are used in cation analysis (see Appendix D); those with two asterisks are cation test solutions (see Appendix C).

APPENDIX G

SOLUBILITY TABLE

	I			II								III					III			IV			IV	V		
	Ag^+	Pb^{++}	Hg_2^{++}	Hg^{++}	Bi^{3+}	Cu^{++}	Cd^{++}	As^{3+}	Sb^{3+}	Sn^{++}	Sn^{4+}	Fe^{++}	Fe^{3+}	Al^{3+}	Cr^{3+}	Mn^{++}	Zn^{++}	Ni^{++}	Co^{++}	Ba^{++}	Ca^{++}	Sr^{++}	Mg^{++}	K^+	Na^+	NH_4^+
$S^=$	I	IA	D	I	I	IA	IA	I	IA	IA	IA	IA	IA	H	H	IA	IA	I	I	HA	HA	HA	HA	S	S	S
I^-	I	I	I	I	IA	D	S	slH	H	slA	H	S		S	S	S	S	S	S	S	S	S	S	S	S	S
$Fe(CN)_6^{4-}$	I	IA	I	I	I	I	I			I	I	I	I	sl		I	I	I	I	sl	S	S	S	S	S	S
Br^-	I	slH	I	I	SH	I	S	SH	SH	S	SH	S	S	S	S	S	S	S	S	S	S	S	S	S	S	S
SCN^-	I	slA	I	slA		D	sl				S	S	S	S	S	S	S	S	S	S	S	S	S	S	S	S
CN^-	I	slA	D	S		D	S					IA	H	H	H	IA	IA	IA	IA	S	S	S	S	S	S	S
$Fe(CN)_6^{3-}$	I	IA	I	S	I	I	I			I		I	S			I	I	I	I	S	S	S	S	S	S	S
Cl^-	I	sl	I	S	SH	S	S	H	SH	S	SH	S	S	S	S	S	S	S	S	S	S	S	S	S	S	S
ClO^-	D	D	D																	S	slA	slA	S	S	S	S
$S_2O_3^=$	D	slA	D	I			S			S	S	S		S				S	S	slA	S	S	S	S	S	S
F^-	S	IA	slA	slA	SH	IA	sl	H	S	S	S	sl	I	S	S	slA	slA	slA	slA	slA	IA	IA	IA	S	S	S
$C_2O_4^=$	IA	IA	IA	IA	IA	IA	IA			IA		IA	S	IA	sl	IA	IA	IA	IA	IA	IA	IA	IA	S	S	S
$SO_3^=$	IA	IA	D	D		slA	slA					IA					IA	IA	IA	IA	IA	IA	slA	S	S	S
PO_4^{3-}	IA	IA	IA	IA	IA	IA	IA			IA	IA	IA	IA	IA	slA	IA	IA	IA	IA	IA	IA	IA	IA	S	S	S
$CO_3^=$	IA	IA	IA	IA	IA	IA	IA					IA	H	H	slH	slA	IA	IA	IA	IA	IA	IA	IA	S	S	S
$SO_4^=$	slA	I	I	slA	SH	S	S		SH	S	S	S	S	S	S	S	S	S	S	I	I	sl	S	S	S	S
$CrO_4^=$	IA	IA	IA	IA	IA	slA	IA			sl	S		S		IA		slA	IA	IA	IA	slA	slA	S	S	S	S
NO_2^-	slA	S	D	S		S	S						S			S	S	S	S	S	S	S		S	S	S
NO_3^-	S	S	SH	S	SH	S	S		SH	SH	H	S	S	S	S	S	S	S	S	S	S	S	S	S	S	S
BO_2^-	slA	IA	slA	slA		IA	IA					IA				IA	IA	IA	IA	slA	slA	slA	slA	S	S	S
CH_3COO^-	slA	S	slA	S		S	S			S	SH	S	SH	SH	SH	S	S	S	S	S	S	S	S	S	S	S

S = soluble in water (greater than 1×10^{-2} g./ml.)
sl = slightly soluble in water (1×10^{-2} g./ml. to about 5×10^{-4} g./ml.)
I = insoluble in water (less than 5×10^{-4} g./ml.)
H = extensively hydrolyzed
A = soluble in dilute solutions of strong acids
D = decomposes

APPENDIX H

SOLUBILITY PRODUCT CONSTANTS *

Substance	K	pK
Aluminum		
$Al(OH)_3$	2×10^{-33}	32.7
Barium		
$BaCO_3$	4.9×10^{-9}	8.31
BaC_2O_4	1.1×10^{-7}	6.96
$BaSO_4$	9.9×10^{-11}	10.01
$BaSO_3$	2.1×10^{-7}	6.68
$BaCrO_4$	2×10^{-10}	9.7
BaF_2	1.7×10^{-6}	5.77
$Ba(OH)_2$	5×10^{-3}	2.3
$Ba(BrO_3)_2$	5.5×10^{-6}	5.26
$Ba(IO_3)_2$	1.3×10^{-9}	8.89
$Ba_3(PO_4)_2$	1.3×10^{-29}	28.89
$Ba_3(AsO_4)_2$	1.1×10^{-13}	12.96
Bismuth		
$BiOCl$	7×10^{-9}	8.15
Bi_2S_3	1.6×10^{-72}	71.7
$BiO(OH)$	1×10^{-12}	12.0
Cadmium		
$Cd(OH)_2$	1×10^{-14}	14.0
$CdCO_3$	2.5×10^{-14}	13.6
CdS	1×10^{-28}	28.0
CdC_2O_4	1.5×10^{-8}	7.82
Calcium		
$CaCO_3$	4.8×10^{-9}	8.32
$Ca(OH)_2$	8×10^{-6}	5.1
$CaSO_4$	2.4×10^{-5}	4.62
$Ca_3(PO_4)_2$	1×10^{-25}	25.0
$CaHPO_4$	5×10^{-6}	5.3
CaC_2O_4	2.3×10^{-9}	8.64
$Ca(IO_3)_2$	1.9×10^{-6}	5.72
CaF_2	3.9×10^{-11}	10.41
$CaSO_3$	1.3×10^{-8}	7.89
$Ca_3(AsO_4)_2$	8.8×10^{-11}	10.06
$CaBO_2$	2.7×10^{-5}	4.57

Substance	K	pK
Chromium		
$Cr(OH)_3$	7×10^{-31}	30.2
Cobalt		
$Co(OH)_2$	2×10^{-16}	15.7
$Co(OH)_3$	2×10^{-43}	42.7
CoS (α)	7×10^{-23}	22.2
CoS (β)	2×10^{-27}	26.7
$CoCO_3$	1×10^{-12}	12.0
Copper		
$CuCl$	1.9×10^{-7}	6.72
$CuBr$	5.3×10^{-9}	8.28
CuI	1.1×10^{-12}	11.96
$CuCNS$	4×10^{-14}	13.4
Cu_2S	2.5×10^{-50}	49.5
$Cu(OH)_2$	6×10^{-20}	19.2
CuS	4×10^{-38}	37.4
$CuCO_3$	1.4×10^{-10}	9.85
$Cu(IO_3)_2$	1.3×10^{-7}	6.89
CuC_2O_4	2.9×10^{-8}	7.54
Iron		
$Fe(OH)_2$	2×10^{-15}	14.7
$FeCO_3$	2.1×10^{-11}	10.68
FeC_2O_4	2.1×10^{-7}	6.68
FeS	1×10^{-19}	19.0
$Fe(OH)_3$	4×10^{-38}	37.4
Lead		
$Pb(OH)_2$	2×10^{-16}	15.7
PbF_2	3.7×10^{-8}	7.43
$PbCl_2$	1.7×10^{-5}	4.77
$PbBr_2$	6.3×10^{-6}	5.2
PbI_2	8.7×10^{-9}	8.06
$PbCO_3$	1.5×10^{-13}	12.82
PbC_2O_4	2.8×10^{-11}	10.55
PbS	1×10^{-29}	29.0
$PbCrO_4$	1.8×10^{-14}	13.75

* Many of these values are given by Latimer (*Oxidation Potentials*, Prentice-Hall, 1938) as the most probable values. Most of them are actually activity products derived from thermodynamic measurements. The error resulting from their use as solubility product constants can be estimated qualitatively from Appendix I for saturated solutions. If ions of electrolytes are present in addition to the ions of the slightly soluble salt, the salt effect on the solubility of salts should be considered. For calculations of solubilities in water, hydrolysis of the ions should be considered.

SOLUBILITY PRODUCT CONSTANTS (*Continued*)

Substance	K	pK
$Pb(IO_3)_2$	3.2×10^{-13}	12.49
$PbSO_4$	1.8×10^{-8}	7.74
$Pb_3(PO_4)_2$	3×10^{-44}	43.5
Magnesium		
$Mg(OH)_2$	5.5×10^{-12}	11.3
$MgCO_3$	1×10^{-5}	5.0
MgF_2	6.4×10^{-9}	8.19
$Mg(NH_4)PO_4$	2.5×10^{-13}	12.6
MgC_2O_4	8.6×10^{-5}	4.07
Manganese		
$Mn(OH)_2$	7×10^{-15}	14.2
$MnCO_3$	8.8×10^{-11}	10.06
MnS	6×10^{-16}	15.2
Mercury		
Hg_2Cl_2	1.1×10^{-18}	17.96
Hg_2Br_2	5.2×10^{-23}	22.28
Hg_2I_2	4.5×10^{-29}	28.35
Hg_2CO_3	9×10^{-17}	16.05
Hg_2SO_4	6.2×10^{-7}	6.21
Hg_2S	1×10^{-45}	45.0
$Hg_2(CN)_2$	5×10^{-40}	39.3
$Hg_2(CNS)_2$	3×10^{-20}	19.53
$Hg_2(IO_3)_2$	1.3×10^{-18}	17.89
$Hg_2(CH_3COO)_2$	2×10^{-15}	14.7
$Hg_2C_2O_4$	1×10^{-13}	13.0
Hg_2CrO_4	2×10^{-9}	8.7
HgS	3×10^{-53}	52.5
Nickel		
$Ni(OH)_2$	2×10^{-14}	13.7
$NiCO_3$	1.4×10^{-7}	6.85
$NiS(\alpha)$	3×10^{-21}	20.5
$NiS(\beta)$	1×10^{-26}	26.0
$NiS(\gamma)$	1×10^{-28}	28.0
Potassium		
$KClO_4$	1.07×10^{-2}	1.97
K_2PtCl_6	1.1×10^{-5}	4.96
K_2PdCl_6	6×10^{-6}	5.22
$KHC_4H_4O_6$	3×10^{-4}	3.52
Silver		
$\frac{1}{2}Ag_2O(Ag^+ + OH^-)$	2×10^{-8}	7.7
$AgCl$	1.7×10^{-10}	9.77
$AgBr$	3.3×10^{-13}	12.48
AgI	8.5×10^{-17}	16.07
$AgCN$	7×10^{-15}	14.15
$AgCNS$	1×10^{-12}	12.0
Ag_2S	1×10^{-51}	51.0
$AgNO_2$	2.4×10^{-4}	3.62
$AgBrO_3$	5.2×10^{-5}	4.28
$AgIO_3$	5.3×10^{-8}	7.28
Ag_2CO_3	8.2×10^{-12}	11.09
$Ag_2C_2O_4$	1.1×10^{-11}	10.96
$AgCNO$	2.3×10^{-7}	6.64
Ag_2CrO_4	1.1×10^{-12}	11.96
$Ag_4Fe(CN)_6$	1.6×10^{-41}	40.8
Ag_2SO_4	1.2×10^{-5}	4.92
Ag_2SO_3	1.9×10^{-11}	10.72
Ag_3PO_4	3.4×10^{-14}	13.47
Ag_3AsO_4	5.6×10^{-14}	13.25
Ag_3AsO_3	1.3×10^{-13}	12.89
$AgWO_4$	5.2×10^{-10}	9.28
$Ag(CH_3COO)$	1.9×10^{-3}	2.72
Strontium		
$Sr(OH)_2$	3.2×10^{-4}	3.49
$SrCrO_4$	3.6×10^{-5}	4.46
SrF_2	3×10^{-9}	8.52
$SrCO_3$	9.4×10^{-10}	9.03
$SrSO_4$	2.8×10^{-7}	6.55
SrC_2O_4	5.6×10^{-8}	7.25
Thallium		
$Tl(OH)_3$	1.5×10^{-44}	43.82
$TlCl$	1.9×10^{-4}	3.72
$TlBr$	3.6×10^{-6}	5.44
TlI	4.5×10^{-6}	5.35
Tl_2S	1.2×10^{-24}	23.92
Tin		
$Sn(OH)_2$	5×10^{-26}	25.3
SnS	8×10^{-29}	28.06
$Sn(OH)_4$	1×10^{-56}	56.0
Zinc		
$Zn(OH)_2$	4.5×10^{-17}	16.35
$ZnCO_3$	6×10^{-11}	10.22
ZnS	1×10^{-23}	23.0
ZnC_2O_4	1.5×10^{-9}	8.82

APPENDIX I

SOLUBILITY PRODUCT CONSTANTS DERIVED FROM ACTIVITY PRODUCT CONSTANTS FOR SATURATED SOLUTIONS OF SALTS

1-1 Salts in Water			2-2 Salts in Water		
K_{AP}	pK_{AP}	K_{SP}	K_{AP}	pK_{AP}	K_{SP}
1×10^{-10}	10	1.001×10^{-10}	1×10^{-10}	10	1.03×10^{-10}
1×10^{-8}	8	1.02×10^{-8}	1×10^{-8}	8	1.22×10^{-8}
1×10^{-6}	6	1.08×10^{-6}	1×10^{-6}	6	2.05×10^{-6}
1×10^{-5}	5	1.16×10^{-5}	1×10^{-5}	5	4.5×10^{-5}
1×10^{-4}	4	1.27×10^{-4}			

$$K_{AP} = (a_{A^+})(a_{B^-}) = [A^+]f_{A^+}[B^-]f_{B^-}$$

$$K_{SP} = [A^+][B^-] = \frac{K_{AP}}{f_{A^+}f_{B^-}}$$

APPENDIX J

IONIZATION CONSTANTS OF WEAK ACIDS

Acids	Formula	K_a	pK_a	Conjugate Base	K_b	pK_b
Acetic	CH_3COOH	1.8×10^{-5}	4.74	CH_3COO^-	5.5×10^{-10}	9.26
Aluminum ion	$Al(H_2O)_6^{3+}$	1.4×10^{-5}	4.85	$Al(H_2O)_5OH^{++}$	7.1×10^{-10}	9.15
Ammonium ion	NH_4^+	5.5×10^{-10}	9.26	NH_3	1.8×10^{-5}	4.74
Antimonous	$HSbO_2$	1×10^{-11}	11.0	SbO_2^-	1×10^{-3}	3.0
Arsenic	H_3AsO_4	4.8×10^{-3}	2.31	$H_2AsO_4^-$	2×10^{-12}	11.69
	$H_2AsO_4^-$	1×10^{-7}	7.0	$HAsO_4^=$	1×10^{-7}	7.0
	$HAsO_4^=$	1×10^{-13}	13.0	AsO_4^{3-}	1×10^{-1}	1.0
Arsenous	$HAsO_2$	6×10^{-10}	9.22	AsO_2^-	1.7×10^{-5}	4.78
Benzoic	C_6H_5COOH	6.6×10^{-5}	4.18	$C_6H_5COO^-$	1.5×10^{-10}	9.82
Boric	H_3BO_3	5.8×10^{-10}	9.24	$H_2BO_3^-$	1.72×10^{-5}	4.76
Carbonic	H_2CO_3	4.3×10^{-7}	6.37	HCO_3^-	2.3×10^{-8}	7.63
	HCO_3^-	4.7×10^{-11}	10.33	$CO_3^=$	2.1×10^{-4}	3.67
Chloracetic	$ClCH_2COOH$	1.4×10^{-3}	2.85	$ClCH_2COO^-$	7.1×10^{-12}	11.15
Chromic	$HCrO_4^-$	3.2×10^{-7}	6.49	$CrO_4^=$	3.1×10^{-8}	7.51
Dichloracetic	$Cl_2CHCOOH$	5.5×10^{-2}	1.26	Cl_2CHCOO^-	1.8×10^{-13}	12.74
Ferric ion	$Fe(H_2O)_6^{3+}$	6×10^{-3}	2.22	$Fe(H_2O)_5(OH)^{++}$	1.7×10^{-12}	11.78
Formic	$HCOOH$	1.8×10^{-4}	3.74	$HCOO^-$	5.5×10^{-11}	10.26
Hydrazoic	HN_3	1×10^{-4}	4.0	N_3^-	1×10^{-10}	10.0
Hydrocyanic	HCN	4×10^{-10}	9.4	CN^-	2.5×10^{-5}	4.6
Hydrofluoric	HF	7.2×10^{-4}	3.14	F^-	1.4×10^{-11}	10.86
Hydrogen peroxide	H_2O_2	2.4×10^{-12}	11.62	HO_2^-	4.2×10^{-3}	2.38
Hydrogen selenide	H_2Se	1.7×10^{-4}	3.77	HSe^-	5.9×10^{-11}	10.23
	HSe^-	1×10^{-10}	10.0	$Se^=$	1×10^{-4}	4.0
Hydrogen sulfide	H_2S	1.2×10^{-7}	6.92	HS^-	8.3×10^{-8}	7.18
	HS^-	1×10^{-15}	15.0	$S^=$	10	−1.0
Hydrogen telluride	H_2Te	2.3×10^{-3}	2.64	HTe^-	4.4×10^{-12}	11.36
	HTe^-	1×10^{-5}	5.0	$Te^=$	1×10^{-9}	9.0
Hypobromous	$HBrO$	2.1×10^{-9}	8.68	BrO^-	4.8×10^{-6}	5.32
Hypochlorous	$HClO$	5.6×10^{-8}	7.25	ClO^-	1.8×10^{-7}	6.75
Hypophosphorous	H_3PO_2	1×10^{-2}	2.0	$H_2PO_2^-$	1×10^{-12}	12.0
Nitrous	HNO_2	4.5×10^{-4}	3.35	NO_2^-	2.2×10^{-11}	10.65
Oxalic	$H_2C_2O_4$	5.9×10^{-2}	1.23	$HC_2O_4^-$	1.7×10^{-13}	12.77
	$HC_2O_4^-$	6.4×10^{-5}	4.19	$C_2O_4^=$	1.5×10^{-10}	9.81
Phenol	C_6H_5OH	1.3×10^{-10}	9.89	$C_6H_5O^-$	7.8×10^{-5}	4.11
Phosphoric	H_3PO_4	7.5×10^{-3}	2.14	$H_2PO_4^-$	1.4×10^{-12}	11.86
	$H_2PO_4^-$	6.2×10^{-8}	7.21	$HPO_4^=$	1.6×10^{-7}	6.79
	$HPO_4^=$	1×10^{-12}	12.0	PO_4^{3-}	1×10^{-2}	2.0
Phosphorous	H_3PO_3	1.6×10^{-2}	1.8	$H_2PO_3^-$	6.3×10^{-13}	12.2
	$H_2PO_3^-$	7×10^{-7}	6.15	$HPO_3^=$	1.4×10^{-8}	7.85

IONIZATION CONSTANTS OF WEAK ACIDS (*Continued*)

Acids	Formula	K_a	pK_a	Conjugate Base	K_b	pK_b
Propionic	C_2H_5COOH	1.4×10^{-5}	4.85	$C_2H_5COO^-$	7.1×10^{-10}	9.15
Silicic	H_2SiO_3	1×10^{-10}	10.0	$HSiO_3^-$	1×10^{-4}	4.0
	$HSiO_3^-$	1×10^{-12}	12.0	$SiO_3^{=}$	1×10^{-2}	2.0
Sulfuric	HSO_4^-	1.2×10^{-2}	1.92	$SO_4^{=}$	8.3×10^{-13}	12.08
Sulfurous	H_2SO_3	1.2×10^{-2}	1.92	HSO_3^-	8.3×10^{-13}	12.08
	HSO_3^-	1×10^{-7}	7.0	$SO_3^{=}$	1×10^{-7}	7.0

Substance	Reaction	K_a	pK_a
Aluminum hydroxide	$Al(OH)_3 + 2H_2O \rightleftharpoons Al(OH)_4^- + H_3O^+$	4×10^{-13}	12.6
Chromium hydroxide	$Cr(OH)_3 + 2H_2O \rightleftharpoons Cr(OH)_4^- + H_3O^+$	9×10^{-17}	16.1
Lead hydroxide	$Pb(OH)_2 + 2H_2O \rightleftharpoons Pb(OH)_3^- + H_3O^+$	2×10^{-16}	15.7
Stannous hydroxide	$Sn(OH)_2 + 2H_2O \rightleftharpoons Sn(OH)_3^- + H_3O^+$	6×10^{-18}	17.2
Zinc hydroxide	$Zn(OH)_2 + 4H_2O \rightleftharpoons Zn(OH)_4^- + 2H_3O^+$	1×10^{-29}	29.0

APPENDIX K

IONIZATION CONSTANTS OF WEAK BASES

Base	Formula	K_b	pK_b	Conjugate Acid	K_a	pK_a
Ammonia	NH_3	1.8×10^{-5}	4.74	NH_4^+	5.5×10^{-10}	9.26
Methyl amine	CH_3NH_2	5×10^{-4}	3.3	$CH_3NH_3^+$	2×10^{-11}	10.7
Dimethyl amine	$(CH_3)_2NH$	7.4×10^{-4}	3.13	$(CH_3)_2NH_2^+$	1.3×10^{-11}	10.87
Trimethyl amine	$(CH_3)_3N$	7.4×10^{-5}	4.13	$(CH_3)_3NH^+$	1.3×10^{-10}	9.87
Ethyl amine	$C_2H_5NH_2$	5×10^{-4}	3.3	$C_2H_5NH_3^+$	2×10^{-11}	10.7
Hydroxyl amine	NH_2OH	6.6×10^{-9}	8.18	NH_3OH^+	1.5×10^{-6}	5.82
Hydrazine	N_2H_4	8.5×10^{-7}	6.07	$N_2H_5^+$	1.2×10^{-8}	7.93
Aniline	$C_6H_5NH_2$	4×10^{-10}	9.4	$C_6H_5NH_3^+$	2.5×10^{-5}	4.6
Pyridine	C_5H_5N	1.4×10^{-9}	8.85	$C_5H_5NH^+$	7.1×10^{-6}	5.15

APPENDIX L

COLOR CHANGES AND pH RANGES OF INDICATORS

Indicator (Trade Name)	Acid Color	pH Range	Base Color
Methyl violet	Yellow	0.0–3.2	Violet
Malachite green (acid range)	Yellow	0.2–1.8	Blue-green
Thymol blue (acid range)	Red	1.2–2.8	Yellow
2,4-Dinitrophenol	Colorless	2.6–4.4	Yellow
Bromphenol blue	Yellow	3.0–4.6	Purple
Methyl orange	Red	3.1–4.4	Orange-yellow
Congo red	Blue-violet	3.0–5.2	Red
Bromcresol green	Yellow	3.8–5.4	Blue
Methyl red	Red	4.4–6.2	Yellow
p-Nitrophenol	Colorless	5.0–7.0	Red
Bromcresol purple	Yellow	5.2–6.8	Purple
Bromthymol blue	Yellow	6.0–7.6	Blue
Phenol red	Yellow	6.4–8.2	Red
Neutral red	Red	6.8–8.0	Yellow
m-Nitrophenol	Colorless	6.8–8.4	Yellow
Litmus	Red	5.0–8.0	Blue
m-Cresol purple	Yellow	7.6–9.2	Purple-red
Thymol blue (basic range)	Yellow	8.0–9.6	Blue
Phenolphthalein	Colorless	8.0–9.8	Red-violet
Thymolphthalein	Colorless	9.3–10.5	Blue
Alizarine yellow	Yellow	10.1–11.1	Lilac
Malachite green	Green	11.4–13.0	Colorless
Trinitrobenzene	Colorless	12.0–14.0	Orange

APPENDIX M

INSTABILITY CONSTANTS FOR COMPLEX IONS

Ion	Equilibrium	$K_{inst.}$	$pK_{inst.}$
AlF_6^{3-}	$AlF_6^{3-} \rightleftharpoons Al^{3+} + 6F^-$	2×10^{-24}	23.7
$Cd(NH_3)_4^{++}$	$Cd(NH_3)_4^{++} \rightleftharpoons Cd^{++} + 4NH_3$	2.5×10^{-7}	6.6
$Cd(S_2O_3)_4^{6-}$	$Cd(S_2O_3)_4^{6-} \rightleftharpoons Cd^{++} + 4S_2O_3^=$	4×10^{-8}	7.4
$Cd(CN)_4^=$	$Cd(CN)_4^= \rightleftharpoons Cd^{++} + 4CN^-$	1.4×10^{-17}	16.9
$CdI_4^=$	$CdI_4^= \rightleftharpoons Cd^{++} + 4I^-$	5×10^{-7}	6.3
$CrCl_2^+$	$CrCl_2^+ \rightleftharpoons Cr^{3+} + 2Cl^-$	1.3×10^{-2}	1.9
$Co(NH_3)_6^{++}$	$Co(NH_3)_6^{++} \rightleftharpoons Co^{++} + 6NH_3$	1.2×10^{-5}	4.9
$Co(NH_3)_6^{3+}$	$Co(NH_3)_6^{3+} \rightleftharpoons Co^{3+} + 6NH_3$	2.2×10^{-34}	33.7
$CuCl_2^-$	$CuCl_2^- \rightleftharpoons Cu^+ + 2Cl^-$	2.9×10^{-6}	5.5
$CuBr_2^-$	$CuBr_2^- \rightleftharpoons Cu^+ + 2Br^-$	1.2×10^{-6}	5.9
CuI_2^-	$CuI_2^- \rightleftharpoons Cu^+ + 2I^-$	1.4×10^{-9}	8.9
$Cu(CN)_2^-$	$Cu(CN)_2^- \rightleftharpoons Cu^+ + 2CN^-$	1×10^{-16}	16.0
$Cu(NH_3)_2^+$	$Cu(NH_3)_2^+ \rightleftharpoons Cu^+ + 2NH_3$	1.4×10^{-11}	10.9
$Cu(NH_3)_4^{++}$	$Cu(NH_3)_4^{++} \rightleftharpoons Cu^{++} + 4NH_3$	4.6×10^{-14}	13.3
$Au(CN)_2^-$	$Au(CN)_2^- \rightleftharpoons Au^+ + 2CN^-$	5×10^{-39}	38.4
$Au(CNS)_4^-$	$Au(CNS)_4^- \rightleftharpoons Au^{3+} + 4CNS^-$	3×10^{-38}	37.5
$Fe(CN)_6^{4-}$	$Fe(CN)_6^{4-} \rightleftharpoons Fe^{++} + 6CN^-$	1×10^{-37}	37.0
$Fe(CN)_6^{3-}$	$Fe(CN)_6^{3-} \rightleftharpoons Fe^{3+} + 6CN^-$	1×10^{-44}	44.0
$Fe(C_2O_4)_3^{3-}$	$Fe(C_2O_4)_3^{3-} \rightleftharpoons Fe^{3+} + 3C_2O_4^=$	1×10^{-10}	10.0
$Fe(CNS)_3$	$Fe(CNS)_3 \rightleftharpoons Fe^{3+} + 3CNS^-$	2.6×10^{-6}	5.6
$Fe(CNS)_6^{3-}$	$Fe(CNS)_6^{3-} \rightleftharpoons Fe(CNS)_3 + 3CNS^-$	3.1×10^{-4}	3.5
$HgCl_4^=$	$HgCl_4^= \rightleftharpoons Hg^{++} + 4Cl^-$	1.1×10^{-16}	16.0
$HgBr_4^=$	$HgBr_4^= \rightleftharpoons Hg^{++} + 4Br^-$	2.3×10^{-22}	21.6
$HgI_4^=$	$HgI_4^= \rightleftharpoons Hg^{++} + 4I^-$	5.3×10^{-31}	30.3
$Hg(CNS)_4^=$	$Hg(CNS)_4^= \rightleftharpoons Hg^{++} + 4CNS^-$	1×10^{-22}	22.0
$Hg(CN)_4^=$	$Hg(CN)_4^= \rightleftharpoons Hg^{++} + 4CN^-$	4×10^{-42}	41.4
$Ni(NH_3)_4^{++}$	$Ni(NH_3)_4^{++} \rightleftharpoons Ni^{++} + 4NH_3$	4.8×10^{-8}	7.3
$Ni(NH_3)_6^{++}$	$Ni(NH_3)_6^{++} \rightleftharpoons Ni^{++} + 6NH_3$	2.1×10^{-8}	7.7
$Ni(CN)_4^=$	$Ni(CN)_4^= \rightleftharpoons Ni^{++} + 4CN^-$	1×10^{-22}	22.0
$PtCl_4^=$	$PtCl_4^= \rightleftharpoons Pt^{++} + 4Cl^-$	1×10^{-16}	16.0
$Ag(CN)_2^-$	$Ag(CN)_2^- \rightleftharpoons Ag^+ + 2CN^-$	3.8×10^{-19}	18.4
$Ag(NH_3)_2^+$	$Ag(NH_3)_2^+ \rightleftharpoons Ag^+ + 2NH_3$	6×10^{-8}	7.2
$Ag(S_2O_3)_2^{3-}$	$Ag(S_2O_3)_2^{3-} \rightleftharpoons Ag^+ + 2S_2O_3^=$	4.2×10^{-14}	13.4
$Ag(SO_3)_2^{3-}$	$Ag(SO_3)_2^{3-} \rightleftharpoons Ag^+ + 2SO_3^=$	3×10^{-9}	8.5
$Zn(C_2O_4)_3^{4-}$	$Zn(C_2O_4)_3^{4-} \rightleftharpoons Zn^{++} + 3C_2O_4^=$	1×10^{-9}	9.0
$Zn(CN)_4^=$	$Zn(CN)_4^= \rightleftharpoons Zn + 4CN^-$	2×10^{-17}	16.7
$Zn(NH_3)_4^{++}$	$Zn(NH_3)_4^{++} \rightleftharpoons Zn^{++} + 4NH_3$	9.8×10^{-10}	9.0
$Zn(OH)_4^=$	$Zn(OH)_4^= \rightleftharpoons Zn^{++} + 4OH^-$	3.5×10^{-16}	15.5

APPENDIX N

OXIDATION-REDUCTION POTENTIALS

Couple (Acid Solution)	E°
$Li \rightleftharpoons Li^+ + e$	3.02
$K \rightleftharpoons K^+ + e$	2.92
$Ba \rightleftharpoons Ba^{++} + 2e$	2.90
$Sr \rightleftharpoons Sr^{++} + 2e$	2.89
$Ca \rightleftharpoons Ca^{++} + 2e$	2.87
$Na \rightleftharpoons Na^+ + e$	2.71
$Mg \rightleftharpoons Mg^{++} + 2e$	2.34
$Al \rightleftharpoons Al^{3+} + 3e$	1.67
$Mn \rightleftharpoons Mn^{++} + 2e$	1.05
$Zn \rightleftharpoons Zn^{++} + 2e$	0.76
$Cr \rightleftharpoons Cr^{3+} + 3e$	0.71
$H_3PO_2 + 3H_2O \rightleftharpoons H_3PO_3 + 2H_3O^+ + 2e$	0.59
$H_2C_2O_4 + 2H_2O \rightleftharpoons 2CO_2 + 2H_3O^+ + 2e$	0.49
$Fe \rightleftharpoons Fe^{++} + 2e$	0.44
$H_2 + 2H_2O \rightleftharpoons 2H_3O^+ + 2e$ (10^{-7}-M H_3O^+)	0.41
$Cd \rightleftharpoons Cd^{++} + 2e$	0.40
$SO_4^= + Pb \rightleftharpoons PbSO_4 + 2e$	0.36
$Co \rightleftharpoons Co^{++} + 2e$	0.28
$2H_2O + \frac{1}{2}C_2N_2 \rightleftharpoons HCNO + H_3O^+ + e$	0.27
$2Cl^- + Pb \rightleftharpoons PbCl_2 + 2e$	0.27
$Ni \rightleftharpoons Ni^{++} + 2e$	0.25
$H_3PO_3 + 3H_2O \rightleftharpoons H_3PO_4 + 2H_3O^+ + 2e$	0.20
$I^- + Cu \rightleftharpoons CuI + e$	0.19
$I^- + Ag \rightleftharpoons AgI + e$	0.15
$HCOOH + 2H_2O \rightleftharpoons CO_2 + 2H_3O^+ + 2e$	0.14
$Sn \rightleftharpoons Sn^{++} + 2e$	0.14
$Pb \rightleftharpoons Pb^{++} + 2e$	0.13
$2HONH_3^+ + 5H_2O \rightleftharpoons N_2O + 6H_3O^+ + 4e$	0.05
$PH_3 + 3H_2O \rightleftharpoons P + 3H_3O^+ + 3e$	0.04
$Fe \rightleftharpoons Fe^{3+} + 3e$	0.04
$HCHO + 3H_2O \rightleftharpoons HCOOH + 2H_3O^+ + 2e$	0.01
$H_2 + 2H_2O \rightleftharpoons 2H_3O^+ + 2e$	0.00
$H_2S + 2H_2O \rightleftharpoons S + 2H_3O^+ + 2e$	−0.14
$Sn^{++} \rightleftharpoons Sn^{4+} + 2e$	−0.15
$Cu^+ \rightleftharpoons Cu^{++} + e$	−0.17
$2S_2O_3^= \rightleftharpoons S_4O_6^= + 2e$	−0.17
$H_2SO_3 + 5H_2O \rightleftharpoons SO_4^= + 4H_3O^+ + 2e$	−0.20
$Sb + 3H_2O \rightleftharpoons SbO^+ + 2H_3O^+ + 3e$	−0.21
$Cl^- + Ag \rightleftharpoons AgCl + e$	−0.22
$As + 5H_2O \rightleftharpoons HAsO_2 + 3H_3O^+ + 3e$	−0.25

Couple (Acid Solution)	E°
$2Cl^- + 2Hg \rightleftharpoons Hg_2Cl_2 + 2e$	−0.268
$HCN + H_2O \rightleftharpoons \frac{1}{2}C_2N_2 + H_3O^+ + e$	−0.33
$Cu \rightleftharpoons Cu^{++} + 2e$	−0.34
$Fe(CN)_6^{4-} \rightleftharpoons Fe(CN)_6^{3-} + e$	−0.36
$Cu \rightleftharpoons Cu^+ + e$	−0.52
$2I^- \rightleftharpoons I_2 + 2e$	−0.53
$HAsO_2 + 4H_2O \rightleftharpoons H_3AsO_4 + 2H_3O^+ + 2e$	−0.56
$2SbO^+ + 9H_2O \rightleftharpoons Sb_2O_5 + 6H_3O^+ + 4e$	−0.64
$H_2O_2 + 2H_2O \rightleftharpoons 2H_3O^+ + 2e$	−0.68
$Fe^{++} \rightleftharpoons Fe^{3+} + e$	−0.77
$2Hg \rightleftharpoons Hg_2^{++} + 2e$	−0.80
$Ag \rightleftharpoons Ag^+ + e$	−0.80
$6H_2O \rightleftharpoons O_2 + 4H_3O^+ + 4e$ (at $H_3O^+ = 10^{-7}$ *M*)	−0.82
$Hg \rightleftharpoons Hg^{++} + 2e$	−0.85
$CuI \rightleftharpoons Cu^{++} + I^- + e$	−0.88
$Hg_2^{++} \rightleftharpoons 2Hg^{++} + 2e$	−0.91
$HNO_2 + 4H_2O \rightleftharpoons NO_3^- + 3H_3O^+ + 2e$	−0.94
$NO + 6H_2O \rightleftharpoons NO_3^- + 4H_3O^+ + 3e$	−0.96
$NO + 2H_2O \rightleftharpoons HNO_2 + H_3O^+ + e$	−0.99
$I^- + 2H_2O \rightleftharpoons HIO + H_3O^+ + 2e$	−0.99
$ClO_3^- + 3H_2O \rightleftharpoons ClO_4^- + 2H_3O^+ + 2e$	−1.00
$I^- + 9H_2O \rightleftharpoons IO_3^- + 6H_3O^+ + 6e$	−1.09
$2Br^- \rightleftharpoons Br_2 + 2e$	−1.09
$\frac{1}{2}I_2 + 9H_2O \rightleftharpoons IO_3^- + 6H_3O^+ + 5e$	−1.20
$6H_2O \rightleftharpoons O_2 + 4H_3O^+ + 4e$	−1.23
$HClO_2 + 4H_2O \rightleftharpoons ClO_3^- + 3H_3O^+ + 2e$	−1.23
$Mn^{++} + 6H_2O \rightleftharpoons MnO_2 + 4H_3O^+ + 2e$	−1.28
$N_2O + 7H_2O \rightleftharpoons 2HNO_2 + 4H_3O^+ + 4e$	−1.29
$Br^- + 2H_2O \rightleftharpoons HBrO + H_3O^+ + 2e$	−1.33
$NH_4^+ + 3H_2O \rightleftharpoons NH_3OH^+ + 2H_3O^+ + 2e$	−1.35
$Cl^- \rightleftharpoons \frac{1}{2}Cl_2 + e^-$	−1.36
$2Cr^{3+} + 21H_2O \rightleftharpoons Cr_2O_7^= + 14H_3O^+ + 6e$	−1.36
$Br^- + 9H_2O \rightleftharpoons BrO_3^- + 6H_3O^+ + 6e$	−1.44
$\frac{1}{2}I_2 + 2H_2O \rightleftharpoons HIO + H_3O^+ + e$	−1.45
$Cl^- + 9H_2O \rightleftharpoons ClO_3^- + 6H_3O^+ + 6e$	−1.45
$Pb^{++} + 6H_2O \rightleftharpoons PbO_2 + 4H_3O^+ + 2e$	−1.46
$Cl^- + 2H_2O \rightleftharpoons HClO + H_3O^+ + 2e$	−1.49
$Mn^{++} \rightleftharpoons Mn^{4+} + 2e$	−1.51
$Mn^{++} + 12H_2O \rightleftharpoons MnO_4^- + 8H_3O^+ + 5e$	−1.52
$Cl^- + 5H_2O \rightleftharpoons HClO_2 + 3H_3O^+ + 4e$	−1.56
$2BiO^+ + 6H_2O \rightleftharpoons Bi_2O_4 + 4H_3O^+ + 2e$	−1.59
$Ce^{3+} \rightleftharpoons Ce^{4+} + e$	−1.61
$MnO_2 + 6H_2O \rightleftharpoons MnO_4^- + 4H_3O^+ + 3e$	−1.67
$PbSO_4 + 6H_2O \rightleftharpoons PbO_2 + SO_4^= + 4H_3O^+ + 2e$	−1.69
$Pb^{++} \rightleftharpoons Pb^{4+} + 2e$	−1.69
$4H_2O \rightleftharpoons H_2O_2 + 2H_3O^+ + 2e$	−1.77
$2SO_4^= \rightleftharpoons S_2O_8^= + 2e$	−2.05
$O_2 + 3H_2O \rightleftharpoons O_3 + 2H_3O^+ + 2e$	−2.07
$2F^- \rightleftharpoons F_2 + 2e$	−2.85

OXIDATION-REDUCTION POTENTIALS (*Continued*)

Couple (Basic Solution)	E°
$Li \rightleftharpoons Li^+ + e$	3.02
$K \rightleftharpoons K^+ + e$	2.92
$Na \rightleftharpoons Na^+ + e$	2.71
$Mg + 2OH^- \rightleftharpoons Mg(OH)_2 + 2e$	2.67
$Al + 4OH \rightleftharpoons Al(OH)_4^- + 3e$	2.35
$H_2PO_2^- + 3OH^- \rightleftharpoons HPO_3^= + 2H_2O + 2e$	1.65
$AsH_3 + 3OH^- \rightleftharpoons As + 3H_2O + 3e$	1.37
$Cr + 3OH^- \rightleftharpoons Cr(OH)_3 + 3e$	1.30
$Zn + 4OH^- \rightleftharpoons Zn(OH)_4^= + 2e$	1.22
$HCHO + 3OH^- \rightleftharpoons HCOO^- + 2H_2O + 2e$	1.14
$HPO_3^= + 3OH^- \rightleftharpoons PO_4^{3-} + 2H_2O + 2e$	1.05
$2NH_2OH + 4OH^- \rightleftharpoons N_2O + 5H_2O + 4e$	1.05
$CN^- + 2OH^- \rightleftharpoons CNO^- + H_2O + 2e$	0.96
$Sn(OH)_3^- + 3OH^- \rightleftharpoons Sn(OH)_6^= + 2e$	0.96
$HCOO^- + 3OH^- \rightleftharpoons CO_3^= + 2H_2O + 2e$	0.95
$SO_3^= + 2OH^- \rightleftharpoons SO_4^= + H_2O + 2e$	0.90
$Fe + 2OH^- \rightleftharpoons Fe(OH)_2 + 2e$	0.88
$H_2 + 2OH^- \rightleftharpoons 2H_2O + 2e$	0.83
$Cd + 2OH^- \rightleftharpoons Cd(OH)_2 + 2e$	0.82
$Sn + 3OH^- \rightleftharpoons Sn(OH)_3^- + 2e$	0.79
$AsO_2^- + 4OH^- \rightleftharpoons AsO_4^{3-} + 2H_2O + 2e$	0.71
$As + 4OH^- \rightleftharpoons AsO_2^- + 2H_2O + 3e$	0.68
$Sb + 4OH^- \rightleftharpoons SbO_2^- + 2H_2O + 3e$	0.66
$S^= \rightleftharpoons S + 2e$	0.51
$NO + 2OH^- \rightleftharpoons NO_2^- + H_2O + e$	0.46
$Mn(OH)_2 + OH^- \rightleftharpoons Mn(OH)_3 + e$	0.40
$Cu + 2OH^- \rightleftharpoons Cu(OH)_2 + 2e$	0.22
$Cr(OH)_3 + 5OH^- \rightleftharpoons CrO_4^= + 4H_2O + 3e$	0.12
$HO_2^- + OH^- \rightleftharpoons O_2 + H_2O + 2e$	0.08
$NO_2^- + 2OH^- \rightleftharpoons NO_3^- + H_2O + 2e$	−0.01
$Co(NH_3)_6^{++} \rightleftharpoons Co(NH_3)_6^{3+} + e$	−0.10
$N_2O + 6OH^- \rightleftharpoons 2NO_2^- + 3H_2O + 4e$	−0.15
$ClO_3^- + 2OH^- \rightleftharpoons ClO_4^- + H_2O + 2e$	−0.17
$Co(OH)_2 + OH^- \rightleftharpoons Co(OH)_3 + e$	−0.20
$I^- + 6OH^- \rightleftharpoons IO_3^- + 3H_2O + 6e$	−0.26
$ClO_2^- + 2OH^- \rightleftharpoons ClO_3^- + H_2O + 2e$	−0.35
$4OH^- \rightleftharpoons O_2 + 2H_2O + 4e$	−0.40
$NH_3 + 2OH^- \rightleftharpoons NH_2OH + H_2O + 2e$	−0.42
$I^- + 2OH^- \rightleftharpoons IO^- + H_2O + 2e$	−0.49
$IO^- + 4OH^- \rightleftharpoons IO_3^- + 2H_2O + 4e$	−0.56
$MnO_2 + 4OH^- \rightleftharpoons MnO_4^- + 2H_2O + 3e$	−0.57
$ClO^- + 2OH^- \rightleftharpoons ClO_2^- + 2H_2O + 2e$	−0.59
$Br^- + 6OH^- \rightleftharpoons BrO_3^- + 3H_2O + 6e$	−0.61
$Cl^- + 6OH^- \rightleftharpoons ClO_3^- + 3H_2O + 6e$	−0.62
$Cl^- + 4OH^- \rightleftharpoons ClO_2^- + 2H_2O + 4e$	−0.76
$Br^- + 2OH^- \rightleftharpoons BrO^- + H_2O + 2e$	−0.76
$3OH^- \rightleftharpoons HO_2^- + H_2O + 2e$	−0.87
$Cl^- + 2OH^- \rightleftharpoons ClO^- + H_2O + 2e$	−0.94
$O_2 + 2OH^- \rightleftharpoons O_3 + H_2O + 2e$	−1.24

APPENDIX O

LOGARITHM TABLES

LOGARITHMS OF NUMBERS

Natural numbers	0	1	2	3	4	5	6	7	8	9	Proportional Parts								
											1	2	3	4	5	6	7	8	9
10	0000	0043	0086	0128	0170	0212	0253	0294	0334	0374	4	8	12	17	21	25	29	33	37
11	0414	0453	0492	0531	0569	0607	0645	0682	0719	0755	4	8	11	15	19	23	26	30	34
12	0792	0828	0864	0899	0934	0969	1004	1038	1072	1106	3	7	10	14	17	21	24	28	31
13	1139	1173	1206	1239	1271	1303	1335	1367	1399	1430	3	6	10	13	16	19	23	26	29
14	1461	1492	1523	1553	1584	1614	1644	1673	1703	1732	3	6	9	12	15	18	21	24	27
15	1761	1790	1818	1847	1875	1903	1931	1959	1987	2014	3	6	8	11	14	17	20	22	25
16	2041	2068	2095	2122	2148	2175	2201	2227	2253	2279	3	5	8	11	13	16	18	21	24
17	2304	2330	2355	2380	2405	2430	2455	2480	2504	2529	2	5	7	10	12	15	17	20	22
18	2553	2577	2601	2625	2648	2672	2695	2718	2742	2765	2	5	7	9	12	14	16	19	21
19	2788	2810	2833	2856	2878	2900	2923	2945	2967	2989	2	4	7	9	11	13	16	18	20
20	3010	3032	3054	3075	3096	3118	3139	3160	3181	3201	2	4	6	8	11	13	15	17	19
21	3222	3243	3263	3284	3304	3324	3345	3365	3385	3404	2	4	6	8	10	12	14	16	18
22	3424	3444	3464	3483	3502	3522	3541	3560	3579	3598	2	4	6	8	10	12	14	15	17
23	3617	3636	3655	3674	3692	3711	3729	3747	3766	3784	2	4	6	7	9	11	13	15	17
24	3802	3820	3838	3856	3874	3892	3909	3927	3945	3962	2	4	5	7	9	11	12	14	16
25	3979	3997	4014	4031	4048	4065	4082	4099	4116	4133	2	3	5	7	9	10	12	14	15
26	4150	4166	4183	4200	4216	4232	4249	4265	4281	4298	2	3	5	7	8	10	11	13	15
27	4314	4330	4346	4362	4378	4393	4409	4425	4440	4456	2	3	5	6	8	9	11	13	14
28	4472	4487	4502	4518	4533	4548	4564	4579	4594	4609	2	3	5	6	8	9	11	12	14
29	4624	4639	4654	4669	4683	4698	4713	4728	4742	4757	1	3	4	6	7	9	10	12	13
30	4771	4786	4800	4814	4829	4843	4857	4871	4886	4900	1	3	4	6	7	9	10	11	13
31	4914	4928	4942	4955	4969	4983	4997	5011	5024	5038	1	3	4	6	7	8	10	11	12
32	5051	5065	5079	5092	5105	5119	5132	5145	5159	5172	1	3	4	5	7	8	9	11	12
33	5185	5198	5211	5224	5237	5250	5263	5276	5289	5302	1	3	4	5	6	8	9	10	12
34	5315	5328	5340	5353	5366	5378	5391	5403	5416	5428	1	3	4	5	6	8	9	10	11
35	5441	5453	5465	5478	5490	5502	5514	5527	5539	5551	1	2	4	5	6	7	9	10	11
36	5563	5575	5587	5599	5611	5623	5635	5647	5658	5670	1	2	4	5	6	7	8	10	11
37	5682	5694	5705	5717	5729	5740	5752	5763	5775	5786	1	2	3	5	6	7	8	9	10
38	5798	5809	5821	5832	5843	5855	5866	5877	5888	5899	1	2	3	5	6	7	8	9	10
39	5911	5922	5933	5944	5955	5966	5977	5988	5999	6010	1	2	3	4	5	7	8	9	10
40	6021	6031	6042	6053	6064	6075	6085	6096	6107	6117	1	2	3	4	5	6	8	9	10
41	6128	6138	6149	6160	6170	6180	6191	6201	6212	6222	1	2	3	4	5	6	7	8	9
42	6232	6243	6253	6263	6274	6284	6294	6304	6314	6325	1	2	3	4	5	6	7	8	9
43	6335	6345	6355	6365	6375	6385	6395	6405	6415	6425	1	2	3	4	5	6	7	8	9
44	6435	6444	6454	6464	6474	6484	6493	6503	6513	6522	1	2	3	4	5	6	7	8	9
45	6532	6542	6551	6561	6571	6580	6590	6599	6609	6618	1	2	3	4	5	6	7	8	9
46	6628	6637	6646	6656	6665	6675	6684	6693	6702	6712	1	2	3	4	5	6	7	7	8
47	6721	6730	6739	6749	6758	6767	6776	6785	6794	6803	1	2	3	4	5	5	6	7	8
48	6812	6821	6830	6839	6848	6857	6866	6875	6884	6893	1	2	3	4	4	5	6	7	8
49	6902	6911	6920	6928	6937	6946	6955	6964	6972	6981	1	2	3	4	4	5	6	7	8
50	6990	6998	7007	7016	7024	7033	7042	7050	7059	7067	1	2	3	3	4	5	6	7	8
51	7076	7084	7093	7101	7110	7118	7126	7135	7143	7152	1	2	3	3	4	5	6	7	8

LOGARITHMS OF NUMBERS

Natural numbers	0	1	2	3	4	5	6	7	8	9	Proportional Parts 1	2	3	4	5	6	7	8	9
52	7160	7168	7177	7185	7193	7202	7210	7218	7226	7235	1	2	2	3	4	5	6	7	7
53	7243	7251	7259	7267	7275	7284	7292	7300	7308	7316	1	2	2	3	4	5	6	6	7
54	7324	7332	7340	7348	7356	7364	7372	7380	7388	7396	1	2	2	3	4	5	6	6	7
55	7404	7412	7419	7427	7435	7443	7451	7459	7466	7474	1	2	2	3	4	5	5	6	7
56	7482	7490	7497	7505	7513	7520	7528	7536	7543	7551	1	2	2	3	4	5	5	6	7
57	7559	7566	7574	7582	7589	7597	7604	7612	7619	7627	1	2	2	3	4	5	5	6	7
58	7634	7642	7649	7657	7664	7672	7679	7686	7694	7701	1	1	2	3	4	4	5	6	7
59	7709	7716	7723	7731	7738	7745	7752	7760	7767	7774	1	1	2	3	4	4	5	6	7
60	7782	7789	7796	7803	7810	7818	7825	7832	7839	7846	1	1	2	3	4	4	5	6	6
61	7853	7860	7868	7875	7882	7889	7896	7903	7910	7917	1	1	2	3	4	4	5	6	6
62	7924	7931	7938	7945	7952	7959	7966	7973	7980	7987	1	1	2	3	3	4	5	6	6
63	7993	8000	8007	8014	8021	8028	8035	8041	8048	8055	1	1	2	3	3	4	5	5	6
64	8062	8069	8075	8082	8089	8096	8102	8109	8116	8122	1	1	2	3	3	4	5	5	6
65	8129	8136	8142	8149	8156	8162	8169	8176	8182	8189	1	1	2	3	3	4	5	5	6
66	8195	8202	8209	8215	8222	8228	8235	8241	8248	8254	1	1	2	3	3	4	5	5	6
67	8261	8267	8274	8280	8287	8293	8299	8306	8312	8319	1	1	2	3	3	4	5	5	6
68	8325	8331	8338	8344	8351	8357	8363	8370	8376	8382	1	1	2	3	3	4	4	5	6
69	8388	8395	8401	8407	8414	8420	8426	8432	8439	8445	1	1	2	2	3	4	4	5	6
70	8451	8457	8463	8470	8476	8482	8488	8494	8500	8506	1	1	2	2	3	4	4	5	6
71	8513	8519	8525	8531	8537	8543	8549	8555	8561	8567	1	1	2	2	3	4	4	5	5
72	8573	8579	8585	8591	8597	8603	8609	8615	8621	8627	1	1	2	2	3	4	4	5	5
73	8633	8639	8645	8651	8657	8663	8669	8675	8681	8686	1	1	2	2	3	4	4	5	5
74	8692	8698	8704	8710	8716	8722	8727	8733	8739	8745	1	1	2	2	3	4	4	5	5
75	8751	8756	8762	8768	8774	8779	8785	8791	8797	8802	1	1	2	2	3	3	4	5	5
76	8808	8814	8820	8825	8831	8837	8842	8848	8854	8859	1	1	2	2	3	3	4	5	5
77	8865	8871	8876	8882	8887	8893	8899	8904	8910	8915	1	1	2	2	3	3	4	4	5
78	8921	8927	8932	8938	8943	8949	8954	8960	8965	8971	1	1	2	2	3	3	4	4	5
79	8976	8982	8987	8993	8998	9004	9009	9015	9020	9026	1	1	2	2	3	3	4	4	5
80	9031	9036	9042	9047	9053	9058	9063	9069	9074	9079	1	1	2	2	3	3	4	4	5
81	9085	9090	9096	9101	9106	9112	9117	9122	9128	9133	1	1	2	2	3	3	4	4	5
82	9138	9143	9149	9154	9159	9165	9170	9175	9180	9186	1	1	2	2	3	3	4	4	5
83	9191	9196	9201	9206	9212	9217	9222	9227	9232	9238	1	1	2	2	3	3	4	4	5
84	9243	9248	9253	9258	9263	9269	9274	9279	9284	9289	1	1	2	2	3	3	4	4	5
85	9294	9299	9304	9309	9315	9320	9325	9330	9335	9340	1	1	2	2	3	3	4	4	5
86	9345	9350	9355	9360	9365	9370	9375	9380	9385	9390	1	1	2	2	3	3	4	4	5
87	9395	9400	9405	9410	9415	9420	9425	9430	9435	9440	0	1	1	2	2	3	3	4	4
88	9445	9450	9455	9460	9465	9469	9474	9479	9484	8489	0	1	1	2	2	3	3	4	4
89	9494	9499	9504	9509	9513	9518	9523	9528	9533	9538	0	1	1	2	2	3	3	4	4
90	9542	9547	9552	9557	9562	9566	9571	9576	9581	9586	0	1	1	2	2	3	3	4	4
91	9590	9595	9600	9605	9609	9614	9619	9624	9628	9633	0	1	1	2	2	3	3	4	4
92	9638	9643	9647	9652	9657	9661	9666	9671	9675	9680	0	1	1	2	2	3	3	4	4
93	9685	9689	9694	9699	9703	9708	9713	9717	9722	9727	0	1	1	2	2	3	3	4	4
94	9731	9736	9741	9745	9750	9754	9759	9763	9768	9773	0	1	1	2	2	3	3	4	4
95	9777	9782	9786	9791	9795	9800	9805	9809	9814	9818	0	1	1	2	2	3	3	4	4
96	9823	9827	9832	9836	9841	9845	9850	9854	9859	9863	0	1	1	2	2	3	3	4	4
97	9868	9872	9877	9881	9886	9890	9894	9899	9903	9908	0	1	1	2	2	3	3	4	4
98	9912	9917	9921	9926	9930	9934	9939	9943	9948	9952	0	1	1	2	2	3	3	4	4
99	9956	9961	9965	9969	9974	9978	9983	9987	9991	9996	0	1	1	2	2	3	3	3	4

LOGARITHM TABLES (*Continued*)

ANTILOGARITHMS

Loga-rithms	0	1	2	3	4	5	6	7	8	9	PP 1	2	3	4	5	6	7	8	9
.00	1000	1002	1005	1007	1009	1012	1014	1016	1019	1021	0	0	1	1	1	1	2	2	2
.01	1023	1026	1028	1030	1033	1035	1038	1040	1042	1045	0	0	1	1	1	1	2	2	2
.02	1047	1050	1052	1054	1057	1059	1062	1064	1067	1069	0	0	1	1	1	1	2	2	2
.03	1072	1074	1076	1079	1081	1084	1086	1089	1091	1094	0	0	1	1	1	1	2	2	2
.04	1096	1099	1102	1104	1107	1109	1112	1114	1117	1119	0	1	1	1	1	2	2	2	2
.05	1122	1125	1127	1130	1132	1135	1138	1140	1143	1146	0	1	1	1	1	2	2	2	2
.06	1148	1151	1153	1156	1159	1161	1164	1167	1169	1172	0	1	1	1	1	2	2	2	2
.07	1175	1178	1180	1183	1186	1189	1191	1194	1197	1199	0	1	1	1	1	2	2	2	2
.08	1202	1205	1208	1211	1213	1216	1219	1222	1225	1227	0	1	1	1	1	2	2	2	3
.09	1230	1233	1236	1239	1242	1245	1247	1250	1253	1256	0	1	1	1	1	2	2	2	3
.10	1259	1262	1265	1268	1271	1274	1276	1279	1282	1285	0	1	1	1	1	2	2	2	3
.11	1288	1291	1294	1297	1300	1303	1306	1309	1312	1315	0	1	1	1	2	2	2	2	3
.12	1318	1321	1324	1327	1330	1334	1337	1340	1343	1346	0	1	1	1	2	2	2	2	3
.13	1349	1352	1355	1358	1361	1365	1368	1371	1374	1377	0	1	1	1	2	2	2	3	3
.14	1380	1384	1387	1390	1393	1396	1400	1403	1406	1409	0	1	1	1	2	2	2	3	3
.15	1413	1416	1419	1422	1426	1429	1432	1435	1439	1442	0	1	1	1	2	2	2	3	3
.16	1445	1449	1452	1455	1459	1462	1466	1469	1472	1476	0	1	1	1	2	2	2	3	3
.17	1479	1483	1486	1489	1493	1496	1500	1503	1507	1510	0	1	1	1	2	2	2	3	3
.18	1514	1517	1521	1524	1528	1531	1535	1538	1542	1545	0	1	1	1	2	2	2	3	3
.19	1549	1552	1556	1560	1563	1567	1570	1574	1578	1581	0	1	1	1	2	2	3	3	3
.20	1585	1589	1592	1596	1600	1603	1607	1611	1614	1618	0	1	1	1	2	2	3	3	3
.21	1622	1626	1629	1633	1637	1641	1644	1648	1652	1656	0	1	1	2	2	2	3	3	3
.22	1660	1663	1667	1671	1675	1679	1683	1687	1690	1694	0	1	1	2	2	2	3	3	3
.23	1698	1702	1706	1710	1714	1718	1722	1726	1730	1734	0	1	1	2	2	2	3	3	4
.24	1738	1742	1746	1750	1754	1758	1762	1766	1770	1774	0	1	1	2	2	2	3	3	4
.25	1778	1782	1786	1791	1795	1799	1803	1807	1811	1816	0	1	1	2	2	2	3	3	4
.26	1820	1824	1828	1832	1837	1841	1845	1849	1854	1858	0	1	1	2	2	3	3	3	4
.27	1862	1866	1871	1875	1879	1884	1888	1892	1897	1901	0	1	1	2	2	3	3	3	4
.28	1905	1910	1914	1919	1923	1928	1932	1936	1941	1945	0	1	1	2	2	3	3	4	4
.29	1950	1954	1959	1963	1968	1972	1977	1982	1986	1991	0	1	1	2	2	3	3	4	4
.30	1995	2000	2004	2009	2014	2018	2023	2028	2032	2037	0	1	1	2	2	3	3	4	4
.31	2042	2046	2051	2056	2061	2065	2070	2075	2080	2084	0	1	1	2	2	3	3	4	4
.32	2089	2094	2099	2104	2109	2113	2118	2123	2128	2133	0	1	1	2	2	3	3	4	4
.33	2138	2143	2148	2153	2158	2163	2168	2173	2178	2183	0	1	1	2	2	3	3	4	4
.34	2188	2193	2198	2203	2208	2213	2218	2223	2228	2234	1	1	2	2	3	3	4	4	5
.35	2239	2244	2249	2254	2259	2265	2270	2275	2280	2286	1	1	2	2	3	3	4	4	5
.36	2291	2296	2301	2307	2312	2317	2323	2328	2333	2339	1	1	2	2	3	3	4	4	5
.37	2344	2350	2355	2360	2366	2371	2377	2382	2388	2393	1	1	2	2	3	3	4	4	5
.38	2399	2404	2410	2415	2421	2427	2432	2438	2443	2449	1	1	2	2	3	3	4	4	5
.39	2455	2460	2466	2472	2477	2483	2489	2495	2500	2506	1	1	2	2	3	3	4	5	5
.40	2512	2518	2523	2529	2535	2541	2547	2553	2559	2564	1	1	2	2	3	4	4	5	5
.41	2570	2576	2582	2588	2594	2600	2606	2612	2618	2624	1	1	2	2	3	4	4	5	5
.42	2630	2636	2642	2649	2655	2661	2667	2673	2679	2685	1	1	2	2	3	4	4	5	6
.43	2692	2698	2704	2710	2716	2723	2729	2735	2742	2748	1	1	2	3	3	4	4	5	6
.44	2754	2761	2767	2773	2780	2786	2793	2799	2805	2812	1	1	2	3	3	4	4	5	6
.45	2818	2825	2831	2838	2844	2851	2858	2864	2871	2877	1	1	2	3	3	4	5	5	6
.46	2884	2891	2897	2904	2911	2917	2924	2931	2938	2944	1	1	2	3	3	4	5	5	6
.47	2951	2958	2965	2972	2979	2985	2992	2999	3006	3013	1	1	2	3	3	4	5	5	6
.48	3020	3027	3034	3041	3048	3055	3062	3069	3076	3083	1	1	2	3	4	4	5	6	6
.49	3090	3097	3105	3112	3119	3126	3133	3141	3148	3155	1	1	2	3	4	4	5	6	6

(PP = Proportional Parts)

LOGARITHM TABLES (*Continued*)

ANTILOGARITHMS

Logarithms	0	1	2	3	4	5	6	7	8	9	PP 1	PP 2	PP 3	PP 4	PP 5	PP 6	PP 7	PP 8	PP 9
.50	3162	3170	3177	3184	3192	3199	3206	3214	3221	3228	1	1	2	3	4	4	5	6	7
.51	3236	3243	3251	3258	3266	3273	3281	3289	3296	3304	1	2	2	3	4	5	5	6	7
.52	3311	3319	3327	3334	3342	3350	3357	3365	3373	3381	1	2	2	3	4	5	5	6	7
.53	3388	3396	3404	3412	3420	3428	3436	3443	3451	3459	1	2	2	3	4	5	6	6	7
.54	3467	3465	3483	3491	3499	3508	3516	3524	3532	3540	1	2	2	3	4	5	6	6	7
.55	3548	3556	3565	3573	3581	3589	3597	3606	3614	3622	1	2	2	3	4	5	6	7	7
.56	3631	3639	3648	3656	3664	3673	3681	3690	3698	3707	1	2	3	3	4	5	6	7	8
.57	3715	3724	3733	3741	3750	3758	3767	3776	3784	3793	1	2	3	3	4	5	6	7	8
.58	3802	3811	3819	3828	3837	3846	3855	3864	3873	3882	1	2	3	4	4	5	6	7	8
.59	3890	3899	3908	3917	3926	3936	3945	3954	3963	3972	1	2	3	4	5	5	6	7	8
.60	3981	3990	3999	4009	4018	4027	4036	4046	4055	4064	1	2	3	4	5	6	6	7	8
.61	4074	4083	4093	4102	4111	4121	4130	4140	4150	4159	1	2	3	4	5	6	7	8	9
.62	4169	4178	4188	4198	4207	4217	4227	4236	4246	4256	1	2	3	4	5	6	7	8	9
.63	4266	4276	4285	4295	4305	4315	4325	4335	4345	4355	1	2	3	4	5	6	7	8	9
.64	4365	4375	4385	4395	4406	4416	4426	4436	4446	4457	1	2	3	4	5	6	7	8	9
.65	4467	4477	4487	4498	4508	4519	4529	4539	4550	4560	1	2	3	4	5	6	7	8	9
.66	4571	4581	4592	4603	4613	4624	4634	4645	4656	4667	1	2	3	4	5	6	7	9	10
.67	4677	4688	4699	4710	4721	4732	4742	4753	4764	4775	1	2	3	4	5	7	8	9	10
.68	4786	4797	4808	4819	4831	4842	4853	4864	4875	4887	1	2	3	4	6	7	8	9	10
.69	4898	4909	4920	4932	4943	4955	4966	4977	4989	5000	1	2	3	5	6	7	8	9	10
.70	5012	5023	5035	5047	5058	5070	5082	5093	5105	5117	1	2	4	5	6	7	8	9	11
.71	5129	5140	5152	5164	5176	5188	5200	5212	5224	5236	1	2	4	5	6	7	8	10	11
.72	5248	5260	5272	5284	5297	5309	5321	5333	5346	5358	1	2	4	5	6	7	9	10	11
.73	5370	5383	5395	5408	5420	5433	5445	5458	5470	5483	1	3	4	5	6	8	9	10	11
.74	5495	5508	5521	5534	5546	5559	5572	5585	5598	5610	1	3	4	5	6	8	9	10	12
.75	5623	5636	5649	5662	5675	5689	5702	5715	5728	5741	1	3	4	5	7	8	9	10	12
.76	5754	5768	5781	5794	5808	5821	5834	5848	5861	5875	1	3	4	5	7	8	9	11	12
.77	5888	5902	5916	5929	5943	5957	5970	5984	5998	6012	1	3	4	5	7	8	10	11	12
.78	6026	6039	6053	6067	6081	6095	6109	6124	6138	6152	1	3	4	6	7	8	10	11	13
.79	6166	6180	6194	6209	6223	6237	6252	6266	6281	6295	1	3	4	6	7	9	10	11	13
.80	6310	6324	6339	6353	6368	6383	6397	6412	6427	6442	1	3	4	6	7	9	10	12	13
.81	6457	6471	6486	6501	6516	6531	6546	6561	6577	6592	2	3	5	6	8	9	11	12	14
.82	6607	6622	6637	6653	6668	6683	6699	6714	6730	6745	2	3	5	6	8	9	11	12	14
.83	6761	6776	6792	6808	6823	6839	6855	6871	6887	6902	2	3	5	6	8	9	11	13	14
.84	6918	6934	6950	6966	6982	6998	7015	7031	7047	7063	2	3	5	6	8	10	11	13	15
.85	7079	7096	7112	7129	7145	7161	7178	7194	7211	7228	2	3	5	7	8	10	12	13	15
.86	7244	7261	7278	7295	7311	7328	7345	7362	7379	7396	2	3	5	7	8	10	12	13	15
.87	7413	7430	7447	7464	7482	7499	7516	7534	7551	7568	2	3	5	7	9	10	12	14	16
.88	7586	7603	7621	7638	7656	7674	7691	7709	7727	7745	2	4	5	7	9	11	12	14	16
.89	7762	7780	7798	7816	7834	7852	7870	7889	7907	7925	2	4	5	7	9	11	13	14	16
.90	7943	7962	7980	7998	8017	8035	8054	8072	8091	8110	2	4	6	7	9	11	13	15	17
.91	8128	8147	8166	8185	8204	8222	8241	8260	8279	8299	2	4	6	8	9	11	13	15	17
.92	8318	8337	8356	8375	8395	8414	8433	8453	8472	8492	2	4	6	8	10	12	14	15	17
.93	8511	8531	8551	8570	8590	8610	8630	8650	8670	8690	2	4	6	8	10	12	14	16	18
.94	8710	8730	8750	8770	8790	8810	8831	8851	8872	8892	2	4	6	8	10	12	14	16	18
.95	8913	8933	8954	8974	8995	9016	9036	9057	9078	9099	2	4	6	8	10	12	15	17	19
.96	9120	9141	9162	9183	9204	9226	9247	9268	9290	9311	2	4	6	8	11	13	15	17	19
.97	9333	9354	9376	9397	9419	9441	9462	9484	9506	9528	2	4	7	9	11	13	15	17	20
.98	9550	9572	9594	9616	9638	9661	9683	9705	9727	9750	2	4	7	9	11	13	16	18	20
.99	9772	9795	9817	9840	9863	9886	9908	9931	9954	9977	2	5	7	9	11	14	16	18	20

INDEX